The Oxford

ILLUSTRATED COMPANION TO THE HISTORY OF

MODERN SCIENCE

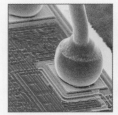 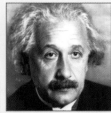 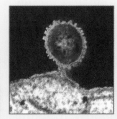  

EDITOR IN CHIEF
J. L. HEILBRON

EDITORS

James Bartholomew Jim Bennett Frederic L. Holmes Rachel Laudan Giuliano Pancaldi

SENIOR CONSULTANT

D. J. Kevles

Tess
Press

CONSULTANTS

Theodore Feldman Loren Graham Norriss Hetherington Mary Jo Nye Kathryn Olesko Naomi Oreskes Alan Rocke

ADVISERS

Janet Browne Robert Bud Regis Cabral Ruth Cowan Matthias Dörries Rivka Feldhay Tore Frängsmyr R. W. Home
Alexei Kojevnikov Sylvia Kraemer Svante Lindqvist Ernan McMullin Dominique Pestre Lewis Pyenson
Laurence Schneider Eri Yagi

PHOTO CREDITS

Granger: 77, 112, 121, 126, 143, 144, 146, 176, 177, 192, 212, 216, 232, 234, 242, 244, 251, 255, 279, 282.

All images below courtesy of **PhotoResearchers.com**, which have additional attributions:

A. Barrington Brown, 200/A. Loll, 296/Adam Hart-Davis, 277/AIP: 75, 171, 202, 257, 261, 262, 264, 266, 268, 309/AKG, 194/Alexander Tsiaras, 74/Alix, 188/Alfred Pasieka, 186/Anatomical Travelogue, 101/Andrew Lambert Photography, 153/Andrew Syred, 284/ArSciMed, 267/ASU, 296/Bill Sanderson, 111/Biophoto Associates, 193/Brian Evans, 5/Bruce Frisch, 225/BSIP, 214/Carl Anderson, 72/CERN: 93, 94, 240, 293/Charles D. Winters, 180/Chris Butler, 85/Christian Darkin, 136/Colin Cuthbert, 213/Cordelia Molloy, 25, 139/Cornell, 197/CSIRO, 300/C.T.R. Wilson, 64/D. Roberts, 41/David Frazier, 105/David Parker, 24/Detlev van Ravenswaay, 283/Edward Kinsman, 302/Emilio Segre Visual Archives: 28, 169, 305/ESA: 202, 296/Eye of Science, 9/F. Evelegh, 211/Estate of Francis Bello, 19/Frank Zullo, 221/Friedrich Saurer, 56/G. Tompkinson, 237/Gary Hincks, 224/Geoff Lane, 300/Georg Gerster, 235/George Bernard: 18, 54/Gunilla Elam, 228/Gusto, 63/Hank Morgan, 132/H. Turvey, 98/Herb Levart, 86/Humanities and Social Sciences Library, 297/Dr. Ian Robson, 7/J. Hester, 296/Jack Fields, 269/James King-Holmes, 46/James Steinberg, 294/Jean-Loup Charmet: 34, 59, 116, 187, 220/Dr. Jeremy Burgess, 307/Jim Dowdalls, 52/John Reader: 84, 129/JPL-CALTECH: 45, 197/Karsten Schneider, 308/Lawrence Berkeley Lab: 253, 303/Lawrence Migdale, 193/LBNL, 68/Library of Congress: 15, 286/Louis Goldman, 13/ Margrethe Bohr Collection, 264/Mark Garlick, 259/Dr. Mark J. Winter, 260/Martin Bond: 103, 280/Mary Evans: Preface, 27, 57, 155, 157, 168, 190, 223, 245, 274/Meggers Gallery: 171, 202/NASA: 30, 45, 164, 197, 229, 246, 278, 287, 289, 296/Michael Abbey, 80/National Library of Medicine: 10, 151, 200, 206/NCAR, 62/New York Public Library, 297/Omikron: 107, 313, 311/P. J. Stewart, 97/Pascal Goetgheluck, 66/Pasieka, 201/Pasquale Sorrentino, 49/Philippe Psaila, 43/Physics Today Collection: 261, 268/Professor Peter Fowler, 32/Peter Menzel, 218/Royal Astronomical Society, 258/Russell Curtis, 278/Sam Pierson, 127/Science Photo Library: 1, 11, 21, 33, 36, 58, 90, 99, 110, 140, 148, 159, 180, 183, 184, 191, 209, 215, 231, 272, 291, 292, 298, 299, 310/Science Source: 40, 82, 89, 92, 124, 150, 162, 164, 165, 174, 185, 195, 202, 214, 222, 270, 278, 306/Sheila Terry: 20, 187, 207, 227, 230, 276, 301/Sinclair Stammers, 294/STSCI, 296/T. Borredon-Explorer, 118/Ted Kinsman, 290/Tek Image, 182/Thomas Deerinck, 78/Dr. Tim Evans, 38/Tomsich, 302/Ton Kinsbergen, 161/Tony McConnell, 236/U.S. Army: 50, 70/U.S. Department of Energy: 16, 248/Professor Vincent Icke, 113/Visum, 115/Volker Steger: 145, 204/WorldSat International Inc., 249

The text of this book was originally published and printed by arrangement with Oxford University Press, Inc.
Oxford is a registered trademark of Oxford University Press

Published by Tess Press, an imprint of
Black Dog & Leventhal Publishers, Inc.
151 West 19th Street
New York, NY 10011

Jacket Design by Lindsay Wolff
Interior Design by Red Herring Design

ISBN: 978-1-60376-036-2

Printed in China

h g f e d c b a

CONTENTS

PREFACE TO ILLUSTRATED EDITION

The present volume derives from the *Oxford Companion to the History of Modern Science* (2003). It differs from its predecessor in its cornucopia of illustrations and in its selection of articles. The *Illustrated Companion* takes about a third of the articles of its parent, some 200 out of 600. The choice was made on the basis of intrinsic interest, accessibility, centrality, and amenability to illustration. On these criteria, we dropped the philosophical, historiographic, and biographical articles, and reduced in number those dealing with individual instruments, institutions, and sub-disciplines. Most of the articles on the major divisions of science and their principal branches have survived in their entirety, unaltered except for the correction of an occasional error.

The following table of organization of the original edition will make clear how the two works differ in coverage.

HISTORIOGRAPHY OF SCIENCE
General concepts and approaches
Examples: Classification, Historiography, Terminology
Articles in original edition: 12
Articles in illustrated edition: 0
Major periods in time
Examples: Enlightenment, Long fin-de-siècle, Scientific Revoluton
Original edition: 8
Illustrated edition: 0
Major divisions of Thought
Examples: Aristotelianism, Hermeticism, Newtonianism
Original edition: 9
Illustrated edition: 5

ORGANIZATION AND DIFFUSION OF SCIENCE
The scientific profession
Examples: Engineer, Scientist
Original edition: 3
Illustrated edition: 0
Generalized institutions
Examples: Academies and Learned Societies, Observatory, Zoological Garden
Original edition: 23
Illustrated edition: 13
Individual institutions
Examples: Bell Labs, CERN, Solvay Congresses and Institutes

Original edition: 11
Illustrated edition: 0
Diffusion (Beyond Science)
Examples: Anatomical Theater, Museum, Textbook
Original edition: 9
Illustrated edition: 4
Communication (Within Science)
Examples: Grand Tour, Journal, Peer Review
Original edition: 9
Illustrated edition: 1
Patronage
Examples: Brain Drains, Courts and Salons, Nobel Prize
Original edition: 7
Illustrated edition: 4

THE BODY OF SCIENTIFIC KNOWLEDGE
Epistemology and Methodology
Examples: Analysis and Synthesis, Magic Model
Original edition: 33
Illustrated edition: 0
Cross-Cutting Concepts
Examples: Cell, Conservation Laws, Ether, Vacuum
Original edition: 75
Illustrated edition: 13
Major Subject Divisions
Examples: Alchemy, Biology, Chemistry, Physics
Original edition: 30
Illustrated edition: 25

LEFT: Antoine Laurent Lavoisier (1743-1794), French chemist and natural philosopher, the principal architect of the modern language of chemistry, and his wife, Marie-Anne Pirette Paulze, who often helped him in his work. Lavoisier was prominent in French society of the old regime, an influential member of the Académie des Sciences, and a tax farmer. The last activity, which amounted to lending money to the government and collecting it from the people, brought him to the guillotine during the Reign of Terror. Oil on canvas by Jacques Louis David (1748-1825).

Minor Subject Divisions
Examples: Analytical Chemistry, Cytology, Quantum
  Physics
Original edition: 69
Illustrated edition: 56
Theoretical Constructs
Examples: Acid and Base, Chromosome, Feedback,
  Supernova
Original edition: 119
Illustrated edition: 42

APPARATUS AND INSTRUMENTS
In General
Examples: Accelerator, Computer, Electrophoresis
Original edition: 12
Illustrated edition: 5
In Particular
Examples: Astrolabe, Micrometer, Pendulum,
  Wardian Case
Original edition: 26
Illustrated edition: 11
In Use
Examples: Dissection, Electrolysis, Space Station
Original edition: 9
Illustrated edition: 1

USES
Intellectual
Examples: Art and Science, Ethics and Science,
  Science Fiction
Original edition: 8
Illustrated edition: 3
Social
Examples: Anti-Science, Fraud, Mad Cow Disease,
  Sputnik
Original edition: 28
Illustrated edition: 11
Geographical
Examples: Africa, Asia, Latin America
Original edition: 6
Illustrated edition: 5
Applied Sciences
Examples: AIDS, Forestry, Klystron, Ultrasonics
Original edition: 53
Illustrated edition: 9

BIOGRAPHIES
Aepinus to Yukawa
Original edition: 100
Illustrated edition: 0

While the present edition necessarily falls short of the original in number of articles, it greatly exceeds its predecessor in its images of the life of science and its content during the last three centuries. We have tried to strike a balance between period illustrations of people and instruments and relatively recent depictions of scientific results. Our frontispiece is the justly famous, and truly companionable, portrait of the chemist Antoine-Laurent Lavoisier and his wife, shown with some of the apparatus from their 18th-century laboratory. There are many other interesting depictions of individuals, which compensate in part for the omission of biographies; a range of instruments and apparatus from the thermometers of the Accademia del Cimento to the Hubble Telescope; and scattered images of modern biology, cosmology, and quantum physics, viruses, phages, cells, galactic catastrophes, particle explosions, which taken together make a significant part of the iconography of our time.

"Eppure si muove"—*"still it moves"*—*quipped Pope John Paul II as he hobbled on his newly repaired hip to preside over a synod of bishops in 1994. Everyone understood the unspoken reference to Galileo's apocryphal muttered defiance 331 years earlier during his forced recantation of his detestable opinion that the earth turns. The Pope joked that he too was a martyr to science. Our boon* Companion *prepares its readers for such unlikely references to the historical culture of science.*

THE CHARACTER OF THE COMPANION

The Oxford Illustrated Companion to the History of Modern Science reliably describes the development and ramification of the main branches and twigs of natural knowledge and their uses in industry, literature, religion, war, entertainment, and much else. In keeping with this serious side of its personality, it can be self-contemplative. It considers various approaches to the history of science including the feminist and Marxist; defines and historicizes terms of art like model and theory; and discusses the fluctuating influence of epistemological notions like hypothesis and proof. By turns the *Companion* is also playful, as in "Slogans from Science," and, in a Pickwickian way, "Quark"; expansive, as in "Asia" and "Latin America"; thoughtful, as in "Race" and "Clone"; and celebratory, as in "Nobel Prize."

The *Companion* depicts its subject with a wider palette than other single-volume and most multi-volume reference works in the history of science and technology. It depicts for a general audience the process by which our colorful, vigorous, demanding, and sometimes off-putting science and its products have come to direct world history. According to George Sarton, the architect of the academic study of the history of science during the last century, "The history of science is the history of civilization." That is at least half true. Our *Companion* is more than an account of a specialized and to some tastes unpleasant human activity. It is also a *Companion* to world history, modern in coverage, proper in demeanor, generous in breadth, and cosmopolitan in scope.

MODERNITY. It may not be easy to say when modernity started or ended, if it is over, but few will dispute that Columbus sailed before it began or that it flourished during the late nineteenth and twentieth centuries, and that it saw the creation and exploitation of natural science as we know it. Hence we limit our coverage to the modern period. Apart from appropriate backward glances, the *Companion* picks up around 1550 and dwells on the seventeenth and eighteenth centuries before turning to the development of the modern scientific disciplines and their interactions with the societies that support them. The earlier period receives emphasis not to allow contributors to expatiate on the so-called Scientific Revolution, which has been the lynch-pin of the historiography of science, but to stress that modern science is a discovery as well as an invention. It was a discovery that nature generally acts regularly enough to be described by laws and even by mathematics; and it required invention to devise the techniques, abstractions, apparatus, and organization for exhibiting the regularities and securing their law-like descriptions.

The discovery of the regularities of planetary motions goes back to antiquity; but the discovery of principles that allowed for ever-finer quantitative agreement between the prediction and observation of astronomical phenomena dates from the seventeenth century. The means by which the agreement was secured—the instruments, computational techniques, and physical models—suggested that the phenomena of physics and chemistry might also be (or with proper definitions and abstractions become) as law-like as astronomy. The systematic production of evidence favorable to the suggestion dates from the last few decades of the eighteenth century.

The redoubtable Immanuel Kant declared in 1786, while deprecating chemistry as no more than an art, that "in every special doctrine of nature only so much science proper can be found as there is mathematics in it." Chemistry went modern from Kant's point of view in the nineteenth century and several of the biological sciences in the twentieth. The trend was resisted by people who deplored the loss of the spontaneous human element from natural science and the coming of professionalization, with its specialization and standardization, and of fraternization with industry and the military. But their resistance did not arrest the trend, which only broadened and strengthened. Modern Western science provides much of the force and substance of globalization. This is not the fault of historians.

Answers to the questions when modern science began and how it grew express values about modernity. Some historians, put off by science's methods of aggrandizement, represent the secularly progressive path of science as a locally bumpy road along which scientists advance by fighting with one another over facts, interpretations, and authority. Others have located the fighting between forward-thinking philosophers of nature and reactionary powers of religion, state, and society. Still others couple the development of science tightly with practical applications, with pharmacy, medicine, mining, and manufactures.

The *Companion* speaks to all of these possibilities and more besides. Readers can choose among them or construct their own stories, aware that the choice matters; that placing the threshold of modern science in the work of Galileo, or the marginalization of women, or the second world war (to pick slight variations of standard candidates) implies and conveys a worldview.

PROPRIETY. The word "scientist" was not seriously propounded before 1840 and not used widely until well into the twentieth century ("man of science" or "scientific man" being preferred). Nonetheless, historians and others who should know better refer readily to doubtful "scientists" of the Renaissance and mythical creatures like "geologists" of the Middle Ages and "biologists" of Antiquity.

This usage can easily hide discontinuities in the subject matters of the sciences and in the circumstances of their cultivation. Anachronistic vocabulary distorts understanding of the nature of modern sciences and their place in the societies that support them.

The *Companion* avoids using the names of modern sciences in reference to the sixteenth, seventeenth, and eighteenth centuries, except for anatomy, astronomy, botany, and chemistry, which then-covered phenomena that now fall to disciplines with the same names. Otherwise it recommends terms of the period, like "natural knowledge," "natural philosophy," and "natural history." It shrinks from labeling as a "scientist" any student of nature active before the middle of the nineteenth century, preferring "scholar," "savant," "man of letters," "academician," "professor," and, where relevant, "anatomist" or "astronomer"; and it prohibits altogether honorifica and horrifica like "the father [or mother] of biology." Earlier students of nature should be allowed the roles they played. Few were, or would have wished to be, professional researchers of today's type.

The *Companion* abates this prissiness when enforcing it would result in pedanticism, which it abhors even more than bad language. Nevertheless, to paraphrase the editor of the *Saggi* or *Essays* issued in 1667 by the Accademia del Cimento of Florence, perhaps the earliest of scientific societies, "if sometimes there shall be inserted any hints of Anachronism, we request that they may be taken always for the thoughts, and particular sense of some one of the Contributors, but not imputed to the whole of the Company."

GENEROSITY. Today's policy analyst blurs the distinction between science and its technological applications: engineering, electronics, and industry now affect the biological sciences as strongly as they do the physical sciences. The *Companion* grants that science and high technology, research and development, have grown cozily close, and that governments now encourage a degree of intimacy between academia and industry previously experienced only in wartime. Consequently the *Companion* devotes much of the space it allots to the uses of science to practical or industrial applications. It makes special provision for scientific instruments and apparatus, which it esteems not only as implements of modernity, but also as products of cooperation between science and industry.

The programs of industrial, governmental, and charitable patrons insure that, no matter what scientists think, science no longer can be a disinterested pursuit of truth. Some philosophers and historians have arrived independently at this last proposition by proving that there is no truth and that, if there were, scientists could not recognize it. The *Companion* gives due weight to the view that modern science is but an engine for the creation and convenient arrangement of facts. It does not disfavor naive realism, however, and generously declines to decide whether existence is more truly predicated of electrons than of readers.

COSMOPOLITANISM. During the seventeenth and eighteenth centuries European centers operated a mercantilist system with respect to science. Information about the flora, fauna, and natural curiosities of colonies returned to the mother country for incorporation in herbaria, botanical gardens, zoos, and books. During the nineteenth century a few colonies acquired their own observatories and gardens, and countries that would challenge European hegemony in the twentieth century began to modernize—Japan, Russia, and the United States. By 1940, leadership had transferred to America, to be challenged in particular sectors after World War II by Europe, Japan, and the Soviet Union. American institutions profited from the migrations of trained people, not only the emigres from the dictatorships of the interwar period but also freely mobile scientists and engineers who clogged the brain drain of the last decades of the twentieth century.

Meanwhile the former colonies strove with varying success to bring home relevant parts of Western science. Some countries in Latin America, notably Brazil, and in Asia, especially India and Pakistan, have managed to create a few institutions that have nourished investigators and prompted discoveries on a par with European and American models. China has followed its own route to the domestication of Western science and is beginning to be a major force in some advanced technologies. But scarcity of resources, lack of international recognition, doubts about the fitness and relevance of high-end science for developing countries, and the difficulty of insuring continuity of purpose in unstable political situations have hampered efforts to transfer Western standards and practices. Our cosmopolitan *Companion* offers accounts of the expansion of science and scientists from their traditional centers throughout the rest of the world. This spread in space parallels the growth of scientific specialties characteristic of the twentieth century. "Spread" and "growth" are key concepts for the *Companion*.

STRUCTURE AND USE. Classifications of science with explicit schemes of subordination, usually with physics on top, go back as far as Aristotle. Something of the same order survives today in the seniority of the Nobel Prizes, although the Swedish Academy of Sciences, Nobel, and Aristotle mean and meant different things by "physics." The *Companion* also has a hierarchical structure. It devotes a primary article to each comprehensive discipline (e.g., Astronomy, Botany, Chemistry) that indicates general historical development, appropriate terminology, and main subdivisions. These subdivisions form the subject matter of secondary articles (Non-optical astronomy, Horticulture, Atom and Molecule), which, in turn, spin off tertiary notices of discoveries, concepts, or instruments (Black Hole, Quark).

The users and browsers we have in mind are the usual audiences for Oxford *Companions*: the casual and general reader, who will want to know where science is in society and how it got there; students preparing papers and (there are some) merely expanding their minds; all who teach, study, apply, or analyze any science whatsoever; every expert in need of breadth and refreshment; and anyone who likes to see a difficult job conscientiously tackled.

ACADEMIES AND LEARNED SOCIETIES. "Ci-gît un qui ne fut rien, pas même académicien" ("Here lies someone who was nobody, not even an academician"). This epitaph, on a tombstone now in the Musée des Beaux Arts in Dijon, suggests the scale and tone of the academic movement during the Enlightenment. Between 1750 and 1774, seventeen learned societies dedicated at least partly to natural science were founded in France alone. But as the epitaph insinuates, most of the academies of the great age of academies had more to do with society than with science. They drew their memberships primarily from the professions—lawyers, doctors, clerics, and military men—and from landed gentry. They discussed local improvements, maintained a library and collection of instruments, and performed, usually irregularly, the two essential offices of a learned society in the age of Enlightenment: giving prizes to winners of essay competitions and publishing papers presented by its members.

Although the various groups, clubs, and societies that occupied themselves with natural knowledge during the modern period elude exact classification, an academy may be defined sufficiently as a formal institution (however meager its statutes) with a restricted membership (never more than a few hundred before the twentieth century) devoted in substantial part to the advancement of all the natural sciences, particularly by the mutual encouragement of its members. A university, professional society, research council, museum, laboratory, or observatory is not an academy, although all of them exercise one or more of the same functions—publishing memoirs, encouraging research, funding expeditions, giving prizes, imposing standards, establishing solidarity, and promoting science among the wider society—first brought together in academies.

The earliest scientific academies of any importance appeared in Italy in the seventeenth century as variants of a common Renaissance type—a group of literary men maintained for a few years by a wealthy aristocrat or prelate. The Accademia dei Lincei (1603–1630), organized but not underwritten by a duke, did not meet together, but it gave its members—including Galileo Galilei, who used to style himself "linceo" (lynx) on the title pages of his books—a sense of common enterprise. Galileo's disciples established a closer-knit body, the Accademia del Cimento (1657–1667), under higher patronage (the Grand Duke of Tuscany and his brother, a cardinal) and with better resources (salaries, instruments, and a meeting place). Inspired also by Francis Bacon's project of improving the arts and sciences through cooperative effort, the dozen or so members of the Cimento, "whose sole Design [was] to make Experiments, and Relate them," published an important collection of their "trials," *Saggi di naturali esperienze* (1667), as a corporate contribution, without attributing discoveries to individuals.

Louis XIV receives the Académie royale des sciences ca. 1670. The Observatoire royal is in the background.

No other academy in seventeenth-century Italy had such lavish support as the Cimento, although several had even higher patronage. Examples are the Accademia Fisico-matematica of Rome, founded in 1677 by a cleric, Giovanni Giustino Ciampini, and encouraged by a cardinal (later elected pope) and by Christina, the converted former queen of Sweden; and the Accademia degli Inquieti (ca. 1690–1714), founded by professors at the University of Bologna, later (when endowed by a private citizen and the pope) the nucleus of the Accademia delle Scienze dell'Istituto di Bologna.

A similar transformation had occurred in France in 1666 when Louis *XIV's* chief minister decided that the king needed royal academicians to map the realm, perfect astronomy, improve navigation, and keep France current in natural knowledge. The Académie Royale des Sciences came into existence with a handful of salaried members including distinguished foreigners, notably Christiaan Huygens. Reorganized in 1699 and again definitively in 1716, the Paris Academy became the exemplar of a learned body in the service of a great monarch. Its forty-four regular members were distributed into six classes, three "mathematical" (geometry, astronomy, and mechanics) and three "physical" (chemistry, anatomy, and botany), and into three ranks (pensionnaire, associé, and adjoint). Its standing secretary had the duties of composing a history of the Academy's work each year as a preface to the annual volume of original *mémoires* presented obligatorily by members and, in due course, of composing their obituaries, which, taken together, became a role model for aspiring contributors to natural knowledge. The Paris Academy set prize competitions, advised the crown, and occasionally sponsored special projects like excursions to determine the shape of the earth. Typically, however, its members did their work at their own expense and in their own rooms or with material and in space provided by other Parisian institutions.

Only a very few monarchs could copy the academy of the King of France. The first to try, the King of Prussia, acting under pressure from Gottfried Leibniz, proved too stingy; the academy he established in 1700 had an uncertain and impoverished existence until refounded by Frederick the Great on Parisian principles. Its new statutes of 1744 provided for four classes (experimental philosophy, mathematics, speculative philosophy, and literature), members divided by rank, and, like the Paris Academy, a variable number of nonresident "correspondents." It published its histories and memoirs in French and, again like its model, engaged distinguished foreigners, notably Pierre de Maupertuis and Leonhard Euler. The westernizing Peter the Great of Russia also had the ambition and wherewithal to create an academy of salaried savants, which he accomplished in St. Petersburg in 1724, without Russian members. Monarchs more modest than the rulers of France, Prussia, and Russia founded smaller academies on similar principles. In 1783 the King of Sardinia transformed a group that had existed since 1757 into the Académie Royale of Turin, at the trifling cost of a building and a budget, and in 1757 the Elector of Bavaria established the Akademie der Wissenschaften of Munich with a meeting place, operating expenses, and half a dozen paid "professors." Closed or proprietary academies of the Paris type placed particular emphasis on mathematics and its applications, which they did much to advance.

Meanwhile, larger academies free to choose their members and able to salary only two or three functionaries flourished. The prototype was the Royal Society of London (founded in 1662), which had nothing from its patron, King Charles II, but a charter, a mace, and the right to call itself "royal."

Like the Accademia del Cimento, it took much of its rhetoric and purpose from Bacon. Its *Philosophical Transactions* constituted, with the *Mémoires* of the Paris Academy, the most important and reliable periodical literature of natural knowledge during the eighteenth century. Like the Paris Academy, the Royal Society set up commissions to investigate debated matters: the calibration of thermometers, the shapes of lightning rods, and the merits of mesmerism. Since the Society depended on the dues and influence of its fellows, it began by enlisting any interested gentlemen or distinguished foreigners and made no distinction of class or rank. During the seventeenth and most of the eighteenth centuries, the number of fellows elected for their social status or professional affiliation exceeded in number those chosen for their contributions to science. Among the latter were many instrument makers.

Several important academies formed on the pattern of the Royal Society in Britain during the eighteenth century: the Royal Society of Edinburgh (1783), a contribution to the consolidation of the United Kingdom as well as a recognition of the flourishing of natural philosophy in the north; the Manchester Literary and Philosophical Society (1781), which reflected the aspirations and discussed the technologies of the industrializing midlands; and the American Philosophical Society (1768), a venture in colonial Philadelphia that became a symbol of intellectual equality with Europe. Important European counterparts of the Royal Society included Kungl. Vetenskapsakademien of Stockholm (1739), which stressed technological problems of Swedish interest, and the Hollandsche Maatschappij der Wetenschappen of Haarlem (1752), which innovated by distinguishing "directors," who paid dues, from "scientific members," who did the work. Few of the many royal regional academies of France could do more than give out an occasional prize or publication. An exception, the Académie Royale des Sciences et Belles-Lettres of Bordeaux (1712), though it had fewer than twenty members at any time, had its own building, library, botanical garden, and instrument collection, all given to it by local philanthropists.

The division of labor in the republic of learning, according to which universities disseminated, and academies increased, knowledge, often created tensions between professors and academicians. Universities sometimes opposed the creation of academies, as the University of Leyden did that of the Hollandsche Maatschappij. The modus vivendi established by the Istituto di Bologna, whereby university and academy exchanged personnel, existed formally in only one other place during the eighteenth century. In 1752 the English Hannoverian government set up a Königliche Societät der Wissenschaften as an adjunct to the university it had established in Göttingen in 1737. A few of the professors ran the academy, which issued publications, including an influential review, the *Göttingische gelehrte Anzeigen*, read all over Europe.

The Bologna-Göttingen model did not become the route by which professors came to dominate the academies during the nineteenth century. Instead, professors added research to their duties. This development, which began at the end of the eighteenth century, accelerated under the transformation of higher education and academic life caused by the French Revolution.

The importance of academies in the advancement of natural knowledge declined as professors took them over. Two factors were chiefly responsible. For one, journals independent of academies came to dominate scientific communication. Traditional academies published only a small fraction of the millions of papers carried in scientific journals between

1800 and 1900. Academies found an important niche in publishing, however, by printing papers rapidly, for example, in the weekly *Comptes rendus* (begun in 1835) of the Paris Academy and in the monthly *Proceedings of* the Royal Society (begun in 1856). Owing to the revolution in communications effected by railroads and the International Postal Union, a professor could send reprints of an article from the unread proceedings of his local academy directly to those who needed to know.

The second factor that diminished the scientific role of learned societies was the confirmation of the research activity of professors and provision for it in the higher schools and universities. With the invention of scientific institutes and departments with their own laboratories and apparatus after the middle of the century, academies ceased to be the main locus for the presentation and criticism of new results, for peer review, or for the financial and rhetorical support of research. This trend continued briskly in the twentieth century with the creation of governmental and industrial research laboratories and central funding agencies. The number of competent research scientists active in 2000 greatly exceeded the number of members in the national and regional academies; and even though more places have been added, academies have long since been unable to meet the expectation implied by the epitaph from Dijon, that they could admit all worthy contributors to science.

The nineteenth and twentieth centuries saw the spread of national academies of the Royal Society type throughout the world and the invention of an important new type, represented by the Akademiia Nauk, successor to the Petersburg Academy. The Soviet Union chose to funnel state support for research and advanced training in science through the Akademiia and its regional dependencies, which thereby captured functions that further west belonged to universities and government laboratories. A senior academician in the Soviet Union had useful perquisites and often enjoyed political influence or protection. Similar arrangements held elsewhere in the Soviet bloc.

Most academies now primarily serve organizational and honorific functions. They are nodes in national and international networks that promote research or outreach beyond their own memberships. The international coupling of major academies began in the nineteenth century as the International Association of Academies. Headquartered in Berlin, it oversaw such projects as the Carte du Ciel and the International Catalogue of Scientific Literature. During World War I, the Paris Academy, the Royal Society, and the U.S. National Academy of Sciences (through a subsidiary it set up called the National Research Council) organized science for military purposes. After the war the allies revived the cooperation of academies under an International Research Council, which at first excluded institutions belonging to the defeated Central Powers. The international network survived World War II in the form of the International Council of Scientific Unions (ICSU). A regional subset of these academies, the European Federation of National Academies of Sciences and Humanities (ALLEA), declares the objectives of its thirty-eight members to be to "promote excellence in science and scholarship . . . value and promote independence from ideological and political interests . . . [and] serve society with advice on science policy." They differ from their forerunners in asserting independence from the regimes that support them.

Although the national academies do advise governments when asked, and also award prizes and research grants (if any), and do what they can to improve public understand-

ing of science, their main function now is honorific. Election to a major scientific academy is itself a distinction. The leading modern institute in the bestowal of prizes is an old academy, that of Stockholm, which exerts a worldwide influence far beyond the scientific work it fosters by giving the Nobel awards in physics and chemistry. Carrying the tendency toward absurdity, "academies" with virtually no purpose but to elect members multiplied in the twentieth century. Examples are the Academia Europaea (founded in 1988) and the Académie International d'Histoire des Sciences (1928). These organizations differ little in function and notoriety from the Baseball Hall of Fame.

J. L. HEILBRON

ACCELERATOR. During the twentieth century physicists developed increasingly powerful artificial means to produce very high-energy particles to transform or disintegrate atoms. At the end of World War I, Ernest Rutherford used alpha particles from naturally occurring sources of radiation to transform nitrogen into oxygen. He called for the development of more energetic sources of charged particles for nuclear experiments. Two of his students, John D. Cockroft and Ernest T. S. Walton, completed the first successful particle accelerator at the Cavendish Laboratory in Cambridge in 1932. By accumulating a potential of hundreds of thousands of volts, Cockroft and Walton accelerated protons to energies sufficient to disintegrate the nuclei of light elements. Owing to the repulsion between nuclei and protons, and the difficulty of creating and maintaining high potentials, their machine could not transform heavier elements.

Physicists soon turned to other means to accelerate particles. In the United States, Ernest Lawrence's magnetic resonance accelerator (the cyclotron), which applied energy to protons or deuterons in successive small steps rather than, as in the Cockroft-Walton machine, in one large jump, provided bombardments able to transform almost all nuclear species. His linear accelerator used the same principle of resonance acceleration to propel heavier nuclei. Another American, Robert Van de Graaff, returned to the one-jump method by a technique that allowed the accumulation of up to about ten million volts on a spherical conductor. The Van de Graaff, cyclotron, and linear accelerators were used at many universities and research institutes in the 1930s to explore the new field of nuclear physics. Financial support for the development of particle accelerators came largely from medical philanthropies. They hoped their high-voltage X rays, neutrons, and other particles as well as the artificially radioactive products of their interactions with other substances would be more effective against cancer and other diseases than the natural radiations from radium and other substances.

Lawrence was especially successful in generating support for his cyclotrons. The parameter most often employed to indicate their power—the diameter of the pole pieces of the magnet that retained the particles in their spiraling orbits as they accumulated energy—grew from a few inches to sixty. The increase in size gave a monumental increase in the energy with which the particles escaped from the magnet—from a few hundred thousand to thirty-two million electron volts. In 1939 Lawrence received the Nobel Prize in physics for his cyclotron and work done with it. The consequent enlargement of his prestige helped him to convince the Rockefeller Foundation to give the money to build a giant cyclotron with pole pieces 184 inches in diameter. Intended to be the last and largest of all particle accelerators and, in that way, the counterpart to the 200-inch telescope the foundation supported at Palomar, the 184-inch proved instead to be the first of a generation of much larger particle accelerators.

The cyclotron did not accelerate electrons because their loss in energy and increase in mass owing to acceleration made them unattractive for work at high energy. Nonetheless, in 1939 Donald William Kerst invented a "betatron," which produced electrons or energies useful in nuclear investigations. After the war linear electron accelerators became competitive with proton accelerators for some purposes, and physicists turned the intense radiation of electrons maintained in circular orbits to advantage in "synchrotrons" whose "light" could be used in materials science and other applications.

The discovery of nuclear fission in uranium in 1939 provided a new role for particle accelerators and nuclear physicists. Cyclotrons at Berkeley and Los Alamos produced the first samples of plutonium, and cyclotroneering principles underlay the electromagnetic separation of isotopes in large banks of "calutrons" (after California University) that separated the fissile isotope of uranium for use in the first atomic bombs. Although other techniques eventually proved more efficient, these wartime successes opened the door to federal funding of nuclear physics by the Manhattan Engineer District and its successor, the Atomic Energy Commission.

The completion of the 184-inch cyclotron as a synchrocyclotron in 1946 was the first successful application of the synchrotron principle discovered by Edwin M. McMillan and Vladimir I. Veksler during the war. This principle enabled designers to accelerate particles in tight bunches by changing the frequency of the accelerating fields in step with relativistic changes in the mass of the particles. A series of accelerators built throughout the second half of the century, ranging from Brookhaven's 'Cosmotron' to the Tevatron, which produces trillions of electron-volts, incorporate the synchrotron principle and advances in magnetic technique that permit the confinement of the beam of accelerating particles to a narrow, evacuated pipe of fixed radius. The only link to the size of these machines is financial. The first version of CERN had a diameter of 200 meters; the one now under construction these extends to 27 kilometers. The largest current machine in the United States, at Fermilab, has a circumference of four miles, within which a herd of bison graze.

The linear accelerator also developed rapidly after World War II. At Berkeley, Luis Alvarez invented a type for protons using war surplus radar equipment. His student Wolfgang Panofsky applied the scheme to electrons at the Stanford Linear Accelerator (1962). Discoveries of new elements and particles by particle accelerators led to Nobel Prizes as well as increasingly larger accelerators in the United States, western Europe, and the Soviet Union. The prestige and power of these machines made them political as well as physical icons. Only after the end of the Cold War did the enormous cost of accelerators prompt the United States to withdraw from the competition by canceling the Superconducting Super Collider.

ROBERT W. SEIDEL

ACOUSTICS AND HEARING. Acoustics, the science of sound, falls at the intersection of several fields, including mechanics, hydrodynamics, thermodynamics, and electromagnetism. Scientific interest in sound also derives from human hearing and hence involves physiology and psychology. Also, acoustics engages fields outside science such as music and architecture. A distinct field of acoustics, including but not limited to hearing, gradually emerged from this disparate background in the eighteenth and nineteenth centuries, aided by the use of quantitative apparatus to produce and detect sound and the mathematical analysis of the results.

Ancient and medieval philosophers of nature studied acoustics mainly as a means to understand music. Mathematical theories of music dated at least to the Pythagoreans, who identified musical intervals as ratios of whole numbers and related musical pitches to lengths of vibrating strings. Although a few ancient writers speculated on the wave nature of sound and the propagation of compressions, Arabic and European natural philosophers through the Middle Ages and Renaissance continued to study acoustics only as part of music theory, if at all. In the early modern period, natural philosophers began to undertake systematic experiments and to extend their investigations to sound in general. Experiments with vibrating strings led Galileo Galilei to posit the relation between pitch and frequency, elucidated around the same time by Giovanni Benedetti and Isaac Beeckman, and also to suggest that pitch depended on the tension and diameter of the string as well as its length. Marin Mersenne in the early seventeenth century used very long vibrating strings, some over one hundred feet long, to arrive at a quantitative relation between pitch and frequency. Mersenne also measured the speed of sound, as did his contemporary Pierre Gassendi, who asserted that soft and loud sounds traveled at the same speed.

The scientific academies that sprang up later in the seventeenth century would make the speed of sound a prime program. Around the same time, experiments with improved air pumps, beginning with Otto von Guericke and extended by Robert Boyle and Francis Hauksbee, convinced natural philosophers that sound did not travel in a vacuum. Experiments on the speed of sound tested in particular the theory of Isaac Newton, whose work on fluid mechanics in the *Principia* included acoustics. But Newton arrived at a figure for the speed of sound, based on the pressure and density of the medium, at odds with contemporary estimates. Mathematicians in the eighteenth century, notably Leonhard Euler, Jean d'Alembert, and Joseph Louis Lagrange, extended Newton's analytical mechanics and pneumatics to explain the discrepancy between theory and measurement, and Pierre-Simon, Marquis de Laplace, Jean-Baptiste Biot, and Siméon-Denis Poisson at the start of the nineteenth century succeeded by suggesting that the passing sound wave heated the medium.

The quantification of acoustics accelerated in the nineteenth century, driven by the use of laboratory apparatus such as tuning forks, vibrating plates, and sirens to produce standardized tones, and sounding boards and the stethoscope to detect them. The new instruments helped bring acoustics into the realm of precision physics and also indicated the increasing quantification of physiology. Hermann von Helmholtz combined knowledge of the physiology and physics of sound in his synthetic treatise *On Sensations of Tone* of 1862, which confirmed that the ear analyzes periodic sound waves into Fourier sums of simple harmonics and predicted the existence of nonlinear summation tones. John Tyndall helped bring Helmholtz's work to English-speaking audiences, elaborating it with his own experiments and generalizing beyond Helmholtz's particular interest in music. Lord Rayleigh then provided a systematic mathematical analysis of sound in his *Theory of Sound* of 1877–78; although Helmholtz provided mathematical details in appendices to his works, he had kept the main text nonmathematical. Rayleigh's two-volume work analyzed diverse phenomena of sound based on the vibration of air, liquids, and gases and of solid strings, plates, and rods under various perturbations; the books completed the edifice of classical acoustics.

New problems and programs were meanwhile emerging from the development of electromagnetism and its application to acoustics. Alexander Graham Bell, familiar with Helmholtz's research and inspired by his own work with deaf students, invented a means for transmitting speech over wires, called the telephone. Bell faced several coclaimants for the invention and strong competition for its development, including an improved system designed by Thomas Edison. Edison in the meantime invented the phonograph, the foundation for the recording industry. The development of radio further spurred the invention of microphones, loudspeakers, amplifiers, vacuum tubes, and oscillators by the burgeoning electrical industry. Industrial engineers also agreed on an international standard for the intensity of sound, the decibel. Magnetostriction, piezoelectricity, and acousto-optics, three more developments of the late nineteenth century, would also provide new ways to produce and detect sound. Electroacoustics opened up a rich new field for the study of sound in the twentieth century.

Electroacoustics also helped to transform architectural acoustics, the study of which dated to the ancients—the Roman architect Vitruvius wrote on the acoustics of theaters in the first century B.C.—and was extended in the seventeenth century by the Jesuit polymath Athanasius Kircher, among others. Around 1900 Wallace Sabine revived the subject with his work relating reverberation times to the volume and building materials of rooms. The introduction of electroacoustic technology, along with new sound-absorbing building materials, provided a means to active control of sound inside buildings, and in 1930 Carl Eyring revised Sabine's results to accommodate the new acoustic environments.

Sound does not just travel through air. The use of submarines in World War I spurred efforts to develop ways to detect them, which soon focused on sound. The subsequent development of sonar for submarine warfare provided much support of acoustics research and also new tools for marine biology and oceanography. Sound also travels through matter, and ultra-high frequency sound, or ultrasound, became an important probe for solid-state research and found application in industrial materials and in medicine in the second half of the twentieth century.

PETER J. WESTWICK

ADVANCEMENT OF SCIENCE, NATIONAL ASSOCIATIONS FOR THE.

During the seventeenth century, naturalists and philosophers emphasized scientific communication among themselves and sought venues for public demonstrations of scientific achievement. Francis Bacon shifted discussion toward what he identified as the "advancement of learning" through human design and proposed a hierarchical model of organization in his fictional work, *The New Atlantis* (1627). Advancing knowledge became associated not only with individual genius but with organizations like the Royal Society of London (1662), which sponsored research activities and publications to share new knowledge. Local voluntary societies provided repositories for specimens, artifacts, and instruments important for advancing research, but these proved expensive to maintain and of benefit primarily to a local membership.

By the nineteenth century, transportation networks of canals and railroads facilitated travel while public interest in science was creating popular audiences and paying occupations for scientists just as cultivators of natural science began to feel a sense of community. German-speaking physicians and scientists, who also felt political isolation, were the first to organize on a national level. Lorenz Oken proposed the

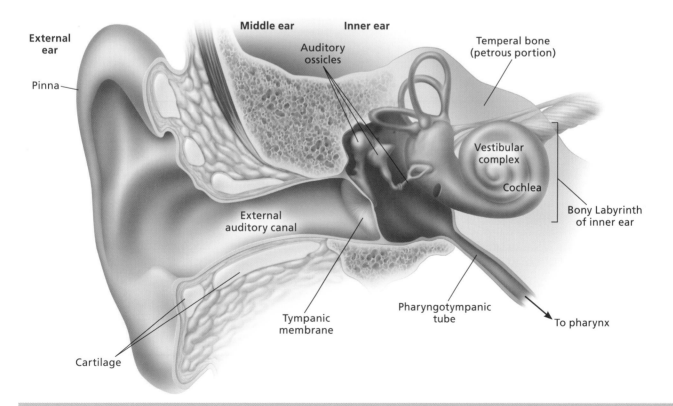

Sound collected by the external ear causes the tympanic membrane (center right) to vibrate; the vibrations are transmitted to the fluid-filled cochlea (the spiral structure); minute hairs lining the cochlea generate the nerve impulses that activate the brain.

foundation of the Gesellschaft Deutscher Naturforscher ünd Arzte (GDNA), modeled loosely on a Swiss organization, in 1822. The GDNA grew quickly, met in a different city each year, and facilitated communication among its members.

Several British attendees at the German meetings, who perceived a decline of science in England, Scotland, and Ireland, rallied colleagues by letter and publication to attend a meeting in York, "the most centrical city for the three kingdoms," in 1831. The resulting peripatetic British Association for the Advancement of Science (BAAS) proved highly successful at attracting public audiences. It quickly became a forum where physical, natural, and social scientists could discuss matters of scientific content and policy, capacities that proved particularly attractive to the visiting North Americans who subsequently established the American Association for the Advancement of Science (AAAS), founded in Philadelphia in 1848. Positioned to enhance the professional ambitions of leaders and serve as advocates for their plans, the AAAS members conducted business at their annual meetings, published proceedings, and created committees to look into special topics from terrestrial magnetism to science education. As a scientific forum the AAAS allowed disputants the opportunity to argue from evidence before peers and to wrestle with such complicated issues as chemical nomenclature and universal species taxonomy. Over the next half century, France, the Netherlands, and Belgium established similar organizations and the movement spread into increasingly independent colonies seeking industrial and government sponsorship for scientific and technological activities. The Italians reinvented a Riunione degli Scienziati Italiani (1839) under various titles over the next century as well.

The BAAS leaders extended membership privileges to British colonials and held five overseas meetings in colonies between 1884 and 1914. The resultant linkages advanced scientific dialogue but sustained international hierarchies as well. Public lectures by distinguished scientists provided stimulus to local science, and sometimes local scientists and visiting experts collaborated on research projects, but inevitably much of the scientific data, and credit, returned home at the conclusion of collaborations. That, at least, was the case for anthropology in Canada, where important early work on northwestern Native Americans and an ethnographic survey of tribes provided unprecedented, immediate opportunities for Canadian amateurs but left no national school in anthropology when the experts went back to England. Far from Britain, the Australia and New Zealand Association for the Advancement of Science (1888) began to link regional scientists and publicize their work. During the first quarter of the twentieth century similar initiatives came in India, South Africa, Hong Kong, and other colonial outposts.

In the twentieth century countries aspiring to democracy as well as technological and scientific progress initiated associations to advance science. Government sponsorship, rather than grassroots voluntarism, became common; for example, the Japan Society for the Promotion of Science (1932) became a channel for funds to large, expensive research facilities. After World War II the model seemed promising for aspiring nations like Brazil, where the Brazilian Society for the Advancement of Science grew from scientific initiatives that persuaded the government to provide financial support. Scientific members, however, found themselves politicized and, indeed, in conflict with policies of a military regime during turbulent times. Nationally based societies, regardless of their financial autonomy, inevitably worked within and through their home political systems, carefully balancing professional norms as they lobbied for scientific budgets, educational policies to support science, and independent peer review for evaluation of research.

National societies varied considerably as they pursued the goal of advancing science. In Britain the early success of the BAAS correlated with the status of scientific activity and high visibility of prominent scientists like Charles Lyell, and was sustained by its outreach in provincial areas to enhance science education. In the United States, members relied on the AAAS to establish a forum for widely dispersed scientists, to maintain links among scientists across the increasingly distinct scientific specialties, and to advocate science to state and federal governments. In the twentieth century the AAAS published *Science* magazine, under editor James McKeen Cattell, the leading journal across the sciences with the largest international readership in the early twentieth century. In this respect the AAAS outdistanced the BAAS, which does not run the leading general British science journal, *Nature*.

The AAAS, with affiliates from most major professional societies, moved to rooms in the Smithsonian Institution until it built its own permanent headquarters in Washington, D.C., where it also reported on research and developments in federal agencies and budgets. By the late twentieth century the AAAS had an administrative and editorial infrastructure whose capacity to report on scientific developments was international, while specific programs in the organization concentrated on science education, promoted gender and racial diversity, and responded to ethical issues raised by advances in science, technology, and medicine. National societies produced a sense of identity even as they provided vehicles for international exchange of publications, visiting status to foreign attendees at meetings, and occasional collaborations.

Efforts to link these national organizations in a formal way have had mixed success. Shortly after World War II, in 1950, the United Nations Educational, Scientific, and Cultural Organization (UNESCO) sponsored an International Meeting for Associations for the Advancement of Science, but the effort faded from lack of support by the well-established organizations like the AAAS and BAAS. An International Federation of Associations for the Advancement of Science and Technology founded in the 1990s persisted, suggesting that the rootedness in particular settings has allowed many national associations to be highly successful but that emphasis on national needs and interests constrained systematic cooperation, at least before the advent of the Internet.

SALLY GREGORY KOHLSTEDT

AFRICA. The history of science in the diverse continent of Africa is best dealt with under four headings: precolonial science in Islamic North Africa, precolonial science in animist Sub-Saharan Africa, European-based colonial science, and science in independent African nations.

Precolonial North Africa

From the eighth century on, North Africa had close ties, culturally and scientifically, with neighboring Islamic regions. From the ninth to the thirteenth century, scholars in Egypt looked to the Baghdad caliphates. In the Maghreb, stretching west of Egypt to Morocco, scholars had close links with Islamic Spain, which saw a flowering of culture and learning through the twelfth century.

For a time, mathematics, astronomy, and medicine flourished under the patronage of the sultans. However, by the fifteenth century, North African Islamic movements had nearly extinguished these intellectual inquiries. Legal scholars and theologians came to view rational study of nature as irrelevant and potentially heretical. Moreover, mystical Sufi orders became widely popular among the people. The role of patient empirical and rational investigation of nature as a way to learn about God was subordinated far below the revelations of the Quran and mysticism. Centers of Islamic learning, such as al-Azhar of Cairo, the Zaituna of Tunis, and the Qarawiyin of Fez no longer supported teachers of natural philosophy. Those who sought such teachers had to search for dwindling numbers of isolated scholars.

What remained was routine work, such as compilation of astronomical tables, which continued to the eighteenth century. Because it was needed to determine the *qibla* (the direction to Mecca) and the five daily times of prayer, astronomy had a privileged status. Even so, it became suspect because of its association with astrology, which was often practiced in the courts of the sultans. Increasingly, folk astronomical methods determined the *qibla* and times of call to prayer in place of the earlier complex, mathematical astronomy. Mathematical usage narrowed to practical matters such as the calculation of inheritances. Medicine too declined; only the vestiges of early Islamic medical science survived. In its place, a folk medicine, which continues to be practiced today, brought together Yunani (Greek) medicine derived from Galen and mystical prophetic medicine associated with the sayings of Mohammed. By the time of European colonization, innovative work in mathematics, medicine, and natural philosophy had long disappeared.

Nor did such work survive along the southern "shores" of the Sahara, the Sahel, a cultural outpost of North Africa. North Africans brought to the Sahel writing and formal education for teaching the Quran. By the sixteenth century, Timbuktu had emerged as a major center of Islamic learning, where mathematics of inheritance was taught, but not natural philosophy. By then other leading Islamic universities, such as the Qarawiyin and the Zaituna, had already jettisoned nonreligious studies.

Precolonial Sub-Saharan Africa

South of the Sahel, traditional medicine and various technologies, including sophisticated iron and bronze metallurgy, flourished prior to European colonization. They did little, though, to point the way to anything resembling modern science. In the African worldview, the natural world was a realm of spirits approachable by sorcery. In this context, analyzing nature according to the rational, disinterested ideal of Western science was unthinkable. Smelting iron required placation of spirits. Traditional healers interpreted the spiritual, psychological aspects of the ill and their communities using mediation with the spirits (although they also turned to herbalists for remedies that had proven effective). Moreover, lack of written languages impeded the progressive accumulation of natural knowledge beyond the limits of oral traditions. Even after the arrival of Christian missionaries, animistic worldviews persisted.

The incursions of the Europeans further discouraged the appearance of science. Importation of European goods, such as weapons, iron, cloth, and glass, undermined traditional technologies. The consequences of the slave trade and warfare in some regions exacerbated the loss of indigenous technology. Traditional knowledge and skills dwindled yet further, sending the societies into cultural decline.

Colonial Africa

Napoleon's invasion of Egypt (1798–1802), with an accompanying body of scientists who studied the riches of its ancient past, marked the beginning of European scientific interest in Africa. The French began colonizing in earnest in Algeria in the 1830s by sending a large medical corps. Under the direction of the French military, doctors investigated Algeria's social structure and environment during their off-duty hours, exploring its potential as a colony. Several meteorological stations were set up extending deep into the Sahara. Also, a small observatory, established in 1858 to provide mariners with accurate time, became the Observatory of Algiers. From these beginnings, French scientific societies took root in North Africa, some of which carried out notable scientific work. For example, research in the Pasteur Institutes in Algeria and Tunisia led to the discovery of the carriers of malaria, typhus, and bubonic plague. These successes were rewarded with Nobel Prizes for Charles Louis Alphonse Laveran in 1907 and Charles Nicolle in 1928. Despite these achievements, the mother institutes in Paris tightly controlled scientific work. Following World War I, the French government founded the Ecole Supérieure d'Agriculture Tropicale and Institut de Médecine Vétérinaire Exotique to train colonial personnel in tropical agriculture and veterinary medicine. However, coordination of research in the colonies had to wait until the Vichy government of World War II formed the Office de la Recherche Scientifique Coloniale, which set long-term research and training goals.

In British colonies, scientific initiative, usually applied to agriculture and medicine, rested with the colonial governments, although fundamental research and training remained in Britain. In particular, research in tropical medi-

The South African Astronomical Observatory in Sunderland, South Africa, is a partner in many international research collaborations.

cine, most importantly work on parasitic diseases and their hosts, which initially fell to medical doctors in the field, centered in Britain with the founding of the London and Liverpool Schools of Tropical Medicine in 1899. After World War I, organizations covering different regions, such as the Forestry and Agricultural Organization of British East Africa and the West African Research Organization, promoted and coordinated research, largely in the agriculture of cash crops such as cocoa and palm oil. Scientific work shifted back to the colonies and regional centers with financing directly through the colonial governments.

Characteristically, European research in Africa was performed to benefit the colonialists or the mother country. Africans rarely advanced beyond assistants. Moreover, education for Africans imbued them with contempt of manual labor. Consequently they eschewed farming and generally did not apply their knowledge to make greatly needed improvements in agriculture.

Medicine had an important role in colonial Africa. The few doctors who went south of the Sahara were typically missionaries employing medicine as a proselytizing vehicle. They deprecated indigenous medical practice, promoting a decline in herbal medicine and spiritual healing. At the same time, the impersonal, antispiritual character of Western medicine and the disdain of doctors for local traditions alienated much of the population.

The only part of Africa to develop leading, independent schools of research was the Union of South Africa. The Royal Observatory of the Cape of Good Hope, established in 1820 to study the southern sky, became a respected observatory under the Scotsman Sir David Gill (director, 1897–1907), a leading proponent for using photography to accurately measure stellar positions. South Africa became the favored site for southern hemisphere observatories owing to its dry highlands and political stability. Sir John Herschel, a celebrated English astronomer, travelled there in the 1830s and made extensive observations of nebulae in the southern skies. In the 1920s, three American universities, Yale, Michigan, and Harvard, each set up astronomical stations in the interior of South Africa to complement their observatories in the northern hemisphere. In the 1920s and 1930s, South Africa moved to the forefront of geological and paleontological research as well, largely through the work of Alexander du Toit, a Huguenot descendent. He was one of the greatest field geologists of the twentieth century and an early supporter of the theory of continental drift, for which he accumulated an impressive amount of evidence. During the same period, research on ancient ancestors of humans began to flourish in Africa with the discoveries of fossils of *Australopithecus africanus* by the South Africans Raymond Dart and Robert Broom. Another field in which South Africa has made a mark is botany. Of the botanical gardens that exist in several African countries, the Kirstenbosch gardens of South Africa (established in 1913) are the largest and most ambitious, with extensive programs devoted to saving endangered plant species.

Independent Africa

Immediately after independence from the colonial powers, which had occurred for most African countries by the mid-1960s, the new governments typically considered support of scientific research unnecessary. Building a national research capability was often deemed to consume too much time and money for young nations with limited resources; besides, the argument went, any research needed could be acquired from the former colonizing countries. On the other side of the coin, the most scientifically advanced country on the continent, South Africa, exploited anthropology and psychology to justify apartheid.

By the late 1960s, African governments began to recognize the need to generate their own scientific research and technological development. Through several conferences held with African governments, such as the International Conference of the Organization of Research and Training in Africa in Relation to the Study, Conservation and Utilization of National Resources (1964), the United Nations played a major role in changing local attitudes toward science and technology. UNESCO has reinforced the idea with dozens of missions to African countries promoting science and technology.

The hurdles are high. Cash-strapped government efforts often lead to routine, uncoordinated, understaffed, and unproductive investigations. African countries face serious shortages of scientists. Many of the brightest students study overseas and remain there. The African universities, having few resources, cannot supply the needed body of scientists. Overwhelmed by increasing enrollments and decreasing funds, the universities do little research. The bulk of research takes place in institutes headed by African scientists and financed by international organizations or governments. For example, the Kainji Lake Research Institute in Nigeria searches for new viral outbreaks, such as Lassa and Ebola fevers.

Africa has a choice between adopting Western science exclusively to solve its problems and bridging the gap between Western and indigenous, traditional approaches. In some countries, Western and traditional medicine are merging into systems to care better for the people. Many Africans today regard traditional medicine as a positive force that can complement the advantages of Western practices. This fresh outlook may help encourage a science in Africa for solving African problems and building the African future.

ROBERT DALE HALL

AIDS. Acquired immune deficiency syndrome (AIDS) was recognized in 1981 as the condition underlying a cluster of several different diseases, notably a type of pneumonia and certain cancers, afflicting certain demographic groups—in the United States, homosexual men in particular. A group headed by Luc Montagnier at the Pasteur Institute in Paris and another under Robert Gallo at the National Cancer Institute in Bethesda, Maryland, sought the cause of the syndrome. Both suspected that the disease agent was a retrovirus similar to the two viruses then known to produce leukemia in human beings. The two groups cooperated. In 1984 both isolated the culprit retrovirus from the tissues of AIDS victims, and characterized it using both serological and molecular techniques. It is much disputed whether Gallo's laboratory succeeded independently of Montagnier's or whether it isolated the retrovirus from material provided by Montagnier's and then failed appropriately to acknowledge the source.

Wholly different from the two leukemic retroviruses, the AIDS agent was soon dubbed the human immunodeficiency virus (HIV) because it attacks the immune system. Scientists in many laboratories learned that HIV targets the white blood cells called "T cells" (because they come from the thymus), particularly the major fraction of them that bristle at their surfaces with a molecule termed CD4 and that direct the body's immune response. In AIDS patients, the number of T cells with CD4 molecules is sharply reduced, steadily compromising the body's ability to mobilize against one or more wasting diseases.

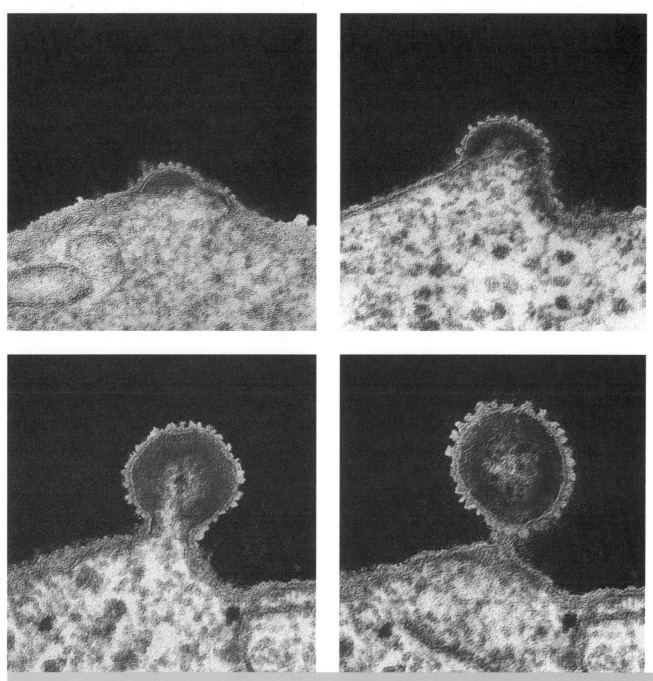

Colored transmission electron micrograph of an AIDS virus (red/green) budding from the surface of a T-lymphocyte white blood cell. The new virus particles erupt to infect other T-lymphocytes.

HIV enters the body mainly by transfusion with infected blood, intravenous drug injection with infected needles, or unprotected sexual intercourse with an infected person. The Montagnier and Gallo groups both quickly developed and patented different blood tests that detect the presence of the virus from antigens produced against its several parts by the body's immune system. A dispute between the governments of the United States and France over which group properly had rights in them was resolved by a compromise in 1987 that divided the revenues. Blood-screening tests greatly diminished the risk of infection to people who depended on blood transfusions, notably hemophiliacs.

Public officials, especially in the United States, were initially skittish towards dealing with AIDS because of its strong link to homosexuality. However, coming to recognize that it posed a major threat to public health, they substantially increased public funding of AIDS research and urged sexual abstinence, monogamy, and the use of condoms to halt the spread of the disease. The search for a vaccine against AIDS has so far proved fruitless. However, during the 1990s several biotechnology firms developed pharmaceuticals that inhibit the reproduction of HIV. Daily cocktails of these drugs have turned HIV infection into a chronic rather than a deadly condition for those who can afford the treatment. Between 1993 and 1997, the incidence of AIDS in the United States fell by almost 50 percent, to about 22 per 100,000 people. But many live in regions where preventative measures are unknown or ignored, and the cocktails unaffordable. Across the globe at the end of 2001, an estimated 40 million people were infected with HIV, and in sub-Saharan Africa AIDS was epidemic.

DANIEL J. KEVLES

ALCHEMY. Scholars can make solid arguments for the rise of alchemical ideas in ancient China or Persia, but most identify its birthplace in the Hellenistic cultural period, probably in

Egypt under the Ptolemaic Kingdom and the early Roman Empire. The sort of alchemy practiced there was born from a mix of Aristotelian theories of matter; Hellenistic religious philosophies such as gnosticism, hermeticism, and the mystery cults; and various ancient metallurgical and chemical techniques. The first practitioners probably were a secretive group or sect, perhaps Hellenized Egyptians in Alexandria.

The earliest definitely known alchemical writer, Zosimus, lived in Alexandria about 300 A.D. and wrote a handbook or encyclopedia of his craft. The allegorical and allusive character of the writing has made its interpretation problematic. Zosimus's book forms a part of the Greek alchemical corpus, a collection of mostly anonymous or pseudonymous writings first assembled a hundred years or more after Zosimus, and known today from a handful of medieval Greek copies. Zosimus and other Greek alchemists aimed to produce valuable metals from less expensive materials, prepare pharmaceutical remedies, and undergo philosophical or religious purification. Important materials in the craft included sulfur, mercury, arsenic, and electrum (a gold-silver alloy).

Leading Islamic scholars, who derived the craft from the Greeks, practiced it, especially in the tenth and eleventh centuries. The number of modern chemical terms that derive from Arabic—alchemy, alkali, alcohol, elixir, and naphtha, for example—indicate the importance of this period to science. The most famous Arabic alchemist, Jabir ibn Mayyan, supposed to have lived in the early ninth century, seems in fact to have

been a mystical Islamic sect that wrote pseudonymously a hundred years after Jabir's death. The celebrated philosophers al-Razi (Rhazes) and Avicenna (Ibn Sīnā) both pursued alchemy. A chief idea of medieval Arabic alchemy held that metals were formed of sulfur and mercury in various proportions, and that altering the proportions in a given metal could change its type, even from lead to gold. Not every alchemist, however, believed in the possibility of such transmutations.

During the twelfth century, scholars in the Christian West translated the ancient Greek philosophical and scientific corpus from Arabic into Latin; among these were works on alchemy elaborated by the Muslims. Albertus Magnus and Roger Bacon occupied themselves, among much else, with alchemical pursuits. A slightly later figure (fl. ca. 1300), perhaps the most important Western alchemist of the Middle Ages, called himself Geber. (Until about a century ago, scholars regarded "Geber" as the Latin form of "Jabir," and Geber's books as Latin translations of the *Suppositions Jabir;* they now regard Geber as a pseudonym of an unidentified Latin scholar.)

In Geber we first see unequivocal evidence for the use of concentrated mineral acids, with proof of distilled alcohol coming around this same period. These new substances, made possible by technological innovations, especially the more efficient cooling of distillates, dramatically altered the operational repertoire of chemists and alchemists. Three fourteenth-century Catalonians—Arnald of Villanova, Ramon Lull, and John of Rupescissa—incorporated these innovations into alchemy. Among other changes, the position of mercury in alchemical manipulations became more central. Despite this activity, interest in alchemy declined, only to reappear with renewed vigor in the Renaissance.

Alchemical ideas grew out of the cultures of which they were a part. Consequently, Greek, Arabic, late medieval, Renaissance, and early modern alchemical traditions each had distinctive characteristics. The craft also diffused within each cultural tradition. Some alchemists devoted themselves to practical tasks: pharmaceutical preparations; techniques of smelting, assaying, and metalworking; or manufacture of dyes and other chemical substances of commercial importance. Other alchemists sought to produce gold from base metals, or the "elixir of life" that would cure any disease. Still others regarded their discipline as an ethical or religious doctrine. Just as one could cure a metal of its imperfections to produce eternally incorruptible gold, or cure a human body of its imperfections to produce eternal life, so also, with the right discipline and approach, could one cure one's soul of its flaws and achieve salvation in heaven. In Renaissance Europe, the hermetic arts experienced a resurgence along with the humanist movement. Alchemy was regarded as one of these secret sciences, and many practitioners were powerfully influenced by Christian mysticism.

A leading early sixteenth-century alchemist was Theophrastus Bombast von Hohenheim, known as Paracelsus. Paracelsus's philosophy mixed gnosticism, cabalism, astrology, magic, and heterodox Christianity, and he gained significant fame (or notoriety) as a peripatetic iconoclastic physician. He championed the role of alchemically prepared mineral remedies, and certain of his treatments—mercury for the new scourge of syphilis, for instance—were doubtless efficacious. Paracelsus's emphasis on chemicals in pharmacy and medicine, called iatrochemistry or chemiatry, influ-

Paracelsus, that is, Theophrastus Bombastus von Hohenheim (1493–1541), from a celebratory broadsheet of the sixteenth century

enced later figures. Lively controversies over his approach still raged around 1600.

Other sixteenth- and seventeenth-century figures expressed doubts about the possibility of alchemical trans-mutations and cures, and gradually the hermetic influence declined in Europe. Two of the chief heroes of the Scientific Revolution, Robert Boyle and Isaac Newton, were active in alchemical pursuits, which provides a measure of the stay-ing power of these ideas. Through most of the seventeenth century, however, no one distinguished between scientific "chemistry" and "alchemy" (eventually viewed as pseudo-science); both words existed, but each indicated the same set of diverse activities, practical and mystical. Only during the 1680s did the popular chemical textbook of Niccolas Lewey open the first of a series of attacks on alchemy as fraudulent. Early Enlightenment thinkers then banished "alchemy" to the discredited category of occult doctrines while restrict-ing the word "chemistry" to the science we know today.

A. J. ROCKE

ANATOMY. In modern parlance, anatomy is synonymous with the dissection of a human or animal body. In histo-ry, however, the term referred more broadly to a metaphor and a model, a method and a practice. In the early modern period, "anatomy" implied an analysis in the sense of taking something apart—not necessarily a body—to its fundamen-tal components. In the early seventeenth century, Francis Bacon advertised "an anatomy of the world," and in 1621 Robert Burton published his *Anatomy of Melancholy.*

Through the eighteenth century, anatomy referred both to the act of dissection and to its subject, the human or ani-mal body. In this era, the act referred to both living and dead bodies, although later anatomy came to denote dissection of the dead. In addition, anatomical models, such as wax ones used for teaching purposes, as well as dried and preserved specimens, came under the rubric. Many anatomy cabinets existed to teach students basic structures before they wit-nessed an anatomy lesson and to reinforce their knowledge afterwards.

Modern anatomy began with the work of Andreas Vesa-lius and his contemporaries in the sixteenth century. By means of human and animal dissection and animal vivisec-tion, they explored and analyzed the structure of the human body. At almost the same time, however, some anatomists began to find the animal body of interest in itself, and com-parative anatomy developed alongside human anatomy.

Anatomy and physiology were not distinct disciplines until the nineteenth century, and early modern anatomists explored both. William Harvey, for example, explained both the form and the function of the human heart and also com-pared the hearts of different species. Researchers in the sev-enteenth and eighteenth centuries dissected and vivisected many animals both to explore morphology and, especially, to answer questions about function. Because of the variety of animals they used, much of the work of men such as Mar-cello Malpighi was broadly comparative. A group of some of the first members of the Paris Academy of Sciences, includ-ing Claude Perrault and Joseph-Guichard Duverney, used the resources of the Jardin des Plantes and the menagerie at Versailles to compile their important *Mémoires pour servir à l'histoire naturelle des animaux* (1676), which notes morpho-logical similarities but without an underlying theory of type.

Public anatomy, in which a human cadaver (and usually several live and dead animals) was dissected before an audi-ence, flourished in the seventeenth and eighteenth centu-

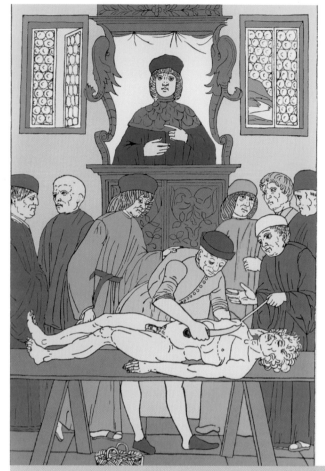

Anatomy lecture and dissection from Joannes de Ketham, *Fasciculus medicinae* (1495)

ries. While such exhibitions taught medical students about the form of the human body, they also attracted members of the general public who found the spectacle entertaining and the contemplation of mortality edifying. The decline of public anatomy at the end of the eighteenth century revealed changing sensibilities as well as a recognition that such dis-section could no longer reveal anything new.

Municipal authorities usually allowed one or two cadavers of executed criminals per year for public dissection, although the number varied according to local custom. Those who gave multiple courses, or wished to do research, usually resorted to grave robbing. Vesalius bragged about his skill at pilfering corpses. Two centuries later Duverney bribed the grave-dig-ger at the Hotel-Dieu in Paris to provide him with bodies. In England, the so-called Murder Act of 1752 gave the College of Surgeons first right to the bodies of executed criminals, but other researchers and lecturers continued to rely on "resurrec-tion men." In Edinburgh in the late 1820s, an entrepreneur-ial pair named Burke and Hare murdered indigent people and sold their bodies to the medical school; this celebrated case helped lead to the passage of the Anatomy Act (1831), which specified that the bodies of the poor who died in workhouses or hospitals be made available for research and teaching.

Over the course of the eighteenth century, Giovanni Bat-tista Morgagni's attention to autopsy indicated the value of revealing pathological conditions. At the end of the century, Marie-François-Xavier Bichat developed his concept of "gen-eral anatomy," which he defined as the study of the constitu-ent tissues of the human body in health and disease. Bichat's tissue doctrine turned attention from the clinical description of pathological phenomena to physiological specificity and physical localization. Following Bichat, Karl von Rokitansky in Vienna brought pathological anatomy to its peak and made it an essential part of medical education in the nineteenth century. The cell theory and improvements in the microscope at midcentury led to Rudolf Virchow's emphasis on the cell as the fundamental unit of anatomy and the ultimate seat of disease, a concept he called his "anatomical idea."

The interest in systematics exemplified by Carl Linnaeus in the eighteenth century also led to a new interest in comparative anatomy as morphological similarities came to be viewed as classificatory signposts. At the Jardin des Plantes, Georges-Louis LeClerc, Comte du Buffon and the anatomist Louis-Jean-Marie Daubenton collaborated on the massive *Histoire naturelle des animaux* (1749–1788), which developed an idea of species based on morphological similarities. In the early nineteenth century, Georges Cuvier continued Daubenton's work on comparative anatomy and combined it with the study of fossils and with Bichat's emphasis on the functionality of the parts of the body to develop his classification of animals. His skills in comparative anatomy and knowledge of the internal structures of animals led to a new classificatory scheme that shattered the old notion of a hierarchical chain of being.

Cuvier's *Règne animal* (1817) identified four principal types of animal form based on structural similarities and functional characteristics: the vertebrates, mollusks, articulates, and radiates. Cuvier's concept of form greatly influenced nineteenth-century work in paleontology and comparative anatomy as well as the theory of evolution. Cuvier's detailed work on fossils confirmed that fossil animals were now extinct, which, to him, did not imply a notion of transformism.

His near contemporary, Etienne Geoffroy Saint-Hilaire, recognized homologous structures in organisms that implied the existence of a generalized type and so opened the door to a transformist, or evolutionary, theory. In the 1830s and 1840s, Richard Owen, who had worked exclusively in comparative anatomy, described an archetype of the simplest vertebrate form. Owen accepted Karl Ernst von Baer's view that embryological development followed a branching, rather than a linear, plan and showed that fossils also show a radiating pattern toward individual specialization rather than a linear progression toward the human form. Charles Darwin did little anatomical work himself. He relied on the investigations of Owen and others on homologies in his theory of evolution by natural selection, published in *The Origin of Species* (1859).

The skeleton, whether animal or human, fossil or new, was at the center of anatomical study. The skeleton appeared at both the beginning and the end of anatomical demonstrations, and took pride of place in anatomy collections. The human skeleton symbolized death and the end of all flesh, and the irreducible bedrock of organic form. In the eighteenth century, some illustrations of skeletons were used to emphasize, and even exaggerate, gender differences. In the nineteenth and early twentieth centuries, skeletons, and especially skulls, were used to adumbrate specious racial theories. The French anthropologist Pierre Paul Broca measured thousands of skulls to confirm his view that skull size (and therefore brain size) correlated with intelligence and with race, gender, and criminality.

By the twenty-first century, anatomical determinism had long been discredited. Dissection, though still important in teaching medicine, had lost its value as a method of discovery. Anatomical atlases display the body in detail and virtual reality computer programs provide three-dimensional views of everything.

Knowledge of the structure of the living body is now gained in many different ways. X rays, discovered at the end of the nineteenth century, were supplemented in the twentieth by ultrasound, the CT scan, magnetic resonance imaging, and the PET scan. Ultrasound employs high-frequency sound waves that form an image on a monitor. The CT (computerized tomography) scan can be one hundred times more sensitive than conventional X rays. It allows a part of the body to be visualized in "slices" in two or three dimensions. Magnetic resonance imagery (MRI) allows visualization of soft tissue by means of magnetic fields and radio waves. Positron emission tomography (PET) shows the entire body at once. A small amount of radioactive glucose is injected into the bloodstream, after which the patient passes through a scanner like that used in CT scans. These new technologies have provided a cornucopia of information about the structure of the human body.

ANITA GUERRINI

ANTHROPOLOGY. While anthropology has existed as an academic discipline only since the beginning of the twentieth century, the perspective it represents has a considerably longer history. Most anthropologists trace its history to the Anglo-French Enlightenment of the eighteenth century and the ensuing period of European global expansion. The Enlightenment is generally acknowledged for its challenge to "time-honored" traditions and for championing reason as the foundation of truth. The Enlightenment relativized customs and beliefs that had been understood as universal. Jean-Jacques Rousseau's essay, *Discourse on the Origin and Bases of the Inequality among Men* (1754), attributes inequality to the development of private property rather than variable natural endowments or the vicissitudes of nature. Despite the criticism of Rousseau's romantic notion of the "Noble Savage," his sympathetic reference to indigenous peoples anticipated anthropology's critical turn 150 years later by emphasizing humanity's diversity and historical character.

The same historical theme is central to Giambattista Vico's *The New Science* (1725). Vico's book has been claimed as ancestral not only to anthropology but the human sciences more generally because it challenged essentialized notions of human nature. Vico argues like Rousseau against an unchanging human nature and for a vision of humanity as historically produced. For Vico, history presented a more suitable means for grasping the human condition than did the emerging natural sciences, a theme that resonates with contemporary anthropology.

The European expansion throughout the eighteenth and nineteenth centuries contributed significantly to the development of anthropology as an academic discipline. The nineteenth century witnessed the reconfigured political and economic landscapes of European and North American nation-states and indigenous cultures worldwide as colonial sources of labor, raw materials, and export commodities. In a manner that betrayed the critical insights of Rousseau, yet in part fulfilled the nature of Enlightenment reason, nineteenth-century colonialism was regarded in moral terms by many Western scholars, colonial administrators, and missionaries as bringing civilization to so-called "savage peoples." A linear and hierarchical mapping of human history consigned indigenous peoples to the dawn of humanity and place Western peoples at the pinnacle of human development.

The nineteenth century saw a critical tension between intellectual commitment to social evolution and opposing discourses that embraced evolution while supporting an alternative vision of indigenous peoples. The encounter with indigenous peoples could be an occasion for the celebration of difference and for exploring alternative possibilities for the human condition. The works of Lewis Henry Morgan, often regarded in anthropology as the founder of modern kinship studies, illustrate the point. In *League of the Iroquois* (1851) and *Ancient Society* (1877), Morgan showed the wide variability of kinship structures in relation to property and changing forms of human community. His work caught the attention of Karl Marx, who used it to show that many of the characteristics nineteenth-century scholars attributed to human nature were in fact particular to the history of capitalism. Morgan and Marx can be claimed as anthropological ancestors because they appreciated the unique historical nature of indigenous societies as a challenge to regnant ideas of unilineal development and progress that ultimately dismissed the humanity of indigenous peoples.

Anthropology Enters the Academy

The founding of American academic anthropology can be attributed to the German immigrant Franz Boas, while English and French anthropology owes much to the intellectual traditions established by Herbert Spencer and Emile Durkheim. Named Professor of Anthropology at Columbia University in 1896, Boas gained the institutional support that enabled him to launch Columbia as the outstanding American center for anthropological research and training of the early twentieth century.

Boas advocated local histories and strongly supported the American four-field approach, integrating cultural anthropology, archaeology, linguistics, and biological anthropology. He criticized nineteenth-century unilineal evolution and argued that ethnographic materials, practices, and culture should be understood from the context of their development. Boas brought linguistic, cultural, archaeological, and biological evidence to bear in studying the historical origins of cultural phenomena. However, his promotion of the American four-field approach came from his ethnographic research on America's indigenous population and his critique of the racist policies espoused by the American Immigration and Naturalization Service at Ellis Island. His numerous students—Margaret Mead, Ruth Benedict, and others—left a lasting mark on American anthropology.

One would expect Edward Tylor's classic *Primitive Culture* (1871), rather than Herbert Spencer's *The Principles of Sociology* (1885) and Emile Durkheim's *Rules of the Sociological Method* (1895), to be the pervasive intellectual influence on British social anthropology given the enduring nature of Tylor's cultural concept of the "complex whole." However, Tylor embraced evolutionism and failed to establish a tradition of field work as the foundation of anthropological practice. Spencer favored an organic model of human society, while Durkheim introduced the notion of the "social fact" to explain the relation between the human individual and the determining cultural influences of groups or communities as the basic unit of social analysis. Spencer and Durkheim served as principal influences on British functionalism and structural-functionalism more generally, which rested on the pervasive idea that social beliefs and practices reinforce the identity and continuity of the social whole.

Bronisław Malinowski was primarily responsible for establishing rigorous field research as the hallmark of socio-cultural anthropology. In contrast to much of late nineteenth- and early twentieth-century anthropology, in which fieldwork was not considered suitable for "gentlemen," Malinowski argued for immersion in the social round of indigenous societies over a sustained period of time. He also emphasized in *Argonauts of the Western Pacific* (1922) the importance of learning indigenous languages, of being able to "think in their symbols." He rejected evolutionary models and was skeptical toward historical approaches he considered too dependent on oral accounts. Malinowski argued for an organic vision of society as consisting of interdependent parts and emphasized individuals and the capacity of culture to satisfy their biological, psychological, and social needs.

Alfred Reginald Radcliffe-Brown's structural-functionalism was the primary competitor to Malinowskian functionalism. Radcliffe-Brown made his reputation through field research in the Andaman Islands and Australia, and, unlike Malinowski, placed a theoretical emphasis on social structure rather than the individual. For Radcliffe-Brown and Durkheim, individuals come and go while social structures endure. However, both Malinowski and Radcliffe-Brown conceived of societies as integrated wholes, and conflict as essentially dysfunctional. They and their students worked during the period of English colonial rule. While the connection between English social anthropology and colonialism was indirect, Malinowski and Radcliffe-Brown's rejection of history and de-emphasis of human agency except as a function of needs and structures precluded a critical understanding of the social, political, and economic circumstances that prefigured the anthropology of their times.

There is little doubt that Claude Lévi-Strauss remains the predominant figure in French anthropology. His work was heavily indebted to Durkheim, especially his *Elementary Structures of Kinship* (1949), as well as to the formalism of the Prague school of linguistics. Lévi-Strauss's most famous book, *Tristes Tropiques,* reported on his sole fieldwork expe-

Margaret Meade (1901–1978), American anthropologist widely known for her best seller, *Coming of Age in Samoa* (1928)

A

rience, in the Amazon. This book is celebrated for its elegant prose and the questions it raises with respect to overcoming the cultural distance that separates the ethnographer from the indigenous "other." However, unlike Malinowski, Lévi-Strauss committed his scholarly career to anthropology from a distance through the formal analysis of myths worldwide. He argued that in spite of the variability of narratives or stories, myths should be understood as permutations of invariable human themes. The structural method, the internal mechanics of the myth's primary oppositions, enabled Lévi-Strauss to transform the surface semantics of a myth to its underlying universal logic.

Structuralism and structural-functionalism continued to be influential right through the colonial era until it subsided in the wake of the critical anthropology of the 1970s. However, with the exception of sociology and political science, the influence of critical anthropology tended to be more pronounced in England and continental Europe than in the United States. Not all versions of structuralism reproduced the original models established by Malinowski, Radcliffe-Brown, and Lévi-Strauss. Edmund Leach introduced a more dynamic version of structuralism than his English predecessors, exhibiting a sensitivity to history and human agency in *Political Systems of Highland Burma* (1954). Although reproducing the functionalism of his mentor Malinowski with an ecological tone, E. E. Evans-Pritchard, like Leach, was more attuned to the importance of history to anthropology. Well versed in the hermeneutic philosophy of Wilhelm Dilthey, Evans-Pritchard identified anthropology with the human rather than natural sciences. The symbolic structuralism of Victor Turner's analysis of rituals and Mary Douglas's use of structure and anti-structure to articulate boundaries and matter out of place also influenced structuralism and functionalism. However, they lacked the deeper reflective and historical perspective necessary to grasp the intellectual contiguity between static theoretical models and the politics of European colonialism.

Mead and Benedict followed up Boas's work on the relation between culture and personality. Mead's books became known worldwide and posed a considerable challenge to dominant ideas of sex and gender. Edward Sapir advanced Boas's initiatives on language by arguing for the close association between language and worldview, a perspective now known as "linguistic relativity." Sapir evaluated the potentials that human cultures offered individuals in his important essay "Culture, Genuine and Spurious" (1924), which engaged Alfred Krober's notion of culture as "superorganic," suspended above the fray of daily practice. Sapir taught that cultures were genuine only if they enhanced the potentials of individuals, and so spoke positively of indigenous societies.

In both the specific traditions of French and British sociocultural anthropology and the American four-field approach, the culture concept served as the common bridge and point of contest among disparate theoretical traditions and practices. Even adamant defenders of the primacy of structure had to concede something to the "cultural other." Throughout the 1930s and 1940s there was wide agreement on fieldwork as central to the identity of anthropology, but "culture" eluded all efforts at operationalization. Perhaps out of resignation, Tylor's view of culture as the "complex whole" served as the minimalist position.

In the 1950s, American anthropology took a dramatic materialist turn through the theoretical contributions of Leslie White and Julian H. Steward. Following the influence of Karl Marx, both White and Steward argued against explaining culture in cultural terms. White embraced in *Evolution of Culture* (1959) a comprehensive theory of unilineal social evolution that had long been criticized and abandoned by the Boasian tradition. According to White, the capacity to harness energy was the primary force in societies' progress from one stage of technological complexity to another. On the other hand, Steward sought, in his *Theory of Culture Change* (1955), to distance himself from the untenable Eurocentric implications of nineteenth-century social evolution. Like Boas, Steward was sensitive to the historically particular in arguing that cultures could evolve in distinct patterns, depending on diverse environmental circumstances. He called this "multilinear evolution." Although Steward emphasized material processes as central to evolution, he did not dismiss the importance of culture. Rather, culture was central to his theoretical framework through the "culture core," the cultural activities most directly related to subsistence.

Contemporary Directions

The end of European colonialism during the 1960s and the political initiatives taken by newly independent states rendered problematic such static theories as structuralism and structural-functionalism, which dismissed history and eclipsed human agency. Anthropologists pursued numerous new directions. Marxist anthropology developed in the United States and France in the 1960s followed by the very important and influential appeal of Dell Hymes, who sought to refigure anthropology along critical lines in his edited *Reinventing Anthropology* (1969). In the United States, three of Steward's students—Stanley Diamond, Sidney Mintz, and Eric Wolf—elaborated Marxist anthropology. Diamond wrote romantically, as had Rousseau and Marx, about alternative potentials of human freedom based upon the reputed equality of indigenous societies. Mintz and Wolf advanced understanding of peasant societies and capitalist accumulation through their work on the Caribbean and Mexico, respectively. Hymes's book of 1969, which included contributions from Diamond, Wolf, Scholte, and others less directly related to the Marxist tradition, called for the political reformulation of anthropology in a manner that acknowledged the close connections between anthropology and colonialism. According to the "reinventing" group, the practice of anthropology should not be divorced from political practice and should be sensitive to the social, political, and historical circumstances that concretely locate anthropology as a discipline.

French anthropology had its own version of Marxism represented in the works of Maurice Godelier and Claude Meillassoux. Godelier and Meillassoux wrote prolifically on the application of mode of production analysis to indigenous societies. They wrote, however, from a largely structuralist perspective that tended to grasp culture as shaped by the forces and relations of production. Godelier invoked the traditional Marxist categories associated with the mode of production and criticized Meillassoux for inventing a new mode of production for every variant in an indigenous social order. Godelier has recently moved away from the strict base-and-superstructure model of Marxism and has been a major figure in establishing a tradition of French anthropology distinct from that of Lévi-Strauss. Recent French anthropologists like Françoise Zonabend have clearly broken from both the colonial past and Lévi-Strauss by focusing on ethnographically detailed and historical accounts of rural France.

White's and Steward's materialism also influenced the development of American cultural ecology. Marvin Harris is perhaps the best known of the cultural materialists. Although hostile to American Marxist and critical anthropology for embracing dialectics and disavowing science, Harris borrowed such concepts as "mode of production," "etic behavioral mode of production and reproduction," and "emic superstructure" strangely reminiscent of Marx. Emics has traditionally referred to the informant's perspective, while etics entails the studied conclusions of the researcher. However, Harris regards culture as derivative of a techno-environmental determinism, a perspective quite remote from Marx and Marxist anthropology. The cultural ecology of Roy Rappaport presents a more subtle and complex rendering of human culture. In *Pigs for the Ancestors* (1967) Rappaport shows how the horticultural Maring of New Guinea use ritual and symbols to mediate the ecology of their gardens, thus avoiding the reductive tendencies associated with ecological castings of culture and daily practices.

Clifford Geertz's *The Interpretation of Culture* (1973), a book whose concept of "thick description" has influenced scholars from history to literary criticism, redefined the concept of culture as lived symbolic beliefs and practices having public meanings. Geertz argued that anthropology was not a science in search of laws but a hermeneutic one in search of meaning, a remark that essentially identifies one of the primary tensions in contemporary anthropology.

Other new directions also seek to bridge political economy and cultural theory. Recently, Marshall Sahlins has sought to reinvigorate structuralism by developing a dynamic, if not dialectical, relationship between structure and agency. George Marcus and James Clifford's *Writing Culture* (1986) contributed importantly to serious discussion of the rhetorical and political dimensions of ethnographic writing, a concern foreshadowed earlier in the writings of historian Hayden White. Marcus, Clifford, Fischer, and especially Tyler have come to be associated with anthropology's postmodern turn through challenging meta-narratives and privileging ethnography as local pastiche.

On another front, contributors to *Recapturing Anthropology* (1991), edited by Richard Fox, and *Anthropological Locations* (1997), edited by Akhil Gupta and James Ferguson, have discussed the reinventing of anthropology to address the problems that ensue from globalization and cultural diaspora. Authors in both volumes argue against the antiquated notion of a circumscribed field site and for what George Marcus calls multisited field research. Moreover, like John and Jean Comaroff and Johannes Fabian, Lila Abu-Lughod argues against univocal views of culture and for culture as contested practice.

Anthropology continues to challenge its own assumptions and to seek to respond to global dislocations and inequalities. Within American anthropology, some academic departments like Stanford's and Duke's have been torn apart by struggles over science and critical practice, while others seek new ways to bridge the subdisciplines. It seems clear that anthropology on a global basis will continue to be relevant to the challenges that face humanity because it is one of the few disciplines that through its critical practice embraces both diversity and interdisciplinary modes of knowing.

ROBERT C. ULIN

ANTINUCLEAR MOVEMENT. From their inception nuclear weapons were controversial, and this ambivalence extended to their civilian counterpart, nuclear reactors, because of the dangers associated with them.

Linus Pauling (1901–94), winner of the Nobel Prize for chemistry in 1954 for work on the chemical bond and of the Nobel Prize for Peace in 1962

Opposition to Nuclear Weapons

The United States used nuclear weapons against Hiroshima and Nagasaki in August 1945 to hasten the end of World War II. Since then, despite calls for their use in the Korean and Vietnamese conflicts and concerns about their employment during the Cuban missile crisis, no nuclear weapon has been fired in anger.

Although the victors of World War II regarded the atomic bomb as the "winning weapon" and expected it to keep the peace, many people considered it an immoral weapon. The Soviet Union's explosion of its first device in 1949 made clear that a nuclear war would be catastrophic for its participants.

The first antinuclear protesters were the Manhattan Project scientists themselves. The wartime Franck Report (named after its principal author, the emigré Nobel Prize-winning physicist James Franck) unsuccessfully urged the U.S. government to issue a warning before dropping a bomb on a city. After the war's end, many scientists joined journalists, clergy, and other citizens in advocating domestic legislation to ensure civilian control of nuclear research and development, and strong international control of weapons through the newly formed United Nations. The Federation of American Scientists (FAS) led these efforts. A best-selling anthology of articles by leading scientists, *One World or None* (1946), helped mobilize public opinion.

During the mid-1950s, testing of newly developed hydrogen bombs revealed the danger of radioactive fallout circulating worldwide. A petition to ban testing, drawn up by the Nobel Prize-winning chemist Linus Pauling and signed by thousands of scientists, raised the level of international con-

The area in the Yucca Mountains on the boundary of the Nevada Test Site was proposed as a repository for high-level nuclear waste.

cern. The National Committee for a Sane Nuclear Policy (SANE) and the Campaign for Nuclear Disarmament (CND) sprang up in the United States and Britain, respectively. These and "ban the bomb" organizations in other countries were often slandered as procommunist. They obtained a following by appealing to the emotions, which allowed opponents to charge, with some accuracy, that they knew little about weapons and strategy. The Limited Test Ban Treaty of 1963, which permitted testing only underground and so removed fallout as an issue, deprived the antinuclear movement of much of its emotional steam. In the 1970s, however, a revitalized FAS, together with the Union of Concerned Scientists, the Council for a Livable World, the Center for Defense Information, Physicians for Social Responsibility, and the American Physical Society, developed arguments that appealed to the intellect as well as the emotions. Composed in large part of scientists, physicians, and retired military officers, their expertise and patriotism could not be impugned.

Organized religion, surprisingly, was not an early and persistent critic of weapons of mass destruction; many churches supported the anticommunist sentiments of the period. During the 1980s, however, several panels of Catholic and Protestant bishops issued reports questioning the morality of nuclear deterrence. Filmmakers created visual images of the horrors of nuclear warfare in *The War Game, Threads, On the Beach,* and *The Day After,* and exposed the danger and absurdity of war initiated by a maniac (*Dr. Strangelove*) or by technological failure (*Fail Safe*).

The United States did not have a monopoly on antinuclear agitation. The Japanese people keep the memory of the bombings of 1945 alive in annual ceremonies in the Hiroshima Peace Park, which has a museum of artifacts and pictures. The government of India, acting as a leader of developing countries, criticized the superpowers' arsenals until it developed its own nuclear weapons. In the Soviet Union, physicist Andrei Sakharov first designed hydrogen bombs and then campaigned vigorously against their use. The Soviet government supported International Physicians for the Prevention

of Nuclear War, a Nobel Peace Prize–winning organization (1985) founded by a Russian and an American. The Pugwash movement, a decades-long series of conferences by scientists from many countries, also received the Nobel Peace Prize (1995). The Green party and other organizations in Germany organized massive marches in the early 1980s to protest the introduction of intermediate-range ballistic missiles with atomic warheads in Europe. Australians and New Zealanders objected to tests by France in the South Pacific as late as the 1990s.

A number of international treaties have created nuclear weapon-free zones in Antarctica (1959), Latin America (1967), the South Pacific (1985), Southeast Asia (1995), and Africa (1996). These accords are more than mere gestures of compliance, but less than enforceable laws. Seeking an outright legal ban on nuclear weapons, a number of nongovernmental organizations requested a ruling from the World Court. The court issued an advisory opinion in 1996 stating that "the threat or use of nuclear weapons would generally be contrary to the rules of international law."

Opposition to Reactors and Radioactive Waste

The United States drew a sharp separation between civilian reactors primarily producing electricity and military reactors primarily growing plutonium. American utilities that owned reactors did not want the albatross of militarism hung around their necks. In other countries, such as Great Britain, reactors served dual purposes. Since all reactors produce plutonium that could become fuel for breeder reactors as well as an explosive, many people feared that terrorists might hijack some of the metal while it was in transit.

During the 1960s and early 1970s, American utilities ordered the building of more than one hundred reactors. Grassroots opposition coalesced around fear of lethal doses of radioactivity released in a meltdown of the core (the theme of the popular film *The China Syndrome*), but other potential problems added to popular concerns: Lesser accidents might release dangerous levels of radioactivity beyond the site perimeter; plans for plants close to urban areas increased anxiety; water from the reactors' cooling system dumped in rivers, lakes, and oceans threatened fish and other animals; and the likely targeting of reactors in a nuclear war made them undesirable neighbors.

By protesting reactor plans at every stage, the opposition (often local citizen groups) slowed the building process so much that the utilities incurred enormous interest charges on the money they borrowed for construction. This often made the proposed reactor uncompetitive with fossil-fuel. By the early 1970s, some utilities had canceled their plans for reactors (not only because of the high costs but also owing to overestimates of the nation's electrical needs). A safety report by the U.S. Nuclear Regulatory Commission in 1975, which minimized the dangers of reactors, was widely criticized. Since 1974, not a single utility in the United States has ordered a reactor, although American manufacturers continue to construct them for other nations. About 100 aging reactors provided around 20 percent of domestic electricity in the United States in 2000. The corresponding numbers were considerably higher in France and Japan.

The U.S. Atomic Energy Commission (AEC) began to promote construction of civilian reactors in the 1950s but did not give sufficient attention to waste disposal. High-level radioactive wastes were planned to be stored "permanently" in abandoned salt mines in Kansas in the 1970s. When Kansas state geologists showed the presence of drill shafts that would allow the entrance of rainwater, the AEC abandoned the site.

No state then volunteered to accept a high-level waste repository. Spent fuel rods accumulated in the already crowded cooling ponds at each reactor location. In the 1980s, the U.S. Congress forced development of the Yucca Mountain site in Nevada, but even after the expenditure of more than four billion dollars by the end of the twentieth century, all the technical problems of containing radioactivity there for ten thousand years had not been solved.

The states of Nevada, Washington, and South Carolina accepted low-level radioactive wastes from universities, hospitals, and industry until the accident at Three Mile Island in Pennsylvania (1979) and the catastrophe at Chernobyl, Ukraine (1986). So-called NIMBY ("not in my backyard") opposition, often based on the fear that radioactivity would reach urban water supplies, then stifled progress in waste disposal. Having brought the nuclear reactor industry to a standstill in the 1970s, the antinuclear movement joined with state and local officials and increasingly sophisticated antinuclear and environmental organizations, such as the Sierra Club, Natural Resources Defense Council, and Union of Concerned Scientists, to challenge proposals for siting storage facilities.

Elsewhere, opposition to reactors has also been effective. In 2000 Germany decided to close all its nuclear power reactors within twenty years. The Green party, one of the few environmental groups to have members elected to a national parliament, turned its once-ridiculed position into national policy. Civilian antinuclear activities have also succeeded in opposing nuclear-powered merchant ships, which many ports now ban. Fears of radioactive contamination faced the American *Savannah* (launched in 1962), the German *Otto Hahn* (1964), the Japanese *Mutsu* (1972), and the Soviet *Sevmorput* (1989). Like reactors used to produce electricity, propulsion reactors changed from a once-promising technology into expensive, controversial, and feared objects. It would be premature to bury nuclear power, however. As

other sources of energy fall behind the world's demand and air pollution from fossil-fuel plants reaches unacceptable levels, there may be no alternative but self-denial to the nuclear reactor.

LAWRENCE BADASH

ARISTOTELIANISM became the philosophy of the newly formed universities of Oxford and Paris and other higher schools during the thirteenth century. The Council of Trent (1545–1563) declared Thomistic Aristotelianism to be the official doctrine of the Roman Catholic church. Aristotelianism retained its cultural, theological, and intellectual dominance even in Protestant countries well into the seventeenth century although Aristotelian natural philosophy met with telling criticism during the Scientific Revolution. Elements of Aristotle's philosophy continued to influence the development of science well into the nineteenth century.

In 1586 the Jesuits introduced the *"Ratio" studiorum* (revised in 1599 and 1616) that established the standard texts used for teaching Aristotelian philosophy at their colleges, including La Flèche (where René Descartes was educated) and their central teaching establishment, the Collegio Romano. Many Christian non-Jesuitical institutions adopted the *Ratio* in one form or another. In general, the texts favored by the Jesuits described a physical world consisting of four elements (earth, air, water, and fire) that in varying combinations composed all earthly bodies. The texts portrayed a geocentric universe and maintained that the Copernican heliocentric theory of 1543 was at best a mathematical tool for calculating the positions of celestial bodies. Traditionalists like the Jesuit cardinal Robert Bellarmine of the Collegio Romano and the authors of the commentaries on Aristotle's *Libri naturales* issued by the University of Coimbra around 1600 showed how to reconcile new observations with Aristotelian theory. Philosophers like Galileo's friend and colleague at the University of Padua, Cesare Cremonini, defended these accommodations because they preserved the systematic explanations of Aristotle against Galileo's piecemeal, unsystematic approach. The close relation between Catholic dogma and Aristotelian doctrine also encouraged continuing with the older philosophy.

Increasingly, the alterations produced by individuals in an attempt to keep Aristotelianism coherent in the face of new observations in astronomy and elsewhere resulted in the erosion of agreement on specific philosophical details. Despite these variations, however, Aristotelianism continued to offer a framework for constructing plausible explanatory systems. The framework considered natural bodies in terms of matter, privation, and form, which gave individual portions of matter the qualities that characterize particular bodies. Four different causes elucidated the generation, construction, or alteration of a body: the material cause out of which the change comes; the formal cause that provides the specifying or defining factor; the agent or efficient cause that initiates the change; and the final cause that provides the purpose *(telos)* for which a thing came into existence.

The mechanical philosophy of the seventeenth century subverted the framework. In his *Discourse on Method* (1637), Descartes rejected the notion of final causality and the theory of four qualititively different elements in favor of one undifferentiated matter. In place of the Aristotelian qualitative approach to explanation, Descartes defended, though he seldom practiced, a quantitative and mathematical method that referred the manifest properties of bodies to the effects of bits of matter in motion. Despite these disagreements of principle, Descartes wrote in a systematic, deductive style agreeable to the Aristotelians, and he presented his works to his former teachers, the Jesuits at La Flèche and Paris, explicitly asking for, although never receiving, their approbation.

In England, Francis Bacon directed his criticism of the Aristotelian framework primarily against its use of syllogistic reasoning to construct elaborate theoretical systems. In *The New Organon* (1620), he argued that the syllogism should serve only as a method of demonstration. It could not be used for the discovery of new knowledge or for the production of new works. In place of the syllogism, Bacon advocated an inductive method based upon the careful compilation and analysis of observational and experimental data. Bacon also rejected the notion of the four elements. He retained the notion of forms, but he described them in a mechanical fashion as the laws that governed the motions of bodies. Although Descartes and Bacon both rejected the Aristotelian conception of final causality, not all mechanical philosophers did. Robert Boyle, who brought together the Baconian and mechanical programs in the next generation, maintained that teleological inferences, such as those used by William Harvey in elucidating his discoveries concerning the circulation of the blood (1628), were a necessary adjunct to mechanical hypotheses in biological investigations.

Parts of the works of Galileo, Descartes, Bacon, and Boyle were placed on the church's *Index of Prohibited Books* and opposed by the Jesuits. Aristotelians such as Antoine

A fanciful portrait from 1702 of the Greek philosopher Aristotle (384–322 B.C.)

Goudin, Jean-Marie-Constant Duhamel, and Jacques Grandamy continued to write well into the eighteenth century, often setting the agenda and parameters for philosophical debate. By the nineteenth century Aristotelianism was no longer viable as a natural philosophy. Even so, remnants of it continued to be influential, primarily in the study of living matter. Thomas Aquinas had used Aristotle's natural philosophy to construct a teleological proof for the existence of God. In the seventeenth century John Ray argued for the necessity of a designer God based upon considerations drawn from observations of the complexity and organization exhibited in living systems. Although belief in the purposefulness of nature opposed strict mechanistic laws, at the end of the seventeenth century Richard Bentley constructed teleological arguments based upon considerations drawn from Newtonian mechanics. William Paley would continue to popularize this type of argument in his *Natural theology* (1802). By the mid-nineteenth century, however, defenders of Darwinian evolution rejected the Aristotelian idea of purposes in nature, and the stage was once again set for a fierce battle between religion and science.

ROSE-MARY SARGENT

ARTIFICIAL INTELLIGENCE. The first machines simply augmented human or animal muscle power, but later pre-industrial inventors introduced devices that also augmented or replaced the human intellect: for example, windmills with sails that adjusted for the intensity of the wind and float valves that maintained water in a tank at a desired level. These devices used the technique of feedback, whereby information about a machine's status or behavior—say the height of water in a tank—is fed back to the input stages—the valve supplying water to the tank. By the nineteenth century, the development of information-processing machines reached a sufficient level to generate speculation about the similarities between self-regulating mechanisms and human thought processes. The most famous publication on this theme was Mary Shelley's *Frankenstein* (1818), whose main character (Frankenstein's creation) has entered popular consciousness not as a person but as anything that becomes dangerous to its creator. Further philosophical speculation on this topic followed. In 1889, Mark Twain discussed the intelligence of the Paige typesetting machine, whose mechanical complexity outdistanced its day and almost bankrupted its inventor. Specifically, Twain believed that the Paige machine's ability to right-justify type automatically—something that he knew required human skill—was an obvious indication of mechanical intelligence.

The invention of the digital computer in the mid-twentieth century once again raised these philosophical questions. In 1948, Norbert Wiener, a mathematician at Massachusetts Institute of Technology, coined the term "cybernetics" in a book that discussed not only the mathematical nature but also the philosophical implications of some machines. These machines could regulate themselves to adjust to changes in their physical environment, select alternative courses of action based on the results of previous actions, and remember what actions they had taken in the past—and their consequences. In short, they could learn from experience, adapt to new conditions, and interact with their human creators.

In England in 1951 Alan Turing published a paper that described a form of parlor game in which players guessed whether they were communicating (through a teletype or similar impersonal device) with a person or a machine (a computer). If players could not distinguish between human and computer, Turing argued, they would have to concede that the computer is "intelligent." The Turing Test for machine "intelligence," a concise, simple, and witty definition of a seemingly intractable conundrum, remains valid. No machine has ever passed the test, although in some restricted domains computers come close.

Similar interests in machine intelligence arose in the United States. At a seminal conference at Dartmouth College in 1956, John McCarthy coined the term "artificial intelligence" (later shortened to AI) to describe ways of making computers act "intelligently." (Some accounts of the Dartmouth conference mention that the group considered Wiener's term "cybernetics," but rejected it so as to avoid introducing a philosophical dimension to their work. Wiener's term resurfaced in the 1990s as "cyberspace," meaning a world existing entirely inside networks of computers.) One of McCarthy's colleagues, Marvin Minsky, defined AI as "the science of making machines do things that would require intelligence if done by men." The term has been criticized for being vague and imprecise; yet it has persisted, perhaps because it captures the imprecision and frustration encountered by humans when they try to understand in an objective way intelligent behavior—what most humans, even children, do effortlessly.

McCarthy developed the programming language LISP (List Processing), which simplified the writing of programs that handled symbolic and logical problems as opposed to numerical problems, which other programming languages were designed to solve. For years LISP remained the preferred language for AI researchers. For nearly all of AI's history, research consisted mainly of writing programs in LISP for ordinary, general-purpose electronic computers. A famous example, ELIZA, mimicked a question-and-answer session between psychoanalyst and patient. AI has focused primarily on computer programming, using text almost exclusively as input and output in keeping with the Turing Test for intelligence. AI has little connection with robotics, the art of building machines that replicate activities carried out by intelligent creatures. Occasionally AI researchers have attempted to couple their programs to microphones, loudspeakers, cameras, electric motors, and so forth, but these projects were exceptions. AI researchers argue that understanding basic cognition gives them enough to do. Also, the U.S. Defense Department's Advanced Research Projects Agency (ARPA), which provided most of the funding for AI research, supported the restricted definition of AI's domain. Since about 1985, AI and robotics have moved much closer together, in part because ARPA's support for AI was drastically cut in that year and because computers, cameras, sensors, motors, and so forth have become much smaller and more capable of putting AI ideas into practice.

Attempts to get computers to perform intelligent tasks have led to new insights into human psychology, and AI has given new life to philosophy as well. But AI research has not led to easier methods of programming computers or to techniques of writing computer programs without errors—both very desirable goals for which the marketplace would pay well. Nor does it have a cupboardful of exemplary programs. As soon as AI perfects a program that can do what was once considered a task requiring human intelligence, computer scientists no longer see it as important and it is demoted from its classification as AI. In the early 1950s computer scientists thought that getting a computer to play a good game of chess would penetrate to the basis of human intelligence. By 1996 a chess program had defeated the human World Champion, and

US mathematician Norbert Wiener (1894–1964), founder of cybernetics, photographed in 1962

pocket chess computers that played a respectable game were selling for $30. Consequently, AI researchers no longer consider chess such an important topic. Pocket computers that recognize handwriting have captured another frontier of AI research.

The branch of AI called expert systems has had some commercial success. Expert systems consist of large structured pools of data on a specific topic—say, medical diagnosis—plus a set of rules acquired by interviewing specialists in the field—in this case, skilled physicians. The resultant system performs as well as and in some cases better than humans. The most famous fictional computer, HAL, of the 1968 Stanley Kubrick film *2001: A Space Odyssey,* could diagnose and suggest repairs for the spacecraft on which it traveled. HAL's voice recognition—really voice understanding—has not been approached in reality, although some progress has occurred with limited vocabularies. And HAL's emotional breakdown suggests a mentality that no computer today comes close to achieving. Researchers have reached no agreement on how to program so sensitive a computer or whether such a program is even possible.

Artificial intelligence continues to defy easy definition. It has not produced any dramatic breakthroughs—something that people seem to demand elsewhere in computing—but over the years it has made genuine progress. Its principal contribution to society may lie more in telling human beings about themselves than in providing us with the more prosaic benefits of computer technology.

PAUL E. CERUZZI

ASIA. As the world's largest and most culturally diverse region, modern Asia displays an exceedingly wide range of scientific achievements and institutions, with historical patterns to match. Japan lies at one end of the spectrum, Bhutan or Laos at the other. Two in the middle, India and China, are among the world's oldest recorded civilizations; both participated in modern science during the twentieth century, and to some extent before. And each can boast of important scientific achievements from the pre-modern era. The fourteen Nobel Prizes in science awarded to

A

銀氣と含まぬあらかひを鑁化して鑁化て去れてれと間吹銅らは

えだ間吹れ圖

Copper production in ancient Japan. From Brian Hickman, *Japanese Crafts* (1978)

investigators from Asia constitute an imperfect indicator of the region's standing in modern science; and it is telling that only half of the prizes went for work done in Asian countries. This record serves as a stark reminder of Asia's strengths in, and contributions to, modern science, on the one hand, and of the weaknesses and continuing difficulties that confront science in the region, on the other.

Origins and Early Growth

Modern science in Asia traces its origins to the arrival of European scientists interested in the region's flora, fauna, minerals, topography, and so on. India, China, the Philippines, and Japan felt the European Scientific Revolution through the activities of Jesuit missionaries in the late sixteenth and early seventeenth centuries, although the Philippines had a European style college by the early seventeenth century. Spain, as the dominant power in the country, long remained marginal to the scientific enterprise. The sustained development of modern science in Asia actually began with the arrival of British scientists in India shortly before 1800. Other European investigators followed, to China, Southeast Asia, Japan, and elsewhere; but developments in India proceeded more rapidly because of the subcontinent's continuing, ever-more intimate association with Britain. British scientists carried out astronomical studies in Bengal and a Trigonometric Survey throughout the whole of India (including today's Pakistan and Bangladesh) beginning in 1800. These and other early investigations simultaneously satisfied curiosity and promoted British commercial and political interests in the region. Direct Crown Rule, however, was not established until 1858.

India's attraction for the British led to a much earlier founding of scientific societies and professional journals than in any other Asian country. British colonial authorities in India provided Western-style education there long before other European powers did so in the regions under their control. In 1813, an Indian reformer with British encouragement established an English-language school for Hindu boys; this school evolved into Presidency College, Calcutta (later the University of Calcutta), and became one of India's leading sites for the growth of modern science. Two other universities, founded at Bombay and Madras by 1857, were modeled on the University of London, and maintained the same academic standards. In 1898, a wealthy Indian business leader, J. N. Tata, dispatched an associate to Europe and the United States to study the operations of universities. After many delays, but with British encouragement, his initiative led in 1911 to the founding of the Indian Institute of Science at Bangalore. It would later constitute the nucleus of the Indian Academy of Sciences. In 1859, the Jesuits established a modern university with a scientific curriculum in the Philippines, the Ateneo de Manila, and added a medical school in 1872. Similarly, Japan and China, which never came formally under European rule, managed to establish universities with programs in science at Tokyo and Peking (Beijing) in 1877 and 1898, respectively. But only later were Indian developments as a whole matched elsewhere in Asia.

Important as the legacy of European scientific activity was for the development of modern science in Asia, no sustained growth occurred before indigenous leaders assumed long-term control. Conditions varied widely from one country to another in this respect. Under the reformist Meiji regime, Japan from 1868 began to lay the foundations required for modern science in a comprehensive manner. An ultramodern engineering school opened in 1869 under the directorship of Henry Dyer, a Scot. After consulting leading scientific authorities in Europe, Japan's government began hiring young European and American scientists, engineers, and physicians at very high salaries to staff several institutions, including Tokyo University. Most importantly, a systematic program to send young Japanese to Europe and the United States for scientific and other modern studies began in 1872. After 1878, scientific societies and academic journals were established in rapid succession. By contrast, China's non-native Manchu regime only grudgingly developed a program for technical translation and modern armaments manufacture at the Kiangnan Arsenal in 1860, but scarcely went beyond it until 1898. Other needed developments—research laboratories, journals, professional societies—only appeared in the twentieth century. Thailand (then Siam) under King Chulalongkorn began to establish French-style *grand écoles* in the 1890s but had no university until 1916, and only a modest number of Thai nationals studied in Europe. Local populations in Vietnam and the East Indies (today's Indonesia) had no prospects for studying science, to say nothing of conducting research, until even later.

Parameters of Development

To what extent did the formation of a local scientific community draw effectively on traditional intellectual culture and the social structure already extant before Europeans arrived? India and Japan enjoyed relatively positive experiences in this respect. Early recruits to scientific and technical studies in India such as Chandrasekhara Raman, India's first Nobel laureate in science, and Srinivasa Ramanujan, the eminent mathematician, came from the traditional Brahmin priestly caste or the Kyasthas scholarly community. In Japan, the first generation of modern scientists (before 1920) arose predominantly from the educated samurai population inherited from the old regime (6 percent of all Japanese); Hideki Yukawa, the first Japanese Nobel laureate, came from a lin-

A

eage of samurai Confucian scholars. In China, however, the first generation of recruits to modern science had tenuous links to traditional intellectual culture and none at all in significant numbers. This was not conducive to the establishment of modern science there.

Political independence, as opposed to colonial dependency or subjugation, was another important variable. Japan's political independence allowed it to define its own agenda, and facilitated rapid progress overall. A government of educated leaders chose which nations, institutions, and laboratories would receive the students sent to the more developed countries of Europe or (less frequently) North America. For example, they could dispatch aspiring Japanese clinicians and medical researchers to German universities at a time when Germany was preeminent in medicine. India did not have this freedom, probably one of the reasons that its modern medicine lagged behind other fields. The lack of political independence was particularly harmful in Southeast Asia. In Vietnam, the Pasteur Institute maintained a significant local research institute for tropical medicine and microbiology at Nha Trang from the 1880s, but it had almost no local educational infrastructure. Well-informed authorities such as Gaston Darboux, permanent secretary of the Académie des sciences in Paris, tried to encourage more forward-looking policies, but the retrograde views of French colonial authorities in Vietnam prevented both the permanent establishment of a university (at Hanoi) and even a permanent scientific mission of French scientists until 1917. Vietnamese had no opportunity to study modern science before 1920; some historians say that as late as 1930, the medical school had the only "serious" scientific program at the University of Hanoi. Dutch colonial authorities in the East Indies at best duplicated French science policy concerning the local population. There was no university at all in this period, only the Institute of Technology at Bandung, which opened in 1920. In 1930, Dutch nationals constituted 60 percent of its student body, Indonesians only a third.

China was neither truly independent nor formally a colony. Taking advantage of the national government's obvious weaknesses under the alien Manchu dynasty, various foreign powers began to establish protected enclaves in several parts of China, and pursued developmental agendas tailored to their own objectives. Some of their strategies favored the growth of science at a time when the Manchu regime was, at best, ambivalent and, at worst, antagonistic to it. The brief spasm of reformism that allowed the establishment of Peking University in 1898 soon spent itself; the anti-foreign Boxer Rebellion, encouraged by reactionary elements of the Manchu elite, broke out in 1900. Although China was forced to pay reparations for damage inflicted on foreign properties by the Boxers, some of this "Boxer Indemnity" was rebated (especially by the United States) to China in support of overseas study by Chinese nationals at (mostly) American universities. This program made possible the formation in 1914 of China's first professional scientific organization, the Science Society of China, a diverse organization of young aspiring scientists then enrolled at Cornell University; in 1918 they returned to China and began promoting the growth of scientific institutions and research projects by Chinese citizens.

Mass education—its presence or absence—has been important for the growth of modern science in Asia. Japan was the first Asian country to provide elementary and mid-level schooling for everyone, and its twentieth-century record in science is the continent's most impressive. India underscores the point. Mass education was only sporadically available in the country during the period of Crown Rule before 1947. Har Gobind Khorana, born in 1922 in a region now part of Pakistan, and one of only two scientists from Asia to win a Nobel Prize in medicine, had the good fortune to come from the only family in his village whose members could read and write. Yet mass education's importance should not be overstated. Partly under U.S. leadership after 1901, the Philippines achieved universal primary education not long after Japan did so; and in recent years, China appears to have followed the Philippines. Yet in technical fields during the first half of the twentieth century, the Philippines achieved only modest distinction, and that only in medicine and meteorology. The consequences of mass education for science in China cannot be evaluated yet.

The degree of political stability and the ease with which private and public interests could be deployed on behalf of scientific ventures have profoundly affected modern scientific achievement in Asia. India, Japan, and Taiwan enjoyed far greater relative stability during the twentieth century than all the other countries in the region. Stability allowed both governments and private patrons to support scientific education and research in the expectation of a positive return on their investments. The British authorities, who stabilized India, did little to support modern science in India directly, but encouraged private individuals and organizations to do so. Thus, J. N. Tata could take a significant part in founding the Indian Academy of Science, with later support from the Maharajah of Mysore, the head of one of India's princely states. Similarly, a trio of wealthy Indian lawyers raised the funds to endow chairs in physics at the University of Calcutta that supported the work of Raman and Meghnad Saha, both Nobel nominees, and one a laureate.

Japan's record in this respect parallels India's. Despite being under American military occupation from 1945 to 1952, following its defeat in World War II, Japan retained control of its own internal affairs, and generally adhered to

Indian physicist Satyendra Bose (1894–1974) is best known for his insight into the quantum property formalized as Bose-Einstein statistics.

A

policies favorable to modern science. Thus were universities founded, laboratories established, journals published, conferences held, and research conducted on a regular basis. Japan had its Imperial Academy of Sciences (founded 1906) and seven comprehensive state ("imperial") universities by 1940, as well as a host of private institutions. Taiwan and Korea, under Japanese rule from 1895 and 1910, respectively, had one imperial university each in addition to private schools. All of the state institutions and many of the private ones were active in research and teaching. Moreover, contrary to some assertions, private interests in Japan supported scientific activities at state as well as at private institutions. Two financial services executives from Osaka endowed the world's first chair of genetics, at Tokyo University, in 1918; the country's leading scientific institution of the inter-war period, the Research Institute for Physics and Chemistry (Riken), was founded in 1917 through substantial private contributions as well as state funding.

While the growth of modern science greatly benefited Japan, its military and related applications did considerable harm to the rest of Asia, with the exception of India. In Manchuria, from the time Japan seized it from China in September 1931 until the end of World War II, the Japanese army conducted research in biochemical warfare, which employed human subjects. Several thousand victims were systematically killed in the process. The U.S. Army later found the data generated sufficiently useful to justify exonerating the perpetrators. Several years before the loss of Manchuria, and after the turmoil of 1911–1927, China experienced an effective central government, which made its capital at Nanking and launched a series of reforms much like those of Japan in the late nineteenth century. During this so-called "Nanking Decade," 1928–1937, the new regime founded a science academy, the Academia Sinica, with more than a dozen research institutes, as well as a number of universities, mostly in coastal cities.

Much of this investment appeared to be lost when Japan invaded China in 1937. Many professors and university students fled to the interior to escape the conflict, taking books, journals, and research equipment with them. Some resumed their activities, at Chunking and Kunming, especially those associated with the newly constituted National Southwest University, created by merging the faculties of the transported coastal schools. Harmful as the Japanese invasion was for modern Chinese science in general, the regrouping that followed had some positive effects. Two young physicists, C. N. Yang and T. D. Lee, who met in Kunming, moved to the University of Chicago to study for their Ph.D.s in theoretical physics after the war. Working together after completing their studies, Yang and Lee surprised the international physics community by challenging the law of the conservation of parity in certain atomic reactions. For this achievement they became in 1957 the first Chinese scientists to receive the Nobel Prize. By providing them with a strong basic education in physics, China's institutional advances in the Nanking Decade and wartime years facilitated their later scientific work. What else might have been accomplished if China's political stability had matched that of India or Japan?

Contributions of Japanese and Indians to world science before 1945 include Shibasaburo Kitasato's collaboration (in 1900) with Emil von Behring on the discovery of natural immunity. During World War I, Katsusaburo Yamagiwa developed the world's first efficient means of creating cancer in the laboratory; many believe he ought at least to have shared the Nobel Prize in Physiology or Medicine for 1926.

In 1920, Meghnad Saha, a professor of physics at the University of Calcutta, published his theory of thermal ionization, a landmark achievement in modern astrophysics. Another Indian colleague, S. N. Bose, then teaching at the University of Dacca (in today's Bangladesh), made what some consider the greatest contribution of an Indian physicist to science when in 1924 he took the first major step in the formulation of quantum statistical mechanics. While Bose never won a Nobel Prize, nor was even nominated, one of the two grand classes of particles in modern physics, the bosons, is named for him. Shortly thereafter, Chandresekhara Vankata Raman published the discovery that did win India's first Nobel in science. This so-called "Raman effect" in quantum optics found important application in spectroscopy. Published in 1928, Raman's achievement, was one of those rare instances in which an important discovery was almost immediately recognized (in this case in 1930) by a Nobel Prize.

More typical were the delays experienced by Hideki Yukawa and Shin'ichiro Tomonaga. Yukawa postulated the existence of a new particle to help explain nuclear forces in 1935, for which he received the Nobel Prize in 1949; Tomonaga solved a difficult problem in quantum electrodynamics in 1944, and shared the prize for 1964. Their candidacies developed rapidly compared with that of Raman's nephew, Subrahmanyan Chandrasekhar. Between 1930 and 1933, working in India and Cambridge, "Chandra" developed the astrophysical theory of white dwarf stars that brought him the Nobel Prize in 1983.

World War II and the Impact of Big Science

The effects of the war on science were felt as strongly in Asia as anywhere else. Seizing power in 1949, China's new Communist regime claimed to be based on scientific principles, and in its first decade appropriated Soviet models that promised a massive expansion of scientific infrastructure and research activity. Academia Sinica merged with another institution to create the powerful Chinese Academy of Sciences in 1950. New institutes and universities were founded, and emigré scientists enticed to return home. Intellectual constraints and Communist dogma offended some; surging nationalism and the dynamic expansion of the scientific enterprise excited others. During a period of relative calm in 1965, a team of biochemists in Shanghai achieved perhaps the most important modern scientific advance ever carried out in China by synthesizing bovine insulin. Seen as a harbinger of future success, the insulin achievement was soon revealed as an epitaph; China descended into the maelstrom of the Cultural Revolution the following year. Between 1966 and 1974, all the nation's universities and most of its laboratories were closed as political chaos engulfed the country.

India, Pakistan, and other Asian nations also sought progress through science after gaining independence. Several countries managed to expand the institutional base of science by building laboratories, universities, or even science academies. But few had the personnel with graduate degrees in sufficient numbers to staff these institutions at an appropriate level. Widespread poverty, illiteracy, and political instability hampered progress. The arrival of big science in the United States and Europe proved a singular spur and challenge. World War II had raised the bar for significant achievement in science, especially in physics. Raman in India wanted to undertake research in nuclear physics after the war, but had to return to optics because of a lack of resources. Abdus Salam had hoped to practice physics in his native Pakistan after completing his doctorate in 1951, but fearing intellectual stagnation, he returned to Cambridge after three years at Lahore. His Nobel Prize came in 1979. In China, Mao had largely shielded the physicists from the destructive forces of the Cultural Revolution; partly at the urging of C. N. Yang and T. D. Lee, Mao and his successors made high-energy physics a target for investment. In 1975, the Chinese leadership endorsed a proposal from the physicists to build a 50 Ge V proton accelerator. Comparable to some earlier accelerators in Europe and the United States, the facility would have brought China welcome prestige. However, the cost of the project and disagreements among likely users led to its termination in the early 1980s.

Because of earlier progress and relative stability, India and Pakistan developed faster than most other Asian countries. Jawaharlal Nehru's prime ministership, 1947–1964, gave India both a rhetorical and a substantive commitment to science that fully matched the new regime of Mao in China but without the cross-currents of revolutionary politics. Nehru's commitment to science expressed itself partly in the foundation of the campuses of the Indian Institute of Technology in five Indian cities with support from Indian and other governments. Focusing primarily on undergraduate education but with some research programs, these schools took MIT as a model, and were widely seen to produce graduates of comparable quality. In a major private initiative of the period, one of Nehru's leading scientific advisers, the physicist Homi Bhabha, persuaded the Tata family to establish the Tata Institute for Fundamental Research at Bombay.

Big science stretched even Japan's resources. Its economy began to recover from the war in late 1950, but the country spent at only half the level of Western Europe on science for the next two decades. Leo Esaki's career in this period illustrates the situation. In 1958, he discovered the tunneling effect in semiconductors while working as a graduate student for the firm that later became Sony. A shared Nobel Prize came to him for this work in 1973, but he worked in the United States after 1960. Susumu Tonegawa's research career followed a similar pattern. After earning a Ph.D. in molecular biology at the University of California, San Diego, he moved to Switzerland, and there investigated the genetic origins of antibody diversity that in 1987 made him the first Japanese recipient of a Nobel Prize in medicine. He was at the time, and has remained, a professor at MIT. Ken'ichi Fukui, however, stayed in Japan, studying chemical reaction theory at Kyoto University. By applying quantum theory to knowledge of hydrocarbons gleaned from wartime work on synthetic fuels, he became in 1981 the first scientist in Asia to win the chemistry Nobel Prize (shared with Roald Hoffmann). In 1984, Y. T. Lee, from Japan's former colony of Taiwan, also won in chemistry, for work done at the University of California, Berkeley.

Only after 1970 did Japan begin to extend the level of support for science long provided by the affluent nations. The founding of Tsukuba University and the Tsukuba Science City in the early 1970s exemplified the new commitment by providing equipment and facilities well beyond those of Japan's other institutions. After 1980, it appeared that Japan intended to raise its level of accomplishment in science, and after 1990 it made explicit declarations to that effect. Convinced by these declarations, Leo Esaki accepted the presidency of Tsukuba University in 1992. Japan's business establishment added weight to expectations by publicly advocating huge increases in funding for research in academic institutions. For Esaki and the Japanese establishment, securing more Nobel Prizes in science became both a public aspiration and a symbolic obsession. Specific initiatives such as the annual Japanese Forum of Nobel Prize Recipients were launched to fulfill this objective. In 2000, a retired professor from Tsukuba University, Hideki Shirakawa, received a share of the Nobel Prize in chemistry for his work on conducting polymers. The following year, another Japanese chemist, Ryoji Noyori, also won in chemistry.

Japan's accomplishments and greater wealth in the region have elicited significant responses on behalf of science in other East Asian nations. South Korea, Taiwan, and Singapore in particular have built substantial new research facilities in recent years, although most have emphasized applied rather than basic science. There is a strong conviction in Asia that greater investment in science will promote more rapid economic growth, as well as cultural prestige. Several nations have launched formal programs to induce emigré nationals to return. In 1957, Chinese authorities tried to persuade C. N. Yang to leave the United States and return to China while he was in Stockholm receiving his Nobel Prize. But few of the efforts succeeded before the early 1990s, when Taiwan successfully invited Y. T. Lee to leave Berkeley to lead Academia Sinica (1993) and Japan enticed Esaki to take the presidency at Tsukuba (1992). Although wealth does not in itself lead directly to distinguished achievement in science, the era of big science makes wealth essential. The major economic reforms set in train by India, China, and other Asian countries in recent years should further raise their collective profile in science.

JAMES R. BARTHOLOMEW

ASTROLABE. The astrolabe is an astronomical and astrological instrument used for calculations involving the positions of the stars and the sun. Although based on the assumption of a spherical sky in daily rotation around a central earth, almost all astrolabes are flat.

The traditional form of astrolabe has a circular, planispheric map of the stars known as the "rete" (Latin for 'net'). This star-chart usually takes the form of a brass plate with most of the metal cut away by fretwork, leaving a network of bands supporting pointers indicating the positions of the stars, and a circular band for the annual path of the sun through the stars, known as the ecliptic. The plane of projection coincides with the equator, while the rectilinear projection lines converge at the south celestial pole. The same projection renders the local horizon of the user, and circles of altitude and azimuth, on a solid brass disc the same size as the rete. These projected lines form the characteristic pattern of the "latitude plate," where circles and arcs cluster around the point that indicates the local zenith, while arcs of azimuth radiate out from it. Both projections extend from the north celestial pole, usually to the tropic of Capricorn. The rete, pivoted at the pole, rotates above the stationary latitude plate; adjusted to any orientation of the sky it will indicate the positions of the stars or the sun above the horizon. Since the position of the sun in its daily rotation measures the time, an hour scale at the edge of the instrument can give the time at any hour of day and night: a rule pivoted at the center carries the sun's position (indicated by a date or zodiac scale on the ecliptic ring) to the hour scale. On the back of the astrolabe is an alidade, or sighting rule, with an altitude scale, for measuring the altitude of the sun or one of the stars included on the rete. By this means the rete can be set to the current position of the sky and the time found. Other scales on the front and back of the instrument allow astrolabes to perform a range of different functions.

Ptolemy described the geometrical basis of the traditional instrument. The earliest surviving astrolabes come from ninth-century Baghdad and Iran. The earliest dated European ones come from the fourteenth century, though astrolabes from several centuries earlier have survived. In the traditional form, separate projections are given for different latitudes, so instruments often have a number of alternative latitude plates. Muslim astronomers found several ways of making a "universal" astrolabe—one that would serve in any latitude—and Europeans devised or rediscovered similar designs in the sixteenth century. The European instrument was in rapid decline by the early seventeenth century, but fine astrolabes continued to be made in parts of the Islamic world through the nineteenth century. Astrolabes have always been treasured and admired, and they remain one of the most desirable instruments for collectors today.

The mariner's astrolabe, by contrast with the complex and ornate instruments for astronomy and astrology, had a simple and robust design. Combining an altitude ring and an alidade, they were used for finding latitude at sea mainly in the sixteenth and early seventeenth centuries).

JIM BENNETT

ASTROLOGY. Astrology is best defined as the set of theories and practices interpreting the positions of the heavenly bodies in terms of human and terrestrial implications. (The positions have variously been considered signs and, more controversially, causes.) The subject—and therefore its study—is fascinating, difficult, and often paradoxical. Although inextricably entangled with what are now demarcated as science, magic, religion, politics, psychology, and so on, astrology cannot be reduced to any of these. The historical longevity and cultural diversity of astrology are far too great for it to have been precisely the same thing in all

Islamic astrolabe made between 1350 and 1450. The top, cut-out plate is the rete; a latitude plate appears beneath and through it.

times and places, yet it has always managed to reconstitute itself as much the same thing in the minds of its practitioners, public, and opponents alike. These points have particular relevance in relation to historians of science, who until recent decades predominantly analyzed astrology anachronistically as a "pseudo-science," the human meanings of which could largely be derived from its lack of epistemological credentials.

Western astrology originated as Mesopotamian astral divination. The planets and prominent stars, identified with gods in ways that have since changed remarkably little, were considered celestial omens in which the divine messages, largely answering royal concerns, could be discerned. The origins of many key elements of the astrological tradition—not only the planetary deities, zodiacal signs, risings, and settings, but also the effort to systematize divination through what we would now consider astronomical and empirical observations—developed between its apparent origins around 2000 B.C. and the fifth century B.C., when natal astrology first appeared. The latter, following Alexander's conquest of Persia, was absorbed and transformed by Greek geometric and kinetic models, which added the aspects, or angles of separation between planets and points, and emphasized the importance of the *horoscopos* or Ascendent, the degree of the zodiacal sign rising on the Eastern horizon. (The first known horoscope dates from 4 B.C.) Astrology was also fruitfully married to Aristotelian cosmology and Greek medicine in the form of Hippocratic humors, and, slightly later, Galenic temperaments. Astrologers tended to develop increasingly flexible interpretive schemes, of which the most famous and influential was formulated by Ptolemy (c. A.D. 100–170) in his *Tetrabiblos.*

Astrology played an important role in Roman life, for the most part in crudely populist and overtly political contexts. A more fruitful course followed in the wake of Alexander the Great's conquests, as Greek astrology spread to Persia and throughout Eastern Asia as far as India. In this way Greek astrology eventually became incorporated into, and benefited from, the learning of the Arabic world. It was introduced into medieval Europe in Latin translations, notably, from the mid-twelfth century onwards, of works by Abu Ma'shar (787–886). These supplied a philosophical basis (largely Aristotelian) for astrology and popularized the idea that conjunctions of Jupiter and Saturn ("grand conjunctions") in particular regions of the heavens signify changes of political rulership. A complete revolution of the conjunctions around the zodiac, which takes 960 years, indicated changes in the fortunes of entire religions. Pierre d'Ailly and Roger Bacon took up this astral historiography.

In the late fifteenth century, a series of influential translations by Marsilio Ficino made available rediscovered Greek texts, including much of Plato, Plotinus, and Iamblichus and the *Corpus Hermeticum.* These placed a renewed magical and/or mystical astrology at the heart of the Renaissance revival of neo-Platonism and hermeticism. Typically, it managed to evade Giovanni Pico della Mirandola's powerful critique of astrology in his *Disputationes* (1494) by finding shelter elsewhere in the set of ideas that had inspired him (for example, occult sympathy and antipathy).

Astrology was controversial within the Christian church. It survived the condemnations of St. Augustine and the early church fathers, who saw it as pagan (and in particular polytheistic) and a transgression of both human free will and divine omnipotence. Augustine did not deny that astrologers could speak truthfully, only that when they did so it was with the help of, and in the service of, demons.

At both popular and elite levels, however, astrology in one form or another remained entrenched. It fell to Thomas Aquinas in the late thirteenth century to arrange a compromise that secured for it a long-lived, if limited, niche. His synthesis of Christian theology and Aristotelian natural philosophy permitted "natural astrology" to influence physical and collective phenomena but not human souls directly; the individual judgments (and in particular predictions) of "judicial astrology" were therefore illicit. Since Aquinas admitted that most people followed the promptings of their bodies, which felt the influence of the stars, he gave a tacit legitimation of astrology in practice. But the Reformation presented a serious new challenge in the sixteenth century. Luther and Calvin objected violently to astrology's idolatry, as they saw it, which they stigmatized as "superstition."

The seventeenth century was pivotal in the history of astrology. Contrary to the argument of Keith Thomas's influential *Religion and the Decline of Magic* (1971), the historical puzzle is not why so many intelligent people then believed in astrology (at a time when most people did), but why did they cease to believe in it?

Strong social and political forces abetted its fall from favor. In the English Revolution the pamphlets and almanacs of astrologers on both sides—but especially those of William Lilly for Parliament—played a major, and highly visible, role. In the late seventeenth and eighteenth centuries the new patrician and commercial alliance sought to put sectarian strife and upheaval behind it, and astrology became firmly identified as vulgar plebeian (rather than religious) superstition, to be contrasted with the spirit of rationalism and realism. This perception was now most often articulated by a new set of opponents: the metropolitan literati. Jonathan Swift's issue of a mock almanac in 1707 predicting the death of the prominent astrologer John Partridge, followed by another putatively confirming its fulfilment, epitomized the attack. Partridge became a laughing-stock in coffeehouse circles, although his almanacs continued to sell. Benjamin Franklin later employed the same tactic in the American colonies.

At the same time, increasing political centralization in France made astrologers' unlicensed prophecies unwelcome there too. After a short period of ambivalence, most prominent European natural philosophers also started to close ranks against astrology, ignoring or criticizing it as part of the old Aristotelian order, and/or as (plebeian or Platonic) magic. Isaac Newton's success set the seal on this development. He borrowed the old idea of attraction at a distance, but substituted a single and quantifiable force for an astrological sine qua non: the planets as a qualitative plurality. Natural philosophy quietly absorbed natural astrology (including the moon's effects on tides), but judicial astrology, as a symbolic rather than mathematical system addressing merely "secondary" qualities and "subjective" concerns, had no place in a newly disenchanted (and commodified) world.

In this context the charge against astrology of "superstition" began to acquire its present meaning as a cognate of stupidity or ignorance. To begin with, natural philosophers made common cause with the guardians of religious orthodoxy; but as natural philosophy moved in the direction of modern science, the hostility to astrology increasingly became a secular opposition.

The early modern period has too often been described, by those mistaking contemporary rhetoric for reality, as the time of the death of astrology. It did decline seriously as it was pushed into largely (but not entirely) rural strongholds dominated by farmers' almanacs, and into a relatively sim-

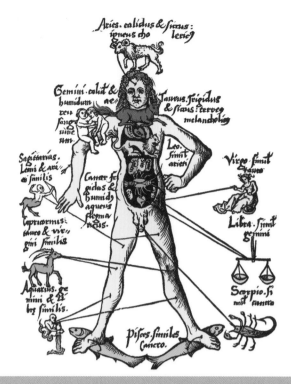

Correspondences between zodiacal signs and body parts; doctors did not bleed patients from a part in whose sign the moon stood. From the popular encyclopedia *Margarita philosophica* (1503) by Gregor Reisch.

ple and magical set of beliefs. But early in the nineteenth century, as the middle classes grew in power and began to break away from patrician hegemony, a new urban astrology appeared that still remains. More individualistic than before, it succeeded in adapting to consumer capitalist society. And in the early twentieth century, through the work of Alan Leo and his commercially canny Theosophy, astrology secured a firm footing in both the popular press and the thriving middle-class market for psychology-cum-spirituality. At present it seems to meet a demand for (re-)enchantment that no amount of technical, technological, or purely theoretical progress can serve.

Thus astrology has managed to adapt to, and even exploit, every challenge history has thrown it. There is no reason to expect it will ever fail to do so, despite the outraged denunciations it continues to attract from contemporary guardians of scientific probity.

PATRICK CURRY

ASTRONOMY. Astronomy, unlike modern sciences formed during the Scientific Revolution of the seventeenth century, has an ancient pedigree. The goals of astronomers, however—their theories, their instruments and techniques, their training, their places of work, and their sources of patronage—have undergone changes as revolutionary as those experienced by other sciences over the past four centuries.

For two millennia before the seventeenth century, a primary problem for astronomy in the Western world was to discover the true system of uniform circular motions believed to underlie the observed and seemingly irregular motions of the planets, Sun, and Moon. Astronomers observed and recorded a few planetary, solar, and lunar positions; attempted to fit geometrical models to the observations; and constructed tables of positions. In addition to the effort for its own sake, there were practical offshoots, including personal horoscopes, more general warnings of man-made and natural catastrophes, and calendars foretelling times of religious celebrations and the agricultural seasons. Solar and stellar navigation became important only later; fourteenth- and fifteenth-century explorers still found their way in sight of land. The rest of the universe scarcely existed for ancient and medieval astronomers other than as the limiting outer sphere of the stars. Nor did they concern themselves with the physical composition of the universe. Beyond the region of the Earth lay one unchanging element.

The Copernican Revolution, begun in the sixteenth century, switched the places of the Earth and the Sun in a geometrical model still composed of uniform circular motions. In other important ways, however, Copernicus radically redefined the astronomical agenda. After new observations refuted the ancient assumption of circular motion, the physical nature and cause of orbital motion, previously outside the province of astronomers, became crucial. Interest in the physical composition of the heavens increased as well once the Earth left the center of the universe, and especially after Galileo's revolutionary new telescopic observations.

In 1609 rumor from Holland of a device using pieces of curved glass to make distant objects on the Earth appear near reached Galileo in Italy. He constructed his own telescope and turned it on the heavens. Among his discoveries were four moons circling Jupiter. These Medicean stars, as he named them, secured him a position at the court of the Grand Duke of Tuscany. Galileo also observed mountains on the Moon and sunspots. Henceforth the telescopic discovery of hitherto unknown planets, moons, asteroids, comets, and nebulae, as well as examination of their more prominent activities, was a standard feature of astronomers. Amateurs wealthy enough to procure relatively large telescopes could excel.

The telescope became an instrument of precise measurement through a happy accident. Noticing that a spider's web spun in the focal plane of his telescope was superimposed on the telescopic image, the Englishman William Gascoigne realized that crosshairs or wires could help center telescopes on objects and also help measure angles between them. By 1700, after some resistance, astronomers had accepted the telescope as the primary instrument of astronomical measurement. The cost of larger telescopes, their operation, and analysis of data speeded the transition from individual observers to organized observatories under government patronage. The Paris Observatory was founded as part of the new Paris Academy of Sciences in 1666, and the Greenwich Observatory began operations a decade later. In a new age of exploration, the task of the Greenwich Observatory, as stated in a royal warrant, was to rectify "the tables of the motions of the heavens, and the places of the fixed stars, so as to find out the so much-desired longitude of places for the perfecting the art of navigation."

The last great achievement of pre-telescopic observations was Tycho Brahe's body of positional measurements at the end of the sixteenth century. He enjoyed inherited wealth and also royal patronage, given in exchange for the glory his discoveries and fame cast over his patrons. Early in the seventeenth century, Johannes Kepler used Brahe's positions to destroy faith in uniform circular motion, showing instead that ellipses more accurately describe planetary motions around the Sun. Aristotelian physics, explaining all motion around a central Earth, did not work in a Sun-centered universe. An explanation of why the planets retrace their elliptical paths around the Sun became a central problem of astronomy.

Near the end of the seventeenth century, Isaac Newton treated celestial motions as problems in mechanics governed by the same laws that determined terrestrial motions. Bodies remain at rest or move uniformly in straight lines unless external forces alter their state. A force of attraction toward the Sun continually draws the planets away from rectilinear paths and holds them in their orbits. Newton showed mathematically that, on his mechanical principles, Kepler's elliptical orbits result from a universal inverse-square law of gravity. The working out of details left undone by Newton focused the energies of many mathematical astronomers during the eighteenth century. Newtonians added quantitative success upon success, though not in the form Newton himself had used. Newton had employed geometry, the accepted medium of mathematical proof, in his demonstrations. His successors used new, more powerful algebraic methods. This change may help explain why Newton's loyal followers in England made little progress compared to scientists on the continent. Royal academies with generous support for astronomers, particularly at Paris, Berlin, and St. Petersburg, also made a difference. London's Royal Society, in contrast, neither received nor paid out royal emoluments, and the astronomers royal at Greenwich had to provide some of their own instruments.

Exact orbital calculations incorporate the influence of small perturbation effects. The Sun alters the Moon's motion around the Earth, and Jupiter and Saturn modify the motions of each other about the Sun. The Swiss-born mathematician Leonhard Euler, at St. Petersburg and later at the Berlin Academy of Sciences, helped develop mathematical techniques to compute perturbation effects. He applied them first to the Moon, and in 1748 to Jupiter and Saturn, whose motions were the subject of that year's prize topic of the Paris Academy of Sciences. Euler, and Joseph Louis Lagrange and Pierre-Simon Laplace, both members of the Paris Academy, applied the newly all-powerful calculus to the perturbations of planets and satellites, the motions of comets, the shape of the Earth, precession (a slow conical motion of the Earth's axis of rotation caused primarily by the gravitational pull of the Sun and the Moon on the Earth's equatorial bulge), and nutation (a smaller wobble superimposed on the precessional motion of the Earth's axis).

Orbital calculations now lie outside mainstream astronomy. NASA scientists use computers to calculate trajectories for their spacecraft. Astronomers would be willing, for additional government funding, to calculate whether various passing asteroids will safely miss the Earth.

The business of astronomy has at times been a family profession. Gian Domenico Cassini, recruited from Italy to set up the Paris Observatory in 1669, was succeeded by a son, a grandson, and a great-grandson, before the French Revolution drove the family from the observatory in 1793. Friedrich Struve, who helped Czar Nicholas I chart his vast empire and also recorded the positions of double stars at the Pulkovo Observatory, opened in 1839 outside St. Petersburg, founded an astronomical dynasty spanning four generations. A son succeeded him at Pulkovo, a grandson directed the Königsberg Observatory, and a great-grandson, having fled Russia in 1921 after the revolution, directed the Yerkes Observatory of the University of Chicago and then, in the 1950s, the astronomy department of the University of California.

In the middle of the nineteenth century, the Pulkovo Observatory shared the honor of possessing the largest refracting telescope in the world. Refractors bend to a focus light passing through curved glass lenses. As late as the end of the eighteenth century, glass of the quality necessary for optical instruments could be cast only in small pieces, up to two or three inches in diameter. The English duty on manufacturing limited production and made further experimentation too costly. Progress occurred on the continent, but even there the largest lens achieved by 1824 was a 9.5-inch disc for the Dorpat Observatory (in what is now Tartu, Estonia). In 1847 the 15-inch refractors at Pulkovo and the Harvard College Observatory were the largest in the world.

British industry made possible the first large reflecting telescope (1780 to 1860), which used metal mirrors to reflect light to a focus. William Herschel built a 48-inch metal mirror in 1789; in 1845 William Parsons, the Earl of Rosse, completed in Ireland his "leviathan," which had a metal mirror 72 inches in diameter. Large reflectors with their tremendous light-gathering power yielded remarkable observations of distant stellar conglomerations. But difficulty in aiming tons of metal and rapid tarnishing of mirrors rendered early reflectors unsuitable for observatories and professional astronomers, who could not harness consistently the instrument's raw power. Something new arrived with the twentieth century: a 60-inch reflecting telescope built and installed at the new Mount Wilson Observatory in 1908. The telescope had a reflective silver coating on a glass disc ground to bring incoming light to a focus, and a mounting system and drive capable of keeping the multiton instrument fixed on a celestial object while the Earth turned beneath it. The mountain observatory, funded by Andrew Carnegie's philanthropic Carnegie Institution, was one of the first located above most of the Earth's obscuring atmosphere. Its reflecting telescope, specifically designed for photographic work, completed the revolution in astronomical practice—which had required the tedious drawing by hand of features seen through telescopes—begun with the invention of photography.

With professional astronomers by definition already employed in research projects, amateur astronomers pioneered in applying photography. The American John Draper took the first known photograph of a celestial object, the Moon, in the 1840s. In 1851 a new process using plates exposed in a wet condition made possible a few photographs of the brightest stars, but not until the introduction of more sensitive dry plates after 1878 did photography become common in astronomical studies. Draper's son Henry took the first photograph of a nebula, the Orion Nebula, in 1880. In England long exposures taken by Andrew Common and Isaac Roberts brought out details too faint for the eye to see. Photography facilitated comparisons over time, produced permanent recordings of positions suitable for more precise measurement, and was essential for exploitation of the other new astronomical tool of the nineteenth century, spectroscopy.

The development of spectroscopy and the subsequent rise of the new science of astrophysics created new activities for astronomers. When attached to telescopes, prisms splitting light into spectra opened to investigation the physical and chemical nature of stars. In 1859 Gustav Kirchhoff, professor of physics at Heidelberg, showed that each element produces its own pattern of spectral lines. In the first qualitative chemical analysis of a celestial body, he compared the sun's spectrum to laboratory spectra. The English amateur astronomer William Huggins seized on news of Kirchhoff's work. By 1870 he had identified several elements in spectra of stars and nebulae. He also measured motions of stars revealed by slight shifts of spectral lines. Early in the twentieth century Vesto M. Slipher at the Lowell Observatory in Arizona was the first to measure Doppler shifts in spectra of faint spiral nebulae, whose receding motions revealed the expansion of the universe. It required an extended photographic exposure over three nights to capture enough light for the measurement.

Astronomical entrepreneurship late in the nineteenth century saw the construction of new and larger instruments and a shift of the center of spectroscopic research from England to the United States. Charles Yerkes and James Lick put up the funds for their eponymous observatories, which came under the direction, respectively, of the University of Chicago and the University of California. Percival Lowell directed his own observatory in Arizona. All three observatories were far removed from cities; the latter two sit on mountain peaks.

A scientific education became necessary for professional astronomers in the later nineteenth century, as astrophysics came to predominate and the concerns of professionals and amateurs diverged. As late as the 1870s and 1880s the self-educated American astronomer Edward Emerson Barnard, an observaholic with indefatigable energy and sharp eyes, could earn a place for himself at the Lick and Yerkes observatories with his visual observations of planetary details and his discovery of comets and the fifth satellite of Jupiter, but he was an exception and an anachronism. A project begun in 1886 at the Harvard College Observatory and continued well into the twentieth century to obtain photographs and catalog stellar spectra furthered another social shift in astronomy. It employed women, for lower wages than men would have received, but at least made space for them in a male profession. Annie Jump Cannon was largely responsible for the Henry Draper Catalogue, published between 1918 and 1924, which gave spectral type and magnitude for some 225,000 stars. Also, she rearranged the previous order of spectra into one with progressive changes in the appear-

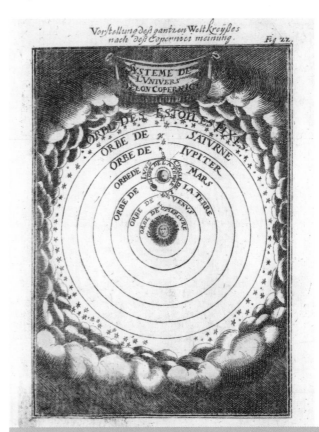

The Copernican system, with the Sun in the center of the solar system. The earth has its moon, but Jupiter still lacks its satellites.

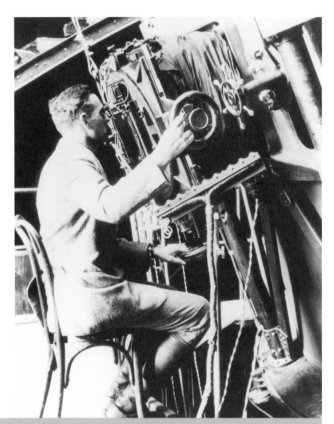

Edwin Powell Hubble (1889–1953), US astronomer and cosmologist, first demonstrated the existence of galaxies outside our own.

ance of the spectral lines. Although she developed her spectral sequence without any theory in mind, astronomers quickly realized that changes in the strength of hydrogen lines indicated decreasing surface temperature.

Spectral class became even more useful when, early in the twentieth century, it was related to luminosity. The relationship could be used to estimate distances. Students of stellar evolution asked what in the constitution of stars gave rise to dwarfs and giants and why brightness increased systematically with spectral type. The source of stellar energy, and with it the constitution of stars, became better known after the discovery of radioactivity at the beginning of the twentieth century. As late as 1920, however, the English astrophysicist Arthur Eddington complained that the inertia of tradition was delaying acceptance of the most likely source of stellar energy: the fusion of hydrogen into helium. Eddington calculated how fast pressure increases downward into a star and how fast temperature increases to withstand the pressure. He used qualitative physical laws regarding the ionization of elements developed in the 1920s by Meghnad Saha, an Indian nuclear physicist. Saha's work also provided a theoretical basis for relating the spectral classes of stars to surface temperatures. World War II produced a deeper understanding of nuclear physics and more powerful computational techniques. The practice of astrophysics has moved from observatories to scientific laboratories to giant computers running simulations.

Cosmology, the study of the structure and evolution of the universe, only belatedly insinuated itself into modern mainstream astronomy. An inability to measure great distances limited cosmology for centuries to philosophical speculations, often focused on the nature of nebulae and the possible existence of island universes similar to our galaxy. Cosmology achieved an observational foundation early in the twentieth century, when Harlow Shapley and Edwin

Hubble at the Mount Wilson Observatory made the observations that revealed the size of our galaxy, the existence of other galaxies, and the expansion of the universe.

At first these observations made little connection with Einstein's relativity theory. Astronomers, especially in the United States, possessed only limited mathematical knowledge, and were largely content to produce observations while leaving theory to theoreticians. In England, in contrast, interest in relativity theory relatively flourished. But the work was strictly mathematical, without observational input. In the 1930s, Hubble attempted to bridge the gulf between observation and theory. Cooperation, he wrote, featured prominently in nebular research at the Mount Wilson Observatory, and he struck up a close collaboration with colleagues at the nearby California Institute of Technology. Not until the 1960s, however, after the discovery of quasars and the intense theoretical effort to find a new energy source to explain them, did relativity theory secure a place in mainstream astronomy.

During the 1970s and 1980s, scientists realized that important cosmological features could be explained as natural and inevitable consequences of new theories of elementary particle physics, and particle physics now increasingly drives cosmology. Also, particle physicists, having exhausted the limits of particle accelerators and public funding for yet larger instruments, now turn to cosmology for information regarding the behavior of matter under extreme conditions, such as prevailed in the early universe.

The greatest change in astronomy during the twentieth century in understanding the universe and also in the backgrounds of astronomers and their activities followed from observations beyond visual light. In the 1930s, the American radio engineer Karl Jansky and the radio amateur Grote Reber pioneered detection of radio emissions from celestial phenomena, and radar research during World War II helped develop radio astronomy, especially in England. X-ray astronomy also took off after the war, first aboard captured German V-2 rockets carrying detectors above the Earth's absorbing atmosphere. NASA subsequently funded a rocket survey program and then satellites to detect X rays. Most of the new X-ray astronomers came over from experimental physics with expertise in designing and building instruments to detect high-energy particles. Their discoveries followed from technological innovations. Gamma rays and infrared and ultraviolet light provided further means of non-optical discoveries in the space age. Unlike the relatively quiescent universe open to Earth-bound astronomers' visual observations, the universe newly revealed to engineers and physicists observing at other wavelengths from satellites is violently energetic.

NORRISS S. HETHERINGTON

ASTRONOMY, NON-OPTICAL. Many recent astronomical discoveries have been made without using visible light. The newly revealed universe is fascinating in its activity. Stars are born, galaxies collide, neutron stars collapse into black holes, quasars vary in hours through luminosities greater than that of our entire galaxy, and pulsars rotate gigantic radio beams in fractions of seconds.

Radio astronomy is the oldest branch of the new astronomy. In 1932, Karl Jansky, an American radio engineer with the Bell Telephone Company, detected electrical emissions from the center of our galaxy while studying sources of radio noise. Neither optical astronomers nor Jansky's practical-minded supervisors cared. Grote Reber, an ardent radio amateur and distance-communication addict, took an interest, and built for a few thousand dollars a pointable radio antenna 31 feet in diameter in his backyard in Wheaton, Illinois. In 1940, he reported the intensity of radio sources at different positions in the sky.

Fundamental knowledge underlying radio astronomy techniques increased during World War II, especially with research on radar, and especially in England. After the war, research programs at Cambridge, at Manchester, and at Sydney, Australia, dominated radio astronomy for the next decade.

Manchester's large steerable radio telescope at Jodrell Bank was rescued from financial disaster in 1958 by its ability to track *Sputnik*. Other uses floated had included mobilizing the telescope as part of a ballistic missile tracking system and for long-range bomber navigation. As an astronomical instrument it detected radar signals bounced off ionized meteor trails in the earth's atmosphere. Other scientists bounced radar signals off the Moon and developed planetary radar astronomy to map the surfaces of planets.

The program at Cambridge was led by Martin Ryle, who received a Nobel Prize in 1974 for his overall contributions to radio astronomy. He completed a survey of almost two thousand radio sources, most of them extragalactic, in 1955. These sources had a bearing on Fred Hoyle's steady-state cosmological theory. Within a few years radio data and their interpretation were more certain, and argued convincingly against Hoyle's cosmology, which allowed for fewer faint radio sources than were detected.

The major blow to Hoyle's theory came in 1965 with discovery of the cosmic microwave (short radio wave) background radiation. It had been predicted in 1948 by nuclear physicists exploring the consequences of the cosmological big bang, but no astronomer looked for it. In 1963, Arno Penzias and Robert Wilson with the Bell Telephone Laboratories detected what the first regarded as noise in an antenna, but soon realized must be excess radiation of cosmic origin. In 1965, Robert Dicke at Princeton interpreted the work for which Penzias and Wilson received a Nobel Prize as a remote consequence of the origin of the universe.

Radio sources were identified in the early 1960s with star-like objects, now called quasi-stellar objects, or quasars. They have luminosities a thousand times that of our entire galaxy. The only known source for so much energy from such a small volume is a black hole. Quasars also have extremely large red shifts, probably a manifestation of an expanding universe. Ryle shared the Nobel Prize with his Cambridge colleague Anthony Hewish, who was credited with discovering pulsating radio sources, although his student Jocelyn Bell made the actual observation, in 1967.

Radio astronomy is increasingly threatened by modern society's growing use of garage-door openers, microwave ovens, wireless telephones, and other sources of interference with radio signals from astronomical objects. The commercial use of radio frequencies is light pollution's invisible cousin.

As did radio astronomy, X-ray astronomy also took off after World War II, first aboard captured German V-2 rockets that took detectors above the earth's absorbing atmosphere. Herbert Friedman at the U.S. Naval Research Laboratory found that the Sun weakly emits X rays, as expected. Astronomers did not expect to find strong X-ray sources, and doubted that brief and expensive rocket-borne experiments could contribute much to observational astronomy. In the immediate post-*Sputnik* period, however, more government money existed for astronomical research than imaginative scientists could spend.

Help came from Italian-born Riccardo Giacconi, who worked at the private company American Science and Engineering and then at the Harvard-Smithsonian Observatory before becoming director of the Space Telescope Science Institute. In 1960, with funding from the Air Force Cambridge Research Laboratories, Giacconi discovered the first cosmic X-ray source, Sco X-1 (the strongest X-ray source in the constellation Scorpius). In 1963, Friedman's group detected a second strong X-ray source, associated with the Crab nebula, the remnant of a supernova explosion.

NASA now funded a rocket survey program and a small satellite devoted exclusively to X-ray astronomy. Launched into an equatorial orbit from Kenya on its independence day in 1970, the satellite was nicknamed *Uhuru*, Swahili for freedom. Its detectors discovered binary X-ray pulsars, neutron stars whose energies arise from infalling matter from companion stars. The Einstein X-ray telescope, launched in 1978, revealed that individual sources account for much of the X-ray background radiation. Giacconi had wanted to name this satellite *Pequod*, from Melville's *Moby Dick*, as a reminder of Massachusetts and the American Indian. The inevitable comparisons of Giacconi and the egomaniacal Captain Ahab indicate the qualities needed to drive a large and complex scientific project to completion. NASA declined to associate its satellite with a white whale.

A single scientific paper was published on X-ray astronomy in 1962, and 311 a decade later. Only 4 out of 507 American astronomers participated in X-ray astronomy in 1962, compared to 170 out of 1,518 in 1972. Over 80 percent of the participants came from experimental physics with expertise in designing and building instruments to detect high-energy particles.

More energetic than X rays, gamma rays arise from nuclear reactions, including those that create elements in stars and bombs. A satellite watching for nuclear tests in the atmosphere made the first observation of cosmic gamma ray sources in 1973. The Compton Gamma Ray Observatory, deployed from a U.S. space shuttle in 1991, has recorded bursts of gamma radiation, about one a day, perhaps from mergers of extremely distant neutron stars into black holes. Gravitational waves from these events may be detectable by the Laser Interferometric Gravitation-wave Observatory, constructed in 1999. The final seconds of such an event would be more luminous than a million galaxies. If it occurred in our galaxy, the burst of gamma radiation would destroy the earth's ozone layer, kill all life on Earth, and leave the earth's surface radioactive for thousands of years.

The ultraviolet is relatively quiet. The Extreme Ultraviolet Explorer Satellite, launched in 1992, has observed hot plasma flares in the outer regions of a few nearby stars. Much of the interstellar medium, however, stops ultraviolet light. The Hubble Space Telescope spans the spectral region from far-ultraviolet through visible to near-infrared.

Cool stars, planets, grains of dust in interstellar space, and also animals radiate most of their energy at infrared frequencies. Frank Low at Texas Instruments developed an infrared detector in 1961 so sensitive that under the impossible ideal condition of no other interfering infrared source, and hooked up to the world's largest telescope, it could have detected the body heat of a mouse on the Moon. Carl Sagan wanted to use it to beat the Russians in the race to detect life on Mars. In 1967 Low, now at the Kitt Peak National Observatory in Arizona, discovered a giant cloud of gas and dust in the constellation of Orion invisible at optical wavelengths but emitting enormous energy in the infrared. The cloud might be an interstellar nursery in which stars are born and grow in their violent way. The Infrared Astronomical Satellite during ten months in 1983 before all its cooling helium evaporated found more extensive dust tails for comets than are visible optically, rings of dust in our solar system, and an extensive ring or shell of gas and dust around the star Vega, perhaps left over from the original cloud of gas and dust from which Vega condensed.

The recent revolution in non-optical astronomy has important policy lessons. Should bureaucrats follow Thomas Kuhn's theory of the structure of scientific revolutions and act as keepers of the paradigm, directing research funds into observations intended to extend and consolidate mature theories? Or should they favor the early stages of development of new fields, when practitioners fumble along without any fixed conceptual framework? Non-optical astronomical discoveries have followed largely from technological innovations, with little advance prediction or justification for their search. Is it, then, nobler of mind and more cost-efficient to serve old paradigms or new technologies?

NORRISS S. HETHERINGTON

ASTROPHYSICS. Telescopes equipped with prisms that split starlight into rainbow-like spectra made possible investigations of the physical and chemical nature of astronomical objects. In 1802, the English chemist William Wollaston found several dark lines in the solar spectrum, and in 1814, the German optician Joseph Fraunhofer observed and catalogued hundreds of solar lines. In 1859, Gustav Kirchhoff, professor of physics at the University of Heidelberg, showed that each element produces its own pattern of spectral lines. In the first qualitative chemical analysis of a celestial body, Kirchhoff compared laboratory spectra from thirty elements to the Sun's spectrum and found matches for iron, calcium, magnesium, sodium, nickel, and chromium.

The English astronomer William Huggins, tired of making drawings of planets and timing the meridian passage of stars, likened news of Kirchoff's work to "coming upon a spring of water in a dry and thirsty land." Huggins suggested to his friend and neighbor, William Allen Miller, a professor of chemistry at Kings College, London, that they commence observations of stellar spectra. Initially Miller doubted the wisdom of applying Kirchhoff's methods to the stars, because of their faint light; but by 1870, Huggins and Miller had identified several elements in spectra of stars and nebulae.

Spectroscopic techniques were also employed to measure motion in the line of sight. In 1842, Johann Christian Doppler, an Austrian physicist, argued that motion of a source of light should shift the lines in its spectrum. A more correct explanation of the principle involved was presented by the French physicist Armand-Hippolyte-Louis Fizeau in a paper read in 1841 but not published until 1848. Not all scientists accepted the theory. In 1868, however, Huggins found what appeared to be a slight shift for a hydrogen line in the spectrum of the bright star Sirius, and by 1872, he had more conclusive evidence of the motion of Sirius and several other stars. Early in the twentieth century Vesto M. Slipher at the Lowell Observatory in Arizona measured Doppler shifts in spectra of faint spiral nebulae, whose receding motions revealed the expansion of the universe.

Instrumental limitations prevented Huggins from extending his spectroscopic investigations to other galaxies. Astronomical entrepreneurship in America's gilded age saw the construction of new and larger instruments and a shift of the center of astronomical spectroscopic research from England to the United States. Also, a scientific education became necessary for astronomers, as astrophysics predomi-

The Compton Observatory (for detecting gamma rays) at the end of the manipulator arm of Shuttle Atlantis. The observatory was launched in 1991.

nated and the concerns of professional researchers and amateurs like Huggins diverged.

George Ellery Hale, a leader in founding the *Astrophysical Journal* in 1895, the American Astronomical and Astrophysical Society in 1899, the Mount Wilson Observatory in 1904, and the International Astronomical Union in 1919, was a prototype of the high-pressure, heavy-hardware, big-spending, team-organized scientific entrepreneur. While an undergraduate at the Massachusetts Institute of Technology in 1889, he invented a device to photograph outbursts of gas at the Sun's limb. He continued studying the Sun at his home observatory and then at the Yerkes Observatory of the University of Chicago. In 1902, Andrew Carnegie established the Carnegie Institution of Washington with a $10,000,000 endowment for research, exceeding the total of endowed funds for research of all American colleges combined. With grants from the Carnegie Institution, Hale built the Mount Wilson Observatory with a 60-inch reflecting telescope in 1908 and a 100-inch completed in 1917. In his own research, Hale in 1908 detected the magnetic splitting of spectral lines from sunspots.

Stellar spectra were obtained at the Harvard College Observatory and catalogued in a project begun in 1886 and continued well into the twentieth century. Women did much of the tedious computing work. Edward Charles Pickering, the newly appointed director of the Harvard College Observatory in 1881 and an advocate of advanced study for women, declared that even his maid could do a better job of copying and computing than his incompetent male assistant. And so she did. And so did some twenty more women over the next several decades, recruited for their steadiness, adaptability, acuteness of vision, and willingness to work for low wages. Initially the stars were catalogued alphabetically, beginning with A, on the strength of their hydrogen lines, but Annie Jump Cannon found a continuous sequence of gradual changes among them: O, B, A, F, G, K, M, R, N, S (mnemonically: Oh, be a fine girl; kiss me right now, Sweet.). Antonia Maury added a second dimension to the classification system by noting that spectral lines were narrower in more luminous, giant stars of the same spectral class. Cecilia Payne-Gaposkin, a graduate student at Harvard, determined from spectra relative abundances of elements in stellar atmospheres. Her Ph.D. thesis of 1925, published as *Stellar Atmospheres,* has been lauded as the most brilliant thesis written in astronomy. She received her degree from Radcliffe College, however—Harvard did not then grant degrees to women—and later when employed at Harvard she was initially budgeted as "equipment."

Ejnar Hertzsprung in Copenhagen and Henry Norris Russell at Princeton University independently, in 1911 and 1913 respectively, related spectral class to luminosity. The Hertzsprung-Russell diagram was used to estimate distances by determining spectral class, reading absolute brightness off the diagram, and comparing that to the observed brightness diminished by distance. Once the source of stellar energy became better known, evolutionary tracks of stars would be drawn on the H-R diagram.

By the middle of the nineteenth century, discussions of the source of solar energy had rejected chemical combustion, which would have burnt away a mass as large as the Sun in only 8,000 years. From 1860 on, William Thomson (Lord Kelvin) switched from an influx of meteoritic matter as the Sun's energy source to gravitational contraction. Thomson estimated the age of the Sun at twenty million years, less than a tenth that required by Darwin's theory of evolution. In 1903 Pierre and Marie Curie measured the heat given off by a gram of radium. This hitherto unknown source of energy opened up vast spans of time for geological and biological evolution, though astronomers were slow to abandon gravitational contraction.

In 1938, the German-born Hans Bethe (b. 1906), then at Cornell University, proposed a plausible mechanism for energy production in stars. He knew much about atoms but little about stellar interiors when he attended a conference in April 1938 reviewing the problem of thermonuclear sources in stars. Shortly thereafter, Bethe worked out the carbon cycle. It begins with a carbon-12 nucleus; adds four protons in stages, converting the carbon to nitrogen and then to oxygen; and ends in nuclei of carbon-12 and helium-4 plus energy. A bit later Bethe also envisioned a proton-proton reaction: two protons (hydrogen nuclei) form a nucleus of deuterium (one proton becoming one neutron); the addition of a third proton creates a helium-3 nucleus (two protons, one neutron), two of which collide to form helium-4 (two protons, two neutrons) while ejecting two protons. The net result in both cases is the fusion of four hydrogen nuclei into one helium nucleus plus a release of energy. The proton-proton reaction provides the main source of energy in stars about the mass of our Sun, 70 percent of which is hydrogen and 28 percent helium. In more massive and hotter stars with more heavy elements, the carbon cycle is more important. Bethe received the Nobel Prize in 1967 for his work on the mechanisms of energy production in stars.

Norriss S. Hetherington

ATOMIC STRUCTURE. By 1890, much evidence had accumulated that the atom of chemistry and the molecule of physics must have parts. The chemical evidence included analogies between the behavior of dilute solutions and of gases, as developed in the ionic theory of Svante Arrhenius (Nobel Prize in chemistry, 1903), and the implication from the periodic table that the elements must have some ingredient in common. The physical evidence included the emission of characteristic spectra, which was likened to the ringing of a bell, and the formation of ions in gas discharges.

Sommerfeld's "Ellipsenverein" showing the linked motions of five electrons described similar precessing elliptical orbits; at any instant the electrons occupy the vertices of a rotating, pulsating pentagon.

Study of the rays emanating from the cathode in these discharges prompted Joseph John Thomson (Nobel Prize in physics, 1906) to assert in 1897 that the rays consisted of tiny charged corpuscles, which made up chemical atoms and constituted their common bond, and also emitted spectral lines and proffered the key to ionization. This hazardous extrapolation quickly received confirmation. Thomson showed that the ions liberated from metals by ultraviolet light had the same low mass-to-charge ratio *(m/e)* as corpuscles, around one one-thousandth the corresponding ratio for hydrogen atoms in electrolysis. Thomson's student Ernest Rutherford (Nobel Prize in chemistry, 1908) determined that the rays from radioactive substances consisted of two sorts, one, alpha, unbendable, the other, beta, bendable, by a magnetic field; he and the discoverer of radioactivity, Henri Becquerel (Nobel Prize in physics, 1903), showed by the degree of bending that beta rays also had a very small *m/e*.

Indication of the presence of corpuscles within atoms came from the magnetic splitting of spectral lines accomplished by Pieter Zeeman (Nobel Prize in physics, 1902) as elucidated by Hendrik Antoon Lorentz (Nobel Prize in

A

New Zealand-born physicist Ernest Rutherford (1871–1937) seen in the Cavendish Laboratory, Cambridge, England, ca. 1930, of which he was the director. He was known for his booming voice as well as for his brilliance.

ford inferred that Thomson's latest estimate was still too high. The scattering experiments indicated that the charges making up an individual scatterer acted as if assembled together at one point. Such an assemblage needed a smaller total charge to deflect an alpha particle through a given angle than a diffuse scatterer. Thus the atomic nucleus, which in Rutherford's original formulation could be either positive or negative, entered physics. He soon chose a positive center carrying the entire mass A and a charge of around $Ae/2$. Rutherford's student Henry G. J. Moseley then (in 1913–1914) deduced from his examination of characteristic X-ray spectra that the nucleus could be characterized by a whole number Z, beginning at 1 with hydrogen and increasing by a unit thereafter through the periodic table. Rutherford's school associated Z (the "atomic number") with the positive charge on the nucleus and recognized it to be a more reliable indicator of chemical nature than atomic weight. Classification by Z allowed an explanation of the few places in the periodic table where chemical properties did not follow weight and provided space for the accommodation of isotopes according to the ideas put forward by Rutherford's former colleagues Frederick Soddy (Nobel Prize in chemistry, 1921), Georg von Gyorgy Hevesy (Nobel Prize in chemistry, 1943), Kasimir Fajans, and others around 1913.

During a study trip to Rutherford's laboratory in 1911, Niels Bohr (Nobel Prize in physics, 1922) convinced himself that the nuclear atom was the route to a theory of atomic structure much better than Thomson's. One cause of his conviction was that ordinary electrodynamics required that a nuclear hydrogen atom with one electron could destroy itself instantly by radiation, whereas atoms stuffed with electrons could last a very long time. By presenting the problem of the existence of atoms in its strongest form, the nuclear hydrogen atom appealed to Bohr's dialectical mind. He solved the problem by fiat, by declaring that electrons could circulate in atoms only on orbits restricting their angular momenta to integral multiples of the quantum of action. With this condition Bohr derived the wavelengths of the spectra of hydrogen and ionized helium and gave indications of the nature of molecular bonding in (1913–1914). Arnold Sommerfeld extended the scheme to spectra containing doublets and triplets, and also to the X-ray spectra investigated by Moseley and Manne Siegbahn (Nobel Prize in physics, 1924).

Physicists returning from World War I found that Bohr (who as a Dane had been neutral), Sommerfeld (who was too old to fight), and their coworkers had made Bohr's combination of ordinary mechanics and quantum conditions into a hybrid, inconsistent, vigorous theory where none had existed before. Reasoning about electrons orbiting nuclei in quantized orbits, they could explain many features of atomic spectra, ionization and electron impact, and molecular bonding. The high point of the hybrid approach, known subsequently as "the old quantum theory," came in 1922, when Bohr claimed to be able to derive the lengths of the periods of the table of elements. But by then quantitative mismatches between theory and data on atoms more complicated than hydrogen had begun to undermine confidence in the internally structured mechanical atom. During the years between 1925 and to 1927, it was superseded by ascribing non-mechanical spin, unsociability (Pauli Exclusion), and exchange forces to the electron, and by replacing the Bohr-Sommerfeld equations with matrix and wave mechanics. Physicists declared that they knew everything

physics, 1902). Lorentz traced spectra to the vibrations of "ions" whose m/e, as determined from Zeeman's magneto-optical splitting, was very close to those of the cathoderay, photo-electric, and beta-ray particles. The omnipresent corpuscle became the electron around 1900 when experiments at Thomson's laboratory at Cambridge indicated that the charge on corpuscles was about the same as that on a hydrogen ion.

Thomson was a leader of the British school, largely Cambridge trained, who, to paraphrase another of its lights, William Thomson, Lord Kelvin, understood a problem best after constructing a physical model of it. Thomson supposed that the corpuscle-electrons constituting an atom circulated within a spherical space that acted as if filled with a homogeneous, unresisting, diffuse, weightless positive charge. On this last assumption, an atom of mass A would contain around $1,000A$ electrons. In 1904 Thomson exhibited analogies between a swarm of electrons circulating in concentric rings and the chemical properties of the elements. He thus introduced the important idea that one element differed from another only in its electronic structure. In 1906, having calculated the capacity of his model atoms to scatter X rays and beta rays, he deduced that the number of scattering centers was more nearly $3A$ than $1000A$, thus giving weight and reality to the positive charge.

In 1910, Rutherford and Hans Geiger showed that alpha particles could be scattered through large angles. Ruther-

about the atom "in principle" and moved their model-making into the recesses of the nucleus.

J. L. HEILBRON

ATOMIC WEIGHT. In his work of the 1770s and 1780s, Antoine-Laurent Lavoisier took weight to be the central measure of amount of material; when he defined a chemical element as a chemically undecomposable substance, he took loss of weight as his criterion for decomposition. In the generation after Lavoisier's death, chemists developed ideas about chemical atoms whose single measurable feature was their weight. Since the absolute weight of an object as small as an atom could not be measured, atomic weights have always been expressed in units relative to a conventional standard.

Determining the relative weights of the atoms of each of the elements involved three pragmatic issues: first, choosing that conventional standard; second, determining the formulas for the compounds used to derive the atomic weights; and third, achieving the greatest possible accuracy in measurement. Among the first generation of chemical atomists, John Dalton, Humphry Davy, and William Prout chose the fiducial standard that the atom of hydrogen = 1 exactly; on the other hand, Thomas Thomson chose oxygen = 1, William Wollaston chose oxygen = 10, and Jöns Jacob Berzelius chose oxygen = 100. By the middle of the nineteenth century, nearly every chemist had adopted the hydrogen standard, which is still used today in modified form (namely, carbon-12 = 12 exactly, which places hydrogen very close to 1).

Throughout the nineteenth century, the chemist had to determine (or to *assume,* if empirical determination proved impossible) the formulas for any chemical compounds used to derive atomic weights. For example, Dalton's data (1810) indicated that water consists of 87.5 percent oxygen and 12.5 percent hydrogen. He assumed that molecules of water consist of an atom of hydrogen united to an atom of oxygen; consequently oxygen weighed 7 using the standard of hydrogen = 1. By contrast, Davy and Berzelius (in 1812 and 1814, respectively) took H_2O rather than HO as the formula for water. In this case, *two* atoms of hydrogen must make up the same quantity that one did in the previous case, so hydrogen must be 0.5 on the scale of oxygen = 7, or if H = 1, then O = 14. Actually, Berzelius's more precise chemical analysis indicated that water consisted of 88.8 percent oxygen by weight, making the weight of an oxygen atom 16 if calculated on the scale H = 1.

Since no physical methods for the determination of chemical formulas existed at the beginning of the nineteenth century, the varying assumptions about formulas led to conflicting systems of atomic weight, many of which gave values for the same atom that differed by small integral multiples (such as O = 8 versus O = 16). Only gradually did chemists learn how to determine formulas in a way that could command a consensus in the specialist community. By the 1860s, most European chemists had come to agreement on a single system of atomic weights and formulas, nearly identical with that used today. Still, many fine chemists in France continued to accept HO as the formula of water, until they too converted to the majority viewpoint in the 1890s.

The dispute between Dalton and Berzelius over hydrogen, oxygen, and water also illustrates the significance of accuracy in gravimetric analyses of compounds to arrive at precise atomic weights. Since many atomic weights appeared to be close to integers on the scale of H = 1, Prout and Thomson both believed that all atomic weights should be integral. If true, all atoms might be built up from subatomic particles that represented the integral weight units—perhaps hydrogen atoms themselves. "Prout's hypothesis," as it came to be known, was formally proposed in 1815.

Berzelius rejected the hypothesis on empirical grounds. Thomson and others, he said, were letting their predilection damage their objectivity. An extended discussion between Berzelius, Justus von Liebig, Jean-Baptiste-André Dumas, Charles Marignac, and others between 1838 and 1849 over the relative atomic weights for the crucial elements hydrogen, carbon, and oxygen established that Berzelius's nonintegral weight for carbon was nearly 2 percent too high. The revised weights (1, 12, and 16 almost exactly) gave another boost to Prout's hypothesis. Subsequent new determinations by the Belgian chemist J. S. Stas established that many elements had nonintegral atomic weights and drew opinion against Prout once more.

Edward Morley and T. W. Richards, who won a Nobel Prize for his work, made the finest atomic-weight determinations using purely chemical means at the end of the century. After the development of the mass spectrometer, atomic weights could be determined with great accuracy and directness. The history of the mass spectrometer is intimately connected with investigations of atomic structure, including the discovery of protons, neutrons, and isotopes. All atomic nuclei consist of integral numbers of unit masses of protons and neutrons, the elemental atomic weight being nothing more than a weighted average of all the naturally occurring isotopes of the element. There was some truth to Prout's hypothesis after all.

A. J. ROCKE

Table of atomic weights of the "elements" together with their symbols, as given by John Dalton (1766–1844) in 1808

BACTERIOLOGY AND MICROBIOLOGY. The science known as bacteriology or microbiology came into existence when the French chemist Louis Pasteur, the German physician Robert Koch, and their associates established the role of specific microorganisms in causing specific fermentations and diseases. Yet the full significance of the new science they wrought extends well beyond providing the evidence to support and the tools to apply what their medical contemporaries called "germ theory." Bacteriology was less a new discipline with its own set of research problems than a new kind of laboratory or experimental system in which myriad physiological, chemical, and biological problems could be addressed and from which new sciences could emerge, notably immunology. Moreover, the development of bacteriology was nearly inseparable from the role it played in wider material, social, and conceptual transformations that unfolded in and beyond the industrializing world in the century after 1860.

Ever since the seventeenth century, the learned and the curious had bent over microscopes to peer at a hitherto unseen new world that seemed to teem with life. These visions inspired everything from philosophical systems by Gottfried Wilhelm Leibniz to comical verse by Jonathan Swift to natural history of "animalcules" and "infusoria" and controversy over the origin of life. By the mid-nineteenth century, field observation and innovation by men like

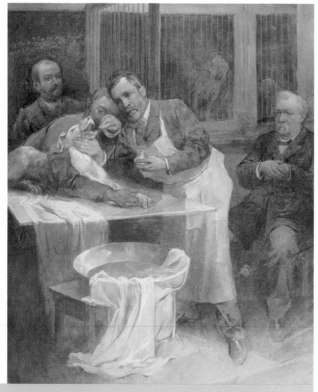

A pencil drawing by artist Alfons Mucha of Louis Pasteur (1822–1895) in his laboratory

the physician Ignaz Semmelweis in the maternity clinic, the civil servant and amateur agronomist Agostino Maria Bassi on the silk plantation, and the surgeon Joseph Lister were yielding the first testable conjectures concerning the role of microscopic life in processes of putrefaction and disease.

Decisive in the transition from this field experimental work to systematic laboratory study of a wide range of specific microorganisms grown in artificial media under controlled conditions were, first, application of chemistry and experimental physiology to the study of apparently "germ"-related processes and, second, radical innovation in methods and materials. The first of these phases, roughly 1835–1875, began in the Berlin physiology laboratory of Johannes Peter Müller. His student Theodor Schwann designed an experimental apparatus allowing him to observe that putrefaction and alcoholic fermentation occurred only in the presence of air that had not been heated to destroy any microscopic life it contained.

Schwann published one important paper and then moved on to other research; twenty years later Louis Pasteur extended Schwann's work to other fermentations and to disease, publishing hundreds of papers and numerous books, training students and gathering associates into his laboratory and thus establishing a school of research on microscopic organisms. Whereas his forerunners and contemporaries were unable to observe microorganisms in isolation from complex natural media such as grape juice, beer, and blood, the chemist Pasteur created a general experimental system for cultivating microorganisms in artificial media. These media were chemically calibrated and their environments controlled so as to favor the growth of any given species over others, thus allowing each to be studied in isolation, its chemical input and output subjected to exact analysis.

The second phase in the emergence of bacteriology, roughly 1875–1890, is associated especially with Robert Koch. The methods and instruments of chemistry and physiology were supplemented and often replaced by novel ways of cultivating, manipulating, and representing microorganisms. Thus the delicate blown-glass globe taken from chemistry by Schwann and Pasteur for use in growing microbial cultures—tricky to manage and precarious to transport, filled with infusions difficult to maintain in biological purity and impossible to scan with the microscope—became the simple, transportable, scannable glass dish named after Koch's associate Richard Petri, now ubiquitous in biomedicine, with its conveniently immobile growing-surface of gelatine or agar-agar, upon which a mixed culture could be sown and then divided into colonies or individual bacteria to be "isolated" and replated as "pure cultures." Whereas Pasteur's difficult methods had been adopted by a mere handful of investigators outside his laboratory, now the new bacteriological technique spread throughout the world.

Koch's fundamental contributions are three-fold. First, his studies on anthrax joined those of Pasteur on silkworm diseases in showing the direct relevance of the laboratory to understanding events in the field. Koch watched the seemingly static "little rods" (bacilli) observed by other microscopists in anthrax blood multiply by division and, in a characteristic life-cycle, change form into highly resistant spores. The spore stage explained the ability of the disease to persist in abandoned pastures. Second, Koch showed that the welter of microscopic life that others had observed in infected wounds could be resolved into a limited number of species, each correlated with a distinct set of pathological effects. Finally, in the work that made him virtually a household name, Koch used his new method of solid-media culture to isolate a microscopic species responsible for the leading cause of death in the Western world, pulmonary consumption or tuberculosis, as well as for the dread disease cholera, while his students Friedrich Loeffler and Georg Gaffky did the same for diphtheria and typhoid fever.

Though these and similar demonstrations are often thought of as the end of etiological research, they were in fact its beginning. By what mechanisms and under what circumstances did microorganisms cause disease and epidemics? Why did some people exposed to infection become ill while others did not? Some early bacteriologists avoided these difficult questions. Others explored them through work on variable virulence, secreted toxins, and, above all, natural and acquired immunity.

In 1880, Pasteur's invention of artificial vaccines launched the study of immunity and immunization. But it also made bacteriology something it had not been before, namely, experimental biology in the strict sense: experimental study of species, inheritance, variation, and the Darwinian evolutionary mechanism of natural selection. Pasteur's vaccines were weakened cultures of pathogenic species, and many bacteriologists understood this weakening or "attenuation" to be biological variation. In the twentieth century, the study of microbial variation and of the associated phenomenon of infection of bacteria by virus (bacteriophage) came to have momentous theoretical consequences for the life sciences through its central role in the origins of molecular biology and genetics.

From its earliest, dramatic achievements, bacteriology was an icon of the triumph of technical skill and experimental discipline over speculation and superstition. Yet as some bacteriologists themselves pointed out, bacteriological research has also been shaped by myths and beliefs concerning purity and danger, life and death: disease-causing germs as demons or enemies, the seeds of disease and the soil of the body, the body as an armed citadel. The scope of meanings of microbiological research has continued ever since to range from the mundane (the quality of beer and the safety of milk) to the cosmic (the origin of life and the cycle of matter) to the political and social (relative importance of "seed" and "soil," or germs and social conditions, in disease causation).

Alongside these wider meanings, the rise of bacteriology involved a conceptual transformation in medicine: from defining diseases by their circumstances, symptoms, and pathologies to defining them by their causes; from clinical and pathological to etiological definitions of disease. Bacteriology gave medicine and hygiene powerful reasons for focusing on the identification and control of necessary, specific causes.

With the conceptual transformations came practical ones. Through bacteriology, not only could diseases be defined and understood in etiological terms, but they could be routinely diagnosed and sometimes even treated according to their causes rather than their symptoms. Bacteriological and serological testing put laboratories, for the first time, at the very center of everyday medical and public health practice. The emergence of routine bacteriological diagnosis in hospitals and municipal health departments may be the single most important event in the wider and longer history by which the means and authority of diagnosis, which once lay solely in the skilled and experienced hands of the physician, was increasingly placed in laboratories and machines.

Beyond the laboratory revolution in medicine, bacteriological methods such as testing of bodies and waters and wastes, products such as vaccines, and technologies such as pasteurization remove the fabric of everyday human existence, consumption, and material production in and beyond the industrializing world. The immediacy of this impact has been unparalleled among the life sciences and comparable to the changes in civilization associated with electromagnetism and synthetic chemistry.

With its array of products and services, the bacteriological laboratory ushered in an era in the history of science in which experiment is often synonymous with invention, inquiry with application. The intimate and constant interaction of Pasteur, Koch, Paul Ehrlich, and others with government and business became a compelling model for the organization of scientific life in the twentieth century. The establishment of the Pasteur Institute in Paris (1888), Koch's institute in Berlin (1891), the Lister Institute in London (1891), Ehrlich's institute in Frankfurt (1899), and the Rockefeller Institute in New York (1901) inaugurated a new kind of large, national, nonuniversity research institution and an expansion in the scale and social role of the sciences of health and life, their growth into an omnipresent complex involving industry, commerce, philanthropy, the state, and the consumer.

ANDREW MENDELSOHN

BAROMETER. The barometer grew out of practical hydrostatics in the early seventeenth century. Italian mining and hydro-engineers had noticed that pumps would not raise water more than about thirty feet. Galileo proposed that "the force of the vacuum" could hold up a column of water only so tall in a pump before it broke, as if the vacuum were a rope holding up a weight. Isaac Beeckman, Giovanni Baliani, and others argued that the weight of the air outside the pump balanced the water column. Around 1641 Gasparo Berti attached a forty-foot lead pipe to the side of his house, filled it with water, sealed the top, and opened a cock at the bottom, which stood in a large vessel of water. Ten feet of water flowed out, leaving a column suspended some thirty feet high and a space above it that posed a difficult puzzle, since the reigning Aristotelian physics held the vacuum to be an impossibility.

Galileo's disciples repeated Berti's experiment with different liquids until, in 1644, Evangelista Torricelli filled a glass tube with mercury, inverted it in a bowl of the same liquid, and watched the silver liquid fall. Torricelli reasoned from the equality of the ratios of the heights of the mercury and water columns and their specific weights that the atmosphere indeed balanced the standing column. He suggested that his instrument "might show the changes of the air," but the meteorological possibilities of the instrument were largely ignored during two decades' debate over the nature of the space above the mercury and the balancing act of the air. The "Torricellian experiment" remained an experiment for the demonstration and investigation of the vacuum. Blaise Pascal pushed the experiment further towards a measuring

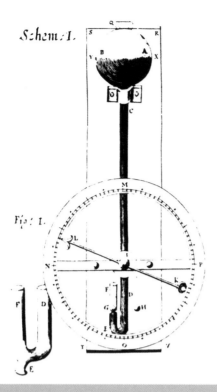

Scheme 1.

Fig: 1.

Wheel barometer designed by Robert Hooke (1635–1703) and depicted by him in his pioneering *Micrographia* (1665)

instrument by fitting the tube with a paper scale and watching the mercury travel "up or down according as the weather is more or less overcast." This arrangement he designated a "'continuous experiment,' because one may observe, if he wishes, continually." The word "barometer" appeared in 1663 in the work of Robert Boyle, who with Robert Hooke had set a tube in a window for weather observation.

Soon many new types of barometers appeared: siphon instruments, in which a recurved lower end replaced the barometer's cistern; double and triple barometers, in which successive liquids magnified the motions of the column; diagonal barometers, whose inclination had the identical function; and others. Many designs aimed at a growing market for philosophical and mathematical instruments among the well-to-do. None increased the barometer's accuracy, which did not concern natural philosophers of the seventeenth and early eighteenth centuries.

Precision became important after the Seven Years' War. European states inaugurated national cartographic projects to provide accurate topographic information for military campaigns, taxation, agricultural reform, and other programs of the late Enlightenment. Barometers provided a convenient, if not the most authoritative, method for measuring heights on these surveys, and a demand arose for their precision. The instruments also proved useful to scientific travelers and for investigations into the properties of the air at a time when philosophers were discovering the different gases constituting it and puzzling over water vapor and its pressure in the atmosphere. The Genevan natural philosopher Jean André Deluc, an avid Alpine explorer, designed the first barometer capable of precise measurement. Deluc's exhaustive *Recherches sur les modifications de l'atmosphère* (1772) included such reforms as boiling the mercury to remove dissolved air, methods for leveling the barometer and for reading the mercury meniscus, and corrections for the expansion with temperature of mercury, glass, and the ambient air. Equally important, Deluc showed how to deploy the instru-

ment in repeated series of exhaustive measurements—a revolutionary technique. Deluc's rule for converting barometric measurements to heights was quickly adopted in England, where a national geodetic survey was underway.

In England, instrument makers, moving away from craft-based organization, implemented industrial techniques such as division of labor, machine manufacture, and research and development financed out of profits from government trade. By 1770, Jesse Ramsden, the most advanced among them, was manufacturing barometers accurate to one-thousandth of an inch. In France, the guilds hobbled efforts by the enlightened monarchy to modernize the instrument trade, though a few excellent instrument makers worked there towards the end of the ancien régime. The dissolution of the guilds during the Revolution and the need for instruments for military purposes and for metrification strengthened the instrument trade in France. Jean Nicolas Fortin's barometer, accurate to two-thousandths of an inch, became the standard model in France.

In the nineteenth century, the popularity of scientific travel and the increasing reach of European imperialism favored the development of the aneroid barometer. At the end of the seventeenth century, Leibniz had suggested an instrument that would balance the pressure of the atmosphere against a spring-loaded, flexible bellows or box. In 1844, Lucien Vidie developed a practical barometer based on this principle. The aneroid became popular among mountaineers and mariners; in the twentieth century, aviation pushed the development of highly accurate aneroid instruments.

The requirements of networks of weather observers organized by national governments in the late nineteenth century helped create a new class of barometers: the high-precision "primary" barometer, against which observers' instruments were calibrated. Manufacturers employed sophisticated methods, including the Sprengel mercury vacuum pump, to clean, fill, and evacuate these instruments.

THEODORE S. FELDMAN

BIOCHEMISTRY is the name most commonly used during the twentieth century to designate the branch of science that investigates the chemical constituents of living matter, the substances produced by organisms, the functions and transformations of these substances within organisms, and the energetic changes associated with them. Many of these topics had been studied under such names as iatrochemistry, animal and plant chemistry, and physiological chemistry.

From the time that chemistry itself emerged as a distinct investigative activity during the seventeenth century, chemical knowledge was regularly applied to the study or explanation of processes occurring in living organisms. The successive stages of digestion and the formation of blood came to be interpreted as a series of interactions of acids and alkalis when their study became prominent in the middle of the century. Alcoholic fermentation, which was often characterized as an "intestine motion," also became a model for the explanation of internal vital processes. Van Helmont was the first of many to suggest that "ferments" caused digestion and other transformations. During the seventeenth and eighteenth centuries, chemists divided their field into three parts according to the three kingdoms of nature. Substances obtained from the animal kingdom were characterized by "volatile alkali," an alkali that sublimed or passed over into the receiver in the distillation procedures central to early chemical analysis. Plant material contained, instead, predominantly fixed alkali. This distinction led to various concepts of nutrition during the eighteenth century, such as that proposed by Herman Boerhaave, who inferred that food entered the body in an "acidescent" condition, gradually becoming "alkalescent" as it transformed into blood, tissues, and eventually excretory products.

The changes in chemistry associated with the chemical revolution at the end of the eighteenth century also marked a transformation in the study of the chemical processes of life. Antoine-Laurent Lavoisier made three central contributions. Through the extension of his studies of combustion to several representative plant substances, especially sugar and oils, he showed that plant matter comprises carbon, hydrogen, and oxygen, individual substances being distinguished by the proportions in which they contain these elements. Drawing on the demonstration by his colleague, Claude Louis Berthollet, that "volatile alkali" is composed of nitrogen and hydrogen, Lavoisier concluded that animal substances contain four elements—carbon, hydrogen, oxygen, and nitrogen. By this time, chemists understood that "animal substances" did not derive from the animal kingdom alone, but constituted a class of substances, including fibrin, albumin, casein, and gluten, some of which came from plant matter.

Adapting his quantitative methods to the study of alcoholic fermentation, Lavoisier showed that the chemical change involved is the conversion of sugar to alcohol and carbonic acid. Determining the elementary composition of each of the substances involved, he produced the first balanced chemical equation for a biologically important process.

Through experiments carried out on birds and guinea pigs breathing in closed chambers and in a calorimeter (the latter experiment in collaboration with Pierre Simon de Laplace), Lavoisier identified respiration as a slow combustion in which carbon converts to carbonic acid and hydrogen to water, and heat and work are derived. To maintain its equilibrium, an animal or human must ingest in its food quantities of carbon and hydrogen equal to those consumed in respiration. Lavoisier could not specify in detail the nature of the substances containing the carbon and hydrogen, or the internal processes connecting the input to the final products of respiration, but his theory has provided ever since the boundaries within which the material exchanges between the organism and its surroundings and the dynamic chemical processes within the organism have been studied.

During the first four decades of the nineteenth century, the rapid development of chemistry provided increasingly powerful methods to study the composition of plant and animal matter and the transformations they undergo. By the 1830s, the three most important general classes of foodstuffs, as well as the major constituents of the organism, had been identified as carbohydrates, fats, and "albuminous" matter (later renamed proteins). The process of chemical change in the organism most open to direct investigation was digestion. A series of investigators, including Friedrich Tiedemann and Leopold Gmelin, Johann Eberle, Theodor Schwann, Louis Mialhe, Claude Bernard, and Willy Kühne, followed the changes that the three classes of foodstuff undergo in their passage through the stomach and intestines. In 1836, Schwann identified pepsin as a "ferment" that induced digestive changes in albuminous foodstuffs. The further characterization of pepsin has occupied investigators ever since. Pepsin became the prototype for the general concept that "ferments," acting in minute quantities as catalysts, direct many key processes in organisms. In 1876, Willy Kühne proposed the word "enzyme" to denote the class of ferments, including pepsin, that can "proceed without the presence of organisms." Later, his term gradually replaced the term ferment to denote the agents of both intracellular and intercellular chemical transformations.

During the 1840s, chemists and physiologists sometimes competed to determine the conditions under which the chemical processes of life could be established, chemists inferring their nature from the chemical properties of the substances involved, physiologists such as Claude Bernard insisting on the need to follow the chemical changes into the living body itself. Among the chemists, Justus Liebig and Jean-Baptiste Dumas showed how the new knowledge of the chemistry of proteins, carbohydrates, fats, and their decomposition products could be used to give more comprehensive meaning to Lavoisier's theory of respiration. Thus they took the first speculative steps toward an account of the intermediate stages connecting foodstuffs with final decomposition products and an ascription to these processes of the sources of animal heat and muscular work. Hermann von Helmholtz gave further meaning to these processes by linking them with his formulation of the general principle of the conservation of energy. Bernard demonstrated the fruitfulness of his approach by discovering through vivisection the special action of the pancreatic juice on fats and the glycogen function of the liver. Others saw the need to establish a new scientific specialty devoted to the study of the chemical processes of life. Carl Lehmann became a professor of physiological chemistry at Leipzig in 1847, and Felix Hoppe-Seyler professor of the same at Strasbourg in 1872. Both argued for the necessity of an independent discipline, but their example did not spread, and the subject continued to be pursued mainly in Institutes of Physiology in Germany, though a series of textbooks of physiological chemistry represented the subject as a coherent and growing body of knowledge and field of investigation.

During the second half of the nineteenth century, organic and physiological chemists identified a number of the amino acids obtainable by decomposing proteins. At the end of the century, Emil Fischer and Franz Hofmeister independently proposed that amino acids linked together through "peptide" (–CO–NH–) bonds compose proteins. Fischer also established the stereospecific formulas for a number of biologically important sugars. By this time it had become clear that starch, glycogen, and other "polysaccharides" were made of many simple sugars linked together. That fats can be decomposed into glycerol and fatty acids had been established early in the century by Michel Chevreul. The general appreciation that each of the three major foodstuffs could be broken down into smaller molecules, and growing evidence that this happened during digestion, led to the "building block" concept. This assigned the creation of proteins, fats, and carbohydrates of the organism to the reconstruction of similar materials, assimilated from the food, and transferred the central problem of "metabolism" from (in the words of Frederick Gowland Hopkins) "complex substances which elude ordinary chemical methods" to "simple substances undergoing comprehensible reactions." This shift in perspective energized the effort during the first decades of the twentieth century to detect the nature of the intermediary steps by new experimental methods. The discovery by Eduard Buchner in 1902 that the archetypical "ferment" (the agent of alcoholic fermentation) could be separated from yeast cells and produce "cell-free" fermentation further energized the search.

At the turn of the century, biochemical processes were studied in many institutional settings ranging from departments of physiology and organic chemistry to internal medi-

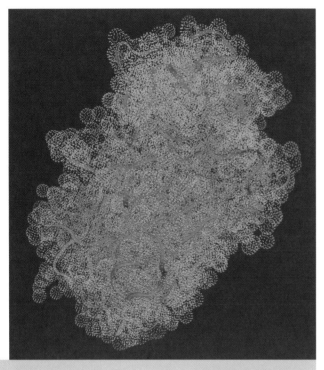

Computer graphic of the protein-digesting enzyme pepsin

lyzed by "dehydrogenases." By the 1930s, these theories could be seen as complementary. Through this and associated research, a further class of smaller molecules essential to enzymatic oxidations and reductions, and named "coenzymes," was discovered.

By the mid-twentieth century, biochemistry appeared to be a flourishing, mature science dealing with a broad range of problems among the chemical phenomena of life. Rather suddenly, there arose a new discipline, named by its founders molecular biology, aimed at explaining biological phenomena at the molecular level. The new field crystallized particularly around the helical structure proposed in 1953 by James Watson and Francis Crick for the molecule of deoxyribonucleic acid, and the genetic implications inherent in it. Biochemistry and its predecessor fields had been involved with the investigation of vital phenomena at the level of molecules ever since chemical molecules had been defined in the early nineteenth century. Why then the need for a new field?

The answer is a mixed intellectual and social one. That the structure of DNA immediately offered a possible explanation of the molecular basis of the classical gene prompted a convergence between structural chemistry and genetics that had not been part of the agenda of biochemistry. Molecular biology hybridized two earlier fields. Also, some of the pioneers of the field of molecular biology, especially those who had moved into biological research from physics, had little training in biochemistry, regarded it as uninteresting, and hoped that they could solve the fundamental problems of life without it. Some biochemists, in turn, regarded newcomers to molecular problems as interlopers, and resisted their assimilation. The institutional separation that resulted has persisted, even though the barrier was artificial. Much of the investigation pursued in biochemical laboratories during the last decades of the twentieth century was indistinguishable from that carried out by molecular biologists, who have long since learned that they, too, need to incorporate biochemistry into their work and thought.

FREDERIC LAWRENCE HOLMES

cine, pathology, and brewery laboratories. In 1914, Hopkins acquired the title of Professor of Biochemistry, in a newly established Department of Biochemistry at Cambridge. Departments of biochemistry sprung up in the United States at leading medical schools, finding an institutional niche in the service role of teaching biochemistry to medical students. Although the discipline in Germany remained subordinate to physiology or organic chemistry, German scientists like Otto Warburg, Otto Meyerhof, Carl Neuberg, Franz Knoop, Heinrich Wieland, and Gustav Embden continued to dominate research in the field until the Nazi takeover in 1933 dispersed much of the German research community. Émigrés from Germany played a substantial role in the rise to prominence of biochemical research in American universities during the 1930s and the postwar period.

While some biochemists worked out metabolic pathways involving small molecules, others studied the structure of the largest biological molecules, the proteins. During the first two decades of the century, they ascribed special properties of proteins to their "colloidal state." After John Northrop crystallized pepsin in 1930, opinion shifted back to the view that proteins were large molecules of definite composition. Frederick Sanger established the complete sequence of amino acids in insulin between 1945 and 1955. But the earlier hope of finding larger patterns in the number and ordering of amino in proteins was not realized.

The crystallization of pepsin settled a long debate over whether enzymes were proteins or whether, as some prominent biochemists such as Richard Willstätter had maintained, proteins only acted as carriers for catalysts of small molecular weight. The study of the specificity and kinetics of enzyme reactions was one of the central focuses of biochemical research during the first half of the twentieth century.

In the 1920s, Warburg and Wieland proposed competing theories about the nature of biological oxidations. Warburg's theory that an iron-containing *Atmungsferment* transferred atmospheric oxygen to substrates undergoing oxidation seemed to be in conflict with Wieland's claim that cellular oxidations were dehydrogenation reactions cata-

BIOLOGY. The word "biology," from Greek "life discourse," was introduced around 1800 by several authors to denote "the science of life" (Gottfried Reinhold Treviranus, 1802), or "everything that pertains to living bodies" (Jean-Baptiste Lamarck, 1802). The word conveyed the new, central role that the notions of life and organism were then acquiring, and a dissatisfaction with the emphasis on the mere classification of natural objects typical of naturalists of earlier generations. However, since Charles Darwin's *Origin of Species* could still do without the word "biology" in 1859, neither the word nor its introduction should be taken as rigid points of departure. Also, the Nobel Prize for "physiology or medicine," first awarded in 1901, did not and does not include the kind of natural history practiced by Darwin.

What we now call biology or the life sciences comprises a rich variety of research traditions and practices. They include, beside the general pursuit of knowledge, medicine, surgery, midwifery, pharmaceutics, agriculture, forestry, hunting, fishing, breeding, collecting, voyages of exploration, veterinary practice, food preservation and industries, biotechnology, and environment preservation. The places devoted to the study of the living world since the Renaissance also point to diversity. The medical school, university, anatomical theater, botanical garden, hospital, doctor's room, school of agriculture, veterinary school, natural history museum, field work, and the laboratory—each with its own set of goals, instruments, and habits—have all contributed to the shaping of what we now call biology.

The historical development of the life sciences fits the transition from natural knowledge to modern science set out in the article "History of Science," which derives primarily from the history of natural philosophy, but with some distinctive traits and contrasts. One such trait is that old research traditions seem to have coexisted with newer traditions more constantly and pervasively than in the physical sciences.

Because of these distinctive traits, the life sciences have received mixed reviews in appraisals of the Scientific Revolution, which until recently focused typically on the physical sciences. Because of these same distinctive traits, the history of biology offers scope for reflections aimed at resisting the recurrent temptation, on the part of scientists, historians, and philosophers alike, to force on science a simplified, unilinear pattern of historical development.

Thus, for example, the adoption of experimental techniques took on different forms in the life sciences depending on the field. Dissection—the main experimental technique revived in anatomy and medicine in the late sixteenth and early seventeenth centuries—stemmed mainly from within medicine itself, and implied no necessary revolt against the Aristotelian tradition, of the kind then frequent among astronomers and natural philosophers. The works of Andreas Vesalius on anatomy, William Harvey on the circulation of the blood, and Marcello Malpighi on development exemplify the shift toward experiment stemming from within the medical tradition.

During the seventeenth and eighteenth centuries, a growing number of new concepts and experimental techniques developed within natural philosophy and chemistry were introduced successfully into the life sciences. The works of René Descartes on physiology, John Mayow on respiration, Hermann Boerhaave on animal heat, Stephen Hales on perspiration, Albrecht von Haller on irritability, Lazzaro Spallanzani on generation, and Antoine-Laurent Lavoisier on respiration indicate how intense and creative the interaction between the life sciences and natural philosophy could be.

Meanwhile, much new information on the animate and inanimate objects of the globe—gathered through the voyages of exploration and the imperial networks set up by European powers from the fifteenth century onwards—was collected, named, and classified along lines suggested by the ancient natural history tradition revived by Renaissance humanists with their interest in erudition, antiquities, and collections. Largely unaffected by the mechanical philosophy of the seventeenth century, this tradition—cultivated by authors like Konrad Gesner, Ulisse Aldrovandi, John Ray, and Carl Linnaeus—continued to bear fruit well into the eighteenth century, especially in the fields of botany, zoology, systematics, the earth sciences, and paleontology.

Repeatedly in the early development of the life sciences, interests and practices that could be regarded as of merely specialist interest impinged upon broad philosophical and religious issues. For example, during the eighteenth century, in the controversy over generation, the concerns of naturalists and physicians merged and occasionally clashed with issues of interest to philosophers, theologians, and public authorities, producing a recurrent battleground for the ideological strands that characterized Enlightenment Europe. Enlightened curiosity and secularization made the egg, the animalcules supposed to be found in sperm, regenerating polyps, the microscopic animals found in vegetable and meat soups (called infusoria), monsters, fossils, as well as topics like the age of the earth, spontaneous generation, and extraterrestrial life subjects of enduring concern to philosophers and cultivated elites. Meanwhile, herborizing, entomology, and an amateur interest in natural history became fashionable among the leisured classes of European countries and their colonies. Similar interests continued to be popular well into the twentieth century and beyond, favored by the creation of natural history museums with their impressive dioramas and dinosaur displays, and by the entertainment and movie industries.

A combination of the traditional concerns and practices of the naturalist with philosophical, secularized theory-building is found also in the development of evolution theories and Darwinism throughout the nineteenth century. The history of evolution theories—a major component of the life sciences over the past two hundred years—reveals the extraordinary power that a blend of the empirical and the philosophical, the scientific and the popular, played in the history of biology. Here the works of Lamarck and Darwin, with their considerable impact on the general public, are emblematic.

A new experimental turn within the life sciences developed after 1839 with the introduction of cell theories and the new microscopic techniques used to explore the fine texture and development of living bodies. The works of Matthias Jakob Schleiden on plant cells and Theodor Schwann on animal cells promoted the idea that the cell was the fundamental unit of life, provided a powerful generalization for biology, and stimulated microscopical research. Together, they contributed to shaping the age of the (compound) microscope, a long, tremendously productive season in the history of laboratory biology and the medical sciences, which lasted until the introduction of the electron microscope in the 1930s.

Early experimental developments in the life sciences were seldom accompanied by the sort of mathematization and quantification that the physical sciences underwent in the same period. Systematic, successful attempts at quantification first materialized in the central decades of the nineteenth century. These had their origins in the gradual affirmation of laboratory biology, the studies of Gregor Mendel on heredity, and biometrics.

The introduction of new instruments and the associated development of new laboratory techniques marked dramatic changes in the life sciences as in other fields of natural science. Chemical analysis and improved microscopes in the eighteenth and nineteenth centuries, X-ray crystallography and electrophoresis in the 1930s, the centrifuge and ultracentrifuge, chromatography and nuclear magnetic resonance from the middle decades of the twentieth century, the introduction of new monitoring techniques throughout the century, and the development of computational biology in the 1990s changed the outlook and perspectives of the life sciences repeatedly. The cumulative effect of these changes in laboratory technique, which had begun to accelerate with the earlier work of Justus Liebig, Claude Bernard, and Louis Pasteur, has been the enrollment of laboratory biology and medicine as major branches of the experimental sciences, and the growth of industries based on biological knowledge and techniques as new, powerful forces in society.

Despite this now recognizable trend, the panorama of the life sciences around 1900 still looked deeply fragmented. The unifying concepts offered by Darwin's theory of evolution in the 1860s and 1870s had only occasionally elicited the commitment of scientists working in other fields, like experimental physiology. The growing number of biologists trained in the laboratory and concentrating on such disciplines as cytology, embryology, or bacteriology felt uneasy about the controversy surrounding evolution theories. Biologists devoted to the empirical work of botany and zoology shared the malaise, while the continuation of Darwin's research tradition in the form of the biometric program developed by Francis Galton, Karl Pearson, and the adepts of eugenics often failed to appeal either to laboratory or field biologists.

The reemergence of Mendelian genetics in 1900, thanks to the works of Hugo de Vries, Karl Correns, and Erich Tschermak von Seysenegg, took place in this fragmented panorama, and for a quarter century seemed unable to contribute to its unification. Only after 1930 did some consensus on the mechanisms of evolution develop leading to the "evolutionary synthesis" or neo-Darwinian theory of evolution. Contemporary and later accounts of developments between 1920 and 1940 suggest, however, that the degree of unification achieved in biology through neo-Darwinism occurred via a federative effort rather than as a movement dominated by only one of the strands making up the field. Current historiography also testifies to the varied impact the synthesis produced in different disciplinary and national contexts.

Meanwhile, the consolidation of the research universities and the growing support given to the biomedical sciences by public and private bodies helped to launch powerful research schools that set new standards in training and research, and favored teamwork that occasionally transcended national borders. The work of Thomas Hunt Morgan and his school on the genetics of the fruit fly *Drosophila* during the 1910s and 1920s may be taken as prototypical. In the fly room—

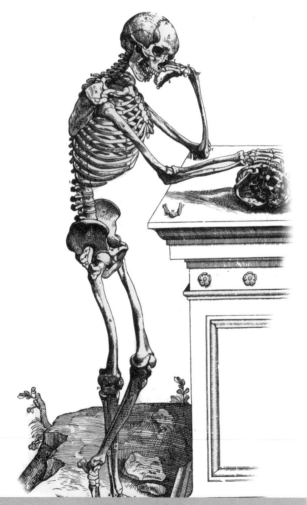

Articulated skeleton from *De humani corporis fabrica* (1543) by Andreas Vesalius (1514–64)

combining the old, simple tools of the naturalists and the sophisticated laboratory apparatus of the cytologists—biologists learned how to combine the laws of Mendelian genetics with laboratory work on the physical basis of the gene. A similar research school developed later in molecular genetics around the study of the viruses called *Bacteriophage*.

Meanwhile, evolution theories underwent important changes. Around 1930, R. A. Fisher, J. B. S. Haldane, and Sewall Wright developed mathematical methods that resulted in population genetics, demonstrating that a theory of natural selection could be based on (rather than, as some believed at the beginning of the twentieth century, refuted by) Mendelian genetics. Population genetics also showed that statistics and mathematical modeling could be basic tools for evolutionary biologists, as they were for physicists.

From the 1940s onwards, two other fronts potentially controversial for evolution theories—systematics and paleontology—fell into line in the works of Theodosius Dobzhansky, George Gaylord Simpson, Ernst Mayr, and their pupils. The evolutionary synthesis could be presented as proof that biology had at last some unification and a widespread consensus around the heritage left by Charles Darwin. Biologists and historians of biology thus represented the synthesis during the centennial celebrations in 1982 commemorating Darwin's death.

The neo-Darwinian synthesis had (and retains) several features appealing to the era of the cold war, when expert and lay audiences alike looking for broad generalizations thought to answer the challenges, and tame the uncertainties, associated with the deep ideological commitments and recurrent conflicts of a divided world order. However, in the early 1980s, just when the synthesis was being celebrated as the major development of twentieth-century biology, it was losing its central position in the life sciences. It no longer reflected the increasingly experimental and instrumentalist ethos attracting biologists and their public.

Since the early 1950s, molecular biology had been shifting the careful balance pursued within the synthesis between the naturalists' and the experimenters' traditions of the life sciences in favor of the experimenters. The shift had been prepared during the 1930s by incursions of leading physicists like Niels Bohr into the terrain of biology, followed by the pathbreaking work of biologists with a background in physics like Max Delbrück, and by books such as Erwin Schrödinger's *What Is Life?* (1942). The new shift of biology toward experiment, the laboratory, and the techniques and metaphors of the new information technologies born of World War II, was later celebrated by biologists in books addressed to a wide public, like James Watson's *The Double Helix* (1968), Jacques Monod's *Chance and Necessity* (1970), and François Jacob's *The Logic of Life* (1970).

The identification of DNA as the carrier of heredity in the 1940s, the discovery of the double-helix structure of DNA by Francis Crick and James Watson in 1953, the breaking of the genetic code in the mid-1960s, and the development of recombinant DNA techniques leading to the emergence of biotechnology industries in the 1970s all can be depicted as the products of a new wave of instrumentalism in biology. So can initiatives like the publicly funded, international Human Genome Project, launched in 1988, and the publication in 2001 of two draft sequences of the human genome produced by biologists participating in the project and by the firm Celera Genomics. Instrumentalism fueled by computer-based techniques and inspired by the conceptual tools of the information sciences seems to constitute the main

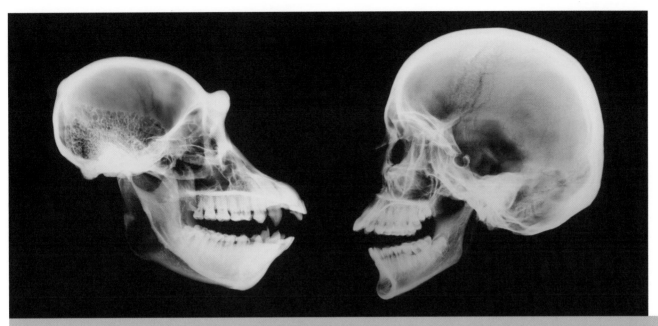

X-ray photographs of chimpanzee and human skulls. The chimp has a bigger jaw bone, the human more brain capacity

connecting thread among these developments, though perhaps not the compass likely to orient biologists toward the long-sought unity of the life sciences.

The detailed recent histories of the people, research schools, laboratory techniques, national institutions, foundations, private industries, and transnational groups of scholars involved in the development of the biomedical sciences during the second half of the twentieth century indicate a complex story. The wealth of stimuli generated by the diverse interests, training, disciplinary traditions, and cultural backgrounds of a growing international population of researchers seems no less important than the overall instrumentalist strategy adopted by the leading actors and programs. A portrait of the life sciences at the turn of the twenty-first century would emphasize the tensions as well as the synergisms among the major, different threads that continue to make up biology. Given the rapid emergence and disappearance of specialties, fields, and subfields, the major threads can best be identified through a few catchwords used by experts, science policy-makers, science journalists, and the public when trying to capture the current focus of biology: "life sciences," suggesting the multiplicity of research traditions and practices that continue to be deployed by humans in order to understand and bend to their own advantage life and its complexity; "evolution," referring to the persistent expectation, associated with the life sciences generally and anthropology in particular, that biology can tell us something about our place in nature; "neurosciences," alluding to the widespread feeling that the brain is the next citadel to be addressed; and "biotechnologies" and "bioethics," currently the most popular of the catchwords, as indicating the powerful, manipulative skills through which biologists have at last joined other scientists and technologists in supplying high-tech goods for the planetary market economy of the turn of the century, and as evoking the mixture of expectations and fears that their new power is generating in the public.

GIULIANO PANCALDI

BIOMETRICS, or biometry, is the statistical study of populations of living organisms and their variations. Biometrics had its origin in the collaboration between W. F. R. Weldon and Karl Pearson at University College London (UCL) from 1891 to 1906. As a morphologist, Weldon was interested in the functional relationships between the physical characteristics of living organisms. But Darwin's theory of evolution by natural selection had changed the context in which morphologists thought about those relationships. His theory challenged future generations of researchers to answer two fundamental questions: how were physical characteristics passed on to offspring, and could the process of natural selection cause the physical character of a population to deviate enough to make it a new and separate species? Investigating the latter question, Weldon realized that before a determination whether natural selection could cause significant deviation in the physical character of a population could be made, ways for measuring the influence of heredity and for establishing the normal degree of variation for a given species had to be established. Weldon concluded, therefore, that the question of the efficacy of natural selection was a statistical question. To make the necessary measurements and calculations, he borrowed the concepts and techniques of correlation and regression developed by Francis Galton in his *Natural Inheritance* (1889). Soon, however, Weldon confronted his own inadequacies as a statistician and turned to Pearson.

Pearson, a Cambridge-educated mathematician, was a polymathic dabbler. Living in London in the 1880s, he made his mark as a freethinking socialist and as an advocate of scientific rationalism. Appointed to the chair of applied mathematics and mechanics at University College in 1884, Pearson found a focus for his mathematical work once he began to collaborate with Weldon, who came to UCL in 1891 as the new Jodrell Professor of zoology.

Pearson also had been impressed with Galton's *Natural Inheritance*, both for its statistical approach and for its eugenic concerns. Under Weldon's influence, Pearson began work on ways to adapt and extend the concepts of correlation and regression to statistical problems presented by the study of dynamic populations. The work done by Pearson between 1891 and 1896 laid many of the foundations of modern statistical theory. By 1900, researchers who applied statistical theory to the study of populations of living organisms were identified as the "biometric school."

The school faced severe criticism of its methods from researchers who, bolstered by the "rediscovery" of Gregor

Mendel's theory of heredity, argued that the study of genetics held the key to understanding evolution. Faced with this challenge, Pearson and Weldon launched *Biometrika* (1901), a journal dedicated to "the statistical study of biological problems." The controversy between the biometricians and the Mendelians raged for more than two decades.

Biometrics continued to be controversial, both for its statistical approach and for its ties to eugenics, until the 1930s, when the final elements of a synthesis of biometrics and Mendelism were put in place. One of the contributors to the synthesis, R. A. Fisher, another Cambridge-trained mathematician, succeeded Pearson in 1933 as Galton Professor of eugenics at UCL. Fisher became interested in evolution by reading Pearson's articles entitled "Mathematical Contributions to the Theory of Evolution." Fisher sought to demonstrate the compatibility between the effects of Darwinian natural selection as described by biometrics and Mendelian genetics. His paper of 1918, "The Correlation Between Relatives on the Supposition of Mendelian Inheritance," did much to establish that compatibility. By the late 1930s, work in a similar vein by Sewall Wright and J. B. S. Haldane had completed the synthesis and laid the foundations for the science of population genetics.

Meanwhile, Pearson's successor as editor of *Biometrika*, his son, Egon Pearson, took advantage of the cessation of hostilities between the biometric and Mendelism camps. No longer needing to defend the legitimacy of the statistical study of evolution, he began to purge *Biometrika* of its anti-genetics rhetoric and of its eugenic concerns, transforming biometrics into the production of statistical tools and data for use by biologists of all persuasions.

JEFFREY C. BRAUTIGAM

BIOTECHNOLOGY. The Hungarian scientist Karl Erky coined the term "biotechnology" in the title of a treatise that he published in 1919 calling for an industrialized agriculture for the production of meat, fat, and milk. Erky's program built on processes that involved fermentation to produce goods like beer. The growing understanding that microbiological processes are chemical ones turned Erky's branch of biotechnology toward the exploitation of biological organisms to work on an industrial scale. After World War II industrial biotechnology expanded into the production of pharmaceuticals such as penicillin and, in the 1960s and 1970s, into attempts to coax single-cell organisms to transform hydrocarbons into edible proteins and barnyard waste into gasohol. Japan, Germany, Britain, and the European Commission encouraged these programs because they promised to yield better medicine and more abundant food and materials, and to bolster international competitiveness in the face of declines in traditional manufacturing.

A new biotechnology, which depended on molecular genetics, particularly the technique of recombinant DNA, was invented in 1973 by Stanley Cohen, at Stanford University, and Herbert Boyer, at the University of California San Francisco Medical School. Their technique allowed biologists to snip out a gene from the genome of one species and insert it into the genome of another, where it might replicate and express itself. The method was first used to insert foreign genes into bacteria to study their function, but molecular biologists recognized that it could be employed to modify virtually any organism, including plants, animals, and perhaps even human beings.

To many scientists, the fact that humans could now easily create combinations of genetic material unknown in nature

was more worrisome than welcome. They feared that, while many DNA hybrids would no doubt prove to be innocuous, some—for example, bacteria containing genes suspected to cause cancer—might be hazardous to human health. In response to that fear, 140 biologists from the United States and Europe convened in February 1975 at the Asilomar Conference Center, on the Monterey Peninsula, in Pacific Grove, California, to probe the promise and hazards of joining DNA across species. The conference agreed that recombinant research could and should be done under guidelines that ensured its safety. Variants of the guidelines were adopted by the National Institutes of Health in the United States and its counterpart research agencies in Europe.

From the mid-1970s onward, recombinant research proceeded with increasing momentum, spurred ahead not only by its scientific but also its commercial possibilities. Molecular biologists predicted that it would revolutionize medicine, by replacing disease-causing genes with normal ones; pharmaceuticals, by turning bacteria into factories for the production of drugs to order; and agriculture, by equipping plants to fix their own nitrogen from the air.

Some of the biologists, including Herbert Boyer, took their case to investment bankers. Together with a young venture capitalist, Boyer scraped up $1,000 to found a biotechnology company to exploit recombinant DNA commercially. The company was formally incorporated (with additional capital including $100,000 from Thomas Perkins of the Kleiner and Perkins firm) as Genentech ("genetic engineering technology").

Boyer and Swanson determined that Genentech's first project should be the production by recombinant techniques of human insulin. The world's supply of therapeutic insulin came from the pancreases of slaughtered cows and pigs. Projections at Eli Lilly & Co., which accounted for at least 80 percent of all insulin sales in the United States, indicated that the insulin needs of the American diabetic population might eventually outrun the animal supply. In early September 1978, at a crowded press conference, Genentech announced that it had bio-engineered human insulin and that, about two weeks earlier, it had entered into an agreement whereby Eli Lilly & Co. would manufacture and market the hormone. When in mid-October 1980, Genentech—assigned the stock symbol "GENE"—went public, investors snapped up its shares at more than twice the offering price of $35, astonishing Wall Street observers.

The financial markets' strong interest in biotechnology was matched by the attention it now received among federal policymakers in the United States. Biotechnological products promised to increase the country's international trade surplus in high-technology goods, which since the mid-1970s had been offsetting a sizable trade deficit in other types of manufactures. In 1980, the government granted the biotechnology industry a triple boost: the National Institutes of Health virtually ended its restrictions on recombinant research; Congress passed the Bayh-Dole Act, which explicitly encouraged universities to patent and privatize the results of federally sponsored high-technology research; and in June, the United States Supreme Court ruled in *Diamond v. Chakrabarty* that a patent could be issued on a genetically modified living organism, holding, over the legal and moral objections of critics, that whether an invention was living or dead was irrelevant to its qualification for intellectual-property protection.

Building on the Chakrabarty case, the United States Patent Office issued its first patent on a genetically engineered plant in 1985 and the first patent on an animal in the history of the world in 1988 (a mouse genetically modified at Harvard to be supersusceptible to cancer). Biotechnology soon received similar encouragement from the European Community. In 1991, the European Patent Office granted Harvard a patent on its mouse, and in 1998 the European Commission, the executive arm of the Community, issued a sweeping directive authorizing patents on a wide range of biotechnological inventions.

By the 1990s, the biotechnology industry had established itself in the United States and Europe and had branches in Asia and Latin America. In 1999, it generated $20 billion in revenues in the United States alone. It comprised start-up firms, many of them spun off from academic laboratories, as well as major pharmaceutical companies and several oil and chemical giants that supported research programs of their own or purchased one or more of the fledglings. Some 80 to 90 percent of the biotechnology companies produced pharmaceuticals and health-service tests.

Agricultural biotechnology accounted for about 10 percent of the industry with plants engineered to resist pests and pesticides or to remain fresh longer after harvest. Some firms in the agricultural area attempted to modify animals genetically with the goal of making sheep that produced more and better wool or cows and pigs that provided more and leaner meat. A few pioneers in "molecular farming" tried to turn common animals genetically into factories for the production of valuable human proteins otherwise difficult and expensive to obtain, if they could be obtained at all.

Yet the new biotechnology had been creating enemies since its inception. Scientists and laypeople both questioned the wisdom of leaping into research with recombinant DNA, holding that the resulting organisms might threaten deli-

cate ecological balances and that, in any case, creating them would be an act of hubris, an assumption of the powers of God. As the biotechnology industry developed, the attention of the critics turned to the patenting of living organisms, the best purchase they could obtain on the advancing biotechnological juggernaut. Some critics declared that such patents would foster monopoly in vital areas such as the food industry; others insisted that the genetic engineering of animals would lead to their suffering; still others contended that patenting them was sacrilegious, turning God's creatures into commodities. In the 1990s, when the Human Genome Project fostered the rapid identification and patenting of genes, one dissident warned the United States Congress that "we are right in the middle of an ethical struggle on the ownership of the gene pool."

The critics made no significant headway until the late 1990s, when genetically modified foods began coming to market. In the United States, these foods, those derived from corn, soy, canola, cotton, and milk, were too widespread to avoid easily. They were also making inroads abroad. Europeans greeted their arrival with protests and boycotts. Critics called them "Frankenfoods" and claimed that they posed hazards to human health because they contained proteins that did not occur in the natural varieties of food crops. The outcry spread to the United States and led a number of food markets to refuse to stock genetically modified products.

Most of the genetically modified food crops available in 2000 had been designed to assist agricultural producers. A notable example, the Monsanto Corporation's Round-Up Ready soybean, was engineered to withstand the company's Round-Up pesticide. Analysts suggested that once the agricultural biotechnology industry produced foods directly

A scientist cultures Chinese artichokes at ENITHP (Ecole Nationale d' Ingenieurs des Travaux de l' Horticulture et du Paysage d' Angers) as part of a project to preserve and improve traditional crops.

beneficial to consumers, the opposition would diminish. But whatever the future may bring to agricultural biotechnology, the biomedical sector of the industry continues to flourish and enjoy the strong support of the public, including investors, because of its promise for health care.

D. J. KEVLES

BLACK HOLE. A black hole in space has a gravitational force so strong that nothing can escape from it, not even light. Hence no one can see a black hole, but astronomers are convinced they exist. An early intellectual precursor to the concept of black holes may be found in John Michell's dark stars. Michell noted in 1783 that if bodies with densities not less than the Sun's, and hundreds of times greater in diameter, really existed, gravity would prevent their light particles from reaching us. Their existence might be inferred from the motions of luminous bodies around them. Michell's idea was ignored even before wave theory, in which gravity does not act on light, overthrew the particle theory from which he reasoned.

Collapsed stars make another intellectual precursor to black holes. After 1915 and Einstein's relativity theory, gravity again could act on light. In the 1930s, Subrahmanyan Chandrasekhar, recently arrived from India to study in England, modeled stellar structures. He found that stars of less than 1.4 solar mass shrink until they become white dwarfs, but more massive stars continue contracting. The British astrophysicist Arthur Eddington noted that at high compression, gravity would be so great that radiation could not escape, a situation he regarded as absurd. Others accepted Chandrasekhar's mathematics but believed that continuous or catastrophic mass ejection would act as a universal regulating mechanism to bring stars below the critical mass. Also, massive stars might evolve into stars composed of neutrons. In 1939, however, the American physicist J. Robert Oppenheimer established a mass limit for neutron stars. When it has exhausted thermonuclear sources of energy, a sufficiently heavy star will collapse indefinitely, unless it can reduce its mass.

World War II and then the hydrogen bomb project diverted research away from stellar structure. Nuclear weapons programs, though, did develop a deeper understanding of physics and more powerful computational techniques, and in the 1960s, computer programs that simulated bomb explosions were modified to simulate implosions of stars. A renewed theoretical assault followed on "black holes" as they were named by the American nuclear physicist John Wheeler in 1967. In contrast to collapsed or frozen stars, black holes are now known to be dynamic, evolving, energy-storing, and energy-releasing objects.

Because no light escapes from black holes, detection of them requires observing manifestations of their gravitational attraction. From a companion star, a black hole captures and heats gas to millions of degrees, hot enough to emit X rays. Because the Earth's atmosphere absorbs X rays, devices to detect them must be lofted on rockets or satellites. A few black holes probably have been found, although other explanations of the observational data are possible.

In another predicted manifestation, two black holes spiral together, gyrate wildly while coalescing, and then become steady. Outward ripples of curvature of spacetime, also called gravitational waves, would carry an unequivocal black-hole signature. Gravitational waves should propagate through matter, diminishing in intensity with distance. On Earth, they should create tides the size of an atom's nucleus, in contrast to lunar tides of about a meter. Gravitational-wave detectors may be operational early in the twenty-first century.

Meanwhile, without benefit of prediction and intent, we may already have observed manifestations of black holes. Extraordinarily strong radio emissions from both the centers of galaxies and from quasars (compact, highly luminous objects) maybe powered by the rotational energy of gigantic black holes, either coalesced from many stars or from the implosion of a single supermassive rotating star a hundred million times heavier than our sun. Other possible explanations for radio galaxies and quasars, however, do not require black holes.

NORRISS S. HETHERINGTON

BLOOD is a complex physiological fluid essential to a wide array of life-supporting functions in the body. Through the circulatory system of arteries, veins, and capillaries, blood transports oxygen from the lungs to cells, and removes waste products like carbon dioxide and other cellular metabolic by-products, delivering them to the lungs, kidneys, and skin for excretion. In addition, blood is the primary vehicle of immunity. White blood cells, or leukocytes, constitute the cellular components of the immune system, responsible for warding off infections and infiltration of foreign proteins.

Since antiquity, blood has been regarded as integral to life. Recognizing that the heart and blood vessels were connected in a unified system, Aristotle defined the blood as a nutritive fluid that sustained the vitality of the solid parts of the body. In the Hippocratic and Galenic traditions, blood was identified as one of the four humors that comprised the human body. In this tradition, health and disease were interpreted as the result of the interaction of these four constituents. Imbalance or disequilibrium in the humors offered a powerful rationale for bloodletting or phlebotomy, which remained an important medical therapy for more than two millennia.

Initial interest in the blood focused on its physical movement in the animal and human body. In the early seventeenth century, English physician William Harvey provided statistical and experimental support in *De Motu Cordis* (1628) for his claims that blood circulated in the bodies of animals and humans. At this time, physicians made little differentiation between the blood of animals and humans, as the earliest efforts in transfusion illustrate. In 1667 French physician Jean Baptiste Denis performed the first human transfusion when he transfused blood from sheep and calves into several patients. At the Royal Society in London, English physician Richard Lower paid a clergyman the sum of one guinea for his willingness to "suffer the experiment of transfusion" with blood from a lamb.

The advent of the microscope revealed that blood was not a simple, uniform fluid. The Dutch lens maker Antoni van Leeuwenhoek, examining his own blood under a primitive microscope, first identified the red blood cells, the small, red globules "swimming in a liquor, called by physicians, the serum." Jan Swammerdam and Marcello Malpighi, who identified the role of the capillaries in the circulatory system, also noted these corpuscles. English physician William Hewson was among the first to describe white blood cells, or leukocytes, and demonstrated some of the essential features of blood clotting or coagulation. In 1851 German physiologist Otto Funke identified hemoglobin, the reddish pigment in red blood cells. Investigations by Felix Hoppe-Seyler established that hemoglobin was responsible for taking up and discharging oxygen. Using new chemical dyes and improved microscopes, Paul Ehrlich profoundly influ-

Black hole at the center of a galaxy, an artist's conception based on data collected by NASA's Galaxy Evolution Explorer. Radiation (blue) is so intense it drives matter away; the gray material is a ring of gas.

enced the development of hematology. Ehrlich identified several new types of white blood cells, described differences between healthy and diseased blood cells, and distinguished the various forms of anemias.

In the early twentieth century, attention focused on the role of blood in the immune system. In 1900, Karl Landsteiner discovered that human blood could be divided into three groups when he combined red blood cells of individuals with the sera taken from others. (The fourth, rarer blood group was identified by two of his associates, who tested a larger group of people.) Although surgeons attached little importance to this work before World War I, the importance of blood grouping to avert transfusion reactions intensified when Landsteiner, with Alexander Wiener, discovered in 1940 the Rh blood group, a major cause of fetal and infant death. In the 1950s, serologists sought to define the antigens on white blood cells. In 1958, Jean-Baptiste Dausset reported his discovery of a gene complex (human leukocyte A complex) that accounted for different immunological responses in blood transfusions. The identification of other human leukocyte antigens (HLA) followed; these formed the basis of the HLA system for typing tissues and organs to reduce the threat of organ and tissue graft rejection in transplantation.

During World War II, the biochemist Edwin Cohn pioneered a new method for plasma fractionation of human blood, fostering renewed interest in blood biochemistry. Cohn's method for separating the protein fraction from plasma and the production of such pharmaceutical products as gamma globulin (used in the treatment of infectious disease) and antihemophilic factor (which altered the lives of thousands of hemophilia patients) ushered in a new era of blood-based research. Extending some of the work on blood fractionation, chemist Linus Pauling studied the physical chemistry of hemoglobin variants and their role in sickle cell disease. In 1949, Pauling concluded that the inherited disorder resulted from a flaw in the molecular composition of hemoglobin, and proclaimed sickle cell anemia to be the first molecular disease. Although significant for the emer-

gence of molecular medicine, these insights did not foster immediate clinical benefits for sickle cell patients.

Over the course of the twentieth century, the therapeutic advances in blood transfusion and blood components provided an important and life-saving medical intervention. At the same time, the therapeutic use of blood fostered new dangers; medically administered blood became the vehicle for the transmission of disease. During World War II, the infection of military personnel with hepatitis raised serious concerns that disease might spread through the blood supply. In the 1980s, blood-borne spread of a hitherto unknown virus, the human immunodeficiency virus (HIV), was linked to a newly identified and lethal disease, AIDS. Although heat treatment and viral antibody testing have decreased the threat of HIV transmission, concern about the transmission of such diseases as Mad Cow Disease continue to trouble blood bankers and health policy makers.

Blood is a potent biological substance studied by physicians and medical researchers; blood is also a complex cultural entity with social meanings that vary considerably with time and place. Ideas about blood purity extend far beyond the physical properties of a biological fluid to encompass notions about social networks and contamination—both moral and physical. In twentieth-century Japan, many believed that a person's blood type determines personality and character. In the American eugenics movement, blood and heredity were often closely linked in ideas about lineage or bloodlines. As Karl Landsteiner had predicted, the science of blood came to play an important role in forensic science and in cases of disputed paternity. By the 1930s, German, Austrian, and Danish courts all accepted blood tests for establishing paternity. In the United States, courts remained reluctant for decades to rely on serological tests to establish paternity, and, in the case of several highly publicized cases in which infants were mistakenly given to the wrong parents, maternity. Serological tests to determine guilt and innocence in criminal proceedings came to play an important role in criminal prosecutions on both sides of the

Atlantic. Even as DNA testing has come to dominate such proceedings, blood remains a powerful signifier.

SUSAN E. LEDERER

BOTANY. Much of the earliest botany was concerned with *materia medica*. An exception, the work of the ancient Greek philosopher Theophrastus, classified plants in the Aristotelian tradition. He included much information on the agricultural techniques of his day. But by far the most famous ancient text was Dioscorides's herbal, a plant encyclopedia written in Greek for physicians. Translated subsequently into Latin and Arabic, and copied and recopied, often with additions and manuscript illustrations because herbalists and apothecaries had to be sure of the plants' identities, Discorides's work underwrote the first printed herbals, particularly those of Otto Brunfels and Leonhart Fuchs. These were expensive books, often hand-colored and annotated, which circulated mainly among physicians, theologians, university dons, and courts.

During the late sixteenth century practitioners increasingly noticed that Arabic or ancient texts did not describe the plants of western Europe and started adding to traditional lists. This enlargement coincided with the colonial expansion of Europe, most notably into the East Indies and the New World, and changing systems of medical education, itself partly a consequence of the new texts available. Plants, remedies, and herbs were introduced to Europe from overseas, encouraging the development of the physic gardens already attached to the main universities, enriching the gardens of the royal courts, and posing questions about geographical distribution. By the end of the century, Rembert Dodoens and William Turner were producing works not so much to supplement but to replace ancient ones. Herbals and botanical compendia continued to be published in large numbers in relatively stereotyped format. Nicholas Culpeper's *English Physician Enlarged; or. The Herbal* (1653) was typical. Through these volumes, countless people learned a utilitarian and domestic combination of medical and botanical science.

Georg Johann Mendel (1822–1884), sixth abbot of the Abbey of Saint Thomas in Brno, Czech Republic, and a founder of genetics

During the seventeenth century, the study of botany broadened to come into contact with other disciplines besides medicine and classification. The use of the microscope in Britain, Italy, and the Netherlands revealed the unsuspected world of the small. Robert Hooke saw "pores" in cork, which he called "cells." Nehemiah Grew and Marcello Malpighi independently identified the principal tissues of the plant body, including stem, root, and leaf. Plant functions were mostly interpreted by analogy with animals. For Grew the xylem vessels resembled animal tracheae; Stephen Hales suggested that plant sap circulated like blood. Grew also identified stamens as the male reproductive organs and supposed that plants possessed two sexes, again like animals. Proof came in the work of Rudolph Jakob Camerarius in 1694, although the sexuality of plants was contested for decades afterwards.

The Swedish doctor Carl Linnaeus transformed botany in the eighteenth century by devising an "artificial" classification system whereby plants were sorted into higher taxa by the numbers of stamens and pistils they possessed. Linnaeus trained and sent plant collectors all over the increasingly accessible globe, to Japan, South Africa, the Carolinas, Asia, and central Spain. They found many specimens of plants unknown in Europe. Linnaeus also set out philosophical principles for the science. He introduced binomial names, the first denoting the genus, the second the specific character of an individual. Furthermore, Linnaeus helped botanical knowledge move out of the elite sphere of universities, museums, and physic gardens to a broader constituency. Many gentlefolk, women, and working men encountered botany through popularizations of Linnaeus's writings. His devout definition of plant species as stable entities, fixed since their creation by God, stimulated studies of hybridization, which even Linnaeus conceded must occur sometimes. Johann Wolfgang von Goethe proposed that all floral parts had been modified from leaves. Later, Augustin-Pyramus de Candolle formulated useful concepts of symmetry, abortion, modification, and fusion.

During the nineteenth century naturalists turned to the functional anatomy of plants. Robert Brown made important investigations into fertilization before making his better known discoveries of the cell nucleus and Brownian motion. Jacob Mathias Schleiden laid the groundwork for the cell theory of Theodor Schwann. Hugo von Mohl summarized advances in cell anatomy in 1851. Meanwhile fundamental observations, including identification of free swimming spermatozoids, were made on the nature of fertilization in algae. René-Joachim-Henri Dutrochet studied osmosis. J. B. J. D. Boussingault elucidated the nitrogen cycle. The essential steps in carbon fixation were recognized when Julius von Sachs showed that the starch present in green cells came from the carbon dioxide absorbed. Gregor Mendel and Charles Naudin did essential experimental work on plant hybridization. Modern perceptions of the overwhelming importance of evolutionary theory have obscured the significance of these physiological, experimental, and microscopic investigations.

Although evolutionary theory gave the geography and morphology of plants new legitimacy, physiology led the way. Sachs's *Lehrbuch der Botanik* (1868) inspired every plant physiologist with the hope of spending time in Sachs's laboratory in Wurzburg. Sachs made significant studies on plant hormones, growth mechanisms, and tropisms like the effect of gravity or light on roots and shoots. The emphasis of research shifted so much toward the physiological, notably in enzyme studies and fermentation, that Joseph Dalton Hooker in Kew

Gardens, England, felt it necessary to reassert the value of taxonomy as an academic discipline in the *Index Kewensis* and his and George Bentham's *Genera Plantarum*. Botany soon became the prime area for genetic research, as in pure-line experiments, cytology, fertilization, and cell division.

In the twentieth century increasing investigations into fossil plants led to debate over the origin of flowering plants (angiosperms) in the Cretaceous period. This also involved controversy over what should properly be considered primitive. Plant paleontology became an important part of science with the rise of quarternary studies, the study of the geology and environment of the recent archaeological past.

JANET BROWNE

BUREAUS OF STANDARDS. The origin of national and international bureaus of standards lies in the interest in metrology during the late eighteenth and early nineteenth centuries. On the eve of the French Revolution, France had over a thousand legal units of measurement with approximately 250,000 local variations. Spurred on by the work of French and foreign natural philosophers, the French government began to revamp its metrological system. French experimental natural philosophers argued that all of the earlier systems of the ancien régime needed to be disposed of, and a new standard based on precision and simplicity needed to be implemented. In 1790 the French Academy approved the decimal metric system. On 22 June 1799 platinum standards of the meter and the kilogram were placed in the Archives in la République de Paris. The leading German physicist and mathematician of the early nineteenth century, Carl Friedrich Gauss, promoted the kilogram and meter, as well as the second, as the units of the physical sciences. His measurements of the earth's magnetic force pioneered the use of these three units and their derivatives. Subsequent research by Gauss and Wilhelm Weber on electrical phenomena also employed this set of units.

James Clerk Maxwell and Joseph John Thomson furthered Gauss and Weber's research under the aegis of the British Association for the Advancement of Science (BAAS). In 1874 the BAAS announced the CGS system, a unit system based on the mechanical units of the centimeter, gram, and second and adding a set of standardized prefixes, from micro to mega, indicating levels of magnitude. During the 1880s, the BAAS and the International Electrical Congress approved a new set of practical units for electricity and magnetism: the ohm for electrical resistance, the volt for the electromotive force, and the ampere for electric current. The schematic origins of Germany's Physikalisch-Technische Reichsanstalt (PTR)—the Imperial Physical Technical Institute for the Experimental Advancement of the Exact Sciences and Precision Technology—can be traced to an essay written by Karl Schellbach, "On the Foundations of a Museum for the Exact Sciences," published in 1872, a year after German unification. The renowned industrialist and engineer Ernst Werner von Siemens was responsible for the actualization of Schellbach's plan. In 1882 Siemens donated the building site that was to house the PTR. The German Reichstag officially approved the PTR on 28 March 1887. It originally comprised physics and technical departments. The physics department was composed of research laboratories for heat, electricity, and optics, while the technical department housed laboratories for precision metrology, heat, and pressure, as well as a second optical laboratory. The first president of the PTR was Germany's premier physicist, Hermann von Helmholtz.

The PTR not only served as the nation's leading metrological laboratory; its governing committee sought to forge links among scientists, engineers, instrument makers, private entrepreneurs, and government officials. In addition to Siemens and Helmholtz, other leading scientists on the advisory board of the PTR included Ernst Abbe, Rudolf Clausius, and Wilhelm Conrad Röntgen. From the very beginning the objectives of the PTR were fourfold: the execution of scientific experiments that necessitated the collaboration of teams of scientists and engineers; the testing and verification of the properties of materials used in precision-measuring devices; the testing and verification of the uniformity of the components used to produce precision-measuring devices; and the testing and verification of measuring tools.

From 1898 until 1945, the PTR was empowered by the Reichstag to provide the legal units of electricity and to monitor instruments for measuring electric current. In 1923 the Imperial Institute for Weights and Measures was integrated into the PTR, rendering the PTR the sole legal arbiter for monitoring calibration and testing offices. The PTR sustained heavy damage during World War II, and was rebuilt in 1946 as the office for the West Berlin Senate. Built in Brunswick in 1950, the Physikalisch-Technische Bundesanstalt (PTB) became the PTR's successor. The PTB, like the PTR, is totally state supported.

The PTR served as the model for the American National Bureau of Standards (NBS, now called the National Institute of Standards and Technology) founded in 1901 and the British National Physical Laboratory (NPL) founded in 1905. The NBS was the first physical science research laboratory funded by the U.S. government. Its directors have included some of the nation's leading physicists and engineers, including Samuel Wesley Stratton, Lyman J. Briggs, and Lewis M. Branscomb. Throughout its history, the NBS has undertaken research on a broad range of topics including electrical standards, aviation technology, uranium calibration research, atomic clocks, electronics, and parity. The NPL was created by the Cavendish physicist Richard Tetley Glazebrook. Starting out with a total of twenty-four physicists, the NPL had sixty-three by the outbreak of World War I. Enjoying less federal support than Germany's standards bureaus, the NPL and NBS have historically relied on a mix of government grants, testing fees, and (particularly in the case of the NPL) gifts from individuals and companies.

Perhaps the most important office of international weights and measures is the Bureau International des Poids et Mesures in France (BIPM). This agency ensures the international uniformity of standards. Its authority is granted by the Convention of the Meter, signed in Paris in 1895, which now represents the collaborative work of fifty-one member nations, including all industrialized countries. The BIPM, operating under the exclusive supervision of the International Committee for Weights and Measures, comprises committees whose members belong to the national meteorological laboratories of these member nations. The BIPM currently conducts research in seven principle areas: laser, wavelength, and frequency standards; mass; time; electricity; radiometry and photometry; ionizing radiation; and chemistry. It also undertakes research in thermometry, pressure, and humidity. During the eleventh Conférence Générale des Poids et Mesures in 1960, the International System of Units (SI) was officially recommended as the basis of scientific measurement. Its seven fundamental units are the meter, kilogram, second, ampere, kelvin, mole, and candela.

MYLES W. JACKSON

CABINETS AND COLLECTIONS. Natural history cabinets and collections took shape in two forms during the Renaissance: the cabinet of curiosities and the botanical garden. The cabinet of curiosities, or *Wunderkammer,* was a repository of objects noteworthy to the Renaissance philosopher: rarities, exotica (from Asia or the New World), monstrosities, artifacts, natural objects, and items of historical interest. The great Renaissance collectors included Ulisse Aldrovandi, whose museum (which he bequeathed to the city of Bologna), or *teatro* or *microcosmo,* as he variously termed it, contained a dragon; and the German Jesuit Athanasius Kircher, whose collection in Rome reflected not only his interests in natural philosophy but also in Egyptian hieroglyphics. Owners restricted access to a discriminating (and carefully chosen) public of fellow scholars and aristocratic or clerical patrons. Aldrovandi kept a ledger of visitors, among them one pope, six princes, twenty-one professors, eighty-seven doctors, six painters, and a notary. Although a few noblewomen visited his museum, they were not enumerated in the roll.

The physical composition and arrangement of an early modern cabinet of curiosities was an idiosyncrasy of its owner. In general, no clear differentiation could be made between objects displayed and the means of display, as cupboards, shelves, drawers, mountings, and frames—the ceiling also served for and as display—were splendid objects in themselves, fully integrated with their contents. Within the room or rooms, objects followed one another according to the three kingdoms of nature: animal, vegetable, and mineral; the importance to collectors of objects like cameos and worked baroque pearls made the boundaries between the artificial and the natural relatively porous and unmeaning.

Besides the splendid display of material objects, the cabinet had another dimension: the catalog, which ordered and described its contents in a form portable beyond its walls. The Dutch merchant and manufacturer Levinus Vincent, whose cabinet had been visited by Peter the Great and Carlos III of Spain, published in 1719 a splendid catalog depicting and describing his holdings. The collection of the Italian antiquary Cassiano dal Pozzo consisted entirely of representations rather than objects: over seven thousand drawings of classical and medieval antiquities, fossils, and botanical, zoological, and horticultural subjects. Several theoreticians of collecting, including the German Samuel Quiccheberg, in his *Inscriptiones vel tituli theatri amplissimi* (1565), discussed the relation of the material cabinet and the idealized catalog.

Botanical gardens began in sixteenth-century Italy as adjuncts to the teaching of medicine and evolved into collections not just of plants useful in *materia medica* but of botanical diversity in general. Over time they developed into repositories of botanical diversity for its own sake. By the mid-eighteenth century the garden was paired with the herbarium, another of the great genres of modern collecting. Botanical gardens through the eighteenth century were laid out almost

exclusively along medical or taxonomic lines (according, for example, to the system of Joseph Pitton de Tournefort, Bernard de Jussieu, or Carl Linnaeus), with little concession to horticultural (rather than architectural) aesthetics. All the earliest gardens (in Padua, Pisa, Leyden, Oxford, and Montpellier) and most later ones were associated with universities, although governments maintained some (the Jardin du Roi, later Jardin des Plantes, Paris) and private individuals others (George Clifford, Holland). In all cases, they restricted admission, generally to students and well-to-do patrons.

From the early eighteenth century, the contents of collections and their administration became ever more standardized. To return to botany, herbarium sheets of the seventeenth and early eighteenth centuries containing pressed and dried plant specimens were often ornamented—dried plants spilling from engraved flowerpots, for example—and had no standard size. Each collector's system of preparation, labeling, sorting, and storage was unique. The growth of networks of botanical collectors and systematists and of widely shared taxonomic systems fostered standardization in the second half of the eighteenth century. The most important botanical authority, Linnaeus, succeeded in imposing his standard size folio herbarium sheet on most of his correspondents, and he ruthlessly cut down sheets he received to the size of his own cupboards, heedless of ornament or aesthetics. At the same time, administrative techniques drawn from commerce and government regulated the contents of collections and kept track of exchanges and purchases among them. The eighteenth century also saw the purchase and transfer of whole collections, like Sir Hans Sloane's assortment of natural objects and antiquarian and ethnological material, bought by the British government in 1753, and Linnaeus's herbarium, sold to J. E. Smith of London in 1784. The first collection formed the core of the British Museum; the second ended up in the Linnean Society, founded in 1788. This new genre of collection, systematic rather than aesthetic, transferable, and increasingly standardized, had almost completely supplanted the cabinet of curiosities by the turn of the nineteenth century. Even amateur collectors of seashells, plants, birds' eggs, and other hobbyists came to order their collections along scientific lines, labeled according to the latest systematics and stored out of sight in boxes, cases, and cupboards analogous to those used in scientific institutions and university collections.

The nineteenth century opened a new era in the typology of collections, still recognizable today and marked by differentiation into three genres: systematic, applied, and aesthetic and didactic. The work of classifying the world's plants and animals begun in the Renaissance went on, but it did so behind the scenes, in herbaria and zoological museums open only to accredited scholars and invisible to the public. The institutions housing this work—Kew Gardens near London, the Jardin des Plantes and Muséum d'Histoire Naturelle in Paris, the Schönbrunn Gardens in Vienna, and later their colonial

Volcanologist Giuseppe Rolandi in the Royal Mineralogical Museum (founded in 1801) at the University of Naples, Italy

satellites in India, Java, Mauritius, Jamaica, and elsewhere—also carried out imperial schemes of acclimatization, hybridization, and plant and animal transplantation. This work was linked to surveys important for systematics and provided revenues both for the gardens and their overseeing governments. Finally, as part of larger nineteenth-century movements for public health, education, and recreation, these institutions came to serve as teaching establishments and places of entertainment for an ever-widening general public.

Parallel to the enclosure of the herbarium as a de-aestheticized, private, and academic space was the opening of the botanical garden as a public park. This theoretical reconception accompanied a shift from the rigidly rectilinear garden plans of the seventeenth and eighteenth centuries taking taxonomy as their planting principle, to more openly aesthetic designs drawing on the picturesque eighteenth- and nineteenth-century English landscape style and organized by geographical or climatic constellations of flora. Guidebooks, identifying labels, and public lectures furthered the education of visitors. Likewise, modern zoological gardens, with their combination of the spectacular and the educational, taking their cue from the zoo founded in Regent's Park, London, in 1828, served an important didactic and recreational function in major European cities. Within doors, the nineteenth century's great museums likewise split their functions between public spectacle and instruction—competing in this in the later part of the century with the great exhibitions—and restricted scholarly collections.

In the twentieth century, this tripartite division continued to hold despite profound changes: transformations in biological theory and systematics (particularly the theory of evolution); political shifts (especially the collapse of the European empires, which altered the context of agricultural interventions); and changing fashions in pedagogical theory and museum display. The modern herbarium, zoo, and science museum would be quite recognizable to a visitor from the mid-nineteenth century, whereas the early modern collector of curiosities would be baffled in spaces epistemologically so foreign. Nevertheless, some new features and types of collections came into existence in the twentieth century. The rise of ecology and conservation biology have led to a return to the collection of biological (and ethnological) diversity for its own sake, reminiscent of the catchall collecting of the sixteenth and seventeenth centuries. The computer has increasingly made information the object of collection, in public media and forums like the World Wide Web. These collections include the genomes of fruit flies, *Arabidopsis,* and human beings, and the widely accessible electronic catalogs of great libraries, themselves collected into metacatalogs like the Karlsruher Virtueller Katalog (http://www.ubka. uni-karlsruhe.de/hylib/virtueller_katalog.html).

A. J. LUSTIG

CALCULATOR. Although calculation had long been a part of the daily routine of commercial life, it was two natural philosophers of the seventeenth century, Blaise Pascal and Gottfried Leibniz, who invented the first machines that could carry out arithmetic processes automatically. Pascal's could add and subtract; Leibniz's did well at addition and multiplication. Although considered mechanical marvels, these devices had little immediate impact on the way people did arithmetic. Of greater practical importance was John Napier's discovery of logarithms, which made it possible to multiply or divide by addition or subtraction. The properties of logarithms were embodied in the slide rule, which soon found use in calculations relating to taxation and, during the nineteenth century, in all sorts of problems considered by scientists and engineers.

In the second half of the nineteenth century, machines that could carry out arithmetic operations came into use in commerce. The most successful of them did addition best. A few—notably the Swiss-made Millionaire—could multiply

Technicians working with ENIAC, a digital calculator built at the University of Pennsylvania, Philadelphia, between 1943 and 1946. The women are rewiring the "program." The US Army paid for ENIAC (Electronic Numeric Integrator and Calculator) to facilitate ballistic computations.

directly rather than by repeated addition, and were of particular use to scientists. Observatories and laboratories hired people called computers to do routine calculations by hand, using published mathematical tables, and by machine.

Nineteenth-century scientists and mathematicians had little to do with the invention of calculating machines. They took a more active role in the development of difference engines, machines that computed values of functions using the method of finite differences. Charles Babbage envisioned and Georg and Edvard Scheutz successfully built a difference engine. One Scheutz difference engine was used briefly at the Dudley Observatory in Albany, New York.

Instruments for carrying out more complex mathematical operations also received the attention of scholars. In 1855 James Clerk Maxwell invented a form of planimeter, a device for finding the area bounded by a closed curve. Planimeters had applications to many scientific and engineering problems, for example, finding the work done by a steam engine from an indicator diagram. In 1876 William Thomson, Lord Kelvin, proposed an instrument for representing a curve as the sum of terms in a harmonic series. The British long used Kelvin's harmonic analyzer and its descendants to predict the tides. Kelvin's instrument inspired several imitators, such as the predictor, designed by William Ferrel of the U.S. Coast and Geodetic Survey in 1880. Larger versions of this machine operated in the U.S. into the 1960s.

In the 1930s, Vannevar Bush at the Massachusetts Institute of Technology developed a much more complex, room-sized mechanical device for solving differential equations. To use Bush's differential analyzer, as well as similar instruments built in Great Britain and Norway, the operator had first to assemble an array of gears, shafts, disk integrators, and electric motors and to enter data by tracing a curve on an input table. The result appeared as a curve on an output table.

During the 1920s and 1930s, punched card equipment, initially developed for census tabulation and then applied to accounting work, came into the social sciences and astronomy. Centers devoted to computation developed at government agencies and universities, particularly Columbia in New York City and Iowa State in Ames. In the late 1930s, a physics graduate student at Harvard University, Howard Aiken, conceived a calculator that could be programmed to carry out calculations. With the help of Harvard faculty, he persuaded International Business Machines (IBM), the most successful maker of punched card equipment, to build the calculator and donate it to Harvard. The machine, called the Automatic Sequence Controlled Calculator, or Mark I, calculated for the U.S. Navy when completed during World War II. As with IBM accounting equipment, calculations were carried out using electromechanical relays. Germany also built relay calculators. During the same period, physicist John Mauchly and engineer J. Presper Eckert designed and built the first general purpose electronic computer, the ENIAC, at the University of Pennsylvania. All of these machines filled a room.

By the 1960s, the introduction of smaller, more reliable electronic components made it possible to make electronic calculators that fit on a desktop. Those introduced by the British firm of Sumlock Comptometer and sold under the name "Anita" used vacuum tubes. In 1964, Sony exhibited a prototype transistorized calculator at the New York World's Fair. Sony and other companies, such as Sharp and Wang Laboratories, soon were selling desktop electronic devices. They cost several thousand dollars, but numerous scientists used them.

In the 1970s, the introduction of the integrated circuit made it possible to build still smaller, hand-held electronic calculators. These initially cost several hundred dollars, but the price quickly fell. The hand-held calculator soon displaced the slide rule and many printed tables. Some early electronic calculators could only do business arithmetic. Others, intended for scientists and engineers, could compute trigonometric functions, exponents, and statistical functions. Early makers of hand-held calculators included the Japanese firm of Busicom and such American companies as Texas Instruments and Hewlett Packard.

As integrated circuits became more powerful, so did calculators. In the mid-1980s the Japanese firm Casio introduced a hand-held calculator that could graph simple functions. Hewlett Packard, Texas Instruments, and other companies soon followed suit; graphing calculators are now widely used in the classroom as well as the laboratory. The more expensive forms of these machines can do symbolic manipulations—not only simple algebra, but also calculus. The programs used in these calculators rely heavily on the results of university mathematicians and scientists, but the devices themselves, like nineteenth-century calculating machines, are very much commercial products.

PEGGY ALDRICH KIDWELL

CANCER RESEARCH. At the end of the nineteenth century, little was known about the causes of cancer, but the prospects for learning more appeared to be brightening with the emergence of evidence that at least some cancers might be produced by infectious microorganisms. Scientists in many laboratories searched for such cancer-causing agents without success until 1909, when a farmer brought Peyton Rous, a young biologist on the staff of the Rockefeller Institute for Medical Research, a chicken with a large sarcoma-type tumor protruding from its right breast. Rous obtained a cell-free extract from the tumor by mincing and then filtering the tissue. He then injected a solution of the extract into healthy chickens of the same breed and found that they, too, developed sarcomas. Rous contended that the tumors might have been stimulated by a "minute parasitic organism" carried in the extract—perhaps a virus.

Other scientists using Rous's methods failed to induce tumors in mice, rats, rabbits, or dogs. By the 1930s the theory that viruses cause cancers had fallen into deep disrepute. John Bittner, a biologist at the Jackson Laboratory in Bar Harbor, Maine, found that a tendency to breast cancer in certain strains of mice could be transmitted from mothers to foster children—that is, independently of the animals' genetic makeup. Bittner suspected that the mothers transmitted a virus to the infant mice when they suckled. Reluctant to challenge the prevailing antiviral paradigm of oncogenesis, he called the agent involved a "milk factor." His suspicion was later validated by recognition of the mouse mammary tumor virus (MMTV).

In the scientific community at large, theories of viral oncogenesis were revived by Ludwik Gross, a refugee from Poland who joined the staff of the Veterans Hospital in the Bronx. In 1944, Gross began injecting healthy mice with an extract obtained from ground-up organs of adult leukemic ones. He failed to induce leukemia in the recipient mice until, probably in 1949, he tried injecting the extract into newborn mice. They all developed the disease within two weeks. In the 1950s, scientists in America and Europe obtained filtrates from a large variety of tumors, injected them into newborn mice, and isolated an abundance of viruses that provoked tumors in many species, including hamsters, rats, apes, and cats. By the early 1960s, animal

Oncogenes influence the mutation, amplification, and proliferation of cancer cells. Here a fission protein (in green), created by abnormal positioning of DNA strands from different chromosomes, initiates the production of oncogenes.

tumor virology had become a major branch of basic medical and biological science. In 1966, at the age of eighty-five, Rous shared the Nobel Prize in physiology or medicine.

Knowledge that viruses are DNA or RNA wrapped in a protein coat allowed tumor virologists to begin reaching into the mystery of what occurs when a virus transforms a normal cell into a cancerous one. In the early 1960s, Renato Dulbecco, at the Salk Institute in La Jolla, California, demonstrated that when a virus invades a cell, its genetic material is incorporated into the cell's native DNA, with the result that it perverts the cell's machinery of regulated growth, and causes it to multiply malignantly. Dulbecco worked with DNA viruses. But Howard Temin, a former student of Dulbecco now at the University of Wisconsin, ran into difficulties pursuing a similar line of research using the Rous sarcoma virus, whose genetic material is RNA. RNA is synthesized using the code that DNA contains, but according to the then-prevailing central dogma in molecular biology, it could not generate DNA and, hence, could not integrate its genetic information into the DNA of a cell.

Temin contended that the central dogma must at least in part be wrong, that Rous viral RNA somehow generated DNA complementary to itself that could integrate into the DNA of the cell. Although ridiculed for his claim, Temin pursued it experimentally through the 1960s, focusing on showing that such integration occurred. In 1969 he turned to a consideration of how the virus's RNA could be physically made into complementary DNA. In 1970, he found the answer—an enzyme that catalyzes the synthesis of DNA from RNA.

The same discovery was made simultaneously and independently by David Baltimore, a member of the MIT faculty who since his graduate-school days had been working on the genetic systems of RNA viruses. In 1970, Temin and Baltimore reported, in separate, back-to-back articles published in *Nature,* the discovery of the enzyme, promptly dubbed "reverse transcriptase" in recognition of its ability to transcribe RNA back into DNA. At the end of his paper

announcing the enzyme, Temin noted that the light it cast on how retroviruses reproduce raised "strong implications for theories of viral carcinogenesis."

No virus had been shown to cause cancer in human beings, but the rapid development of tumor virology had convinced a coalition of scientists and influential laypeople to agitate for a stepped-up federal cancer program. In 1971, the agitation yielded the National Cancer Act, inaugurating a "War on Cancer" that would more than triple the budget of the National Cancer Institute by 1976. Biomedical scientists managed to divert resources from the war to research into the interaction of tumor viruses with the cell. They argued that victory over cancer would come not with searching for human tumor viruses but from understanding how the integration of a virus's genetic information into a cell's DNA transformed the cell into a source of malignancy.

In 1969, the biologists Robert J. Huebner and George J. Todaro, addressing the transformation puzzle, theorized that the cells of many, if not all vertebrates must naturally contain two kinds of cancer-related DNA: "virogenes," to create RNA viruses, and "oncogenes," a term they coined to denote genes with the power to transform normal cells into tumor cells. They speculated that both genetic substances lie latent in the cell, having entered it by some ancient infection, until activated by natural causes or environmental carcinogens.

In the early 1970s, J. Michael Bishop and Harold E. Varmus, both young faculty members of the medical school of the University of California in San Francisco, began investigating the virogene/oncogene hypothesis. They sought to determine whether any stretch of DNA in a normal chicken cell resembles the Rous virus's transforming gene, a tentative identification of which had recently been established by several other scientists in the San Francisco area. Bishop and Varmus dubbed the transforming viral RNA the "sarc" gene and sought to determine whether the viral "sarc" gene has a cousin—scientists call it a homologue—in the DNA of a normal chicken.

Between 1976 and 1978, the Bishop-Varmus group found that the viral "sarc" fragment is homologous not only to a region in the DNA of chickens but also to regions in the DNA of quail, turkeys, ducks, emus, calves, mice, and salmon. They even had detected evidence of them in human DNA. "Sarc" seemed to have cousins in DNA everywhere. The "sarc" homologues were obviously not the oncogenes—the latent oncogenic DNA—that Huebner and Todaro had originally proposed. Evolutionary reasoning helped identify them. The major groups of species—birds, mammals, and fish—that carry the "sarc" cousins had separated at least 400 million years earlier. To Bishop and Varmus, the plain evidence that the "sarc" homologues had been conserved through so much time and speciation indicated that they might be involved in some critical cellular function such as growth and development. They appeared to be normal genes that can be turned into oncogenes by viral action or by a physical or chemical agent.

In 1979, the laboratory of Robert Allan Weinberg at MIT reported that normal cellular DNA could indeed be transformed into oncogenic DNA with a chemical carcinogen. Soon, experiments in other laboratories detected transformed DNA—DNA changed from that of a normal cellular gene—in a variety of cancer cells, including carcinomas taken from rabbits, rats, mice, and people. Most of these cellular genes seem to exist all over the tree of animal evolution, just like the cousins to the viral "sarc" gene (now designated *src*, in conformity with the classical rules of three-letter genetic nomenclature). Like the *src* gene, these other cellular genes probably have a role in the fundamental cellular processes of growth, regulation, and differentiation. They are thus normal cellular genes that can be turned into oncogenes by chance processes within the cell as well as by environmental carcinogens, including tobacco smoke. These "proto-oncogenes"—potential agents of cancer—comprise, as Bishop has said, a kind of "enemy within."

The multiple steps that led to the discovery of oncogenes revolutionized cancer research and widened opportunities for the study of normal cell growth and regulation. Parts of the work earned Nobel Prizes, including one, in 1975, for Dulbecco, Baltimore, and Temin and another, in 1989, for Bishop and Varmus. Coupled with increasing knowledge of the oncogenic role of environmental carcinogens, the oncogene revolution has shown that cancer can arise from genes alone or from interactions between our genes and what we ingest, inhale, or encounter.

D. J. KEVLES

CARTOGRAPHY, the art and science of making representations of areas of the earth and other spatially extended objects, has been connected with the history of modern science both as a field of inquiry and as a tool. As a field, it has supplemented and stimulated geodesy and, later, planetary science. As a tool, it has been indispensable to geology, geophysics, oceanography, meteorology, and biology, all of which rely on thematic maps to represent and analyze spatially distributed phenomena such as magnetic variation, rock outcrops, or warm and cold fronts.

Three major events around 1500 triggered an explosion of cartographic activity in Europe. First, cartographers assimilated the lessons of Claudius Ptolemy's *Geographia*, the greatest cartographic achievement of the ancient world. Brought to Italy from Constantinople, the complete text was translated into Latin early in the fifteenth century. By the century's end, at least seven different editions had been published. From Ptolemy, cartographers learned to arrange geographical knowledge according to a coordinate system of parallels (latitudes) and meridians (longitudes) and to project the system onto flat surfaces. Second, thanks to the invention of printing and advances in engraving, cartographers found ways to reproduce maps, first as wood engravings and, in the sixteenth century, by copper engravings that made much clearer maps. Third, the voyages of discovery and increased international trade that followed produced a demand for more accurate maps of the world. Thus the chief focus of cartographers became the production of atlases.

The Low Countries were the center of atlas-making in the sixteenth century. There, Gerardus Mercator invented the famous projection that showed lines of constant direction (rhumb lines) as straight lines, just as the portolan charts of the late Middle Ages had done earlier. Mercator used this projection in the marine chart he published in 1569. In 1599, Edward Wright used the newly invented logarithms to lay out the mathematical basis of this projection. In 1570, Abraham Ortelius published one of the most comprehensive early atlases, the *Teatrum Orbis Terrarum,* with 53 maps by various authors. Numerous other atlases followed. By the eighteenth century, France had become the center of cartography. Guillaume Delisle published an atlas of 98 maps, and Jean-Baptiste Bourguignon d'Anville included 211 maps in his *Atlas général* (1737–1789).

Part of France's lead in cartography came from its research in geodesy, which led not only to a determination of the earth's shape and the length of a degree, but also to the first detailed topographical map of any nation, the *Carte géométrique de la France* (or *Carte de Cassini*). Its 182 sheets were finally completed and published by 1793, the culmination of decades of work.

Across Europe, nations founded surveys, mostly run by the military: the Ordnance Survey of Great Britain in 1791, the Institut Géographique National in France, the Landestopographie in Switzerland. The Spanish set up their topographic survey in the eighteenth century, the Austro-Hungarians, Swiss, and Americans in the nineteenth century. The Germans combined the existing state surveys into a national survey following unification in 1871. In 1888, Japan instituted its Imperial Land Survey. European nations also surveyed their overseas territories. The most ambitious of these surveys, the Great Trigonometrical Survey of India, established early in the nineteenth century, not only mapped the subcontinent but raised gravimetric problems that quickly led to the theory of isostasy.

Already in the seventeenth century, scientists had designed maps for specific scientific purposes. Between 1698 and 1700, Edmund Halley sailed the Atlantic, measured the variations in magnetic declination, and charted them on a pioneering map that appeared in different editions between 1701 and 1703. By drawing lines between points of equal variation, he pioneered the technique of isogonic lines that would be used often in later thematic maps. In the early nineteenth century, geologists invented the stratigraphic map that represented each kind of rock that outcropped at the earth's surface by a different color. Constructing such maps became the major goal of newly instituted national geological surveys. So important was stratigraphic mapping, so urgent its need for good underlying base maps, that in the United States the government gave the Geological Survey, established in 1878, the responsibility for producing the prerequisite topographic maps.

As national topographic surveys designed to promote national military and commercial interests began to publish their results, entrepreneurs founded private companies to exploit the information in maps for the use of the general public. Among the more important of the companies they founded were Bartholemew in Great Britain, Justus Perthes in Germany (an enterprise begun in the late eighteenth century), and Rand McNally in the United States.

From the 1880s to World War I, cartographers, like many other scientists, created international institutions. In 1875, the Convention of the Meter, attended by twenty nations, accepted the metric system, initially proposed in France in 1791, as the universal system of measurement. This aided the systematization of map scales. In 1884, the International Meridian Conference in Washington, D.C., decided on Greenwich, London, as the site of the prime meridian; the choice was universally accepted by World War I. At the International Geographical Congress of 1891, the German geographer Albrecht Penck proposed an International Map of the World on a scale of 1:1,000,000 in 1,500 sheets. The proposal was accepted but the work proceeded slowly. The most significant accomplishment of this still incomplete project was the 107-sheet *Map of Hispanic America* published by the American Geographical Society in 1945.

World War I brought a halt to international cooperation and ushered in the most productive century ever in cartography. In succession, the airplane, aerial photography, seismic techniques, echo sounders and sonar, radar, satellites, and computers made possible the mapping of features of the land, ocean bottoms, and extraterrestrial objects with an accuracy, ease, and variety hitherto undreamed of.

Without a growth industry in aeronautical charts, aviation would have foundered. Conversely, airplanes made aerial photography and reconnaissance mapping possible once cartographers had developed techniques to translate photographs into maps. Meteorologists responded to the needs of the aviation industry, and benefited from it as they developed theories of high- and low-pressure systems and hot and cold fronts, all of them represented on maps. Today, meteorology is a map-intensive enterprise. Seismology, the echo sounder, and sonar displaced sounding as methods of mapping underwater. The unexpected topographic features detected with these new tools helped bring about the plate-tectonic revolution.

In the 1960s, the already-important remote-sensing systems came into their own. Electronic measuring helped extend continental surveys to oceanic areas. Soon thereafter, satellite triangulation became possible, helping to tie the triangulation of the continents together into a single system. Innovations multiplied. For example, scientists developed SLAR (side-looking airborne radar) in the 1970s. After SLAR had been tested in Ecuador and Nicaragua, RADAM (Radar Amazon Commission) of Brazil and Aero Service of Philadelphia mapped the hitherto inaccessible Amazon Basin. Wide-angle cameras and improved film allowed the mapping of the earth and the moon and planets.

Computers were quickly harnessed for the purposes of mapping by institutions such as the Laboratory for Computer Graphics and Spatial Analysis at Harvard. They made the previously tedious business of laying out projections routine. After experiments in the 1970s, computers by the 1980s could translate aerial photographs into topographic maps complete with contours, allowing rapid and accurate contour mapping for the first time. Statistical mapping also became much easier.

The greatest change brought about by computers was a shift from considering the map as a completed object to the map as a manipulable tool. In the 1960s, geographers devel-

A map constructed on principles laid down by the Greek astronomer Ptolemy around 150 A.D., showing Europe, Asia, and Africa. (The Mediterranean Sea is at middle left.) Editions of Ptolemy's *Geographia* containing such maps were published before 1500.

oped computerized information systems. Instead of entering data on a two-dimensional surface, they digitalized it. This meant they could easily superimpose different sets of information and, even more important, draw conclusions based on the superimposition. With this new tool in hand, cartographers were better equipped to prepare specialized maps for business, law enforcement, natural-disaster prediction, or other specialized interests.

Today, cartography flourishes as never before. The military remains heavily involved, and the private companies multiply. Most nations have their surveys. Non-governmental groups such as the American Geographical Society and the National Geographic Society promote cartography. Professional societies such as the American Congress on Surveying and Mapping, the American Society of Photogrammetry, and the American Society of Civil Engineers (focusing here on the United States) have multiplied. They publish journals such as the *Manual of Photogrammetry, Photogrametria,* and *Surveying and Mapping*. Finally, a variety of international organizations attempt to coordinate mapping worldwide. Among them are the U.N. Office of Cartography, the Inter-American Geodetic Survey, the Pan-American Institute, and the International Hydrographic Organization in Monaco.

During most of the twentieth century, historians of cartography described how their discipline had achieved increasing scope and precision. At the end of the century, the critical cartography movement led by J. B. Harley and other British cartographers emphasized instead that, however exact maps may be, they are far from neutral. Cartographers' choice of projections, scales, symbols, and units reflect their own and their patrons' interests. According to these historians, maps depend not only on scientific knowledge but also on political interests.

RACHEL LAUDAN

CHAOS AND COMPLEXITY. Nature is complicated. Scientists trying to understand it have to simplify and approximate in order to discern regularity in phenomena and describe it mathematically. In the late twentieth century a new field called chaos theory emerged that instead embraced complexity and the nonlinear mathematical equations that expressed it.

Scientists and mathematicians had previously addressed the topic of complexity and nonlinear equations, notably Henri Poincaré, who worked on the theory of differential equations and dynamical systems. In 1908 Poincaré pointed out that small differences in the initial conditions of a system could result in large changes in their long-term evolution, and noted as an example the unpredictability of the weather. But Poincaré's work did not immediately spark a new line of research; physicists at the time were fruitfully exploiting linear differential equations in the development of relativity and quantum theory.

Chaos theory first emerged from the increasing use of computers in meteorology after World War II, when computer scientists viewed the complex, nonlinear problems of meteorology as a testing ground and meteorologists used computers as a way to handle their accumulations of data and to model weather systems. In 1961 Edward Lorenz, a meteorologist at the Massachusetts Institute of Technology (MIT), was running simplified atmospheric models through his computer. He decided to retrace a run, but instead of starting at the beginning he started halfway through, typing in the numbers for the initial conditions from the printout for the first run.

The printout had rounded off the six decimal places used by the computer to just three, but Lorenz assumed a difference of one part in a thousand would be inconsequential. Instead he found that the second run, from almost the same initial conditions, diverged wildly from the first. He first thought he had blown a vacuum tube, but then recognized the importance of the small difference in initial conditions.

Using a still simpler system of three nonlinear equations modeling convection, Lorenz demonstrated sensitive dependence on initial conditions, as the phenomenon was called, and cast doubt on the prospects of long-range weather forecasts. But he also revealed a sort of abstract order within the disorderly behavior that resulted: a plot of the results in three dimensions traced a complex double spiral, nonintersecting and non-repeating yet with distinctive boundaries and structure. The image, later called a Lorenz attractor, appeared with Lorenz's results in 1963, in a paper entitled "Deterministic Nonperiodic Flow" in the *Journal of the Atmospheric Sciences*. The title asserted the persistence of determinism; the avenue of publication indicated the source of Lorenz's interest in the problem and ensured that most physicists and mathematicians would miss its initial appearance.

In the meantime Stephen Smale and several other mathematicians at the University of California at Berkeley were developing ways to model dynamical systems through topology, folding and stretching plots in phase space to reproduce the unpredictable histories of nonlinear systems; two points on the plot could be close together or far apart depending on the sequence of folds, thus exhibiting sensitivity to initial conditions. In the early 1970s, mathematician James Yorke came across Lorenz's paper and publicized it in a mathematics journal, in which he applied the term "chaos" to the subject. Yorke drew on the work of Robert May, a mathematical physicist who had turned to population biology. May had found that nonlinear equations describing cyclic changes in populations could begin doubling rapidly in a period before giving way to apparently random fluctuations; but within the random behavior, stable cycles with different periods would reappear, then start doubling again toward randomness. Yorke explained May's results with chaos theory. A review article in *Nature* in May 1976 brought chaos to a still wider audience.

Yorke learned that Soviet mathematicians and physicists had been pursuing similar lines of research, starting with the work of A. N. Kolmogorov in the 1950s and extended by A. N. Sarkovskii, who arrived at the same conclusions as Yorke, and Yakov Grigorevich Sinai, who developed the theory in the framework of thermodynamics. Physicists in the Soviet Union, the United States, and Europe saw in chaos a way to tackle long-standing problems in fluid dynamics, especially regarding turbulence and phase transitions. The appearance of periodic order within longer-term disorder found visual expression in the geometry developed by Benoit Mandelbrot and other mathematicians in the 1970s. Mandelbrot coined the term "fractal" to describe the new class of irregular shapes that seemed to duplicate their irregularity when viewed at different scales and dimensions. In 1976, Mitchell Feigenbaum found that a single constant described the scaling or convergence rate—that is, the rate at which cycles doubled in period on the way to chaos—no matter the type of physical system or mathematical function (quadratic or trigonometric). Shortly after Feigenbaum announced the single universal scaling law, the first conference on chaos convened in Como, Italy. That was in 1977, fifty years after another conference of physicists there had considered the competing interpretations of quantum mechanics.

Computer-generated image derived from a Mandelbrot Set, which defines complex mappings that often resemble structures found in nature

Chaos theory emerged from diverse disciplinary and institutional origins: from Lorenz, an academic meteorologist; to Mandelbrot, working at International Business Machines (IBM) Corp. on mathematical economics; to Feigenbaum, a theoretical physicist at Los Alamos National Laboratory. Los Alamos eventually created a Center for Nonlinear Studies, and other centers for chaos theory emerged at the University of California at Santa Cruz, at Gorky in the Soviet Union, and elsewhere. Chaos theory served to bridge disparate disciplines dealing with apparent disorder: biology, ecology, economics, meteorology, and physics. Digital electronic computers were central to all of the work. Chaos also connected abstract mathematics with real-world problems. The theory provided tools for astronomers studying the red spot on Jupiter and galactic structure, population biologists modeling the fluctuations of species, epidemiologists charting the cycles of disease, physiologists investigating cardiac fibrillations, and urban engineers tracking traffic flows. A few enterprising chaos theorists sought to predict the stock market and make investors, and themselves, rich. Some practitioners viewed chaos theory as a subset of a wider field called complexity, which studied neural nets, cellular automata, spin glasses, and other exotic systems exhibiting complex interconnections among individual components.

Chaos theory emerged in the 1960s and 1970s, a time of general cultural ferment often manifested in antiscientism. Chaos theory itself seemed to reject reductionism and determinism in favor of a holistic embrace of complexity and flux, even if it still found rules and regularity buried deeper in disorder, and it thus resonated with critics of deterministic science. Several chaos pioneers themselves drew inspiration from the romanticism of Goethe. The emergence of centers for the field in Santa Cruz and Santa Fe, towns with New Age reputations, suggest the countercultural component in the chaos community.

PETER J. WESTWICK

CHEMICAL BOND AND VALENCE. In the eighteenth century and earlier, chemical combination was thought to be ruled by the laws of "chemical affinity" as measured (among other ways) by the energy and proportions in which acids and bases combine to form salts. When atomic theory and electrochemistry began to be developed almost simultaneously shortly after 1800, most theorists thought that the atoms that form chemical compounds must be held together by polar electrostatic forces. The electronegativity or electropositivity of a substance could be measured by its behavior in an electrochemical cell; the sign and intensity varied with the substance, and was a primary characteristic of each element. Developed primarily by Jacob Berzelius in the 1810s and 1820s, the theory of electrochemical dualism worked well for inorganic compounds, but by the 1830s it ran into increasing difficulties in organic chemistry.

Certain elements seemed to be able to substitute for one another in compounds irrespective of their electrochemical character. A study of inorganic and organometallic compounds led Edward Frankland in 1852 to point out that atoms of nitrogen, phosphorus, antimony, and arsenic seemed always to combine with either three or five other atoms, regardless of electrochemistry. In the late 1850s, Frankland's friend Hermann Kolbe began applying this concept to organic compounds. Even before Frankland's paper of 1852, Alexander Williamson had pointed out the "bibasic" nature of certain organic radicals, and soon he applied this concept to the oxygen atom as well. Following Williamson's lead, Charles-Adolphe Wurtz, William Odling, and August Kekulé also explored the same concept in organic chemistry, with regard to hydrogen, oxygen, sulfur, nitrogen, and ultimately carbon.

Kekulé summarized this emerging theme in two articles published in 1857–1858. He stated that atoms of each element appear to have a certain fixed capacity to combine with atoms of the same or of other elements; he called these components of combination capacity "affinity units." Hydrogen and chlorine atoms had one such unit; oxygen and sulfur two; nitrogen, phosphorus, and antimony three; and carbon four. About a decade later this concept was renamed "valence." Kekulé wrote that the formula for water, H_2O, signifies two monovalent hydrogen atoms combined with one divalent oxygen atom; ethane, H_3CCH_3, holds together because each methyl group (CH_3) has one unused valence unit of the tetravalent carbon atom, and the two valences satisfy each other in hooking together; and so on with other formulas.

This theory of atomic valence seemed to be supported by abundant evidence, and most leading chemists rapidly accepted it. Kekulé used valence concepts to develop a theory of "chemical structure." Carbon atoms, he wrote, could use some of their valences to bond together to create carbon "chains," forming the "skeleton" of a molecule. Following the valence rules, atoms of other elements, such as hydrogen, oxygen, and nitrogen, could add onto (or into) this skeleton, to form molecules of (potentially) all the organic compounds then known.

The gradual formulation of accessory assumptions, such as that of multiple bonds (ethylene as $H_2C=CH_2$, formaldehyde as $H_2C=O$, and so on), demonstrated that the structure theory could cover a wide range of organic formulas. In 1865 Kekulé showed how carbon tetravalence could be used to derive a promising candidate formula for the crucially important benzene molecule, C_6H_6, the prototype of all so-called aromatic compounds. This formula suggested a closed ring of six carbon atoms with alternating single and double bonds, and with a hydrogen atom attached to each carbon. Chemists soon accepted Kekulé's benzene theory.

Despite their important roles in its initial formulation, Frankland and Kolbe rejected the full implications of valence and structure theory, though Frankland's resistance collapsed quickly in the early 1860s. One problem they identified was the number of additional assumptions necessary to make the theory work well. Moreover, it was not clear whether valence was a constant property, characteristic of each element, or variable with chemical circumstances, as Frankland had initially proposed. Disputes about the fixity of valence continued for decades.

Some chemists objected that the valence connections between atoms resembled crude "hooks" or "glue" rather than an isotropic (spatially uniform) natural force such as gravitational or electrical attraction. Frankland referred to valence connections as chemical "bonds," but demurred at describing them further. Gravitation seemed to be excluded as the cause of valence owing to the complexity and stability of chemical compounds; electrical attraction seemed impossible because atoms of a single element could bond to each other. Therefore, accepting the idea of valence appeared to require renouncing the possibility of understanding chemical affinity as a familiar macroscopic physical force. It was a new and uniquely chemical concept.

The residual anomalies associated with Kekulé's highly successful benzene theory led to new proposals by Lothar Meyer, Henry Edward Armstrong, and F. K. Johannes Thiele that invoked partial or center-directed valence bonds. In 1874, J. H. van't Hoff and Joseph Le Bel began to explore valence bonds in three dimensions. In the 1890s, Alfred Werner used a modified valence theory successfully to represent the molecular composition of certain complex inorganic substances ("coordination compounds"). In this endeavor he made use of the recently formulated theory of ionization of Svante Arrhenius.

When J. J. Thomson demonstrated the existence of the electron (1897), some physicists and chemists immediately began to inquire whether this offered a new way to understand valence. In 1904, Thomson developed an atomic model in which electrons were supposed to circulate in exterior shells. In the same year in Berlin, Richard Abegg formulated a more explicit "rule of eight," corresponding to periodic valence regularities.

During and just after World War I, Walther Kossel and Gilbert N. Lewis began independently to develop electronic theories of the chemical bond, a concept fruitfully extended shortly thereafter by Irving Langmuir. Neutral atoms have as many electrons outside the nucleus as protons within. In the new theory, the second and third periods of the periodic table each have eight members, the last of which has a stable nonbonding "octet" of electrons in a shell. Beyond the octet shells are the odd electrons in the outer shell, the "valence electrons," which can be shared with adjacent atoms to form chemical bonds. For instance, aluminum, with atomic number 13, is eleven places past helium in the periodic table, or three places past the first stable octet. The aluminum atom therefore has three valence electrons available to share with other atoms—a valence of three.

Joseph John Thomson, discoverer of the electron and director of the Cavendish Laboratory, Cambridge, England, at work in 1904

C

La calcination Solaire de l'antimoine.

a *la Table*
b *le miroir avec son soutien qui se peut hausser et baisser*
c *la pierre ou la plaque sur laquelle est l'antimoine en poudre*
d *l'artiste qui gouverne le miroir et qui remue l'antimoine*
e *la lumiere qui est concentree par le miroir.*

Some early photo-chemistry: the chemist is focusing the sun's rays so as to oxidize a piece of antimony.

Langmuir thus distinguished an "ionic" bond, where an electron transferred from an electropositive to an electronegative atom, from what he called a "covalent" bond, where the two electrons, one from each atom forming the bond, were shared more or less equally. In the first case, coulombic attraction held the atoms together; in the second case, electricity was involved in a manner not understood until the advent of quantum mechanics.

Neils Bohr and his collaborators began to develop their theories of electronic structure by examining atomic spectra with reference to quantum principles and the basic patterns revealed by the periodic table. Meanwhile, work on wave mechanics by Louis de Broglie and Erwin Schrödinger began to provide theoretical explanations for the spatially directed nature of valence bonds. In the late 1920s and early 1930s, Walter Heitler, Fritz London, John Slater, Linus Pauling, and others developed "valence-bond theory" as an application of the new quantum mechanics of Erwin Schrödinger and Werner Heisenberg. This involved constructing wave functions to represent the older Lewis-style electron pairs of a covalent bond.

At about the same time, Robert Mullikan developed an alternative quantum-mechanical technique for understanding chemical bonding based on what he called "molecular orbitals." Erich Hückel applied both valence-bond and molecular-orbital methods to the problem of aromatic compounds and found Mullikan's method superior. The molecular-orbital approach seemed to many to provide a cleaner and more satisfying model, and after World War II it gradually displaced the valence-bond model championed by Pauling.

Both valence-bond and molecular-orbital approaches had led to the idea of "resonance": the bonds between the carbon atoms of the benzene ring could not be considered either as single or as double bonds, but rather as uniform "resonance hybrids" halfway between the two states. Theories of resonance have successfully accounted for the curiously passive character of aromatic compounds toward addition to the double bonds of the ring, and the concept of "aromaticity" has broadened to include nonbenzenoid compounds.

After welcoming and then abandoning electrical theories of chemical bonding in the course of the nineteenth century, chemists in the twentieth century, armed with physical theories of the atom and quantum-mechanical principles, embraced them once more, and with considerable success. Chemists still have a long way to go, however, in developing theoretical models for the observed chemical behavior of molecules.

A. J. ROCKE

CHEMISTRY. The term chemistry first appeared in references to a practice consolidated in Alexandria at the beginning of the Christian era, and known later as the "Egyptian" art. Historians of chemistry have characteristically distinguished chemistry from alchemy, a product of the Arabic and European Middle Ages and later depicted as a secrecy-laden search for methods to produce noble metals by transmutation and to obtain the mysterious philosophers' stone. According to this story, chemistry emerged during the late sixteenth and seventeenth centuries. Drawing on practices of alchemy, metallurgy, and herbalist distillers, chemistry distinguished itself from its earlier roots both by its openness and its goal: the determination of the composition of substances drawn from the plant, animal, and mineral kingdoms by separating them into their elementary constituents. Recent historians, however, believe that until well into the seventeenth century alchemy and chemistry were synonymous terms that denoted a broad range of inquiries, and that only after practitioners of chemistry wished to distance themselves from the seekers of gold and the philosophers' stone did they narrow the definition of alchemy to activities they discountenanced.

The remarkable stability of the identity of chemistry despite deep mutations in its aims and conceptual frameworks rests on the nature of the place in which it has been practiced, from the earliest times of which we have records to the present. The original meaning of "laboratory" was the space in which chemists "elaborated" chemical and medicinal substances. Chemists traditionally assembled in their laboratories a characteristic set of apparatus capable of a well-defined repertoire of operations. With furnaces and distillation apparatus constructed from components made of earth, metal, or glass, they attempted through the agency of fire to separate substances into their volatile and fixed components. Filtration, solution, precipitation, maceration, solvent extraction, and other operations were usually subsidiary to the central procedures of distillation and sublimation.

During the seventeenth century, a series of textbooks, of which the prototype was Andreas Libavius's *Alchemie* (1597), organized knowledge of chemical substances and operations into teachable form. They culminated in the popular *Cours de Chymie* of Nicolas Lemery, first published in 1673. He and other chemists in France gave chemical lectures and demonstrations at the Jardin des plantes and in their apothecary shops. In the German principalities, chemical instruction entered the universities during the seventeenth century, an early example being the teaching of chemical medicine at the University of Marburg (1609). By the end of the century, chemistry had become a sufficiently distinct branch of natural knowledge to form, together with physics, anatomy, and botany, the physical section of the French Academy of Sciences. In England, Robert Boyle led those who sought to make chemistry part of the broadly forming new natural philosophy.

Seventeenth-century chemists interpreted their separations by theories of matter through hybrids drawn in part from the three "principles" (salt, sulfur, and mercury) adapted by Paracelsus from alchemical views, and in part from the four-element theory of Aristotle. The most common compromise identified the products of a distillation as oils (characterized by the combustible principle, sulfur); "spirituous" liquids (mercury); insipid liquids (water); substances soluble in water (salt); and fixed insoluble substances (earth). At a more pragmatic level, there gradually emerged a scheme in which metals, alkalis, and "absorbent earths" could be separated from and recombined with the three known mineral acids and a "vegetable" acid. Boyle's systematic application of color indicators able to detect the presence of acids and alkalis facilitated these identifications.

The incorporation of the mechanical philosophy into chemistry during the second half of the seventeenth century abetted the interpretation of chemical processes as consequences of the particular shapes of the ultimate participating particles. Sharp-pointed acid particles embedded themselves in pores in alkali particles, resulting in a salt that displayed neither the properties of the acid nor the alkali, but from which both could later be recovered.

During the first half of the eighteenth century, chemists gradually subordinated early theories of matter to the more pragmatic concept of neutral salts formed of an acid and a base. Elaborate mechanistic explanations gave place to the more generic particulate picture. In 1718, Etienne-François Geoffroy systemized the well-defined chemical changes then known in a Table of Rapports, the columns of which indicated the order in which substances would replace one another in combination with the substance shown at the top of each column. During the following decades, chemists adopted Newton's idea that differential short-range forces of attraction, or "affinities," drove these replacements.

Chemists continued to support their activities largely from apothecary shops. The teaching of chemistry in German medical faculties expanded. A group of chemists in the reformed Paris Academy of Sciences became a leading forum for the pursuit of experimental chemistry in the first three decades of the eighteenth century. At the Prussian Academy of Sciences, reformed by Frederick II, Andreas Marggraf and Johann Pott became prominent after 1750 in the investigative expansion of the chemistry of salts and in their application to both plant and mineral analysis. The growing sense of a chemical community in Germany gave rise in 1778 to the first specialized chemical periodical, *Chemisches Journal,* edited by Lorenz Crell.

Because fire figured so prominently in their operations and distinctions, chemists were much concerned to explain combustion. Chemists long associated combustibility with the sulfur principle because common sulfur conspicuously burned. The dominant form of this approach in the eighteenth century was Georg Ernst Stahl's theory of phlogiston. Stahl recognized that the calcination of metals and the reduction of metallic ores to their metallic form, as well as the relationship between sulfur and vitriolic acid, could all be explained as exchanges of the same principle. Phlogiston served to link an extensive series of the most impor-

tant chemical changes known at the time into a coherent system.

Until the late eighteenth century, chemists operated mainly on solids and liquids. Since vapors could not be handled by ordinary techniques, they were usually neglected in accounting for the substances that entered or left during a chemical change. Atmospheric air was regarded as an elementary, homogeneous, elastic fluid, which could contain various impurities. In 1756, following up earlier work by Stephen Hales, Joseph Black showed through quantitative balance experiments that ordinary alkalis contain a distinct species of air, which he named "fixed air." During the next two decades, several British natural philosophers discovered other "airs." In 1775, the most prolific of these discoverers, Joseph Priestley, discovered (by reducing mercury without charcoal), a "purer and more respirable" air than the atmosphere. Extending the phlogiston theory to explain the properties of the various new airs, Priestley named his discovery "dephlogisticated air."

In 1772, Antoine Laurent Lavoisier took up the problem of the absorption and release of air. His discoveries that phosphorus and sulfur gain weight when burned, and metallic calces lose weight when reduced, led him to a distinctive quantitative style of experiment, the so-called "balance-sheet method," which many historians identify as the basis of the modern science of chemistry. In 1777, Lavoisier proposed a new general theory of combustion, dispensing with phlogiston, in which "pure" air combined with metals and combustible bodies, releasing the material principle of heat. Soon he renamed this principle "caloric" and pure air "oxygen," which, as its Greek root implies, is regarded as the principle of acidity.

By 1785, Lavoisier's demonstration of the decomposition and synthesis of water consolidated his theoretical structure and converted several influential French chemists to his side. They lobbied chemists who visited Paris, founded a new journal, and collaborated to reform chemical nomenclature. Although Priestley never acceded to the "French chemistry," other British chemists, as well as the Germans who remained loyal to the Stahlian viewpoint until 1790, rapidly adopted the essential features of Lavoisier's reform during the last decade of the century.

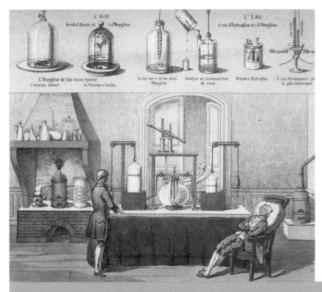

An engraving from 1860 depicting pneumatic experiments done with the apparatus of the late 18th century

C

To help consolidate what supporters and opponents alike were calling a revolution in chemistry, Lavoisier published a *Traité élémentaire de chimie* (1789) that summarized the experiments and theories on which he had based his movement, incorporated into the new framework earlier knowledge of the chemistry of salts, and presented recent applications of the new theory of combustion to organic substances. In addition, the *Traité* replaced the traditional chemical elements, which Lavoisier regarded as "metaphysical," with a pragmatic definition of elements as substances that "we have not been able to decompose by any method." His list of elements provided the basis from which the modern periodic table of elements has grown.

In principle, eighteenth-century chemists recognized a hierarchy of levels of composition, from elements to various orders of "mixtes," but the only levels generally established through analysis and synthesis were salts and their constituent acids, metals, alkalis, and alkaline earths. Chemists often assumed that these constituents were present in fixed proportions because a specific quantity of an acid was required to neutralize a particular quantity of a base. At the end of the century, Claude-Louis Berthollet challenged this assumption. From the principle that substances combine because of general laws of attraction, Berthollet inferred that compounds could form in an indefinite series of proportions, depending on the relative masses of the constituents placed together. Joseph Proust argued that true compounds occurred only in fixed proportions. Their debate ended indecisively, but contributed to a clearer distinction between chemical compounds and solutions, mixtures, or alloys.

Along with his attack on fixed proportions, Berthollet broke with eighteenth-century affinity theory, according to which a substance with greater affinity for one of two substances combined together will completely displace the substance of lesser affinity. Instead, according to Berthollet, an equilibrium sets in that depends on the relative masses of each of the substances present. His idea took hold gradually, culminating in the 1860s to quantitative laws of mass action.

Considerations about the composition of the atmosphere led John Dalton during the first years of the nineteenth century to identify chemical atoms with characteristic atomic weights. By assuming that when only one compound of any two elements was known it consisted of one atom of each, that when two were known one of them consisted of one atom of each, the second of two of one and one of the other, and so on, Dalton calculated, from the measured proportions by weight of the elements, the relative weights of their atoms. In 1808, he published atomic weights for thirty-six elements relative to hydrogen = 1. Dalton conceived of his atoms as hard, spherical bodies, and depicted their assumed spatial arrangements in the compounds they formed.

Several prominent English chemists, including Thomas Thomson and William Hyde Wollaston, adopted Dalton's atomic theory after obtaining independent evidence for multiple combining proportions. To avoid commitment to the reality of the atoms, Wollaston referred to "equivalent" rather than atomic weights, but he calculated them in Dalton's manner. In Sweden, Jöns Jacob Berzelius accepted the general principle of the atomic theory, but established more rigorous standards of experimental precision for determining atomic weights. Those that he established during the first two decades of the century were generally accurate to within 1 percent. In place of Dalton's "law of simplicity," Berzelius devised rules and analogies by which to decide on the empirical formula for a given compound. Since chemists operated with several sets of rules, they produced atomic weights for some elements that differed by small integral multiples.

The invention of the battery (pile) by Alessandro Volta in 1800 influenced chemistry powerfully. Anthony Carlisle and William Nicholson found even before Volta's paper was published that the current generated by the pile can decompose water into its elements. During the next decade, Humphry Davy passed a current through alkaline solutions to isolate the metals potassium and sodium. Later he recovered magnesium, strontium, calcium, and barium from amalgams of the alkaline earths. Because the electric current could overcome the force of the affinities supposed to hold substances together in compounds, Davy inferred that affinities were electric forces. Berzelius, who also experimented extensively with Voltaic currents, developed a general theory of chemical composition based on the same assumption. According to Berzelius's "dualistic theory," oxides formed between highly negative oxygen and positive, or less negative, atoms. The remaining net positive or negative charges of these oxides allowed them to combine into neutral salts and other more complex compounds.

The discovery in 1810 by Joseph Louis Gay-Lussac that gases combine in ratios of small whole numbers by volume provided a potential resolution of uncertainties over atomic weights. One needed only the additional assumption that a given volume of any gas contains the same number of atoms (or molecules). Some, including most famously Amedeo Avogadro and André Marie Ampère, devised theories based on this conclusion, but Dalton rejected the generalization that all gases contained the same number of particles in the same volume. The consequence that individual molecules of several elementary gases must then be composed of multiple identical atoms caused other prominent chemists to reject or restrict the generalization.

By the second decade of the nineteenth century, chemists had established fundamental principles sufficient to support rapidly growing investigative and educational activities. New institutional arrangements strengthened the role of chemistry in higher education. In France, the École Polytechnique, set up during the Revolution, included lectures and laboratories in chemistry. Leading chemists, such as Gay-Lussac and Louis Jacques Thenard, became professors there, at the Collège de France, or at the University of Paris, and gave lectures that attracted large audiences. Aspiring foreign chemists came to Paris to learn from these masters of rigorously logical exposition and experimental demonstration. In London, Davy achieved great popularity through his chemical lectures at the Royal Institution. Chemical instruction took place in Germany in several universities, and especially in small proprietary pharmacy schools. One of those who began his education in Germany, but continued it in Paris, was Justus Liebig. After working with Gay-Lussac, Liebig returned to his native state of Hesse in 1824 with an appointment to teach chemistry at the small University of Giessen. There he developed a teaching laboratory, intended at first to train pharmacists toward instruction in general chemistry. By the mid 1830s, Liebig's laboratory was training dozens of chemists and pharmacists in a systematic program that moved from elementary exercises to original research projects.

The laboratories in which these activities took place resembled earlier ones but now were also centers for innovations in apparatus and procedures. Lavoisier had initiated the break from the traditional array of material objects that had long characterized the places where chemists worked.

Sometimes adapting and combining customary retorts and pneumatic troughs, sometimes designing, for particular purposes, apparatus that was quite unfamiliar, Lavoisier increased both the range and the cost of chemical equipment dramatically. Some of his designs, such as the Baroque gazometer depicted in his *Traité*, his successors simplified. But by the 1820s, chemists so regularly designed and redesigned apparatus for more special operations and for better precision that publications began to appear to keep them informed of the latest developments in laboratory organization and equipment.

As modern chemistry emerged in the nineteenth century, the traditional small-scale commercial producers of various chemicals grew into a heavy chemical industry. By the 1830s, factories rather than shops produced sulfuric acid and soda. Historians often treat this early stage of industrialization as independent of the Scientific Revolution. Chemical crafts and deliberate chemical experimentation with the intention to advance the science were closely interwoven by the early eighteenth century. What each owed to the other differed from case to case.

By the mid-nineteenth century, chemists comprised the most prominent class of the new genre of scientists. With roots in long-established practices, driven forward first by the chemical revolution identified with Lavoisier, and then by the atomic theory associated with Dalton, chemists led the way into what fin-de-siècle spokesmen called the "century of science." The laboratories that had been their peculiar abodes for several centuries now became the prototypes for the places in which other fields, such as physiology, began to establish themselves. Whatever may have been the source of the earlier development of industrial chemistry, chemists were confident that further advances depended on the application of chemical science to factory production. By the 1840s, Justus Liebig could proclaim in his *Familiar Letters on Chemistry* that the wealth of a nation could be measured by its chemical production.

No sooner had chemistry crystallized as a modern scientific discipline than it began to split into subfields. First, organic chemistry separated from inorganic chemistry. Lavoisier had already applied his theories and methods of combustion analysis to determine the elementary composition of plant and animal matters. A generation later, several leading chemists took up the problem of obtaining the quantitative precision that had eluded him. By the 1820s, they had shown that organic compounds conformed to the laws of combining proportions. The application of principles of composition derived from the study of inorganic compounds ran into severe difficulties. The discovery of compounds identical in elementary composition, but different in properties, showed that empirical formulas did not fully characterize them, and set off decades of controversy. A series of "radical" theories proposed during the 1830s posited groups of elements that remained constantly associated while taking part in the reactions that transformed the organic compounds of which they formed constituent parts. The substitution theory asserted, on the other hand, that one element within a radical or compound could be exchanged for another, such as chlorine for hydrogen, without deeply altering the properties of the molecule.

Meanwhile, as the focus in organic chemistry shifted from the analysis of substances derived from plants or animals to the derivation of carbon compounds from them by partial decomposition, substitution, and later by synthesis, another field, most often called physiological chemistry, arose to take up the problems lost in the shift. By the early twentieth century, physiological chemistry had evolved into biochemistry. Liebig's efforts, beginning in 1840 to apply the new chemical knowledge to improve agriculture, had already become a focal point for the formation of agricultural chemistry.

Around 1850, organic chemists still used competing theories of composition, different systems of atomic weights, and several versions of the letter symbols that Berzelius had introduced to represent atoms. In addition to using empirical formulas, chemists used various "rational" formulas that grouped the atoms within a molecule into several "types." Generally they regarded these types not as literal descriptions of the spatial arrangement of the atoms, but as means to classify organic compounds, to understand their relationships to one another and their reactions. From these efforts emerged generalizations about the proportions in which elements and radicals combined with one another that gradually produced theories of chemical combination applicable to both organic and inorganic compounds. Put in their most general form by August Kekulé beginning in 1857, these new views underwrote the classical theory of valence and the basis for structural formulas of organic compounds. Organic chemistry enjoyed a rapid expansion, remaining the dominant subfield of chemistry for the rest of the century.

Debates over the constitution of organic compounds during the 1850s ended in reforms of the system of atomic weights that achieved consistent interpretations of the relations between compounds. Among the most influential proposals were those of Charles Gerhardt, based in part on the views of Auguste Laurent. These efforts culminated at the first international Congress of chemists, which met in Karlsruhe in 1860 to standardize atomic weights and chemical notation. There, Stanislaus Cannizzaro circulated a proposal that although not immediately accepted, afterward quickly resolved the outstanding differences.

From the time it first coalesced during the seventeenth century, chemistry shared a wide borderland with other branches of physical science. Its theories of matter borrowed from Aristotelian natural philosophy and then from the mechanical philosophy. Even within their own operational domain, chemists of the eighteenth century distinguished between the "physical" and the "chemical" properties of the substances they studied. At the end of the eighteenth century, the exploration of the properties of heat and of gases again blurred the boundaries between chemistry and what was by then emerging as a discipline of experimental physics. The rapid growth of chemical investigations oriented around accurate combining proportions, the atomic theory, and the isolation and analysis of organic compounds seemed to distance chemistry from a physics defined around a different set of problems and methods. Nevertheless, the investigation of electricity and other phenomena common to both fields often pierced the boundaries. During the second half of the nineteenth century, a new subfield arose, deliberately situated at this persistent interface.

The discipline of physical chemistry was formed by Jacobus Henricus van't Hoff, Svante Arrhenius, and Wilhelm Ostwald. They concentrated on the application of thermodynamics to chemical processes the causes of chemical affinity, and the properties of solutions. The central importance of Arrhenius's theory of ionization to the new field earned them and their followers the sobriquet "ionists." Begun in Germany, the field spread most rapidly after 1900 in the United States under the leadership of a generation trained in the laboratories of Ostwald and Van't Hoff.

C

Until nearly the end of the nineteenth century, the atom as conceived and employed by chemists and physicists had little in common. The physical atom, usually called "molecule," was defined mainly by the kinetic theory of gases, while chemical atom functioned as a unit of composition defined by its atomic weight. The situation changed after physicists identified the electron and the nucleus as the principal subunits of the atom. During the first decades of the twentieth century, several chemists proposed theories of chemical affinity and valence based on the view that electrons in the outer shells of atoms form chemical bonds. The most influential of these theories, published by Gilbert N. Lewis in 1916, connected the electronic structure of the atom with the properties of the elements defined by their place in the periodic table. Reviving in a new form the electrochemical theory of Berzelius, Lewis postulated that covalent bonds consist of an electron pair shared by two atoms, whereas an ionic bond results from the transfer of an electron from one atom to another atom to form a pair that holds the molecule together electrostatically.

The development of physical chemistry and the elucidation of the electronic structure of the atom gave rise to a school of chemists who sought to describe the reaction mechanisms of organic compounds in terms of the positive and negative regions of molecules, the displacements of electrons, and the formation of transient intermediate compounds. Systematized by Christopher Ingold during the 1930s, these efforts culminated in the formation of the subfield of physical organic chemistry.

Meanwhile, quantum mechanics declared that the properties of the chemical elements and their combinations could be explained by the basic laws of physics. It referred the chemical bond to the distribution of the electrons believed to form both ionic and covalent bonds. In the event, however, the quantum mechanical equation could not be solved for complex molecules. Chemists and physicists had recourse to approximate solutions, combined with other knowledge of the properties of compounds and the nature of their reactions. The leading figure in this development was Linus Pauling.

Chemical laboratories and chemical industries continued to grow in size and complexity during the second half of the nineteenth century. The synthetic dye industry became possible through the growing capabilities of chemists both to synthesize naturally occurring organic compounds and to produce previously unknown compounds by modification of the natural ones. German industry led the way in this development. At first drawing on the knowledge of academic chemists, these industries soon began to hire chemists to work directly on the discovery of new dyes, creating the first industrial research laboratories. The special problems and expertise required to scale up laboratory operations for volume production gave rise to the profession of chemical engineering.

During the early twentieth century, new classes of chemical industry emerged. The increasing worldwide demand for fertilizer led to the invention of catalytic processes requiring very high temperatures and pressures to obtain nitrogen from the atmosphere. The best known of these was the Haber-Bosch process for ammonia synthesis. World War I deprived France, Great Britain, and the United States of the supplies of chemicals previously acquired from Germany and stimulated the growth of chemical industries that afterward became strong competitors with Germany. World War I also saw a great expansion of chemical plants devoted to munitions and poison gas.

After World War II, the traditional character of the chemical laboratory began to change. Physical instrumentation became more prominent, and automated analytical methods replaced some of the chemist's traditional skills. To some observers, chemistry lost its status as a fundamental science. Quantum chemistry appeared to be merely an application of physics to the particular phenomena that chemists studied. As the applications of chemistry to many other fields of science and technology multiplied, concern whether it retained any core unity intensified. It had come to be, in the words of one general history of the subject, a "field without a territory," existing both "everywhere and nowhere." Others have argued, however, that even though its most fundamental principles may be borrowed from physics, extension of these principles to the wide range of chemical phenomena still requires methods of reasoning and investigation that have long been characteristic of chemistry.

FREDERIC LAWRENCE HOLMES

CLIMATE CHANGE AND GLOBAL WARMING. Theories of climate change date from very early times; Theophrastus (371–287 B.C.) wrote on desiccation wrought by deforestation. His work, revived in the Renaissance, helped fuel concern over deforestation in European colonies, and

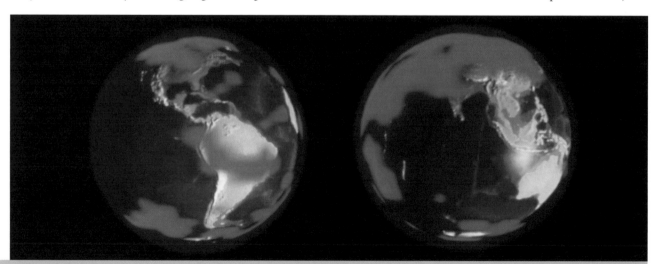

Computer-generated models of the earth showing the effects of global warming after twelve years during which the CO_2 content of the atmosphere is twice that at present. Red marks regions where the surface temperature has risen by more than 5°C.

In 1996, British embryologist Ian Wilmut (born 1944) created "Dolly," the world's first sheep cloned from an adult sheep cell.

from the late eighteenth century onward, colonial governments established forest reserves that were among the earliest measures of environmental conservation. Meanwhile, Enlightenment students of the classical world uncovered literary evidence for climate change since ancient times, while Americans such as Thomas Jefferson argued that deforestation from European settlement had moderated the climate, rendering it fit for civilization. Nineteenth-century climatologists, applying more exacting historical and scientific analysis to these questions, found no convincing evidence of climate change in historical times.

Climate change on astronomical and geological timescales on the other hand was more nearly certain. From Buffon, Kant, and Laplace to Lord Kelvin and beyond, cosmologists speculated about the long-term cooling of the earth from its origin as a molten ball and about the longer-term cooling of the sun. Nineteenth-century geologists found indisputable evidence in fossils of a warmer climate in ancient times, and around the middle of the century, discovered the ice ages. In order to reconcile these discoveries with his belief in a uniform state of the earth, Charles Lyell developed a theory of cyclical climate change, according to which "all... changes are to happen in future again, and iguanodons...must as surely live in the latitude of Cuckfield as they have done so."

Several eighteenth- and early nineteenth-century natural philosophers and mathematicians, including Horace Bénédict de Saussure, Joseph Fourier, and Claude Pouillet, had noted the atmosphere's selective transmission of heat; Fourier compared the atmosphere to the glass of a greenhouse. Beginning in 1859, John Tyndall began experiments on the radiative properties of atmospheric gases, and speculated that variations in their amounts might have altered the earth's climate on the geological time scale. In 1895, Svante Arrhenius, trying to explain the Ice Ages, calculated temperature changes from variations in carbon dioxide. Two decades later, he pre-

dicted that industrial generation of CO_2 would protect the globe from recurring ice ages and allow increased food production for a larger world population. Arrhenius's ideas were welcomed by the American geologist T. C. Chamberlin, who, in the first three decades of the twentieth century, developed a theory of the atmosphere as a large-scale geological agent based on a carbon cycle. Crustal uplifts expose large surface areas to weathering, a process that absorbs CO_2; global cooling and glaciation follow. The cycle turns about when mountain ranges reduce to nearly base levels.

By the 1950s, alteration in insolation—solar radiation received by the earth—orbital changes, mountain building, and volcanism had all been identified as agents of climate change. Water vapor eclipsed CO_2 as an agent of global warming until G. S. Callendar published a series of articles from 1938 to 1961 emphasizing anthropogenic influences on the amount of carbon dioxide in the atmosphere. Political tension feeds fears of climate degradation, and the Cold War intensified anxiety over both global cooling and global warming. Proposals were floated for large-scale interventions such as damming the Bering Strait, orbiting fleets of mirrors in space, and spraying sulfur dioxide into the upper atmosphere. Today, the scientific community has reached a consensus that CO_2 levels have increased owing to industrial activity and that warming is taking place on a global scale. The relation between these two phenomena remains in doubt, as well as the role of other factors and the future course of climate change.

THEODORE S. FELDMAN

CLONE. Clones, genetically identical copies of living organisms, were first produced with certain plants by the cultivation of a stem or branch of the original. The process originated in ancient times and is widely used by horticulturalists and home gardeners to obtain reproductions of fruit trees, vines, and roses. The biologist J. B. S. Haldane took

C

the word "clone," which he coined in 1963, from the Greek word for "twig." Scientists applied the term to the replication of genes themselves beginning in the 1970s, when the new techniques of recombinant DNA permitted them to snip out individual genes from an organism's genome and insert them into bacteria, where they would multiply with the bugs. The chemist Kary B. Mullis's invention of the polymerase chain reaction (PCR) in 1983 enabled scientists to produce a billion clones of a gene in a test tube.

In the late 1920s, the German embryologist Hans Spemann had achieved a type of animal cloning by inserting the nucleus from a salamander embryo cell into a denucleated egg that then developed into an independent salamander. In 1938, by then a Nobel laureate, Spemann proposed that it might be possible similarly to clone an adult animal. But he described the experiment as "fantastical," partly because he did not know how to do it, partly because he did not know whether the nucleus from an adult animal's fully differentiated cells possessed the capacity to direct the full development of the organism from the egg.

In 1951, Americans Robert Briggs and Thomas J. King, biologists at the National Institutes of Health, cloned embryonic frog cells but failed in attempts to clone more differentiated ones. Their results, along with those from other laboratories, indicated that the older the cells from which the nuclei came, the less likely the clones would develop. In 1962, John Gurdon, a developmental biologist at Oxford University, reported that he had been able to produce fully

One of the first photographs of tracks of subatomic particles in a cloud chamber. Alpha particles from radium made the tracks; the chamber's inventor, C. T. R. Wilson (1869–1959), made the picture at the Cavendish Laboratory, Cambridge in 1911.

developed frogs by cloning putatively differentiated cells from the intestinal linings of tadpoles. Gurdon argued that his experiment, although successful only 2 percent of the time, confirmed that fully differentiated cells retained the genetic capacity to direct development. Other embryologists could not replicate his results. Biologists working on farm animals were able to clone horses, pigs, rabbits, and goats from early embryo cells, but most considered cloning from adult cells impossible.

In the mid-1990s, however, Ian Wilmut, a biologist at the Roslin Research Institute in Scotland, resolved to try to improve the efficiency of "molecular farming," the genetic engineering of animals to produce valuable human proteins such as blood clotting factors. Animals were then being engineered for the purpose by injecting the gene for the protein into newly fertilized eggs that a surrogate mother brought to term. The gene generated the desired protein in only about 5 percent of the resulting animals. But if those animals could be cloned, the 95-percent failure rate could be turned into a 100-percent success rate. That prospect brought Wilmut support for his research from PPL Therapeutics, a biotechnology firm.

Wilmut thought that adult cells might be clonable if the nucleus was taken from cells in the right condition. Keith Campbell, an embryologist whom he hired to assist him in the research, suggested that cells in the G0 condition—a state of quiescence they enter when near starvation—might do. They confirmed this possibility in March 1996 when two lambs were born that they had cloned, using the G0 approach, from differentiated embryo cells. They then attempted to clone a sheep from adult udder cells. The effort produced 277 failures and one success—a sheep, born in July, that they named Dolly, in honor of the singer and actress Dolly Parton. "No one could think of a more impressive set of mammary glands than Dolly Parton's," Wilmut explained.

The announcement of Dolly's birth the following February—it was delayed to give PPL Therapeutics time to file a patent on the cloning technology—prompted immediate international debate about the application of cloning to human beings. Opponents demanded that it be legally banned. They prevailed in several countries, but not absolutely, since the biotechnology industry and many biomedical scientists backed human cloning for research purposes. Proponents see in cloning opportunities to study cellular differentiation and development and to obtain human stem cells for medical purposes.

D. J. KEVLES

CLOUD AND BUBBLE CHAMBERS. C. T. R. Wilson built the first cloud chamber in 1895 to satisfy his interest in the weather. Previous work by John Aitken had examined the role of dust as a nucleating agent for water vapor in air, and hence as a source of fog and clouds. Like Aitken, Wilson built a chamber to reproduce in the laboratory the condensation of clouds: sudden expansion of the volume of a closed vessel containing saturated air produced a temperature drop and supersaturated the air. Unlike Aitken, Wilson brought a background in physics and the program of the Cavendish Laboratory at Cambridge University, especially in ion physics and discharge tubes, to bear on the subject. Instead of dust, Wilson focused on the role of ions as nuclei for water droplets. He also began photographing the formation of drops. Then in 1910 Wilson thought to use the device as a detector of charged particles, whose passage through the chamber would leave a trail of ions and hence water droplets. The next year Wilson obtained his first photographs of the tracks left by alpha and beta rays, as well as evidence of X and gamma rays through the beta rays they produced, and thus provided compelling visual evidence of individual atoms and electrons and their interactions.

The cloud chamber then became a popular tool for the study of particles given off by radioactivity, nuclear physics, and cosmic ray physics. Commercial firms helped propagate the device by providing affordable, experiment-ready Wilson chambers. P. M. S. Blackett, also at the Cavendish, used a Wilson chamber in the early 1920s to confirm Ernest Rutherford's transmutation of nitrogen into oxygen. In the early 1930s Blackett and Giuseppe P. S. Occhialini built a countercontrolled chamber, with a Geiger counter wired to trigger the expansion of the chamber whenever a cosmic ray passed through it. They used the chamber in 1932 to confirm the existence of the positron, which Carl Anderson of the California Institute of Technology (Caltech) had just detected in his own cloud chamber.

The Wilson cloud chamber suffered from a slow cycle time, and its diffuse gas offered few chances for interaction with incoming particles. The solid film of nuclear emulsions yielded more interactions and hence grew in popularity in the 1930s; but emulsions also constantly recorded tracks and hence complicated the resolution of occurrence times. In 1952, Donald Glaser, a physicist at the University of Michigan, tried to solve these problems by turning to a liquid analogue of the cloud chamber: instead of supersaturated gas, Glaser used a superheated liquid. He filled a small glass bulb, a couple of centimeters wide, with liquid diethyl ether held under pressure above its boiling point, then suddenly released the pressure, superheating the liquid. A charged particle passing through the chamber further heated the liquid and left a line of vapor bubbles in its wake. A high-speed camera filmed the first tracks in late 1952, and Glaser announced his results in 1953.

Glaser's bubble chamber provided sufficient density for numerous interactions and a fast cycle time. He intended to use his bubble chamber to detect cosmic rays and hence tried various means of triggering the expansion as Blackett had done with the cloud chamber. The bubble chamber instead became an important particle detector for high-energy accelerators, whose predictable output dispensed with the need for countercontrolled expansion. A particular implication of the bubble chamber intrigued accelerator physicists: the possibility of using liquid hydrogen, which, because of its simple nucleus, already served as a target for interaction experiments at accelerators. A hydrogen bubble chamber would combine target and detector in one device.

Accelerator laboratories soon began building bubble chambers, including a group at the University of California at Berkeley under Luis Alvarez. The Berkeley group produced the first tracks in a hydrogen chamber in late 1953 and soon scaled up to larger chambers, culminating in a 180-cm. (72-in.) version to accommodate the greater interaction lengths of hyperons and other strange particles. The massive chamber, completed in 1959, presented new problems in cryogenics, optical systems, and computerized data analysis. The coordination of the physicists, engineers, and technicians building the chamber produced a complex, corporate organizational structure.

The Berkeley bubble chamber signaled the growing importance accorded the detector in accelerator experiments. It also marked a decisive shift from the table-top device of Glaser, built for cosmic-ray physics, to the big science of high-energy physics. Bubble chambers at several accelerator laboratories paid dividends in evidence of new particles and resonances that supported the SU(3) theory for classifying strange particles in the early 1960s and of neutrino interactions that helped confirm the electroweak theory in the early 1970s. Both Glaser and Alvarez won Nobel Prizes in physics for their work with bubble chambers, and both eventually drifted away from the field, disillusioned with the routinization, specialization, and automation that the bubble chamber had brought to particle detection.

PETER J. WESTWICK

COLD AND CRYONICS. Artificially produced cold has always been welcome. From the time ice was brought from the mountains so that the Roman emperors could enjoy their wine chilled in the summer to our days of high temperature superconductivity, the wonders of low temperatures have been publicly displayed and their benefits privately pursued. From unexpected phenomena of the very cold to dramatic changes in food production and eating habits, the production and harnessing of cold has probed nature and shaped society.

The first systematic researches on cold were reported by Robert Boyle in his *New Experiments Touching Cold* (1665)—the subject that the master of experimenters found "the most difficult" of all. The ingenious experiments of Joseph Black to determine the latent heat and specific heat of water involved ordinary ice. Cryogenics received a boost from Michael Faraday's liquefaction of nearly all the gases known in the 1820s. Among the gases he could not liquefy were oxygen, nitrogen, and hydrogen. By the end of the nineteenth century all gases except helium had been liquefied. Raoul-Pierre Pictet in Geneva and Louis Paul Cailletet in Paris first obtained small droplets of oxygen and nitrogen in 1877. Zygmunt Florenty von Wróblewski and Karol Stanisław Olszewski liquefied oxygen in appreciable quantities in 1883. Carl von Linde and William Hampson made significant improvements to the apparatus for reaching low temperatures. James Dewar liquefied hydrogen in 1898 at the Royal Institution in London. Heike Kamerlingh Onnes managed to liquefy helium on 10 July 1908 at the Physical Laboratory of the University of Leiden. Using the regeneration method and starting from liquid hydrogen temperatures, he made liquid helium and found its boiling point to be $4.25°K$ and its critical temperature $5°K$.

The development of thermodynamics, especially James Prescott Joule's and William Thomson's proofs that the temperature of a gas dropped when it expanded very quickly, provided the necessary background for the investigation and the understanding of the properties of matter in the very cold. Thomas Andrews's experiments determining the critical point—the temperature at which a gas whose pressure is increased at constant volume liquefies—and Johannes Diderik van der Waals's discussion of the continuity of the gaseous and liquid states brought further insight into the characteristics of very cold fluids.

The nineteenth century saw remarkable developments in the large-scale production of cold, especially through the development of the vapor compression process that led to different types of refrigerating machines and refrigeration processes. The plentiful availability of artificial cold transformed the preservation, circulation, and consumption of food. By the end of the nineteenth century the Linde Company had sold about 2600 gas liquefiers: 1406 were used in breweries, 403 for cooling land stores for meat and provi-

C

Apparatus at the Laboratoire Kastler Brossel, Paris, for producing liquid helium to create a Bose-Einstein condensate, a state of matter near absolute zero in which many atoms act like one

sions, 204 for cooling ships' holds for transportation of meat and food, 220 for ice making, 73 in dairies for butter making, 64 in chemical factories, 15 in sugar refining, 15 in candle making, the rest for other purposes.

In 1911, the Institut International du Froid was founded in Paris to regulate the industry and to formulate directions of further research on cold. The preservation and transport of agrarian, fish, and dairy products, the standardization of the specifications for home refrigerators, the construction of trains and ships with large refrigerators, the installation of special refrigerators in mortuaries and slaughterhouses, the building of new hotels with air cooling systems, the design of breweries, the manufacture of transparent ice, and the possibilities of medical benefits from cold were some of the issues on which the national delegates who founded the Institut reached consensus.

In 1911, Kamerlingh Onnes observed that certain metals become superconductors, losing all resistance to electrical current, below 4°K. In recent decades materials have been made that reach the superconducting state at much higher temperatures. Another bizarre bit of cold behavior, which came to light in the 1930s, is the superfluidity that liquid helium acquires below 2.19°K in virtue of which it does not display any of the features of classical fluid. These two phenomena turned out to be explicable only on the principles of quantum mechanics. The explanation forced quantum mechanics to negate one of its basic methodological and historical tenets—that it made a difference only in the microscopic world. Superconductivity and superfluidity showed that macroscopic quantum phenomena exist.

With the availability of liquefied gases, the variation of the electrical resistance of metals with temperature was persistently studied. Dewar and John Ambrose Fleming made the first systematic measurements in 1896. Their results derived at liquid oxygen temperatures suggested that elec-

trical resistance would become zero at absolute zero. But the same measurements at liquid hydrogen temperatures showed that the resistances after reaching a minimum started increasing again. In 1911, Kamerlingh Onnes measured the resistance of platinum and that of pure mercury at helium temperatures. At 4.19°K the value of the resistance dropped abruptly and became 0.0001 times that of solid mercury at 0°C. Impurities did not affect the superconductivity of mercury, but a high magnetic field could destroy it.

The first successful quantum mechanical theory of electrical conduction, proposed by Felix Bloch (1928), predicted that superconductivity was impossible. This theory considers the electrons in a metal as uncoupled, though it calculates the field in which any one electron moves by averaging over the other electrons. If the metal was at absolute zero, its immobile lattice determined a periodic potential field for the electronic motions and offered no electrical resistance. Bloch used an analogy to ferromagnetism to try to understand superconductivity. He found that the most stable state of a conductor, in the absence of an external magnetic field, had no currents. But since superconductivity was a stable state displaying persistent currents without external fields, his theory did not explain how superconductivity could come about in the first place.

At the beginning of November, 1933, there appeared a short letter in *Naturwissenschaften* by Walther Meissner and Robert Ochsenfeld. It presented strong evidence that, contrary to every expectation and belief of the previous twenty years, a superconductor expelled the magnetic field after the transition to the superconducting state and the magnetic flux became zero (the Meissner effect). Superconductors were found to be diamagnetic and, hence, superconductivity a reversible phenomenon, thus allowing the application of thermodynamics.

In 1934, Fritz London and his brother Heinz, on the assumption that diamagnetism must be an intrinsic property of an ideal superconductor, and not merely a consequence of perfect conductivity, proposed that superconductivity involved a connection not with the electric, but with the magnetic field. Their assumption led to the electrodynamics of a superconductor consistent both with the zero resistance and the Meissner effect. Fritz London, in his discussion of superconductivity in 1936, formulated for the first time the notion of a macroscopic quantum phenomenon.

Because ionic masses are so much larger than the electron mass, physicists doubted that ions played an important role in the establishment of the superconducting state. Herbert Frohlich in 1950 asserted the opposite and found that the interaction of the electrons in a metal with the lattice vibrations would lead to an attraction between the electrons. Experiments confirmed his assertion. The mass became an important parameter when the motion of the ions was involved, and this, in turn, suggested that superconductivity could be derived from an interaction between the electrons and zero-point vibrations of the lattice. Soon after learning about these results, John Bardeen showed that superconductivity might arise from a new attraction between the electrons and the phonons resulting from lattice vibrations, thus laying the foundations for the electron pair theory. In 1956, Leon Cooper argued that such an interaction could provide what was needed. Based on these ideas, in 1957 Bardeen, Cooper, and John R. Schrieffer worked out the details of a microscopic theory of superconductivity, and shared the Nobel Prize in physics of 1972 for their successful explanation of this elusive phenomenon.

All liquids solidify under their own pressure at low enough temperatures. Helium can only be solidified under a pressure of 26 atmospheres. The densities and specific heats of all liquids follow a continuous change and increase as the temperature goes down. In the case of helium, however, these parameters display a maximum at 2.19°K and then decrease. The two methods for measuring the viscosity of any liquid—rotating a disk in it or forcing it through very small capillaries—give identical results. Not so for liquid helium below 2°K. The first of these methods gives a value a million times larger than the second. Finally, all liquids can be deposited in open containers, kept in containers with extremely small holes through which they cannot flow, and remain at rest when exposed to light. Liquid helium does not tolerate any such constraints. It goes over open containers, leaks through the smallest capillaries, and springs up in a fountain when light falls on it. Below 2.19°K liquid helium becomes a superfluid.

In 1938, Fritz London proposed that the transition to the superfluid state can be understood in terms of the Bose-Einstein condensation mechanism, first discussed by Albert Einstein in 1924. For an ideal Bose-Einstein gas, the condensation phenomenon represented a discontinuity in the derivative of the specific heat. London argued that the sudden changes in the properties of helium at 2.19°K could result from such discontinuities. Below a certain temperature and depending on the mass and density of the particles, a finite fraction of them begins to collect in the energy state of zero momentum. The remaining particles fly about as individuals, like the molecules in a normal gas. Laszlo Tisza proposed to regard superfluid helium as a mixture of a normal and a superfluid. These two components had different hydrodynamical behaviors as well as different heat contents. At absolute zero, the entire liquid became a superfluid consisting of condensed atoms, while at the transition temperature the superfluid component vanished.

Excluding some applied fields, low-temperature physics became the high point of Soviet physics, especially during World War II. After receiving his doctorate under the supervision of Ernest Rutherford, Pyotr Kapitsa served as an Assistant Director of magnetic research at the Cavendish Laboratory, before becoming the director of the Mond Laboratory in Cambridge. There he liquefied helium in 1934. Though he was not allowed to return to England by the Soviet authorities after a trip in 1934, he was, by 1935, appointed as director of a new Institute of Physical Problems within the Academy of Sciences in Moscow. That is where he conducted his experiments with liquid helium in 1941 and coined the term "superfluid" when he discovered the remarkable characteristics of its viscosity. In 1941, Lev Landau developed a quantized hydrodynamics that explained the transition to the superfluid state in terms of rotons and phonons. The ground states and the excitations played the roles of the superfluid and normal state, respectively. The excitations were the normal state because they could be scattered and reflected and, hence, exhibit viscosity. The ground state described the superfluid because it could not absorb a phonon from the walls of the tube or a roton unless it met some conditions on the velocity. Landau's formalism led to two different equations for the velocity of sound. One was related to the usual velocity of compression, while the other depended strongly on temperature. Landau named it "second sound." Victor Peshkov demonstrated the existence of standing thermal waves in 1944 for the first time, and in 1949 the experiments of Maurer and Herlin settled the issue of the temperature dependence of the second sound velocity below 1°K. By 1956, Richard Feynman could show that some of Landau's assumptions could be justified quantum mechanically and that the rotons were a quantum mechanical analog of a microscopic vortex ring.

KOSTAS GAVROGLU

COLLIDER. During the final quarter of the twentieth century, particle colliders emerged as the preferred instruments in high-energy physics. Their defining characteristic, besides their great size—the largest are measured in kilometers—is their manner of generating collisions. They accelerate two beams of subatomic particles and bring them together at interaction points, where a particle in one beam can collide with a particle in the other. Surrounding each interaction point, a particle detector records the tracks, energies, and other characteristics of particles emanating from these collisions, allowing physicists to analyze what transpired.

The great advantage of colliders over conventional "fixed-target" machines (such as cyclotrons), in which particle beams strike stationary objects, is that essentially all the energy of the individual colliding entities can be used to create new subatomic particles. The available "center-of-mass" energy, or total collision energy, grows in proportion to the beam energy rather than to its square root, as in fixed-target experiments. All discoveries of massive new subatomic particles since 1975 have been made using colliders, while fixed-target experiments have excelled at examining the structures of known particles such as protons. To permit meaningful experiments, colliders must attain sufficient luminosity, a key measure of the rates of interaction between particles in the opposing beams.

The idea of particle colliders occurred to Rolf Wideröe and Donald Kerst in the mid-1950s, but the first significant work on developing such an instrument began at Stanford University in 1958. Led by Gerard O'Neill of Princeton University, a small group of physicists built two evacuated "storage rings" in a figure-eight configuration. Beams of electrons circulated in opposite directions within these rings at energies of up to 500 million electron volts (MeV); collisions occurred in the shared segment where the rings touched.

In parallel with this effort, physicists at the Frascati National Laboratory in Italy, led by Bruno Touschek, built a single-ring collider in which electrons circulated one way and positrons (their antimatter opposites) the other. Following the success of this prototype, the Italian physicists developed a full-scale electron-positron collider called ADONE, with beam energies of up to 1,500 MeV, or 1.5 billion electron volts (GeV). Experiments using this instrument began in 1968, recording electron-positron annihilations that usually created other subatomic particles.

Physicists at the European Center for Nuclear Physics (CERN), led by Kjell Johnsen, pioneered proton-proton colliders. In 1971, they successfully operated the Intersecting Storage Rings, in which beams of protons circulated at energies of up to 28 GeV. Collisions occurred at six interaction points where the interlaced rings crossed.

The most productive electron-positron collider was the SPEAR facility built at the Stanford Linear Accelerator Center (SLAC) under the direction of Burton Richter. Completed in 1972, SPEAR generated collisions at combined energies of up to 8 GeV. It yielded the discoveries of the massive psi particles and tau lepton, and Nobel Prizes for Richter (in 1976) and SLAC physicist Martin Perl (in 1995).

Following these advances, physicists built colliders at all leading high-energy physics laboratories. Especially noteworthy was a proton-antiproton collider built at CERN as an upgrade of its existing Super Proton Synchroton, stimulated by ideas and inventions of Peter McIntyre, Carlo Rubbia, and Simon Van der Meer. By observing proton-antiproton collisions at total energies of up to 540 GeV in 1982–1983, two teams of physicists discovered the massive W and Z bosons, the mediators of weak interactions and key elements of the standard model.

These significant discoveries and the development of superconducting magnets for the Tevatron proton-antiproton collider at the Fermi National Accelerator Laboratory (Fermilab) encouraged U.S. physicists to design the Superconducting Super Collider (SSC), a 40,000 GeV proton-proton collider that was to have a circumference of 86 km (54 miles), several interaction points, and a cost of $5.9 billion. Those were its parameters in 1989 when construction began south of Dallas, Texas. Congress terminated the project in 1993 owing to cost overruns, lack of major participation from other countries, and a concern to reduce budget deficits after the Cold War.

Since the SSC's demise, the development of particle colliders has continued largely through upgrades of existing instruments at CERN, Cornell University, Frascati, Fermilab, and SLAC, and at national laboratories in China and Japan. A prime example was the conversion of the Stanford Linear Accelerator into a linear electron-positron collider. The new machine accelerated individual "bunches" of the two types of particle and brought them together after a single pass through the linear accelerator. This approach contrasts with that of storage-ring colliders, in which the bunches of particles circulate continuously in fixed, intersecting orbits.

MICHAEL RIORDAN

COMPLEMENTARITY AND UNCERTAINTY constitute the foundation of the "Copenhagen interpretation" of quantum physics, an acausal understanding of physics that remains predominant today. Both concepts were introduced in 1927, by Niels Bohr and Werner Heisenberg, respectively. They arose as part of the development of quantum physics when the field was in tremendous flux. Several institutions—notably the Bohr Institute for Theoretical Physics and the physics institute at the University of Göttingen—and many individual physicists had placed high stakes on establishing an acceptable theory as well as its interpretation.

Bohr had been a leader in the development of quantum physics since he published his revolutionary atomic model in 1913. In Bohr's model, atomic electrons could exist only in orbits determined by the quantum of action and emit electromagnetic radiation only when jumping from one orbit to another. During the "old quantum theory" (1913–1925), theorists invoked a mixture of Bohr's "correspondence principle" (which specified a numerical connection between quantum and classical physics) and arguments based on the quantum of action. As one of a long line of increasingly radical attempts to arrive at an overarching theory, in 1924 Bohr, his assistant Hendrik Kramers, and an American postdoctoral researcher, John Slater, published a paper based on a denial of the well-established principle of energy conservation. In their view, the principle held only statistically and not for individual atomic processes. Experimental results showing energy conservation in collisions between

Danish theoretical physicist Niels Bohr (1885–1962) photographed around 1920

individual photons and atomic electrons in the Compton effect quickly forced the abandonment of this view, and others took the lead in seeking to formulate a quantum theory. In the fall of 1925, Heisenberg, then working as Bohr's assistant, devised a means to calculate spectral data without explicit appeal to the correspondence principle. Whereas Heisenberg's severely operationalist, as well as particle-oriented, theory involved complicated matrix calculations, Erwin Schrödinger's wave-oriented version of "quantum mechanics," published in the fall of 1926, involved mathematics with which the average physicist felt more comfortable. In spite of this, and although Schrödinger's "wave mechanics" seemed at first to allow the visualization of atomic processes by emphasizing continuity and retaining causality, Schrödinger and others soon showed that his approach was mathematically equivalent to Heisenberg's.

In September 1926, Schrödinger paid a now famous visit to Copenhagen. Bohr stubbornly sought to convince him of the reality of quantum jumps. In this tense environment Heisenberg wrote the article containing his "uncertainty principle," which stated that in the atomic domain the quantum of action set a limit to the precision with which two conjugate variables, such as a particle's position and momentum, or the time and energy of an interaction, could be measured. Since the present therefore cannot be fully specified, Heisenberg argued, neither can the future. By explaining the indeterminism of quantum physics in this way, Heisenberg tried to make his presentation more visualizable (anschaulich) and hence more acceptable to his fellow physicists.

Heisenberg overstepped common practice by submitting his article from Copenhagen without asking Bohr's permission. It turned out that Bohr disagreed so strongly with Heisenberg's presentation of the quantum that Heisenberg felt compelled to add a correction in the proofs that allowed a greater role for the wave picture. Bohr was then perfecting his own formulation of the foundations of quantum theory. At the end of a lecture surveying the general situation given in Como in September 1927, he proposed his notion of complementarity for the first time. The new notion provided an understanding of quantum mechanics in general and of Heisenberg's uncertainty principle in particular. Bohr maintained that, unlike in classical theory, a description of processes in space-time and a strictly causal account (by which Bohr meant an account recognizing conservation laws) of physical processes excluded one another. This meant in practice that the investigator could choose which aspect of microphysical reality he wished to see expressed by his choice of experimental setup. Although the setup required for realizing one aspect excluded the realization of the other—for example, an apparatus for exhibiting light with particulate properties cannot also show it as a wave—both sets of properties had to be invoked to obtain a complete description of the microphysical reality. While presented as a direct result of quantum mechanics, Bohr's interpretation and his subsequent elaborations of it resonated with philosophical views with which he had struggled in his youth. Only with Bohr's complementarity of 1927 did his work and that of Heisenberg, Max Born, Wolfgang Pauli, Pascual Jordan, and others begin to converge into what came to be seen as the unified "Copenhagen interpretation" of quantum mechanics.

The group surrounding Bohr soon came to perceive complementarity and uncertainty as so closely intertwined that in 1928 Heisenberg gave Bohr's concept precedence over his own. In 1935, Albert Einstein and two collaborators challenged Bohr's interpretation for being inherently incomplete; they thought that they could obtain more information by experiment than complementarity allowed. Bohr repelled their attack by widening the divide between classical and quantum ideas. In the larger physics community, however, the uncertainty principle became inseparable from any presentation of quantum mechanics, while complementarity figured little in the teaching of the new physics. It tended to be regarded as overly philosophical, vague, and irrelevant.

In recompense, complementarity took on a life beyond physics. Bohr sought to generalize its application, first to psychology, then to biology, and ultimately beyond the scope of natural science. Although he did not complete the book on the topic that he had hoped to write, Bohr conceived complementarity as a general epistemological argument of great import for humanity. It constituted a guiding principle for his own activities, inside and outside physics. At the same time, Bohr's disciples sought to spread their understanding of Bohr's word, sometimes—as in the case of Jordan, who tried to use it to save the freedom of the will—to Bohr's embarrassment. Variations of complementarity became part of severe ideological struggles in Nazi Germany and the Soviet Union.

While extremely devoted, the audience for Bohr's philosophical statements was never large, and today consists largely of a specialized set of philosophers. Nevertheless, complementarity played an important role in providing a conceptual basis for the early work on quantum mechanics.

FINN AASERUD

COMPUTER SCIENCE. Computer science is the study of the principles and the use of devices for the processing and storing of usually digital data using instructions in the form of a program. Before the existence of modern computers, people who performed calculations manually were known as "computers." The term "computer science," signifying a particular combination of applied mathematics (particularly logic and set theory), and engineering (normally electronic) first occurred as the name of a university department at Purdue (U.S.) in 1962. The two key areas of development have been hardware (the computers themselves) and more recently software (the intangible programs that run on them).

Mechanical computing devices long preceded electronic ones. The earliest known mechanical adding machine, the creation of the German inventor Wilhelm Schickard, dates from 1621. The mechanical calculators created by Blaise Pascal (1623–1662) and Gottfried Leibniz (1646–1716) received wider attention than Schickard's machine, which fell into oblivion, and formed part of the intellectual inheritance of Charles Babbage (1792–1871), often celebrated as a pioneer of computing. Alarmed by the number of mistakes in hand-computed mathematical tables, he invented the Difference Engine and subsequently the Analytical Engine with many of the features of a modern computer. The "mill" (the gears and wheels that performed the arithmetical operations) corresponded to a modern central processing unit (CPU) for computation and the "store" was a mechanical memory for reading and writing numerical values. Ada Lovelace (1815–1852), the daughter of Lord Byron, provided the earliest comprehensive description of this first programmable computer partially based on notes by the Italian Luigi Menabrea (1809–1896). Babbage never completed the Analytical Engine, which would have stretched cogwheel machinery to its limits at the time.

Leibniz was the first mathematician thoroughly to study the binary system, upon which all modern digital comput-

Technician working on EDVAC, an improvement of ENIAC and, like it, intended for ballistic calculations. ENIAC operated from 1951 to 1961 at the University of Pennsylvania.

ers are based. George Boole presented what became known as Boolean algebra or logic in his masterwork of 1854, *An Investigation of the Laws of Thought*. Boole's laws can be used to formalize binary computer circuits. Later, David Hilbert (1862–1943) argued that in an axiomatic logical system all propositions could be proved or disproved, but Kurt Gödel (1906–1978) demonstrated otherwise, with important implications for the theory of computability. Propositional and predicate logic, together with set theory, as formulated by Ernst Zermelo (1871–1953) and Adolf Fraenkel (1891–1965) among others, provide important underpinnings for computer science.

Analog computers use continuous rather than discrete digital values. They enjoyed some success before digital technology became established for systems of related variables in equational form. Vanne var Bush devised the successful Differential Analyzer for solving differential equations at the Massachusetts Institute of Technology during the 1930s. Later he wrote a seminal article, "As We May Think" (1945), that predicted some of the features of the World Wide Web, illustrating a very broad appreciation of computer science.

In 1936, the English mathematician Alan Turing, influenced by Gödel, devised a theoretical "universal machine," later known as a Turing machine, that helped to define the limits of possible computations on any computing machine. Turing had a practical as well as a theoretical bent. He played a significant part in the building of Colossus, at Bletchley Park, which made possible the breaking of German codes during World War II. Although it has a claim to be the first modern digital computer, Colossus had little influence since it remained secret for several decades. Turing subsequently worked on the design of the Pilot ACE computer at the National Physical Laboratory and the programming of the

Manchester Mark I at the University of Manchester, both successful postwar British computers. Turing's standing in modern computing is indicated by the Turing Award, computer science's highest distinction. It has been given annually since 1966 by the Association for Computing Machinery (ACM), the subject's foremost professional body, founded in 1947.

John Atanasoff built what may have been the first electronic digital computer, the Atanasoff-Berry, prototyped in 1939 and made functional in 1940. It influenced John Mauchly, who with J. Presper Eckert constructed the famous ENIAC at the Moore School of Electrical Engineering in Philadelphia between 1943 and 1945. EDVAC, the first U.S.-built stored-program computer, followed in 1951. Maurice Wilkes attended a summer program at the Moore School in 1946, returned to the University of Cambridge in England, and completed the EDSAC in 1949. Its run on 6 May 1949 made it the world's first practical electronic stored-program computer. The Lyons company copied much of EDSAC to produce the first commercial data processing computer, the LEO (Lyons Electronic Office), in 1951. Other important early computer pioneers include Konrad Zuse, who worked separately on mechanical relay machines, including floating-point numbers, producing the Z1-Z4 models in Berlin between 1936 and 1945. Significant U.S. engineers include Howard Aiken, who developed the electromechanical calculator Harvard Mark I, launched in August 1944, and George Stibitz, who illustrated remote job entry in September 1940 by communicating between Dartmouth College in New Hampshire and his Model 1, first operational in 1939, located in New York. Aiken established programming courses at Harvard long before the university computer science courses of the 1960s.

Programming facilities for early computers initially operated at the binary level of zeros and ones. Assembler programs allowed the input of instructions in mnemonic form, but still matching the machine code very closely. Higher-level programming less dependent on machine language requires a compiler program run on a computer. Noam Chomsky provided influential formal characterizations of grammars for languages, including programming languages, in the late 1950s and early 1960s.

Early high-level programming languages for scientific and engineering applications included Fortran, developed between 1954 and 1957 by John Backus and others at IBM in New York City. Backus also devised Backus Normal Form (BNF) for the formal description of the syntax of programming languages. Successive versions of Fortran have kept it in use. COBOL was another important programming language, developed for business applications in the late 1950s. U.S. Navy Captain Grace Hopper played a key part in its creation. ALGOL, the first programming language described using BNF, included in its 1960 version important new features such as block structuring, parameter passing by name or value, and recursive procedures that greatly influenced subsequent programming languages.

Pascal, designed by Nichlaus Wirth in Zurich between 1968 and 1970, embodied the concepts of structured programming espoused by Edsger Dijkstra and C. A. R. Hoare. Its simplicity suited it for educational purposes as well for practical commercial use. Wirth went on to develop Modula-2 and Oberon and is widely considered as the world's foremost designer of programming languages. Ada was developed in the 1970s for U.S. military applications. It proved to be the opposite of Pascal in the scale of complexity.

Dennis Ritchie created "C" as a general-purpose procedural language. It served as a basis for the highly influential Unix operating system, developed by Ritchie and Kenneth Lee Thompson at Bell Laboratories in New Jersey and refined still further there into C++. C++ encourages information hiding, as suggested by David Parnas, or encapsulation within "objects" considered as instances of classes, a technique first used in the SIMULA language, produced by Ole-Johan Dahl and others in 1967. The highly successful language Java, designed as a portable object-oriented programming language for distributed applications, dates from the early 1990s.

The languages so far considered follow an order of instructions. Some higher-level languages, such as LISP (late 1950s and early 1960s, at MIT), widely used in artificial intelligence, express computations in the form of mathematical functions, and so reduce the importance of the ordering of execution. Logic programming, as in Prolog (1970s), is a relational approach admitting nondeterministic answers. An extension, constraint logic programming, allows the convenient inclusion of extra conditions on variables.

A von Neumann machine, similar but not identical to a theoretical Turing machine, refers to the standard arrangement of early sequential computers with CPU and memory still widely used. However, parallel architectures have become increasingly important, as computer-processing power presses against physical limits. Architecture has evolved through valves or tubes, solid-state transistors, and integrated circuits of increasing complexity.

Theoretical underpinnings for computer science include the definition of computability incorporated in the Turing machine, the λ-calculus of Alonso Church (1903–1995), and recursive functions. Complexity theory aids reasoning about the efficiency of computation. Other theoretical computer science subdisciplines include automata theory, computational geometry (for computer graphics), graph theory, and formal languages.

Software engineering encompasses the process of producing programs from requirements and specifications via a design process. Dijkstra from Holland has been a major contributor to the field. His influential paper *GO TO Statement Considered Harmful* (1968) led to the acceptance of structured programming, a term he coined, in the 1970s, in which abstraction is encouraged in the design process and program constructs are limited to make reasoning about the program easier. Dijkstra, Dahl, and Hoare wrote the widely read *Structured Programming* (1972). Hoare has also made important contributions to formal reasoning about programs using assertions, sorting algorithms, and the formalization of concurrency. Donald Knuth of Stanford University has been a major innovator in computer algorithms. His multivolume and still unfinished magnum opus, *The Art of Computer Programming*, is one of the best-known and influential books in computer science. He has contributed especially to parsing, reasoning, and searching algorithms, all important computer science techniques. Like all good computer scientists, he has expertise in both theory and practice. As well as major theoretical contributions, he has produced the TeX document preparation system, still widely used by computer scientists internationally for the production of books and papers.

Artificial intelligence (AI) has held out huge promises that have been slower to mature than expected. Major contributions have been made by John McCarthy, latterly at Stanford University, and Marvin Minsky at MIT. Important aspects of AI include automated reasoning, computer vision, decision making, expert systems, machine learning, natural language processing, pattern recognition, planning, problem solving, and robot control. A successful outcome of the Turing test, where the responses of a human are essentially indistinguishable from those of a computer, has proved elusive in practice unless the knowledge domain is very limited. Connectionism, using massively parallel systems, has opened up newer interesting areas for machine learning such as neural networks (similar to the workings of the brain) and also genetic algorithms (inspired by Darwin's theory of evolution). Databases are an important method of storing, organizing, and retrieving information. The Briton Edgar Codd created the relational model for databases in the late 1960s and early 1970s at the IBM Research Laboratory in San Jose, California. The two important categories of database objects are "entities" (items to be modeled) and "relationships" (connections between the entities) for which a good underlying theory has been established. Communication has become as significant as computation in computing. Claude Shannon provided an important theoretical approach in his paper of 1948, *A Mathematical Theory of Communication*. He contributed to both network theory and data compression. Donald Davies of NPL and others developed packet switching in the 1960s, a precursor to the Internet, originally established in 1969 and known as the ARPAnet for many years. More recently, the expansion of the Internet has made possible the proliferation of the World Wide Web (WWW), a distributed information system devised in the early 1990s by the British scientist Tim Berners-Lee at CERN in Switzerland. His unique insight combined a number of key principles: a standard network-wide naming convention for use by hyperlinks in traversing information; a simple but extensible markup language to record the information; and an efficient transfer protocol for the transmission of this information between the server and a client user.

Computer science has had an enormous social impact in recent years. Yet it is still a relativity young and perhaps immature science. Quantum computers offer the possibility of removing some of the stumbling blocks encountered today and could theoretically render useless many of the data security mechanisms currently in place. The future of computer science looks even more interesting than its past.

JONATHAN P. BOWEN

CONSERVATION LAWS. Isolated physical and chemical systems possess certain unchanging properties, for example, mass and energy, and, if in thermal equilibrium, temperature. Conservation laws refer to a subset of these properties conserved when these systems interact (conservation of energy, conservation of mass). Natural philosophers first explicitly set out such rules in the eighteenth century. Conservation laws have guided theory in the physical sciences ever since. Many instructive conflicts have erupted over the identity of the property conserved and the conditions of its conservation.

The first of these conflicts, fought out in the early eighteenth century, concerned the "force" of a particle or set of particles. "Force" could mean a particle's mass m multiplied by its velocity v (momentum), mv^2, or $mv^2/2$ (vis viva). Colin Maclaurin, Gottfried Leibniz, and Johann Bernoulli I put forward conflicting claims for the conservation of "force" based in metaphysical principles logically developed and eventually expressed mathematically. Experimental data was incorporated into various metaphysical schemes. These arguments intensified with the 1724 prize competition of

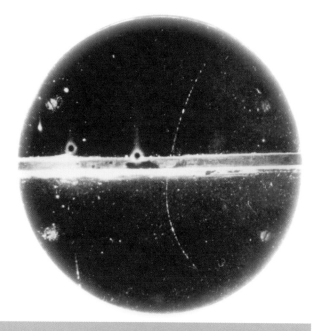

Discovery photograph of the positron, which revealed itself by the curvature of its track on either side of the lead plate in the middle of the cloud chamber. The photo was taken by Carl David Anderson (1905–1991) at Caltech in 1932.

the Paris Royal Academy of Sciences. Other laws and controversies followed including conservation of angular momentum (Jean d'Alembert, 1749). These quarrels died with their adherents after d'Alembert rooted rational mechanics in virtual velocity rather than conservation. The physical conditions governing momentum, vis viva, energy, force, and so on were disentangled only in the nineteenth century.

Another conserved quantity of the eighteenth century was weight, which became an important guide to chemical theory with the discovery and identification of the several sorts of air. Conservation of weight became a foundation of the reformed chemistry of Antoine-Laurent Lavoisier. A third conservation law developed during the eighteenth century had to do with static electricity. Benjamin Franklin's theory of positive and negative electricity (1747) explicitly conserved charge and, moreover, made good use of the law in explaining the operation of the Leyden jar. Later natural philosophers, who used two electrical fluids where Franklin had made do with one, also practiced, if they did not make explicit, the conservation of electricity. Most theories of caloric, the weightless matter supposed to cause the phenomena of heat also supposed its conservation. Conservation laws in physical sciences were thus well established by 1800.

During the nineteenth century, conservation became a tool for discovery. In 1824, the military engineer Sadi Carnot (1824) applied the principle of conservation to caloric considered as the fuel of steam engines. The work extracted from the engine came from the cooling of the caloric from the temperature of the boiler to that of the environment just as the fall of water works a mill. Carnot's analysis, which resulted in the important insight that no engine more efficient than a reversible one can exist, was put into mathematical form by Benoit-Pierre-Émile Clapeyron in 1837 and largely ignored. Meanwhile, Michael Faraday, William Grove, and others explored the conservation of force, including electricity and magnetism.

In the 1840s, this work changed direction and several men from various backgrounds became "discoverers" of the conservation of energy. William Thomson, Lord Kelvin, developed Clapeyron's work, which led him to the definition of absolute temperature. In 1847 Thomson heard James Joule present an account of his measurements of the heat produced by an electrical current (Joule's law) and by mechanical motion. Joule had concluded that the forces of nature were not conserved but transformable one into another in accordance with an exact calculus. A certain amount of heat will always generate the same amount of mechanical work (mechanical equivalent of heat).

In *The Conservation of Force* (1847), Hermann von Helmholtz announced a general principle of nature that he extracted from a representation of matter as a collection of atoms held together by central forces. He equated the change in vis viva of a particle moving under the influence of a center of force to the change in the "intensity of the force." He identified the latter with the potential function introduced earlier by Carl Friedrich Gauss. Helmholtz showed how the results of experiments, like Joule's measurements of the production of heat in current-carrying wires, supported his principle of the interconvertibility of force.

In 1850, Rudolf Clausius put forward the clearest statement of the conservation of energy. He redid Carnot's analysis, replacing the conservation of caloric by the conservation of the "energy" of the perfect gas he assumed as the working substance of his heat engine and gave a mathematical expression for the conservation of energy, the first law of thermodynamics. Later he presented heat as the vis viva of gas molecules and the raising of a weight by the engine as the transformation of one type of mechanical energy (kinetic) into another (potential). In the second half of the nineteenth century, the conservation of energy became a mainstay of the physical sciences.

The conservation of energy had no prominent place in James Clerk Maxwell's kinetic theory or statistical mechanics but was central to Ludwig Boltzmann's work on both mechanics and thermodynamics. J. Willard Gibbs extended thermodynamics from physics into chemistry and developed, along with Helmholtz, other conservation laws (enthalpy and free energy) useful in physical chemistry. Energy conservation underwrote a new philosophical approach to physics, developed by Wilhelm Ostwald and Georg Helm. Also, Maxwell reworked his theory of electromagnetism and light within an energy framework using Thomson and Peter Guthrie Tait's *A Treatise on Natural Philosophy* (1867) as a guide.

Despite these substantial acquisitions, physicists had trouble making energy conservation fit certain phenomena of heat and radiation, and its applicability to radioactivity at first appeared doubtful. The bleak situation, which Thomson described as clouds over the otherwise sunny landscape of physics, was saved by the quantum theory of Max Planck and the demonstration of the conservation of weight and energy in radioactive decay through measurements by Marie Sklodowska Curie, Ernest Rutherford, and others and the mass-energy law ($E = mc^2$) of relativity.

Conservation of energy was an integral part of Niels Bohr's theory of atomic structure (1913). As the problems of his quantized atoms mounted in the early 1920s, however, he limited conservation of energy to the average of all the interactions of atoms with the electromagnetic field, and freed individual interactions from the necessity of obeying the first law of thermodynamics (1924). This *lèse majesté* played a part in Werner Heisenberg's quantum mechanics (1925), which changed the place of conservation laws in physics. Conservation laws now sprang from the mathematical symmetries inherent in the expressions for the matrices representing the operations that take a physical system from one state to another. Symmetry here required that under geometrical change or time reversal the mathematical form remains the same: a rotation in space implied conservation of angular momentum; time reversal, conservation of energy; and linear translation, conservation of momentum. In addition, there was a nonclassical symmetry associated with the intrinsic angular momentum (the spin) of a particle at rest. In the 1930s, an associated concept, isospin, was introduced and developed into a method of classifying the known nuclear particles. During the 1950s, isospin helped in classifying and predicting antiparticles and in generating a new conservation law, the conservation of nucleons.

To explore the nucleus physicists had to incorporate light into their theories of the atom and nucleus. The simplest problem, the interaction of the electron and the electromagnetic field, included a synthesis of quantum mechanics and the special theory of relativity. Techniques developed to bring convergence (renormalization) often forced changes in the conception of the nucleus and its constituents. P. A. M. Dirac's derivation of the wave equation for the electron (1928) implied the existence of negative energy states, which he interpreted as the domain of an "antiparticle" with the same mass as the electron but with positive charge. In Dirac's theory the two sorts of electrons could be created and annihilated together and contradicted an implicit assumption in quantum mechanics—the conservation of particles. Dirac's interpretation gained credence through Carl David A. Anderson's observation in 1931 of the positron (positive electron) in tracks made in his cloud chamber by cosmic rays.

The problem of beta decay further undermined assumptions as basic as the conservation of energy and momentum. Wolfgang Pauli suggested in 1931–1932 that an undetected particle of zero mass and electrical charge, named the neutrino by Enrico Fermi, carried away the missing energy and momentum. The neutrino first revealed itself directly in experiments done by Frederick Reines and Clyde L. Cowan in 1956.

The development of particle accelerators resulted in the discovery or manufacture of more and more "fundamental" particles and graver and graver problems for conservationists. Novelties included particles produced in associated pairs under circumstances so improbable that physicists gave them a quantum number named strangeness. Scientists postulated a new force within the nucleus, the weak force. The neutrino became a left-handed particle and the antineutrino right-handed. Conservation laws again needed revision, including those springing from the assumption of parity (P) conservation in weak interactions. (Parity requires that a device and its mirror image, if made of the same materials, function in the same way.) Nonconservation of parity led to investigations of other symmetry relations and their conservation laws, including charge conjugation (C), in which all the charges entering an equation become their opposites, and time reversal (T), in which the time variable t is changed to $-t$. The strongest result that physicists could produce was the conservation of CPT, in which the transformations C, P, and T simultaneously take place, with the corollary that if T conserves the relations, so does CP.

Experiments to test nonconservation under P demonstrated that some particles are intrinsically right-, and others intrinsically left-handed. By the 1970s a generally accepted model for particle behavior emerged, the so-called Standard Model, whose fundamental building blocks, the quarks, have fractional charges 1/3, 2/3, −1/3 of the electron's. In this model, however, all hadrons (protons, neutrons, etc.) should have the same mass, which they do not. The theory "breaks" this unwanted symmetry by introducing different sorts or "flavors" of quarks. Further symmetries and conservation laws emerged from the requirement that quarks be confined by the strong force. This led to further symmetries and new conservation laws. The dependence of physical interpretation on difficult mathematics seemed justified by the experimental identification of the different quarks in the 1970s and 1980s.

Thus conservation laws, at first intuitive expressions of physical regularities and lately of esoteric mathematical symmetries, have guided physics over the past 250 years.

ELIZABETH GARBER

CONSTANTS, FUNDAMENTAL. The belief that numbers constitute the essence of the universe runs deep in the human experience. The patterns of the sky and seasons provided the first opportunity for discovering nature's numbers, and the agricultural, commercial, and religious needs of early civilizations provided the motivation for inscribing them in calendars. The Greeks in particular anchored thought in number, both in the metaphorical, as in the speculations of the Pythagoreans and the Platonists, and in the practical, as in the exact geometrical astronomy of Hipparchus and Ptolemy. These two approaches came together from time to time, notably in the work of Johannes Kepler, who combined numerological beliefs in the literal harmonies of the celestial spheres with Tycho Brahe's precision measurements to discover that the cube of a planet's average orbital diameter divided by the square of its orbital period was the same value, no matter the planet.

Galileo Galilei confined his numerical endeavors to terrestrial bodies. He measured the rate of fall of various weights and found that the ratio of the distance traveled and the time of fall squared was the same for each body examined. Galileo's falling bodies and Kepler's fruitful numerology came together in Isaac Newton's theory of universal gravitation. Newton's theory implied the existence of a fundamental constant (later labeled G) that specified the force of attraction not only between a planet and the Sun but also between a falling object and Earth.

Not much attention was paid to these constants of gravity. The mathematical methods of the time, which focused on the form of ratios between quantities and not their proportionality constants, veiled the importance of the constants themselves. Even in the late eighteenth century, Henry Cavendish devised his famous torsion balance experiment not to measure the force between two weights and thus what modern physicists call the gravitational constant, but to measure the density of the earth. A significant exception to the lack of interest in the natural constants prevalent in early modern science was the measurement of the speed of light by Ole Rømer in 1675. A possible explanation of this exception is that, in contrast to gravitational acceleration, speed was conceptually familiar and, in the case of light, would be determined by astronomical phenomena—Rømer used eclipses of Jupiter's satellites—frequently subjected to measurement.

Not until the middle of the nineteenth century did the modern interest in fundamental constants in physics evolve. A broad-based quantifying spirit that had arisen during the eighteenth century supplied the general motivation, and the burgeoning telegraph industry, in dire need of well-defined electrical units and standards, supplied the immediate requirement. In 1851, Wilhelm Weber proposed a system of electrical units founded on the metric system. A decade lat-

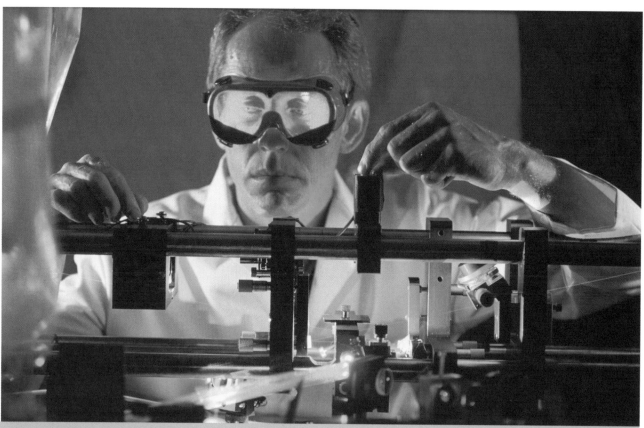

Researcher using a tabletop dye laser to drive an atomic clock. Very exact measurement of time figures are used in the determination of fundamental constants.

er, the British Association for the Advancement of Science, under the leadership of William Thomson, Lord Kelvin and James Clerk Maxwell, took up the challenge of promulgating an international system of electrical units and standards that could meet the needs of both science and industry. In such a system, certain fundamental quantities of nature played a key role, such as the magnetic permeability and electrical permittivity of the ether. The work also raised the possibility of defining a "natural," non-arbitrary system of units, perhaps based on the wavelength, mass, and period of vibration of the hypothesized atoms.

Meanwhile, certain key numbers were appearing in pathbreaking physical theories. James Joule demonstrated the mechanical equivalent of heat and calculated its value. Ludwig Boltzmann reframed thermodynamics in terms of statistics and an important constant, later called k, relating a molecule's average energy to temperature. Max Planck introduced another key constant related to molecular energy, h, in his blackbody radiation law. Maxwell's electromagnetic theory emphasized that the speed of light c was actually the speed of electromagnetic radiation in general. Albert Einstein's theory of special relativity and his mass-energy equivalence, $E = mc^2$, further established the fundamental status of c. And Joseph John Thomson's discovery of the electron introduced its mass and charge (m_e and e) as candidates for the fundamental quantities of matter and electricity.

As the recognized physical constants multiplied into the twentieth century, they raised the question, how fundamental? Although they could be categorized by type, such as properties of objects or factors in physical laws, and some clearly possessed deeper and broader significance than others, it became apparent that many of them were interrelated and that the term "fundamental" always hid some arbitrariness.

A second question was, how precise? The 1920s and 1930s saw an informal international effort to identify not only the best extant value of each fundamental constant but also its precision. The technologies of World War II, and offspring like the laser and atomic clock, assisted by enabling revolutionary increases in decimal places. In the 1960s the project gained a formal footing with the establishment by the International Council of Science of a Committee on Data for Science and Technology (CODATA) and its Task Force on Fundamental Constants. It surveyed the literature and produced a set of "best" values for fundamental constants in 1973, 1986, and 1998.

The hard-eyed quest for the next decimal place did not eradicate interest in numerology, however. Certain combinations of e, h, and c seemed to contain deeper magic. The dimension-less constant e^2/hc, for example, was revealed by quantum electrodynamics to be the constant that defined the strength of the electromagnetic force. Dimensionless constants held great allure because their value did not depend on the system of units chosen, but seemed to be pure numbers of the universe. Moreover, some simple combinations of fundamental constants yielded very large dimensionless numbers all on the order of 10^{40}. In his "large number hypothesis," P. A. M. Dirac proposed that this coincidence hinted at an undiscovered law of the universe. The large number hypothesis also raised the question, how constant?, as it implied that some fundamental constants, such as G, might vary as the universe evolves. On some cosmological theories, small changes in the values of the constants can trigger large consequences for the development of the universe. Only for values close to those observed could complex life develop. Thus a consideration of the fundamental constants renewed interest in the anthropic principle and raised hopes that nature's numbers could be derived from the fact of human existence.

LARRY R. LAGERSTROM

COSMIC RAYS. The first explorers of radio-activity found it in air and water as well as in the earth. Shielded electroscopes placed out of doors lost their charges as if they were exposed to penetrating radiation. Since leak diminished with height, physicists assigned its cause to rays emanating from the earth. As they mounted ever higher, however, from church steeples to the Eiffel Tower to manned balloons, the leak leveled off or even increased. In 1912–1913, Victor Hess of the Radium Institute of Vienna ascertained that the ionization causing the leak declined during the first 1,000 m (3,280 ft) of ascent, but then began to rise, to reach double that at the earth's surface at 5,000 m (16,400 ft). Hess found further, by flying his balloon at night and during a solar eclipse, that the ionizing radiation did not come from the sun. He made the good guess—it brought him the Nobel Prize in physics in 1936—that the radiation came from the great beyond.

The need to know the meteorological state of the upper atmosphere for directing artillery during the Great War improved balloon technology. Robert Millikan, who would receive the Nobel Prize in 1923 for his measurement of the charge on the electron, was a powerful organizer of American science for war. His observations made with Army balloons seemed to show that the ionization in the atmosphere declines continually from the earth's surface. Experiments in lakes at different heights showed him his error and he became the champion of what he called "cosmic rays." He regarded them as the "birth cries of infant atoms" since, by his calculations, the relativistic conversion of mass into energy during the formation of light elements from hydrogen would produce high-frequency radiation (photons) of the penetrating power of Hess's rays.

The advance of electronics transformed the study of cosmic rays from a guessing game to an exact, expensive, and productive science. In 1929, Werner Kolhörster, who had confirmed Hess's measurements, and Walther Bothe placed two Geiger counters one above the other, separated them by a lead block, and arranged a circuit to register only when both counters fired simultaneously. They detected too many coincidences for photons to produce and they inferred that cosmic-ray primaries must be charged particles with at least a thousand times more energy than the hardest rays from radioactive substances. After learning the coincidence method from Bothe (who received a Nobel Prize for it in 1954), Bruno Rossi, one of the Italian pioneers in the field, set three counters in a triangular array and deduced the existence of showers of particles produced by stopping the primaries (1932). A new particle, the positive electron (positron), was found among the secondaries in cloud chambers by Carl David Anderson, who worked with Millikan at the California Institute of Technology (Caltech), and by P. M. S. Blackett and Giuseppe P. S. Occhialini, who used Rossi's electronics. Anderson and Blackett received Nobel Prizes in 1936 (sharing with Hess) and in 1948, respectively.

Cosmic rays became big science when Arthur Holly Compton (Nobel Prize, 1927) undertook to annihilate Millikan's primary photons. Compton designed a method to show that the sea-level intensity of cosmic rays at the poles exceeds that at the equator. If the primaries were charged particles, they would be deflected by the earth's magnetic field more strongly the lower the magnetic latitude.

Compton's project mobilized sixty investigators who carried expensive standardized apparatus on eight expeditions. Government agencies used to funding geophysical work and the Carnegie Institution of Washington paid the bills. By 1934 Compton's company had confirmed the latitude effect and silenced the birth cries of infant atoms.

The victory at first appeared to have a heavy cost, however, since quantum electrodynamics required that the charged primaries, if electrons or protons, be absorbed more quickly by the atmosphere than was compatible with their intensity at the surface. Anderson's cloud chamber soon disclosed the existence of a secondary particle (now called the μ meson or muon) whose intervention would slow the absorption of cosmic rays. At first identified with the particle Hideki Yukawa (Nobel Prize,1949) had postulated as the carrier of nuclear force (now called the π meson or pion), the muon has played an important role in the systematics of the standard model. It also afforded, through the difference in time between its decay in flight and at rest, the first experimental confirmation of the time dilation required by the theory of relativity.

The last major contributions of students of cosmic rays to fundamental physics occurred just after World War II. With the help of photographic emulsions developed for wartime use, Cecil Powell (Nobel Prize, 1950) and his colleagues at the University of Bristol (including Cesar Lattes) caught a pion as it turned into a muon, confirming the growing realization that Anderson's meson was not Yukawa's. In the same year, 1947, two other British physicists, George D. Rochester and Clifford C. Butler, found evidence in cloud chamber tracks of the decay of unknown neutral particles (now called hyperons) into neutrons, protons, and pions. Two years later, Powell, immersed again in emulsions, found a particle (the K meson) that decayed into three mesons.

The data needed to unravel the relations among elementary particles did not come from cosmic rays, however, but

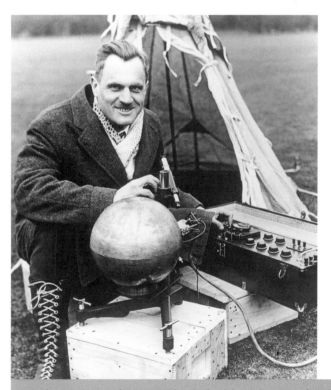

Arthur Compton (1892–1962), US physicist, who won the Nobel Prize in physics in 1927 for showing that high-energy photons behave like particles in collisions with electrons. Here he is shown some years later in the field chasing cosmic rays.

from accelerators. Already in 1947 the Berkeley synchrotron was making μ and π mesons in greater quantity than cosmic rays furnished. Whereas the synchrotron confirmed and extended the discoveries of mesons made through the study of cosmic rays, cosmic-ray physicists could find the antiproton only by scanning emulsions exposed to the beam of the Berkeley Bevatron, where it was first made and detected in 1955. In compensation, cosmic-ray physicists came to agree that the primary radiation striking the atmosphere consists almost entirely of protons, a substantial sprinkling of alpha particles and other nuclei, and a few electrons.

The invention of artificial satellites gave cosmic-ray physicists a needed fillip. *Sputnik I* and the U.S. runners-up, *Explorer I* and *Explorer III,* all carried counters to measure cosmic-ray intensity. The *Explorers'* counters stopped working high above the earth. The man in charge of the instrumentation, James A. Van Allen of the University of Iowa, interpreted the silence as evidence that the satellite had passed through a region so full of charged particles that the counters jammed. The region, now known as the Van Allen Belt(s), consists of cosmic-ray and solar particles trapped in the earth's magnetic field. Hess's assertion that the Sun does not contribute to cosmic radiation succumbed to technological advances that replaced the balloons of the years around World War I with the rockets of the Sputnik era.

J. L. HEILBRON

COURTS AND SALONS. Since the middle ages, European princely courts were populated by practitioners of natural philosophy, mostly physicians and astrologers catering directly to the sovereign's body and peace of mind. Their number increased in the early modern period as courts became larger and wealthier, and their activities diversified. Natural history, alchemy, natural magic, clocks, automata, lodestones, anamorphic devices, mirrors, telescopes, microscopes, and, eventually, experiments took their places at court.

These subjects did not share the same courtly spaces or visibility. Some were incorporated in court pageants, played out in court disputations, or displayed in botanical gardens, cabinets of curiosity and, later, galleries and museums. Others were confined to the prince's study or to the workshops of court jewelers, glassmakers, or apothecaries. Princes and courtiers had an eye for intriguing objects and intriguing philosophers. They did not care where the objects fell in classifications of knowledge or academic disciplines. As shown by the remarkable variety of objects included in early modern aristocratic cabinets of curiosity, the line between *naturalia* (natural objects) and *mirabilia* (spectacular human artifacts) often blurred. Similarly, the courtly interest in artistic representations of botanical and zoological specimens was rooted in their location at the intersection of natural history and the visual arts.

Spectacle was serious business at court. The power of the prince and the relative positions of his aristocratic subjects were continuously staged through a multitude of rituals, some of them quite spectacular. Natural philosophy moved from serving the prince's personal and bodily needs to strengthening and legitimizing his political role and authority through the production of novelties and curiosities—objects that would help to cast him as a unique person entitled to a unique, exalted political role. The personal demeanor and the writing and argumentative style of the natural philosopher also adapted to fit courtly standards of elegance, wit, and nonchalance.

The court employed natural philosophers, paid them well, and, most importantly, provided them with a social status they could attain nowhere else. The implications of a court position extended well beyond material rewards or personal status to the authority of the natural philosopher and his discipline. Disciplinary hierarchies (quite rigid in the university and the craft guilds) could be easily redrawn if the prince wished it so. Artisans could become artists and (here Galileo is the exemplar) mathematicians could become philosophers.

On the other hand, court life demanded a certain level of social and linguistic skill and only topics that were novel, spectacular, and nontechnical were likely to be approved. Moreover, the court favored objects, not theories or long-term projects. Although princes appreciated and often promoted philosophical disputations, they worried more about the quality of the performance than the truth-value of the debate. Ultimately, natural philosophers at court, being courtiers, existed at the whim of the prince. Reaction to these disadvantages of the court system was a central impetus in the establishment of scientific academies—institutions often connected to courts but with relative stability and some tools for self-governance.

Salons were gatherings in the urban homes of nobles or patricians. Their size, schedule, discussion topics, exclusivity, or internal structure varied greatly, as did the role of women in them. Usually organized and managed directly by the host, they relied in some cases on a litterateur or philosopher (the "secretary") to run the salon's activities. As an institution, the salon resembled both the court and the academy. In mid-seventeenth-century Paris, some salons amounted to small full-fledged courts; others were the direct ancestors of royal academies of science. In turn, in the eighteenth century many provincial academies resembled seventeenth-century urban salons in the scope of their interests and the nature of their membership.

Like courts, salons played an important role in the development of the scientific community and, more generally, the so-called republic of letters. They provided forums for discussion of the members' work or, more often, of philosophical literature and news. Their polite conversation helped to prepare non-noble savants for careers at court or in academies. But conversation could turn contentious, disrupting the sociability that underpinned the salons, and cast them as places where natural philosophy was consumed, not produced.

The salons supported and constrained natural philosophy the way the court did. The court could be more effective in providing social legitimation and financial support. The salons offered social training, more leeway in discussion topics, somewhat greater accessibility, and contacts that might make a career—Bernard de Fontenelle and Jean d'Alembert's careers were made in this way. Unlike the court, the salon came with schedules for meetings and activities but, like the court, might come to an end with the death of its patron. Also like courts, salons tended to blend natural philosophical interests with literature, poetry, and moral questions.

Salons have been celebrated as hotbeds of Enlightenment thought and as crucial sites for women natural philosophers—an association that can be traced back to the seventeenth century. But even as they reached an apex of cultural prominence, salons came to be associated with scientific marginality. By the eighteenth century, academies had taken over as the main scientific institutions, relegating the salons to the role of launching pads for future academicians or merely occasions for the nonprofessional consumption of academic science.

Mario Biagioli

CREATIONISM is a popular movement arising from deep-seated objections to perceived religious and social consequences of the acceptance of evolution and from the conviction that evolution has never been satisfactorily demonstrated. These objections predate Charles Darwin. "If the book be true," Cambridge geologist Adam Sedgwick wrote of the evolutionary speculations published (anonymously) by Robert Chambers in *Vestiges of the Natural History of Creation* (1844), then "the labours of sober induction are in vain; religion is a lie; human law is a mass of folly, and a base injustice; morality is moonshine; our labours for the black people of Africa were works of madmen; and man and woman are only better beasts."

Modern creationists raise similar concerns, linking evolution with racism, sexual promiscuity, totalitarianism, nihilism, and various forms of irreligion. Many philosophical and empirical objections to evolution voiced today—the existence of significant "gaps" in the fossil record (which Darwin admitted and modern paleontologists continue to debate), questions about the limits of variability in organisms, the difficulty of explaining the origin of complex organs such as the eye (also admitted by Darwin), and the denial that the earth has existed long enough for natural selection to produce all forms of life—were likewise expressed in the mid-nineteenth century, for example in the review of the fourth edition of Darwin's *On the Origin of Species* by Scottish engineer Fleeming Jenkin (*North British Review,* 1867). Political and social objections—including the argument (detailed by biologist Vernon Lyman Kellogg in *Headquarters Nights* [1917]) that there were close links between the teaching of evolution and German militarism—drove prominent American politician and lawyer William Jennings Bryan to head efforts to outlaw the teaching of evolution in publicly funded American schools, culminating in the staged trial of John Scopes in Dayton, Tennessee (1925).

Although modern creationists still try sometimes to prevent the teaching of evolution, more often they push for "equal time" to teach their ideas alongside evolution in public schools. They challenge the ways in which evolution is presented in standard textbooks, calling for more attention to its perceived difficulties and clearer statements about the nature of evolution as a "theory" rather than a fact. Creationists have also developed their own alternative textbooks; most are written for fundamentalist religious schools though some are intended for public schools, which do not use them, as a rule.

Where most earlier antievolutionists, including Bryan, accepted evidence for an old earth and universe and did not see the biblical flood as a major geological event, the self-styled "scientific creationists" of today insist on a young earth (roughly the traditional biblical age of six thousand years) and embrace "flood geology," the claim that most fossiliferous rocks are relics of the flood and therefore not evidence for evolution. These ideas are central to *The Genesis Flood* (1961) by engineer Henry Morris and theologian John C. Whitcomb, Jr., the single most important creationist book since the 1920s. This work, which popularized flood geology for a wide audience of conservative Protestants, rests on an idea that had circulated for many years within the thoroughly creationist Seventh-day Adventist religious tradition—an idea ultimately derived from prophetess Ellen Gould White but directly taken from Canadian schoolteacher George McCready Price, author of *The New Geology* (1923) and many other works. Morris helped found two organizations, the Creation Research Society and the Institute for Creation Research (San Diego), that are leading disseminators of creationism. Their reach extends beyond the United States to a number of other countries, though creationism—as has been true for most of its history—remains largely an American phenomenon.

Edward B. Davis

CRYSTALLOGRAPHY. Crystals have attracted attention because of their striking and often beautiful forms since early in human history. As an object of systematic study, they have attracted the attention of very different investigators: natural philosophers, mineralogists, chemists, physicists, mathematicians, metallurgists, and biologists. Only in the twentieth century did crystallography become an institutionalized scientific discipline. Perhaps for this reason a comprehensive history of the study of crystals is yet to be written.

In the sixteenth and seventeenth centuries, natural historians thought that crystals, like snowflakes and fossils, bridged the conventional categories of the material world. Like living things, their symmetric form indicated organization. It was even possible to see them growing. Yet they did not seem to be fully alive. Some observers speculated that the variety of crystalline appearance indicated astrological influence, others that it evidenced nature's ability to impose form on matter. Crystals were thought by some to grow from seeds in the earth; by others, from circulating fluids. Mechanical philosophers such as Robert Boyle and Robert Hooke saw in the regular form of crystals a reflection of the underlying arrangement of corpuscles or atoms. Nicolaus Steno, in his *Produmus to a Dissertation on Solids Naturally*

Clarence Darrow, lawyer for the defense of John T. Scopes, tried for teaching evolution in the public schools, and William Jennings Bryan, lawyer for the prosecution, during a lull in the proceedings at Dayton, Tenessee, in 1925

Contained within Solids (1669), explored possible manners of growth and stated the principle that crystals of the same kind have the same angles between adjacent faces.

In the eighteenth century, the study of crystals advanced on a number of fronts. Carl Linnaeus proposed that minerals could be classified by counting their faces, a suggestion of limited utility at the time since most minerals do not appear crystalline to the naked eye and since the polarizing microscope was yet to be invented. René-Just Haüy, professor of mineralogy at the Muséum d'Histoire Natural in Paris, followed earlier work by Romé de l'Isle on the relation of visible crystal forms to the units composing them. In his *Traité de cristallographie* (1822), Haüy suggested that cleaving a crystal divided it into one of six basic polyhedral units, themselves formed of smaller units that might or might not have other polyhedral forms. William Wollaston's invention of a reflecting goniometer that used light rays to measure crystal angles made possible much more precise measurements of crystal forms.

Haüy assumed a univocal relation between crystal form and chemical composition. The chemist Eilhard Mitscherlich dissented. He observed that substances with different chemical compositions could crystallize in the same form, a property he called isomorphism. This bothered the young Louis Pasteur who took advantage of the peculiar optical properties of crystals to investigate the matter further. He carefully separated tartrate crystals that differed just slightly in their facial angles. Polarized light passed through a solution of one set of crystals rotated in one direction; when passed through a solution of a second set, in the reverse—indicating, Pasteur argued, crystalline asymmetry at the molecular level.

The optical properties of minerals proved a reliable aid in identifying them. Henry Clifton Sorby's polarizing microscope enabled mineralogists to examine rocks in thin section and identify their previously invisible crystal constituents. This became a basic technique of petrography. In the

Micrograph of copper sulphate crystals taken with polarized light; the crystals appear as a bright, intense blue to the naked eye.

second half of the nineteenth century, physicists studied the elasticity, density, and electrical properties of minerals. In 1880, Pierre Curie and his brother Jacques-Paul discovered that pressure exerted at the right point on a crystal produced an electric field, a phenomenon known as piezoelectricity. Pierre later incorporated this effect in an electrometer used in the detection of radioactivity. Other scientists worked out the mathematical possibilities for crystal structure: Auguste Bravais, professor of physics at the École Polytechnique of Paris, showed in his *Études cristallographiques* (1866) that only fourteen possible arrangements of points in space lattices were possible.

The discovery of X rays revolutionized crystallography. In 1912, Max von Laue and his group at the University of Munich photographed the diffraction pattern produced by a copper sulphate crystal, showed that X rays passed through a crystal scattered and deflected at regular angles. William Henry Bragg, professor of physics at the University of Leeds, and his son William Lawrence Bragg, then a student at Cambridge, realized that the pattern depended on the atomic structure of the crystal and succeeded in analyzing the crystal structure of the mineral halite (sodium chloride). This in turn led to the invention of the X-ray powder diffractometer. X-ray crystallographers began organizing themselves into formal bodies shortly after World War I. In 1925, they held an informal meeting in Germany to restore disrupted relations. At the Royal Institution in London and the University of Manchester, the Braggs trained students from all over the world in the techniques of X-ray crystallography. Societies were founded in Germany in 1929, the United States in 1941, and the United Kingdom in 1943.

Zeitschrift für Kristallographie became the leading journal in the field in 1927 when it started accepting papers in French and English as well as in German. International cooperation in crystallography revived immediately after World War II. The International Union of Crystallography was founded and quickly joined the International Council of Scientific Unions, the intermediary for UNESCO funding. Soon after came the debut of *Acta crystallographica*, quickly to become the premier journal in the field. X-ray crystallography proved crucial to the rapidly expanding field of molecular biology, itself the result of the coalescence of biochemistry and crystal structure analysis. After the discovery that proteins could be crystallized, W. T. Astbury began exploring their structure with X rays. In the late 1950s, the double-helix structure of nucleic acid, predicted by Francis Crick and James D. Watson, was confirmed by Maurice Wilkins and Rosalind Franklin; in the same period Max Perutz and John Kendrew determined the structure of hemoglobin and myoglobin.

In the 1960s, X-ray crystallographers began adding computers to their apparatus, increasing the speed and precision of analysis. X-ray crystallography remains the most powerful, accurate tool for determining the structure of single crystals. It is widely used in disparate fields including mineralogy, metallurgy, and biology.

RACHEL LAUDAN

CYBERNETICS is the discipline that studies communication and control in living beings and machines or the art of managing and directing highly complex systems. Concepts investigated by cyberneticists include systems (animal or machine), communication between systems, and their regulation or self-regulation.

The MIT mathematician Norbert Wiener invented the term in 1947 (first used in print, 1948) from a Greek term for "steersman" or "governor." The origins of cybernetics lie in the development of feedback mechanisms such as the spring governors for steam engines invented by James Watt and Matthew Boulton (1788), James Clerk Maxwell's consideration of ships' steering engines (1868), and Weiner's involvement in developing automated range finders (1941), which led to the construction of the ILLIAC computer.

Wiener joined MIT in 1919 as a professor of mathematics. Together with MIT neurophysiologist Arturo Rosenblueth he established small interdisciplinary teams to investigate unexplored links between established sciences. Working with the engineer Julian Bigelow, Wiener developed automatic range finders for antiaircraft guns able to predict an aircraft's course by taking into account the elements of past trajectories. Wiener and Bigelow observed the seemingly "intelligent" behavior of these machines and the "diseases" that could affect them. The servomechanisms appeared to exhibit "intelligent" behavior because they dealt with "experience" (recording of past events) and predictions of the future. They also observed a strange defect in performance. With too little friction, the system entered a series of uncontrollable oscillations. Rosenblueth pointed out that humans exhibited similar behavior and Wiener inferred that in order to control a finalized action (an action with a purpose) the circulation of information needed for control must form a closed loop, allowing the evaluation of the effects of previous actions and the adaptation of future conduct based on them. Wiener and Bigelow thus discovered the negative feedback loop.

Rosenblueth's multidisciplinary teams approached the study of living organisms from the viewpoint of a servomechanism engineer and considered servomechanisms from the perspective of the physiologist. Rosenblueth and neurophysiologist Warren McCulloch (then director of the Neuropsychiatric Institute at the University of Illinois) brought together mathematicians, physiologists, and mechanical and electrical engineers in 1942 at a seminar at Princeton's Institute for Advanced Study. After ten more meetings, two seminal publications resulted: Wiener's *Cybernetics, or Control and Communication in the Animal and the Machine* (1948) and Claude Shannon and Warren Weaver's *The Mathematical Theory of Communication* (also 1948), which established information theory. Although it had an interdisciplinary orientation, early cybernetic studies employed an engineering approach focusing on feedback loops and control systems and on constructing intelligent machines. Influenced by the changing and challenging perspectives, McCulloch moved from neurophysiology to mathematics and then to engineering.

The new disciplines inspired biologist Ludwig von Bertalanffy to found the Society for General Systems Research. The society included disciplines far removed from engineering: sociology, political science, and psychiatry. The excitement attracted researchers such as mathematician Anatole Rapoport, biologist W. Ross Ashby, bio-physicist Nicolas Rashevsky, economists Kenneth Boulding and Oskar Morgenstern, and anthropologist Margaret Mead. Mead urged Wiener to extend his ideas to society as a whole. The Society's *Yearbooks* first appeared in 1954 and exerted a profound influence on those interested in applying the cybernetic approach to social systems and to industrial problems.

Early interest in cybernetics in the USSR was stifled on ideological grounds but in 1955 Aleksandr Mikhailovich Lyapunov, founder of Soviet cybernetics and programming, along with Sergei Sobolev and Anatoly Kitov, published the first permitted paper on cybernetics in *Voprosy Filisofii* (Problems of Philosophy). Soon thereafter, V. M. Glushkov established the Institute of Cybernetics in the Ukraine though its independent work does not appear to have had much impact on western studies.

Cybernetics was closely related to the development of ENIAC (1946), EDVAC or EDSAC (1947), Whirlwind II (1951), and other early computers. The latter used a superfast magnetic memory invented by an electronics engineer from MIT's Lincoln Laboratory, Jay Forrester. Beginning in 1952, he coordinated the SAGE (Semi-Automatic Ground Environment) alert and defense system for the U.S. Air Force. It combined radar and computers for the first time to detect and prevent attacks by enemy rockets. Forrester designed SAGE to be capable of making vital decisions as information arrived while interacting in real time with humans inputting data and with other humans making decisions on appropriate reactions.

Ten years later, back at MIT, Forrester created industrial dynamics, which regards all industries as cybernetic systems in order to simulate and predict their behavior. In 1964, confronted with the problems of the growth and decay of cities, he extended industrial dynamics to urban systems (urban dynamics), generalized his theories as system dynamics, and published its definitive text, *World Dynamics* (1971).

Heinz von Foerster coined the term "second-order cybernetics" in 1970. First-order cybernetics concerned observed systems, and second-order cybernetics observing systems. Biologists like von Bertalanffy stayed at the first level. Second-order cybernetics deals with living systems and not with developing control systems for inanimate technological devices and explicitly includes the observer(s) in the systems under study. These living systems range from simple cells to human beings. From the 1970s, "cybernetics" has served as an umbrella term for several related disciplines: general systems theory, information theory, system dynamics, dynamic systems theory (including catastrophe theory), and chaos theory, among others. Cybernetics and systems science now constitute an academic domain encompassing recently developing "sciences of complexity," including artificial intelligence, neural networks, dynamical systems, chaos, and complex adaptive systems such as those used in flexible or multi-mirrored astronomical telescopes. Problems that appear beyond solution now may one day succumb to quantum computers able to mimic more closely the analytical powers of the human brain.

RANDALL C. BROOKS

CYTOLOGY. The term "cytology," denoting the study of plant and animal cells, has been in use from the 1880s, but it only acquired widespread currency in the early decades of the twentieth century. The seventeenth-century British natural philosopher and first Curator of the Royal Society of London, Robert Hooke, may, however, be regarded as the first cytologist. He observed, named, and figured vegetable cells using the recently invented compound microscope. Nehemiah Grew, using the same sort of microscope as Hooke, published many illustrations of vegetable cells. During the last quarter of the seventeenth century, the Dutch draper Antoni van Leeuwenhoek reported observations of structures including what would later be identified as protozoa and blood globules.

These were the efforts of a handful of individuals and did not amount to a concerted program of research into the min-

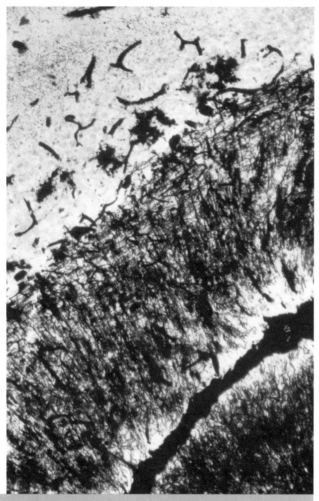

Purkinje cells in the human cerebellum, magnified 150 times

1855, however, on the basis of his microscopic investigation into disease processes, Virchow rejected this concept of cytogenesis.

Later developments in cytology were closely associated with the increasingly refined techniques for fixing and staining tissue that became available to investigators. The German anatomist Walther Flemming elaborated techniques to reveal the internal structure of the cell. He was the first to describe the presence of thread-like bodies, later named chromosomes, in the nucleus, and to describe the role they played in cell division. Flemming coined the term "mitosis" for this process in 1879. In the 1890s, the mode of division characteristic of reproductive cells ("meiosis") was distinguished.

Oscar Hertwig had reported in 1876 that the fertilized ovum contained nuclear matter from both parents. Edouard van Beneden expanded upon these observations in 1883, giving a definitive account of the processes involved in the production of the new nucleus in the fertilized egg. The full significance of these cellular phenomena for the understanding of heredity came in the early twentieth century after the rediscovery of Gregor Mendel's ideas.

During this period cytology and genetics became increasingly intertwined. The work of the American biologist Edmund Beecher Wilson summed up what had been done in cytology in the previous half century and made a bridge to later developments: his *The Cell in Development and Inheritance* (1896) synthesized what was known about the structure and functions of the cell. In his later researches on the role of chromosomes in reproduction, he supplied the cytological basis for the researches of his associate, Thomas Hunt Morgan, on the mechanisms of heredity.

Although attention thus focused on the nucleus, the cell contents, or "cytoplasm," also received intensive study. Several observers discerned a reticular structure in the cytoplasm. By the end of the century, however, these appearances had been dismissed as artifacts produced by the fixatives employed. A considerable debate broke out during the mid-nineteenth century over whether the animal cell, like the vegetable, in all instances possessed a true "wall" or dividing membrane. Ernst Wilhelm von Brücke and Max Schultze argued against the traditional view of the cell as a bounded cavity. The essential parts of the cell were the nucleus and its surrounding "protoplasm."

Around the turn of the twentieth century, Carl Benda employed sophisticated staining methods to identify cytoplasmic inclusions to which he gave the name "mitochondria." Microscopy offered little insight into the functions these bodies might perform, although Benda speculated that they might play a role in heredity. Later biochemical analysis revealed that they participated in cell respiration. The structure of the mitochondria was elucidated after World War II by the use of the electron microscope.

In the second half of the twentieth century, cytology became increasingly detached from its early reliance upon the light microscope. At the same time its links with cognate disciplines like microbiology, genetics, biochemistry, and molecular biology have become ever more intimate. Using techniques drawn from these sciences, cytologists have been able to provide fuller accounts of how the different parts of the cell perform their metabolic and reproductive functions.

STEPHEN JACYNA

ute structure of living tissue. Only in the mid-nineteenth century did schools of histological inquiry began to develop. These histologists made use of new achromatic microscopes that corrected some of the optical defects of earlier microscopes. Among the most important figures in this first generation of microscopic anatomists were Jan Evangelista Purkyn, Professor of Physiology at Breslau, and Johannes Peter Müller, Professor of Physiology at Berlin. Müller in particular produced a school of microscopic observers who went on to produce important original research. One of these, Theodor Schwann, was to make a fundamental theoretical contribution to cytology.

In 1831, the Scottish botanist Robert Brown identified a nucleus in vegetable cells. Jacob Matthias Schleiden came to the conclusion in 1838 that cells were a ubiquitous feature of plant organization and that the nucleus played a crucial role in the growth of plant cells. When Schwann became acquainted with the results of Schleiden's researches, he recognized an analogy between these nucleated cells and certain structures he had himself discerned in animal tissue. In 1839, Schwann argued that the cell was the common unit of structure, function, and development in both plants and animals. This "cell theory" became a fundamental tenet of biology.

In 1846, Schleiden's former associate, Carl Wilhelm von Naegeli, concluded that in almost all cases new plant cells arose through the division of preexisting ones. Embryological studies made by Robert Remak supported the view that the same held for animal cells. The pathologist Rudolf Virchow was at first a proponent of free cell generation. By

DEVELOPMENTAL MECHANICS (*Entwicklungsmechanik*) is the name given in the 1890s by the German anatomist Wilhelm Roux to his experimental program for causal analysis of the transformation of fertilized eggs into multicellular organisms. More generally it also denotes the discipline of experimental embryology that flourished from the 1880s to the 1950s.

In France, Laurent Chabry was the first to apply the methods of experimental teratology—the mutilation of an embryo and comparison of its development to that of a normal embryo—to ascidian fertilized eggs. He built his own micro-tools to observe, manipulate, and kill a single blastomere (one of the segments formed by the division of the ovum) at the two-cell or four-cell stage. In his experiments he obtained half individuals or larvae with anomalies and concluded that each blastomere contained potential parts that were lost if destroyed. In Germany, Wilhelm His, who much improved research techniques by introducing serial microscopic sections, accepted descriptive embryology as essential for understanding the development of individual organs, but criticized its inability to reveal the factors responsible for differentiation. Chabry, His, and their colleagues criticized Ernst Haeckel for studying embryos only for the sake of establishing phylogenetic relationships, and mistrusted his so-called biogenetic law (ontogeny recapitulates phylogeny—the development of the individual follows that of the species).

Eduard Pflüger, professor of physiology at Breslau University, tested whether factors additional to ones internal to the fertilized egg directed development. In 1883, he analyzed the effects of gravitation on the cleavage of fertilized frog eggs and concluded that their development depended on external factors. Gustav Born and Roux, both then also working in Breslau, contested this interpretation. Roux refined Pflüger's experimental techniques and maintained that embryos developed normally even in altered environmental conditions, and that after the second cell division they were self-differentiating.

In 1888, Roux performed his celebrated experiment of puncturing one of the blastomeres of the frog's egg at the two-cell stage with a heated needle. Since in some cases the surviving blastomere developed into a well-formed hemiembryo, Roux concluded that the experiment confirmed his theory of self-differentiation. According to Roux, every cell of a developing embryo has a capacity for self-determination that resided in the structure of the nucleus. He suggested that each cell division separated structurally differentiated nuclear material. He described the process as the production of a mosaic-work (mosaicism) in which each cell gives rise to different tissues and organs.

By shaking water containing sea urchin eggs, Hans Driesch separated the blastomeres from each other and demonstrated, in 1891, that isolated blastomeres at the two-cell and four-cell stages could give rise to complete but dwarf embryos. Since these results contrasted with Roux's theory of self-differentiation by nuclear division, Driesch argued that the isolated blastomeres could produce all the parts of the organism by responding to the needs of the whole. Conflicting views over the interpretation of these experiments provoked a debate reminiscent of that between preformation and epigenesis in the eighteenth century. Roux's embryonic development was mechanistic and neo-preformationist, Driesch's vitalistic and neo-epigenetic.

Roux's research program acquired a commanding position in experimental embryology, which by innovating manipulative operations with extirpation, transplantation, and explantation techniques obtained astounding results usually published either in the *Archiv für Entwicklungsmechanik der Organismen,* a journal founded by Roux in 1893, or in the *Journal of Experimental Zoology.* The leading figures studying heredity and development at the cellular level were Theodor Boveri, Hans Spemann, Kurt Herbst, and Johannes Holtfreter in Germany; Charles Otis Whitman, Edmund Beecher Wilson, Thomas Hunt Morgan, Edwin Grant Conklin, Charles Manning Child, and Ross Granville Harrison in the United States; and Jean Eugène Bataillon and Etienne Wolff in France. Although experimental results did not give rise to a comprehensive theory concerning the transformation of a fertilized egg into a multicellular organism, they did clarify the external conditions necessary for development and showed that the factors guiding differentiation reside in the nucleus. Transplantation experiments in early embryos have shown the existence of organ-forming areas exhibiting various characteristics (Harrison's morphogenetic fields) and the capacity for integrated inductions of the upper lip of the blastopore (Spemann's organizer).

RENATO G. MAZZOLINI

DOUBLE HELIX. The double helix is the name associated with the molecular structure of deoxyribonucleic acid (DNA). Although isolated in the nineteenth century and identified chemically by 1909, its structure was not clarified until 1953 when Francis Crick and James D. Watson published their now famous model. The world authority on the nucleic acids, Phoebus Aaron Levene, had formulated the now infamous tetranucleotide structure, according to which the DNA molecule comprised four bases—adenine, guanine, cytosine, and thymine—attached to each other by a sugar-phosphate backbone. So small and boring a structure did not seem able to serve as a repository for the subtle and diverse specificities of the genetic material, yet DNA was long known to be the chief constituent of the chromosomes, the material bearers of our genes. Hence arose the suggestion that it acted as a "midwife" molecule assisting protein genes to duplicate. When in the 1940s it became clear that DNA was a macromolecule implicated in the transfer of genetic material in bacteria and bacte-

D

Rosalind Franklin (1920–58), British X-ray crystallographer

fraction photograph of the B form in 1952 was stunning in its clarity and simplicity.

James D. Watson and Francis Crick were not officially working on DNA, but were so convinced of the importance of solving the structure and concerned that Franklin was going in the wrong direction, that they made two attempts on it themselves. Their first attempt failed. Their second, aided by knowledge of the contents of Franklin and Raymond Gosling's report to the Medical Research Council of December 1952, led to their famous double helical model. Unlike Franklin they had long been convinced that the DNA molecule is helical. Both also understood the potentially great biological significance of the structure.

Franklin told Watson and Crick that the sugar-phosphate backbone had to be on the outside. Her data suggested more than one helical strand. Crick realized that the symmetry of the crystalline A form indicated that the sugar-phosphate chains should run in opposite directions (anti-parallel). This proved to be a fundamentally important point in solving the structure. Watson solved the problem of putting the bases inside the helical cylinder of the two backbones by his innovation of the matching of the large purine bases (adenine and guanine) with the smaller pyrimidine bases (thymine and cytosine), so that adenine pairs with thymine and guanine with cytosine—another fundamental feature.

As refinements to the crystallographic data appeared, the double helix enjoyed growing support. Details were modified, but the basic structure has remained. Admittedly it was a shock when in 1959 the first single-crystal pictures of mixed nucleotides gave like-with-like pairing of the bases. Another seventeen years passed before data from single-crystal pictures supported the Watson-Crick scheme of pairing. A year later the non-helical "zipper" model was introduced as an alternative to the double helix. Not being a double helix, it could open out more easily for replication and transcription. But as we now know, nature long ago solved the problems associated with opening up the double helix.

ROBERT OLBY

rial viruses, DNA became a contender for the role of the genetic material.

Mounting an attack on the structure called for the skills of the X-ray crystallographer, good knowledge of chemistry, and much patience. The physical chemist Rosalind Franklin had all of these. When she took over the work on DNA at King's College London, she distinguished the crystalline A form and the wet B form, established the crystal parameters of the former, assigned it to its correct crystalline group (C2 monoclinic), and determined the change in length of the fibers in the transition from one form to the other. Her dif-

EARLY HUMANS. The modern study of early humans depended on two major intellectual developments in the second half of the nineteenth century: rejection of the belief that human beings had existed only for the six thousand years of biblical time, and acceptance of the biological principle of human evolution. The major proponents of the antiquity of humans came from geology (Charles Lyell), paleontology (Hugh Falconer), and archaeology (John Lubbock and John Evans). Chance finds of flint tools predated the discovery of Brixham cave (1858), but the human-made artifacts and fossilized animal bones uncovered during its meticulous excavation proved conclusively that humans coexisted with extinct animals like mammoths of the late Pleistocene. The field methods of geology and relative dating using the fossil index had become a means to study our ancestors.

The comparative anatomy of great apes and humans provided evidence for human evolution. A committed Darwinian, T. H. Huxley argued in *Evidence as to Man's Place in Nature* (1863) for a common ancestor of humans and simians, and suggested searching for it in the fossil record. Some fossil discoveries, at Engis Cave, Belgium (1829), and Neander Valley, Germany (1856), predated the finds at Brixham. But the robustly built Neanderthal Man, with its prominent brow ridges, was often dismissed as a pathological aberration of a modern skeleton.

Gabriel de Mortillet organized the artifacts known in 1872 into a developmental sequence, an important improvement on the earlier systems of naming an object after the location where the "type specimen" was found. Mortillet's sequence overlay Édouard Lartet's for the Paleolithic based on supposedly predominant animal species. Edward B. Taylor and other anthropologists added a developmental perspective to studies of primitive societies, seeking observations of the "living Stone Age" in remote tribes. Further discoveries of Neanderthals in Europe, however, including almost complete skeletons at Spy, Belgium (1886), encouraged the search for fossils. Human paleontology (later paleoanthropology) thus became the dominant discipline in modern studies of early humans. While at first this work consisted of description and naming, the use of anthropomorphic measuring techniques (Aleš Hdrli ka) and later complex statistical analysis (William H. Howell) changed the search for type specimens into a much more dynamic endeavor.

Ernst Haeckel championed the idea that fossils would provide evidence for the "missing link" between humans and other animals. He also believed that Asia had been the cradle of humankind. Inspired by his writings, the young Dutch doctor Eugène Dubois went to search in Java (now Indonesia) where, in 1891, he found a primitive skullcap. Further finds indicated that this hominid had walked upright. As with the Neanderthals, debate raged over the place of *Pithecanthropus erectus* in human evolution, but the notion of a large-brained, bipedal hominid ancestor received a strong fillip. Authors speculated for many years about the order in which the four main events purported to be essential for "humanness"—bipedalism, a large brain, descent from the trees, and tool-use/sociability/language—had occurred. Speculation had dangers, though. Grafton Elliot Smith, Arthur Smith Woodward, and Arthur Keith's belief in the primacy of a large brain led to their acceptance of the Piltdown fossil (1908), famously proved a hoax in 1953.

Marcellin Boule's analysis of the Neanderthal skeleton from La Chapelle-aux-Saints as brutish, shambling, and semiupright (1911–1913) unequivocally restored to this group its fossil status, but sidelined its ancestral role. The archaic modern fossil skeletons found at Cro-Magnon, France (1868), apparently provided a more acceptable forerunner for *Homo sapiens*. Boule championed the "pre-sapiens" theory, according to which a large-brained human ancestor with modern body proportions had been present as far back as the Pliocene. The ramifications of this idea resonated throughout the twentieth century. In South Africa (1924) the "Taung baby" (*Australopithecus africanus*)—a juvenile face and fossilized brain, about two million years old (myo)—was rejected by all save Raymond Dart and Robert Broom. It looked too apelike to belong in the human family. Moreover Asia was still the favored continent for human evolution despite Broom's finds of adult *Australopithecine* skulls in South African caves at Sterkfontein, Swartkrans, and Kromdraai. The Taung child was not accepted until the 1950s, after the exposure of Piltdown.

American vertebrate paleontologist Henry Fairfield Osborn continued to promote an Asian origin of the human family. He sponsored a series of expeditions to Central Asia. Davidson Black's later work (1927–1929) at Chou Kou Tien near Beijing, China, unearthed "Peking Man" (*Homo erectus*). Africa too had champions. In the 1920s, Louis Leakey returned to his native Kenya from Cambridge committed to the pre-sapiens theory, but with an African origin. Together with his second wife Mary, also an archaeologist, Leakey established the significance of Africa. Their son Richard took up the mantle with spectacular success in the latter half of the twentieth century, becoming with Donald Johanson one of the most celebrated "fossil hunters"—academics with a media profile, useful in funding increasingly complex and costly expeditions. The East African fossil finds—including "Zinj" (*Australopithecus boisei*, 1959), 1.7 myo; "1470" (*Homo habilis*, 1972), 1.9 myo; "Lucy" (*A. afarensis*, 1974), 3 myo; "the first family" (*A. afarensis*, 1975), 3 myo; "Homo erectus boy" (1984), 1.6 myo; "the black skull" (*A. aethiopicus*, 1985), 2.6 myo; and the preserved footprints of an upright hominid (1978), 3.5 to 3.7 myo—have extended our lineage back in time and suggested the coexistence of more than one species of hominids in Africa at intervals in the past. Charles Loring Brace and Milford Wolpoff in rehabilitating the Neanderthals argued that the same may be true in Europe and the Near East. The importance for paleoanthropology of thinking of populations as biological units, according to the new evolutionary synthesis launched by Ernst Mayr, Theodosius Dobzhansky, and George Gaylord Simpson in 1947, has become clear.

Increasingly sophisticated radiometric dating techniques have helped determine the absolute age of fossils. Computerized tomography scanners now allow paleontologists to see within fossils. Molecular biologists have suggested divergence dates based on similarities among human deoxyribonucleic acid (DNA) and mitochondrial DNA. An intellectual overhaul of archaeology, helped by Lewis Binford's view that we should not seek current behavior patterns in the historical record, turned attention away from the past search for "humanness." Allied with the rise of ecological thinking and general principles such as the effects of climate as an evolutionary lever, fossil hominids have been freed from the legacy of humans' once unique position in the nat-

Full-size reconstruction of Java Man (*Pithecanthropus erectus*, later *Homo erectus*) by the Dutch anatomist Eugène Dubois (1858–1940) on the basis of fossil remains found in 1898

ural order, to take their place in the changing environment of the planet's evolving ecosystem.

HELEN BYNUM

EARTH, AGE OF THE. Before the mid-eighteenth century, few scholars or scientists in the Christian West questioned the adequacy of the chronologies derived from the Mosaic narrative. They believed that the earth was little older than the few thousand years of recorded human history. Beginning in the second half of the eighteenth century, however, investigations of the earth's strata and fossils suggested that the earth's crust had undergone innumerable cycles of formation and decay and that it had supported an ever-changing sequence of living beings long before the first appearance of humans. For geologists such as James Hutton and Charles Lyell, the earth's age seemed too vast for human comprehension or measurement. By 1840, geologists had identified most of the major subdivisions of the stratigraphic column and arranged them in a chronological sequence, but it was a chronology without a measurable scale of duration, a history of the earth without dates.

In 1859, Charles Darwin attempted to determine one geological date by estimating how long it would take to erode a measured thickness of the earth's strata. His conclusion that 300 million years had been required to denude even the relatively recent strata of the Weald, a district of southern England, brought an immediate reaction. In 1860, the geologist John Phillips rebutted with an estimate that the composite thickness of the whole stratigraphic column could be denuded in only 100 million years. Soon afterward, the physicist William Thomson, Lord Kelvin calculated that 100 million years would be sufficient for the earth to cool from an assumed primordial molten condition to its present temperature. Kelvin's conclusions, based on the widely held hypothesis that the earth had been formed from the scattered particles of a primordial nebula, and supported by the latest theories of thermodynamics, carried great weight during the remainder of the century. Subsequent estimates of rates of erosion and sedimentation, of solar radiation and cooling, and of the time of formation of the Moon and the oceans converged on his figure of 100 million years.

All this was changed by the discovery in 1903 that radioactive elements constantly emit heat. A year later, Ernest Rutherford suggested that the ratio of the abundance of radioactive elements to their decay products provide a way to measure the ages of the rocks and minerals containing them. Robert John Strutt and his student, the geologist Arthur Holmes, pursued Rutherford's idea. By 1911, Holmes had used uranium/lead ratios to estimate the ages of several rocks from the ancient Precambrian period. One appeared to be 1,600 million years old. Many geologists were initially skeptical, but by 1930, largely as a result of the work of Holmes, most accepted radioactive dating as the only reliable means to determine the ages of rocks and of the earth itself. The discovery of isotopes in 1913, and the development of the modern mass spectrometer of the 1930s, greatly facilitated radioactive dating. By the late 1940s, the method produced an estimate of between 4,000 and 5,000 million years for the age of the earth. In 1956, the American geochemist Clare Cameron Patterson compared the isotopes of the earth's crust with those of five meteorites. On this basis, he decided that the earth and its meteorites had an age of about 4,550 million years. All subsequent estimates of the age of the earth have tended to confirm Patterson's conclusion.

JOE D. BURCHFIELD

EARTH SCIENCE. The discipline of earth science was invented during the 1960s. It replaced geology as the major institutional framework for studying the earth just as geology had replaced mineralogy in the early nineteenth century. As with the simultaneous invention of planetary science, geologists had additional reasons for rethinking the status quo. Geology had lacked focus and exciting new ideas and techniques for the previous half century. Oceanographers and geophysicists had new instruments and techniques, particularly in submarine gravity studies, submarine seismology, deep ocean drilling and paleomagnetism.

The needs of submarine warfare during World War II and the Cold War gave a strong boost to seismology and studies of submarine gravity. Before World War II, the Dutch physicist Felix Andries Vening-Meinesz had developed a pendulum apparatus (now named after him) that made it possible to measure gravity at sea as accurately as on land. Using this apparatus, Vening-Meinesz and others mapped the gravity anomalies of the ocean floors and discovered the areas of downbuckling frequently associated with island arcs. Following the War, Maurice Ewing developed sea-floor seismic equipment, measured velocities in the sediments of the deep ocean, and contributed importantly to the understanding and detection of long range sound transmission in oceans.

In the late 1950s, the International Geophysical Year (IGY), which included gravity, geomagnetism, oceanography and seismology in its areas of concentration, further encouraged these lines of research. Deep ocean drilling that brought up cores from the sediments on the ocean floor began in the 1960s with the establishment of JOIDES (Joint Oceanographic Institutions for Deep Sea Drilling). At the same time, scientists at the United States Geological Survey, the University of Newcastle, and the Australian National University were racing to produce time scales of global magnetic reversals and theories of the motion of the magnetic north pole.

The promotion of the nascent discipline of earth science owed much to a few pioneering individuals and institutions. Among the individuals, in addition to those already mentioned, were J. Turzo Wilson, who led the Canadian contribution to the IGY and made major contributions to plate tectonics, and W. H. (Bill) Menard of Scripps Institution of Oceanography, later Director of the United States Geological Survey. The institutions that saw some of the important early work were spread across the English speaking world: Princeton University, Cambridge University, the University of Toronto, and the Australian National University, together with Lamont Doherty Geological Observatory (founded by Columbia University as a result of Ewing's successes) and Scripps Institution of Oceanography.

By the early 1970s, geophysicists, oceanographers, and geologists had pieced together the theory of plate tectonics. By the end of the decade, the theory had won worldwide acceptance, except in the Soviet Union. The theory vindicated the new approach to the science of the earth. It showed that expensive oceanographic surveys were necessary because the geology of the ocean floor turned out to be unexpectedly different from that of the land surface. It demonstrated that theorizing on a global scale led to the detection of patterns that would never have emerged from the laborious mapping of one square mile of the earth after

Artists concept of the position of Earth's continents about midway through the Cretaceous Period (136 to 165 million years ago). Africa and South America are shown before they split to form the Atlantic Ocean.

another. And it showed once and for all that sophisticated instruments and high levels of funding need not be a waste of public money.

Simultaneous developments in other areas supported these conclusions. Geologists showed that the earth had suffered multiple impacts from meteors, asteroids, and other extraterrestrial bodies, ending the century-long convention that extraterrestrial phenomena were irrelevant to the study of the earth. When geologists found evidence supporting the thesis, put forward by Walter Alvarez, that one of these impacts precipitated the widespread extinctions at the Cretaceous-Tertiary boundary, the move to integrate earth and planetary science gained further momentum. The growing environmental movement and the popular belief that in some way all earth systems were interconnected doubtless also helped accelerate the shift to earth science.

During the 1970s and 1980s, established geology departments changed their names to earth science, or earth and ocean science, or earth and planetary science. They hired professors trained in physics and chemistry as well as in geology, and overhauled their curricula. Geological surveys rethought their missions, broadened their scope, and began using new instruments. The movement spread beyond research science. In 1982, a group of scientists founded the History of the Earth Sciences Society, and shortly thereafter began publishing *Earth Sciences History,* now the major journal for the history of geology and earth science. In 1983, the National Earth Science Teachers Association was chartered in the United States and began publishing *The Earth Scientist* to promote the teaching of earth science in the school system. Since the 1970s, instruments have continually improved. Magnetometers for measuring fossil magnetism which in the 1950s and 1960s were so new and intricate that many scientists believed the instruments created the effects observed by "paleomagicians" became standard, everyday, off-the-shelf tools. Theorizing has continued apace. Plate tectonic theory, which at first swept all before it, has been refined, and to some extent reformulated.

For all the success of earth science, traces of its roots in the formerly distinct areas of geology, geophysics, and oceanography remain. Major societies founded before the disciplinary transition, such as the American Association of Petroleum Geologists, the Geological Society of London, and the American Geophysical Union, still exist and continue to publish journals specializing in their traditional interests. And although histories of plate tectonics and biographies of its creators abound, as yet we have no comprehensive history of the disciplinary change to earth science.

RACHEL LAUDAN

ECOLOGY. In his groundbreaking 1927 textbook, *Animal Ecology,* Charles Elton characterized "ecology" as a new name for an old subject, or simply "scientific natural history." Much of ecology does concern phenomena that have been observed and pondered since antiquity, such as patterns in the geographical distribution of organisms, population fluctuations, predator-prey interactions, food chains, life cycles, and cycles of materials. Before the twentieth century, most of these phenomena fell within the domain of natural history. However, experts took up the many pieces of the subject in different studies in which the individual organisms, not their interrelationships, were the chief objects of study. The process by which the interrelationships

themselves became the objects of study is the process by which ecology became a science.

The name came earlier than the science. In 1866 Ernst Haeckel coined the word "ecology," with more or less its current meaning, in a long treatise on animal morphology that owed much of its inspiration to Charles Darwin's theory of evolution. Haeckel wanted a name for a new branch of science that examined the collection of phenomena Darwin characterized as the "conditions of existence," that is, everything in the physical and biological environment of an organism that affects its survival in the broadest sense. Haeckel coined the term but did not make much use of it. The first to do so were botanists working during the 1890s mainly on the geographical distribution of plants. Although this line of research owed something to Darwin, it had deeper roots.

The leader of this older line of research, and one of Darwin's major sources of inspiration, was the German polymath Alexander von Humboldt, whose treatise on plant geography (or phytogeography), based upon a turn-of-the-century expedition to South America, became a model for the entire field. Humboldt's central contribution was to identify particular assemblages of plants, characterized by vegetation type, with particular environmental regimes. He divided the globe into discrete vegetation zones and made the observation, not unique to him, that the zones traversed in ascending high mountains, such as those he had climbed

Navy technicians check water pollution in the Arctic Ocean, Point Barrow, Alaska.

in the Andes, paralleled the zones passed through in traveling from the equator to the poles.

Over the course of the century, Humboldt's line of inquiry would be expanded, elaborated upon, and modified by a succession of European researchers. By the 1890s, a rich collection of observations and descriptions existed alongside a growing vocabulary of phytogeographical terms. This geographical tradition then meshed with a laboratory tradition, born in the revitalized and now thriving German university system, to produce detailed studies of plant adaptation under natural conditions—studies aided considerably by opportunities for travel opened up for European scientists as a result of intense colonization efforts in Asia and Africa and continued economic ventures in South America. In the United States, the maturation of the university system, combined with the expansion of the nation into the western regions of the North American continent, afforded similar opportunities for botanists. The science of ecology emerged out of this combined functional and geographical emphasis in botany around the turn of the century. North American botanists quietly adopted Haeckel's new term in 1893, and the Danish botanist Eugenius Warming published the first textbook to employ both the term and the concept in 1895.

With his knowledge of the laboratory methods taught in the German universities and his extensive travel experiences in South America and Europe, Warming developed his own classification scheme for plant communities based mainly upon available soil moisture in the habitats in which the characteristic plant groups are generally found. He also offered a discussion of ecological succession, the process by which different communities replace one another in the occupation of a particular site, such as a recently exposed rocky slope, a sand dune, or a burnt-over patch of forest. Warming's counterpart in Germany, Andreas Franz Wilhelm Schimper, in 1898 produced a similar textbook oriented toward plant geography, although with less emphasis on community structure. Schimper, to whom we owe the term "tropical rainforest," came from a school of laboratory-trained botanical field researchers who found more inspiration in Darwin's natural selection theory than did most early plant ecologists. Like many of his colleagues, Schimper traveled widely in the American tropics as well as in Germany's newly acquired Pacific island territories and the island of Java, where the Dutch colonial authorities maintained a botanical laboratory and garden. His textbook, like Warming's, provided a wealth of examples drawn from nature and became a source of inspiration for many budding ecologists in Europe and North America.

Meanwhile, young American botanists found ample opportunities for applying the latest insights and practices from European science to the study of North America's forests and grasslands, fast disappearing under the ax and the plow. A dynamic approach to plant ecology took shape, with emphasis on the process of succession and its inevitable culmination in the climatically determined "climax" community. This conception received its most thorough and persuasive treatment in the hands of Nebraska-born Frederic E. Clements, who spent most of his career in the western United States as a special ecological researcher for the Carnegie Institution. Although Clements's notion of "climax" came under attack at home and abroad, it nevertheless served as a productive focal point for the study of plant communities throughout the first half of the twentieth century. Clements's ideas found modest support among British plant ecologists, but numerous rival schools of plant ecology

emerged in Germany, France, Switzerland, Scandinavia, and Russia, most of them promoting versions of what came to be known as phytosociology, or plant sociology—essentially the identification, often by elaborate sampling techniques and statistical methods, of natural plant groups associated with particular sets of environmental conditions. Whereas Clements and his followers focused on the climax community as the single, natural endpoint of a successional sequence, as well as a self-regulating, integrated whole, most European phytosociologists recognized multiple outcomes of successional sequences and did not necessarily emphasize the plant community as a stable, self-sustaining entity.

Studies of animal distribution began in the nineteenth century, but the formal development of animal ecology did not occur until the 1920s. British zoologist Charles Elton, whose field research emphasized the study of populations in the wild, was perhaps the most influential figure. Elton's work, often involving northern fur-bearing animals of commercial value, made a number of concepts part of the naturalist's vocabulary, including the ecological niche, the food chain, and the pyramid of numbers, that is, the decrease in numbers of individual organisms, or total quantity (weight) of organisms, at each successive stage in a food chain, from plants and plant-eating animals at the bottom to large carnivores at the top. Just as with plant ecology, diverse schools of animal ecology emerged in Europe and the United States during the first half of the twentieth century. Some schools, like Elton's, focused on empirical studies of predator-prey interactions and population fluctuations, others focused on animal community organization, still others on broader patterns of distribution and abundance.

Although some of the early work in animal ecology, particularly in the United States, attempted to model itself on plant ecology, by the 1930s animal ecology had emerged as an independent field. There was little overlap or interaction between the work of animal and plant ecologists. Effective impetus for an integrated perspective in ecology came from work in aquatic biology, best exemplified in the late nineteenth century by Karl Möbius's studies of the depleted oyster bank off Germany's north coast and the pioneering limnological (freshwater) studies of François Alphonse Forel on Swiss lakes. This work was continued and refined in the early twentieth century by many researchers, including August Thienemann in Germany and Einar Naumann in Sweden. Möbius's concept of the "biocenosis," the integrated community consisting of all living beings associated with a given habitat or a particular set of environmental conditions, was adopted widely by German and Russian ecologists in the 1920s and 1930s. An integrative perspective also emerged in soil science, as in Sergei Winogradsky's turn-of-the-century studies of soil microbiology, and in studies of biogeochemical cycles, as in the work of Russian geochemist Vladimir Vernadsky, who introduced the term "biosphere" in 1914. However, the integrative concept that had the broadest appeal and played a central role in bringing together the many different strands of ecological science was that of the "ecosystem," introduced by British botanist Arthur G. Tansley in 1935 but first used effectively in an aquatic setting.

Tansley was Britain's foremost plant ecologist and the founder in 1913 of the British Ecological Society, the first such national organization, formed two years earlier than its American counterpart. A pioneer in vegetation surveys, a critic of Clements's idea of the climax community, a passionate conservationist, and a student of Sigmund Freud, Tansley brought his broad experience and erudition to bear on the problem of identifying the ideal ecological unit of study. He suggested that the term "ecosystem" captured this concept best without implying any mysterious vital properties. The new term received its fullest early treatment in a seminal paper published in 1942 by a young American limnologist, Raymond Lindeman. Making use of the concept of ecological succession, Elton's pyramid of numbers and food chains, earlier studies of energy flow in aquatic systems, and Clements's notion of the stable climax community, Lindeman traced the flow of energy through the different trophic (feeding) levels (producers, primary consumers, secondary consumers) in a small Minnesota pond as a way to map its structure as an ecosystem and to demonstrate its progress in development toward a stable, equilibrium state.

World War II proved to be a watershed for ecology. Although earlier preoccupations with community classification and structure, population dynamics, and patterns of distribution continued in the postwar years, newer methodologies, practices, and conceptual schemes took hold, and ecology as a science and a profession grew in size, status, and organization. In the postwar period, Lindeman's groundbreaking work on ecosystem ecology found a home among biologists funded by the U.S. Atomic Energy Commission, who used radionuclides to trace the flow of materials and energy through natural ecosytems. Ecosystem research soon expanded from its base in the Atomic Energy Commission. It also prospered among a small group of Tansley's followers at the new Nature Conservancy in Britain. It became an essential feature of modern ecological science, a message conveyed to several generations of students worldwide through the successive editions of Eugene P. Odum's *Introduction to Ecology,* first published in 1953. Meanwhile, the prewar synthesis of Darwinian natural selection theory with Mendelian genetics resulted in the gradual postwar emergence of a more strongly Darwinian perspective in population and community ecology.

The postwar years also saw a shift toward quantitative aspects of ecology. Mathematical techniques developed in the United States, Europe, and the Soviet Union during the interwar period joined with war-born techniques involving information systems and cybernetics to produce a movement toward mathematical modeling and computer simulation of populations, communities, and ecosystems. Much of this modeling and its techniques came under attack during the last decades of the twentieth century. Some ecologists abandoned model building for empirical studies, others worked on refining and improving the models, and many called into question the underlying notions of stability and equilibrium upon which most of the models were based.

The devastation brought by World War II also contributed to greater postwar interest in the conservation of natural resources, protection of wildlife, and preservation of natural environments, a trend that, when linked in the 1960s with social criticism, blossomed into an international environmental movement that drew heavily upon concepts and theories of ecology. As had occurred before the war in a more limited way among a few visionaries, ecology now came to be widely viewed not only as the source of remedies for environmental ills but also as the scientific underpinning for a new social order. This proved to be a mixed blessing for ecologists. On the one hand, funding for ecological research increased considerably, and many more people were drawn into the field. On the other hand, the theoretical framework of ecological science, being neither unified nor consistent, could not provide easy, unambiguous solutions to environmental problems, let alone unified and consistent social visions. Toward the end of the twentieth century, this disagreement and uncertainty among ecologists was used as fuel in legislative and legal debates arguing against the protection of endangered species and the maintenance of pristine nature reserves. This situation encouraged the further refinement and integration of ecological science toward the incorporation of human disturbance and the notion of managed ecosystems.

EUGENE CITTADINO

ELECTRICITY was originally the term used to describe the power acquired by certain substances, notably amber, when rubbed, to attract nearby small objects. This power, known to the Greeks, was carefully distinguished by William Gilbert (1600) from magnetism. Seventeenth-century philosophers were unanimous in believing that the rubbing agitated a subtle matter associated with ordinary matter, causing it to be ejected into the surrounding air, where it (or perhaps air rushing in to fill the space left empty) swept up any light objects in the way.

Francis Hauksbee (c. 1666–1713) obtained more powerful effects by mounting a glass globe on a spindle and rubbing it as it rotated. He showed that electrification was linked to the emission of light—indeed, in Hauksbee's experiments it seemed that the subtle matter streaming from electrified bodies could be felt, seen, and heard. As elaborated by Jean-Antoine Nollet in the 1740s, the theory envisaged fiery matter streaming from electrified bodies, while other streams flowed in to replace the matter that had left.

In 1731, Stephen Gray discovered that the electrical attracting power could be transmitted over great distances, provided that the conducting line was made of an appropriate material and suitably supported. This led to a distinction between "electrics"—substances electrifiable by friction but poor conductors—and "non-electrics"—substances not electrifiable by friction but good conductors.

In 1746, Petrus van Musschenbroek announced a sensational discovery, the "Leyden experiment," in which a bottle filled with water and electrified by means of a conductor leading from a generating machine into the water delivered a terrible blow when contact was made simultaneously with the conductor dipping into the water and the outer surface of the bottle. "I thought it was all up with me," Musschenbroek reported. Enthusiasts everywhere rushed to repeat the experiment. Nollet delighted the French king by discharging a bottle through a line of monks, making them leap into the air simultaneously. In America, Benjamin Franklin and his friends amused themselves with electrical party tricks.

Franklin also devised a new theory of electricity that in time became generally accepted. He, too, supposed that ordinary matter was suffused with subtle fluid. For Franklin, however, electrification consisted in the redistribution of this fluid between rubber and rubbed, one finishing up with more than its natural quantity, the other with less. The notion of electrical "charge" thus acquired a meaning, the bodies becoming electrified "plus" and "minus" respectively. Noting the ability of pointed conductors to discharge nearby charged objects, Franklin conceived an experiment, first successfully performed near Paris in May 1752, to demonstrate that thunderclouds were electrified and lightning was an electrical discharge. His conclusion that erecting pointed conductors (lightning rods) on buildings could protect them from lightning strikes was hailed as a triumph of reason over nature.

A fanciful painting of Alessandro Volta showing his electric battery to Napoleon Bonaparte (seated) and other men of science in Paris in 1800

Franklin's theory worked well in explaining when a shock would be experienced in a variety of situations. He did not provide a coherent dynamical basis for his theory. In 1759, Franz Ulrich Theodosius Aepinus published a fully consistent version of Franklin's theory, based explicitly on forces acting at a distance between particles, whether of fluid or of matter. By adding the forces acting in various situations, he gave satisfactory explanations for a wide range of effects, and successfully predicted others. His ideas were taken up by leading investigators of the next generation such as Alessandro Volta and Charles Augustin Coulomb, who showed in 1785 that the forces involved obeyed an inverse-square law with respect to distance. On this basis, Simeon-Denis Poisson developed a full mathematical theory of electrostatics in 1812.

To make his theory consistent with elementary observation, Aepinus found it necessary to assume that particles of ordinary matter repelled each other. Many people rejected this idea, supposing instead the existence of two electric fluids that normally neutralized each other but that became separated in electrification. This theory attributed to the second electric fluid the additional repulsive force that Aepinus invoked. Operationally, the one-fluid and two-fluid theories could not be distinguished, and each found adherents.

In the 1790s, controversy erupted between Alessandro Volta and Luigi Galvani over Galvani's experiments in which frogs' legs jerked spasmodically when a conducting circuit was completed between the crural nerve and the leg muscle. Galvani attributed the effect to the discharge of "animal electricity" accumulated in the muscle, which he saw as analogous to a Leyden jar. Volta believed the cause was ordinary electricity, and concluded that dissimilar conductors in contact generate an electromotive force. He built a "pile" comprising pairs of silver and zinc disks separated by pieces of moist cardboard, the electrical force of which he managed to detect with a sensitive electroscope.

Volta's device was the first source of continuous electric current. Its operation was accompanied by chemical dissociations within the moist conductor and in any other conducting solutions forming part of the electrical circuit. These became a focus of research, leading to Humphry Davy's successful isolation of potassium and sodium in 1807 by electrolyzing molten potash and soda, respectively, and eventually to large-scale industrial applications of electrochemical processes.

In 1820, Hans Christian Oersted discovered that a wire carrying an electric current deflects a magnetic needle. André-Marie Ampère quickly showed that a current-carrying loop or solenoid was equivalent to a magnet, and proposed that all magnetism arose from solenoidal electric currents in molecules of iron. Ampère's discovery led to the construction of electromagnets—iron-cored solenoids carrying ever-larger currents—that produced magnetic effects far more powerful than any previously known. Then, in 1831, Michael Faraday discovered electromagnetic induction: when an electrical conductor cuts across lines of force, an electromotive force is generated in the conductor. These discoveries underpinned the development, first, of the electric telegraph and, later in the nineteenth century, the electrical power industry, which provided a continuous supply of electrical power for industrial or domestic use from generators in which coils of conducting wire placed between the poles of a powerful electromagnet were rotated by steam or water pressure. In the twentieth century, the increasing availability of such power, and the rapid proliferation of appliances to exploit it, transformed civilized life.

But what is electricity? For most nineteenth-century physicists, sources of electromotive force literally drove a current of the electric fluid (or fluids) around a conducting circuit. In an electrolytic cell, the electrodes acted as poles, attracting the constituent parts of the solute into which they were dipped. For Faraday, however, and later for James Clerk Maxwell, the energy resided not in electrified bodies but in the medium surrounding them, which was thrown into a state of strain by the presence of a source of electromotive force. If the medium were a conductor, the tension would collapse, only to be immediately restored; the product of this continuous repetition, the "current," was a shock wave propagated down the conductor. Static electric charges represented the ends of lines of unrelieved electric tension.

These ideas were widely influential in late-nineteenth-century physics, even though they left the relationship between electricity and matter far from clear. Following the discovery of the electron by Joseph John Thomson in 1897, however, and the recognition that it was a universal constituent of matter, electric currents again came to be conceived in terms of a flow of "subtle fluid"—now clouds of electrons semidetached from their parent atoms, driven along by an electromotive force. No longer, however, was "charge" defined in terms of accumulations or deficits of this fluid. Rather, charge became a primitive term, a quality attributed to the fundamental constituents of matter that was itself left unexplained. Some kinds of fundamental particles, including electrons, carry negative charge, whatever that might be, whereas others carry an equally mysterious positive charge: in combination, these two kinds of charge negate each other. After Robert Millikan's experiments (1913), most physicists accepted the notion that there is a natural unit of electricity, equal to the charge on the electron. The current standard model in elementary particle physics, however, assumes the existence of sub-nucleonic constituents ("quarks") bearing either one-third or two-thirds of the unit charge. Neither these quarks nor their fractional charges have been detected in a free state.

R. W. HOME

The Danish natural philosopher Hans Christian Oersted (1777–1851) apparently thinking about possible interactions between electricity (generated by Volta's battery) and magnetism (detected by a compass needle)

ELECTROMAGNETISM. The study of electricity and magnetism has alternated between theories that represented the two as manifestations of a single effect and the view that they were separate phenomena, with general inflection points around 1600 (when the two fields were divided) and 1820 (when they reunited).

Ancient and medieval philosophers did not distinguish between the ability of amber to attract objects and the action of the lodestone on iron. In 1600, William Gilbert insisted on a distinction between the two, coining the term "electricity" to describe the effect of amber and attributing it to many other substances; the lodestone remained for Gilbert the sole source of magnetism, around whose force he constructed an entire cosmology. Gilbert's successors spent the seventeenth century searching for the source of electrical and magnetic phenomena and generally finding it in material emanations, such as René Descartes's theory of magnetic effluvia that swarmed around iron and accounted for magnetic action.

Over the course of the eighteenth century, natural philosophers incorporated the distinct fields of electricity and magnetism within a new quantitative, experimental discipline of physics, aided by new instruments to produce phenomena—electrostatic machines like Francis Hauksbee's spinning glass globe, and the Leyden jar, an early form of capacitor—and to measure them, such as the electroscope, which indicated electrical force by the displacement of threads, straws, or gold leaf. Quantification allowed mathematicians, notably Henry Cavendish and Charles Augustin Coulomb, to follow Isaac Newton's example for gravitation and reduce electro- and magnetostatics to distance forces. Philosophers around 1800 explained their measurements in terms of a system of imponderable fluids, with one (or two) weightless, elastic fluid(s) each for electrical and magnetic forces. But despite similar mathematical and conceptual approaches to electricity and magnetism, the phenomena still appeared unrelated. Electricity produced violent action like lightning or sparks, unlike milder magnetic effects, and did not have the same polar behavior.

One of the new instruments, Alessandro Volta's battery, produced a flow of current electricity. It thus enabled the unification, or reunification, of electricity and magnetism, whose interactions stemmed from dynamic electric and magnetic effects. In 1820, Hans Christian Oersted noticed that a current-carrying wire displaced a nearby compass needle. Oersted's response reflected his adherence to Naturphilosophie, a metaphysical system advanced at the time by German philosophers who sought single polar forces underlying various domains of natural phenomena. Oersted thought his experiment gave evidence of such a unifying force and proposed a connection between electricity and magnetism. André-Marie Ampère soon mathematized Oersted's experiment, providing a force law for currents in wires. In 1831, Michael Faraday, who may also have dabbled in Naturphilosophie, explored the reverse effect, the ability of a moving magnet to generate electric currents. Oersted, Ampère, and Faraday thus established electromagnetism, although all three noted a difference between the linear action of electricity and the circular action of magnetism.

Faraday formulated the concept of fields to explain the action of electric and magnetic forces at a distance. Instead of material, if weightless, fluids carrying the force, Faraday attributed the source of electromagnetic action to lines of force in the medium between currents and magnets: lines of force ran from one magnetic pole to the opposite pole, and between opposite electrical charges; magnets or conductors experienced pushes or pulls as their motion intersected these lines of force. James Clerk Maxwell in the 1860s and 1870s systematized the field concept and the interaction of electric and magnetic forces in a set of differential equations, later simplified into four basic equations. Maxwell's theory, which interpreted light as very rapidly oscillating electric and magnetic fields, received experimental confirmation by Heinrich Hertz, who starting in 1887 demonstrated the propagation of electromagnetic waves through space.

Over the course of the nineteenth century, experimental work on electromagnetism, especially in Germany, spurred the emergence of precision physics, which in turn promoted the establishment of academic research institutes. Electromagnetism provided one of the two main lines of development of nineteenth-century physics, along with thermodynamics and the kinetic theory. Whereas thermodynamics derived from the first industrial revolution of the late eighteenth century, specifically the program to describe the working of the steam engine, electromagnetism stimulated the second industrial revolution of the late nineteenth century.

Electromagnetism gave rise to industries around the telegraph, a result of Oersted's discovery of mechanical motion produced by electric current; electric power generation and transmission, with the dynamo deriving from Faraday's work on the transformation of mechanical motion into electric current; and radio, a consequence of Hertz's experiments on the free propagation of electromagnetic radiation. Together with chemistry and the chemical industry, electromagnetism and its applications exemplified the science-based industry of the second industrial revolution. But the electrical industry did not just apply scientific theories developed in isolation from commercial concerns; rather, prominent scientists, such as William Thomson (later Lord Kelvin) and Oliver Heaviside tackled practical problems, especially in telegraphy, and thus advanced the state of electromagnetic theory.

Since Maxwell's theory established a conception of light as a form of electromagnetic waves, electromagnetism merged with theoretical optics. At the end of the century, some physicists sought to extend the domain of electromagnetism to all physical phenomena, including mechanics and gravity, in what was called the electromagnetic worldview. Many electromagnetic theories relied on an all-pervasive ether as the medium for electromagnetic waves. Albert Einstein's theory of relativity at the outset of the twentieth century enshrined the interchangeability of electrical and magnetic forces and banished the ether, leaving electromagnetic waves to propagate through empty space at the speed of light. The concurrent development of quantum theory, which itself arose from the application of thermodynamics to electromagnetic waves (in the form of heat radiation), led to the wave-particle duality, in which electromagnetic radiation at high frequencies may behave either as a wave or a particle. The elaboration of quantum electrodynamics starting around 1930 provided a quantum theory of electromagnetism and a description of the duality.

Physicists later in the twentieth century came to view electromagnetism as one of four fundamental forces, the others being gravity and the strong and weak nuclear forces. Particle physicists hoped to show that each force was a particular manifestation of a more general force; they thus joined the unified electromagnetism with the weak (in the so-called electroweak force) and then the strong force (in quantum

chromodynamics), and sought in vain for final unification with gravity in a so-called theory of everything.

PETER J. WESTWICK

ELECTROTECHNOLOGY. The first practical (and very questionable) application of electricity occurred in the eighteenth century. Using electrostatic machines and Leyden jars, natural philosophers, doctors, and various charlatans administered sparks to paralytics and otherwise tried to repair the body by shocks and effluvia. Another early example of electrical technology, the lightning conductor, was comparatively reliable. Alessandro Volta's invention of the electrochemical cell or battery grandly enlarged the range of application of electricity. The battery's current could produce electrolysis, generate a bright light across a gap between two carbons, and act upon a magnet. Michael Faraday's discovery that the relative movement of wires and magnets induce electric currents made motors possible. But the very first electromagnets, electric motors, generators, and lamps were little more than scientific toys, at home only in laboratories and in lecture rooms. Also, despite countless improvements introduced after Volta, the battery remained an inefficient and expensive source of energy. The first electric motors could not compete with steam engines. Electric arc lights, too bright for domestic application and requiring a complex regulating apparatus, were confined to lighthouses until technical improvements suited them for public buildings and street illumination in the later decades of the nineteenth century.

The first successful practical applications of electricity were electroplating and electric telegraphy in the 1840s. Around the beginning of the decade, an electrochemical process was discovered for depositing a thin layer of gold or silver on a non-noble metal (or a conductive mould made of graphite-covered gutta-percha). Electroplating and electroforming permitted the bulk production of inexpensive "artistic objects" for the growing middle class. Decoratively wrought metal objects (cutlery, vases, statuettes, candlesticks), previously manufactured only in limited numbers by skillful craftsmen, could be multiplied cheaply and accurately.

Telegraphy also boomed in the 1840s, the development of transmission lines accompanying the growth of national railroad systems. In the second half of the nineteenth century, entrepreneurs pressed the creation of an international telegraphic network that demanded an unprecedented effort from physicists, engineers, and electrical manufacturers. New materials (e.g., for insulating cables) had to be developed, and measuring instruments refined. New technologies for making and laying underwater cable had to be invented. Universal electrical standards were needed to allow interconnection of apparatus of diverse origins into a world network; new apparatus was required for detecting the weak signals traveling over thousands of miles. The scientific and technical community, industrialists, tycoons, and politicians joined their efforts for the achievement of this global enterprise. The first transatlantic cables were laid in the 1860s with physicist William Thomson, Lord Kelvin, in charge of testing the cable as it paid out.

The telegraphic industry supported many spin-offs and trained many inventors of electrical devices. Pantelegraphy, invented by the Italian Giovanni Caselli in the late 1850s, a primitive form of fax, allowed transmission of images by telegraph. It was deployed in France during the Second Empire, but the market was too small to sustain it after 1870. At the turn of the century, however, electric transmission of static images returned (with a better technology) to supply news-

E

papers and magazines with photographs from around the world. Thomas Edison got his start as a telegraphist; his contributions to the field, such as the stock ticker, laid the groundwork for a number of his later inventions, including the phonograph.

In the late 1860s, a number of inventors and scientists with telegraphic experience, notably Charles Wheatstone and Ernst Werner von Siemens, introduced the first self-excited generators, far more powerful and efficient than earlier models. Another major step, taken by the Italian physicist Antonio Pacinotti in the 1860s, was a reversible dynamo machine, an ideal prototype for a direct current electric motor and generator. Pacinotti did not find a favorable industrial environment in Italy and tried to commercialize his apparatus abroad. In 1869, the Belgian Zénobe-Théophile Gramme, a skilled mechanician, transformed "Pacinotti's ring" into an industrial product. With better generators and motors electricity could be used not only for arc lighting, which gained ground in the 1870s, but also for mechanical power.

During the last decades of the nineteenth century several inventors proposed types of incandescent lamps to challenge gas and oil illumination. The new lamps required a complex system of generators, cables, switches, electricity meters, fuses, and lamps. Edison developed the first commercially successful system in the early 1880s—a triumph based not only on technology, but clever advertising and lobbying as well.

Supplying electricity was one thing, metering it another. The standard laboratory instruments were too delicate and temperamental for extended use in factories and power plants. In the 1880s the American electrical engineer Edward Weston patented a series of solid, reliable voltmeters and ammeters easy for unskilled workers to use. Weston's measuring instruments proved to be so well designed that they were used with few modifications for more than a century.

In 1885, both the Italian physicist and engineer Galileo Ferraris and the Serbian-born American electrician Nikola Tesla discovered the principle of the rotating magnetic field and the induction motor. Ferraris, a university professor, did not care to develop his discovery industrially and built only a few pieces of demonstration apparatus. Tesla, an inventor, patented various types of motors and generators and laid down the principles of modern polyphase electrical systems, which the industrialist George Westinghouse exploited. The alternating-current system met with fierce opposition from the supporters of the existing direct-current technology. The subsequent "battle of the currents" turned more on economic and industrial strategies than on scientific arguments.

In 1888, physics professor Heinrich Hertz demonstrated the existence of the electromagnetic waves deducible from James Clerk Maxwell's equations. For several years these radio waves remained a lecture demonstration. Pioneers of wireless such as Oliver Joseph Lodge and Guglielmo Marconi faced the problem of detecting the waves over distances wider than lecture halls and transforming successful technology into a reliable commercial system. At the end of the nineteenth century, wave propagation was still mysterious; no one understood fully how antennas and detectors worked and the invention and improvement of wave detectors depended more on empirical trial and error, practical savoir-faire, and technical skill than on scientific research. Wireless experimenters advanced in an almost virgin field, or rather forest, and their work opened new perspectives to scientific research.

In the twentieth century, the booming electrical (and later electronic) industry increased demand for systematic

Nicola Tesla (1856–1943) entertaining electricians ca. 1900

research and development. The growing complexity, variety, and cost of apparatus, components, networks, and systems, necessitated rational planning. Industries developed their own research and development units. The boundary between laboratory research and workshop activity became even vaguer. Science tended increasingly toward industrialization and industry toward subordination to science.

PAOLO BRENNI

ELEMENTARY PARTICLES. Modern particle physics began with the end of World War II. Peace and the Cold War ushered in an era of new accelerators of ever increasing energy and intensity able to produce the particles that populate the subnuclear world. Simultaneously, particle detectors of ever increasing complexity and sensitivity recorded the imprints of high-energy subnuclear collisions. Challenges, opportunities, and resources attracted practitioners: the number of "high energy" physicists worldwide grew from a few hundred after World War II to some 8,000 in the early 1990s.

Developments in 1947 shaped the further evolution of particle physics. Experimental results regarding the decay of mesons observed at sea level presented to the Shelter Island conference led Robert Marshak to suggest that there existed two kinds of mesons. He identified the heavier one, the π meson, with the meson copiously produced in the upper atmosphere in nuclear collisions of cosmic-ray particles with atmospheric atoms and with the Yukawa particle responsible for nuclear forces. The lighter one, the μ meson observed at sea level, was the decay product of a π meson and interacted but weakly with matter. A similar suggestion had been made earlier by Shoichi Sakata in Japan. Within a year, Wilson Powell identified tracks showing the decay of a π into a μ meson in a nuclear emulsion sent aloft in a high altitude balloon. During the early 1950s the data obtained from particles produced in accelerators led to the rapid determination of the characteristic properties of the three varieties of π mesons.

The two-meson hypothesis suggested amendments to the list of particles. Some particles ("lep-tons")—the electron, muon, and neutrino—do not experience the strong nuclear forces. Others ("hadrons")—the neutron, proton, and the π-mesons do interact strongly with one another. It proved useful to split the hadrons into baryons and mesons. Baryons, of which the proton and neutron are the lightest representatives, have odd-half integer spin and (except for the proton) are unstable, one of the decay products always being a proton. Mesons have integer spin and when free ultimately decay into leptons or photons.

In January 1949, Jack Steinberger gave evidence that the μ-meson decays into an electron and two neutrinos, and shortly thereafter several theorists indicated that the process could be described in the same manner as an ordinary β-decay. Moreover, they pointed out that the coupling constant for this interaction had roughly the same magnitude as the constant in nuclear β-decay. Attempts then were made to extend an idea Oskar Klein had put forth in 1938, that a spin 1 particle, the "W boson," mediated the weak interactions and that the weakness of the β-decay interaction could be explained by making the W mesons sufficiently heavy.

During the first half of the 1950s theoretical attempts to explain pion-nucleon scattering and the nuclear forces were based on field theoretical models emulating quantum electrodymics (QED). The success of QED rested on the validity of perturbative expansions in powers of the coupling constant, $e^2/hc = 1/137$. However, for the meson theory of the pion-nucleon interaction the coupling constant had to

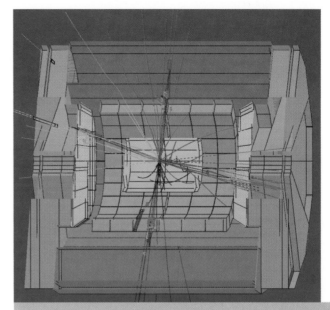

Computer graphic of the first creation of W particles at CERN in 1996 by a collision between a proton and an antiproton. Each W decays into a quark and an antiquark, which give rise to the four sprays of particles shown in pink, purple, and blue.

be large—around 15—to yield nuclear potentials that would bind the deuteron. No one found a valid method to deal with such strong couplings. By the end of the 1950s quantum field theory (QFT) faced a crisis because of its inability to describe the strong interactions and the impossibility of solving any of the realistic models that had been proposed to explain the dynamics of hadrons. Theorists abandoned efforts to develop a theory of the strong interactions along the model of QED, although Chen Ning Yang and Robert L. Mills advanced a local gauge theory of isotopic spin symmetry in 1954 that proved influential later on. Local gauge invariance, however, implies that the gauge bosons are massless. This is not the case for the pion and thus Yang and Mills's theory was considered an interesting model but not relevant for understanding the strong interactions.

The crisis in theoretical particle physics at the end of the 1950s inspired several responses. It led to the explorations of the generic properties of QFT when only such general principles as causality, the conservation of probability (unitarity), and relativistic invariance figured and no specific assumptions regarding the form of the interactions were made. Geoffrey Chew's S-matrix program that rejected QFT and attempted to formulate a theory that made use only of observables was more radical.

Another response to the crisis made symmetry concepts central. First applied to the weak and the electromagnetic interactions of the hadrons, symmetry considerations were later extended to encompass low-energy strong interactions. Symmetry became one of the fundamental concepts of modern particle physics, used as a classificatory and organizing tool and as a foundational principle to describe dynamics. Interest in field theories, and in particular in gauge theories, revived after theorists had appreciated the notion of spontaneous symmetry breaking (SSB). SSB allows a field theory to have a much richer underlying symmetry than that observed. Usually a symmetry expresses itself in such a way that the vacuum state of the theory is invariant under the symmetry that leaves the description of the dynamics (the Lagrangian) invariant. In the early 1960s, Julian Schwinger, Jeffrey Goldstone, Yoichiro Nambu, Steven Weinberg,

Engineer working on the BCDMS particle detector at CERN near Geneva, Switzerland, in 1978

Abdus Salam, and others noted that in quantum field theories symmetries could be realized differently: the Lagrangian could be invariant under some symmetry, without the symmetry applying to the ground state of the theory. Such symmetries are called "spontaneously broken" (SBS).

In 1967 Weinberg, and in 1968 Salam, independently proposed a gauge theory of the weak interactions that unified the electromagnetic and the weak interactions and made use of the Higgs mechanism, which generates the masses of the particles associated with the gauge theory. Their model incorporated previous suggestions by Sheldon Glashow (1961) for formulating a gauge theory in which the gauge bosons mediated weak forces. The renormalizability of such theories—the existence of consistent algorithms for extracting finite contributions from every order of perturbation theory—was proved by Gerard 't Hooft in his dissertation in 1972. The status of the Glashow-Weinberg-Salam theory changed dramatically in consequence. As Sidney Cole-man noted in his article in *Science* describing the award of the Nobel Prize to Glashow, Salam, and Weinberg in 1978, "'t Hooft's kiss transformed Weinberg's frog into an enchanted prince."

As presently described, a common mechanism underlies the strong, weak, and electromagnetic interactions. Each is mediated by the exchange of a spin 1 gauge boson. The gauge bosons of the strong interactions are called gluons, those of the weak interactions, $W^{\pm}$ and Z bosons, and those of electromagnetism, photons. The charges are often called "colors": QED, the paradigmatic gauge theory, works with a single gauge boson, the photon, coupled to a single "color," namely the electric charge. The gauge bosons of the strong interactions carry a three-valued color, those of the weak interactions carry a "two-dimensional" weak color charge. Weak gauge bosons interact with quarks and leptons and some of them, when emitted or absorbed, can transform one kind of quark or lepton into another. When these gauge bosons are exchanged between leptons and quarks they are responsible for the force between them. They can also be emitted as radiation when the quarks or leptons accelerate.

Quantum chromodynamics (QCD) describes the strong interactions between the six quarks: the up and the down, the charmed and the strange, and the top and the bottom. They are usually denoted by u, d, c, s, t and b. Evidence for the top quark was advanced in the fall of 1994 and confirmed in the spring of 1995. Quarks carry electrical charge and in addition a "three dimensional" strong color charge. QCD is a gauge theory with three colors, eight massless gluons, and color-carrying gauge bosons, six that alter color and two that merely react to it. Gluons do not carry color in the same way as quarks do; they carry a color-anticolor, which enables them to interact with one another.

In QFT the vacuum is a dynamic entity. Within any small volume of space-time the root mean square values of the field strengths (electric and magnetic in QED, color-gluon field in QCD) averaged over the volume do not vanish. Virtual particle-antiparticle pairs are constantly being created, and as demanded by the energy-time uncertainty relations, particle and anti-particle annihilate one another shortly thereafter without traveling very far. These virtual pairs can be polarized in much the same way as molecules in a dielectric solid. Thus in QED the presence of an electric charge e_0 polarizes the "vacuum," and the charge that is observed at a large distance differs from e_0 and is given by $e = e_0/\epsilon$, with ϵ the dielectric constant of the vacuum. The dielectric constant depends on the distance (or equivalently, in a relativistic setting on energy) and in this way the notion of a "running charge" varying with the distance being probed, or equivalently varying with the energy scale, is introduced. Virtual dielectric screening tends to make the effective charge smaller at large distances. Similarly virtual quarks and leptons tend to screen the color charge they carry.

It turns out however that non-Abelian gauge theories like QCD have the property that virtual gluons "antiscreen" any color charge placed in the vacuum (and in fact overcome the screening due to the quarks). This means that a color charge that is observed to be big at large distances originates in a charge that is weaker at short distances, and in fact vanishingly small as $r \rightarrow 0$. This phenomenon has been called asymptotic freedom. The discovery of the antiscreening in spin 1 non Abelian gauge theories was made independently by 't Hooft in 1972, and by David Politzer and by David Gross and Frank Wilczek in 1973: non-Abelian gauge theories behave at short distances approximately as a free (non-interacting) theory. This behavior, called *asymptotic* freedom, could explain in a natural way the SLAC experiments on deep inelastic scattering of electrons by protons. Some physicists speculate that in non-Abelian gauge theories the complement to asymptotic freedom at short distances is confinement at large distances. This would explain the nonobservability of free quarks. In other words, even though the forces among quarks become vanishingly small at short distances, the force between them increases very strongly at large distances. Although to this day confinement has not been proved in a rigorous fashion, nonperturbative calculations point to the correctness of the assumption.

The past two decades have seen many successful explanations of high-energy phenomena using QCD. The detection and identification of the $W^{\pm}$ and of the Z_0 in 1983 by Carlo Rubbia and coworkers at CERN gave further confirmation. Similarly, the empirical data obtained in lepton and photon deep inelastic scattering, and in the study of jets in high energy collisions, can be accounted for quantitatively by QCD. Furthermore, computer simulations have presented convincing evidence that QCD confines quarks and gluons inside hadrons. Frank Wilczek, one of the important contributors to the field, remarked at a conference in 1992 devoted to an assessment of QCD that it had become mature enough to be placed in its "conceptual universe with appropriate perspective."

SILVAN S. SCHWEBER

ELEMENTS, CHEMICAL. Antoine-Laurent Lavoisier's *Traité élémentaire de chimie* (1789) introduced the modern definition of elements. Lavoisier explicitly rejected the obsolete four-element theory of matter, dating to Empedocles and Aristotle, in which everything was believed to be composed of earth, air, fire, and water, combined in varying proportions. The supposed four elements conveyed different pairs of essential qualities: earth the cold and dry; water, cold and wet; fire, hot and dry; air, hot and wet. One prediction from the four-element theory that Lavoisier specifically refuted was the transmutability of water into earth.

Lavoisier proposed that the term "elements," or principles of bodies, should refer only to the endpoint of observational analysis—those substances into which bodies have been reduced by decomposition. This made experiment the final arbiter and so improved on Robert Boyle's earlier more metaphysical definition of elements as perfectly unmixed bodies. Lavoisier drew up a list of thirty-three elements, or simple substances, including metallic and nonmetallic solids; earthy substances; the gases oxygen, nitrogen (azote), and hydrogen; and light and heat (caloric). Louis Bernard Guyton de Morveau, Antoine François de Fourcroy, and Claude Louis Berthollet were among Lavoisier's collaborators who also contributed to what became known as an eighteenth-century revolution in chemistry.

The new chemistry regarded an element as a simple substance with observable properties; compound substances were made up of one, two, or more simple substances. In his *New System of Chemical Philosophy* (1808–1810), the natural philosopher John Dalton identified each of the simple substances or elements with indivisible atomic particles and characteristic combining weights. Dalton devised combinatorial rules and visual images to describe the composition of ordinary bodies by fixed numbers of atom elements, taking hydrogen to be the smallest and lightest element, with an arbitrary atomic weight of 1 unit.

Between 1790 and 1844, thirty-one new elements were discovered, although in some cases without separation from their oxides. Chemists identified these elements and their properties by traditional analytical techniques, supplemented in the early nineteenth century by electrochemical decomposition and replacement by potassium. No further elements were identified until 1860, when Robert Bunsen and Gustav Kirchhoff noted unusual blue spectral lines in the spectrum of a salt. They gave the name "cesium" (from Latin *caesius*, "blue of the firmament") to the supposed emitter. The following year they discovered rubidium from its dark red spectral lines in certain alkaline compounds. The spectroscope figured in the discovery of thallium by William Crookes in 1861, and of indium in 1863, gallium, the rare earths, and the noble gases.

With the proliferation of elements beyond Lavoisier's table of thirty-three, many natural philosophers and chemists speculated that there must be an underlying basic material in all simple substances. In 1815, William Prout proposed hydrogen as the basic building block, citing the experimental result that gas densities appeared to be exact multiples of the density of hydrogen. Tests of Prout's hypothesis continued over the next decades, even as chemists disagreed whether to take hydrogen or oxygen as the most effective standard for calculating relative combining weights of chemical elements, or atoms. By 1860, chemists were convinced that the careful measurements of Jean-Servais Stas demonstrated that atomic weights could not be multiples of 1 or 0.5 or 0.25 as a fundamental protyle.

In 1860, approximately 140 chemists convened at an international chemistry congress in Karlsruhe to discuss standardization of conventions for atomic weights and molecular formulas. Charles Frédéric Gerhardt's system, in which water has the composition H_2O (H = 1, C = 12, and O = 16), was widely adopted. During the era, scientists including Johann Wolfgang Döbereiner, Alexandre-Émile Béguyer de Chancourtois, and John Newlands attempted systematic groupings of the elements. During the 1860s, Dmitrii Mendeleev, professor of technical chemistry in St. Petersburg, used Gerhardt's formula convention, along with combining values, or valences, and the analysis of other properties to develop what he called a natural system of the elements. By early 1869, Mendeleev arrived at a law relating atomic weights to periodicity of properties. His periodic table left blank spaces for unknown elements. The idea of natural families also informed the table of elements published in 1864 by Lothar Meyer. In 1870, Meyer first used increasing atomic weights as the basis of vertical arrangement, complemented by horizontal arrangement of families, and a separate graphical figure plotting atomic weights against atomic volumes. Meyer's short paper of March 1870 brought wide attention to Mendeleev's publication of the previous year.

In 1875, Paul Émile Lecoq de Boisbaudran discovered the element gallium, which fit neatly into Mendeleev's blank space below aluminum, an important confirmation of his law of periodicity. Other predicted elements followed in 1879 (scandium) and 1886 (germanium). The known rare earths doubled in number from 1869 to 1886 and proved difficult to classify. In 1913, Henry G. J. Moseley demonstrated the existence of a constant relationship between the frequency of the shortest x-ray line emitted by an element and what Moseley, following A. Van den Broek, termed atomic number, beginning with 1 for hydrogen. Moseley correctly predicted that there must be ninety-two natural elements up to and including uranium. Atomic number replaced atomic weight as the organizing principle for the periodic table of the elements.

Radioactivity produced elements possessing the same atomic numbers and chemical properties as well-known chemical elements, but with different atomic weights. Frederick Soddy coined the term "isotope" to signify any of these chemically identical "elements." In 1912, Joseph John Thomson obtained results suggesting that the inert gas neon (atomic number 10) is a mixture of neon atoms weighing 20 and 22. After World War I, Francis Aston designed a mass spectrograph that sorted out ions by weight and determined that isotopes can be found generally among the chemical elements. Thus a chemical element had a unique atomic number, but an average atomic weight determined by the relative abundance of its isotopes.

Following James Chadwick's discovery of the neutron in 1932, physicists and chemists systematically irradiated elements of the periodic table. Enrico Fermi and his collaborators found that neutrons that had been slowed down were more effective than fast neutrons in producing radioactive isotopes. Fermi's group believed that it had created elements heavier than uranium (atomic weight 238 and atomic number 92) when, in 1934, their irradiations of uranium produced new activities. Similar work by Irène Joliot-Curie and Frédéric Joliot and by Lise Meitner, Otto Hahn, and Fritz Strassmann, resulted in the discovery of uranium fission.

In 1940, Edwin M. McMillan and Philip H. Abelson produced the transuranium element 93 (neptunium) by bombarding uranium with neutrons in a Berkeley cyclotron. Glenn T. Seaborg and his colleagues produced element 94 (plutonium) in the same way in 1941.

At the end of the twentieth century, scientists recognized 112 elements. Of these, 90 occur in nature either free or in combination with other elements; three (atomic numbers 110–112) had not been named formally by the end of 2000. Since the introduction of Mendeleev's and Meyer's tables of 1869 and 1870, the form for the classification of the elements by means of a periodic system has changed remarkably little. The current asymmetrical rectangular table, in which the lathanide series (numbers 57–70) and the actinide series (numbers 89–102) fall outside the main body of the table was largely the design of Seaborg. A pyramidal periodic table, a form originally favored by Niels Bohr, has been proposed but has not come into general use despite its more symmetrical appearance. The elements are today recognized not as simple substances in the physical meaning of undecomposable primary matter, but as basic substances in

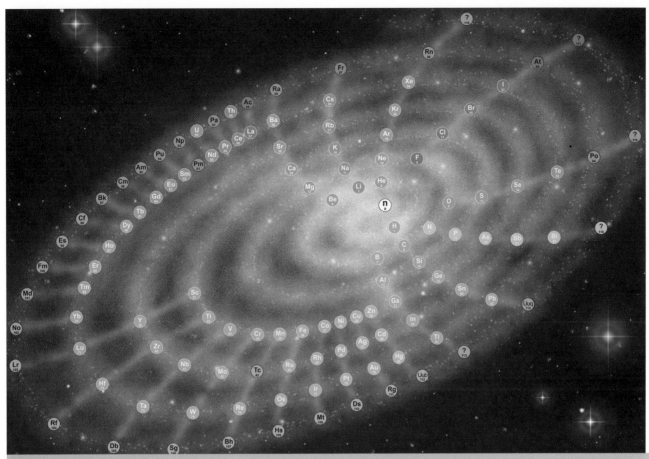

Periodic table represented as a galaxy, the lighter elements nearer the center. The halogens are in red, transition metals in green, lanthanides and actinides in blue.

E

the chemical sense of fundamental matter that exists freely or virtually in all known bodies.

MARY JO NYE

EMBRYOLOGY. The embryo and its development have been investigated since antiquity and, with few exceptions until the early nineteenth century, under the heading "generation." During the mid-1900s, the term "embryology" denoted the branch of anatomy or physiology concerned with the development of the individual before birth. At the end of the nineteenth century the perception of embryology as a distinct discipline encouraged some universities to establish chairs in "embryology and histology." Given the sensitive character of their subject matter, embryological investigations often reflected deep religious, philosophical, and gender beliefs and influenced legal and social issues.

By breaking open day after day eggs hatched by a hen, Aristotle recorded a sequence of observations on the development of the chick. On the third day he observed a palpitating heart and later distinguished a head with prominent eyes clearly separate from the rest of the body. Aristotle held that the first organ to develop in the embryo was the heart, which he considered to be the control core of animal life and the source of vital heat. He also maintained that death occurred when the heart stopped beating. During the Renaissance Aristotle's observations on the developing chick, a subsidiary part of his theory of generation, were replicated and examined by Ulisse Aldrovandi, Volcher Coiter, and Girolamo Fabrici, who investigated many viviparous animals using a comparative approach (*Deformatione ovi et pulli*, 1621).

Drawing an analogy with shipbuilding, Fabrici believed that the embryo would build itself up from a bony frame-

work, a view harshly criticized by his pupil William Harvey in his *De generation animalium* (1651). Harvey based his theories on numerous observations and dissections of domestic fowl and deer carried out over many years. Although he never saw the ova of vivipera, he postulated that all female animals produced them and that their development followed the pattern of ovipera. Because his dissections of the uteri of fowl and deer after mating never revealed conception in the form of a mixture of male and female semen, he rejected ancient doctrines of conception. Instead, he held that females produced eggs endowed with a vitality that, with no material contribution, could be stimulated to develop by the male's semen. By focusing on a little scar (Fabrici's *cicatricula*, i.e., the blastoderm) on the surface of the hen's fertilized egg, Harvey made his most important discovery, namely that after the first day it started germinating. He also described how the chick developed from the *cicatricula* by budding and subdivision in sequence. He named this process "epigenesis." Contrary to Aristotle, Harvey maintained that the blood and not the heart formed first.

During the second half of the seventeenth and the eighteenth centuries, many scholars opposed Harvey's epigenesis with the alternative theory that development consisted in the unfolding and growth of all the parts of the adult organism, which pre-existed miniaturized in the egg. In his *Dissertatio epistolica de formatione pulli in ovo* (1673), Marcello Malpighi compared the development of the chick to that of plants, considered the intake of food from the yolk and albumen, and described how the parts of the embryo change shape and position before acquiring resemblance to their adult form. His description of embryogenesis and his discoveries (e.g., of

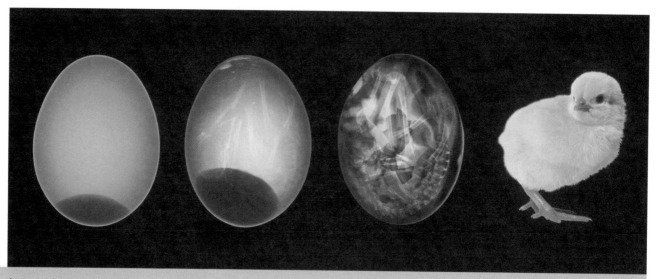

Colored X-ray photographs of the development of a chicken. Left to right: at six days, twelve days, eighteen days, and 21 days

the cardiac tube, the neural folds, and the neural tube) had a profound impact upon embryological research.

During the eighteenth century the opposition between these two main views of embryogenesis culminated in the controversy between Albrecht von Haller's mechanistic preformationism and Caspar Friedrich Wolff's vitalistic epigenesis. Wolff maintained that, just as plants formed from the structureless substance of the vegetational bud, so the chick emerged from a homogeneous primordium through the secretion and solidification of fluids regulated by a *vis essentialis* (essential force) present in living matter (*Theorie von der Generation*, 1764). Despite Wolff's denial that organs pre-existed in a latent form and his insistence that preformation was a chimera, epigenesis acquired preeminence only during the nineteenth century.

The period 1820 to 1880, the age of classical descriptive embryology, saw the seminal works of Christian Heinrich Pander, Karl Ernst von Baer, Martin Heinrich Rathke, Rudolf Albert von Koelliker, Robert Remak, Ernst Haeckel, Oscar Hertwig, Richard Hertwig, Francis Maitland Balfour, Aleksandr Kovalevsky, and others. Improvements of the microscope first, and then the combined introduction of the microtome and staining techniques, helped overcome some of the technical barriers that had frustrated previous investigators in their observations. Study of the embryo was much influenced by morphology in the 1820s and 1830s, by cell theory in the 1840s and 1850s, and by the theory of evolution from the 1860s onwards. It was also influenced by the ideal, typical of the century, of furnishing historical explanations. Applied to the embryo, this ideal postulated that knowledge of the organization of living entities could be achieved only by investigating their gradual development. It also suggested a parallelism between the stages of development of the individual organism and the long-term transformations of the entire animal series.

One major contribution of early nineteenth century embryology was the doctrine of germ layers. In 1817, Pander described how the chick's blastoderm (a term he introduced) developed into three separate layers, which he considered to be the antecedents of later structures (*Beiträge zur Entwicklungsgeschichte des Hühnchens im Eye*). In the 1820s, von Baer maintained that the germ-layer concept applied to other vertebrates as well, and Rathke extended it to invertebrates. In papers published between 1850 and 1855, Remak demonstrated that germ layers consisted of cells. Thus the

goal of much embryological research of the time became that of tracing the origin of a single organ to a specific germ layer. In 1867–1871 Kovalevsky reported compelling observations that evidenced the universality and specificity of the germ layers. "Mesoderm" was coined in 1871, and "ectoderm" and "endoderm" in 1872, to denote the three germ layers. The doctrine of the absolute specificity of the germ layers has been disputed by more recent embryological research, which has emphasized the interactions among the layers as they develop.

Perhaps the most significant contribution of embryology during the early eighteenth century was the clarification of the fertilization mechanism. In papers published in 1824–1825 Jean-Louis Prevost and Jean-Baptiste-André Dumas described filtering experiments that showed that spermatozoa played an essential role in fertilization, and in 1827 von Baer announced the discovery of the egg, first in dogs and then in other mammals (*De ovi mammalium et hominis genesi*). In 1841, Koelliker argued for the cellular origin of spermatozoa and in 1844 suggested that the ovum is a cell. In the early 1850s Remak proved the cellular nature of the egg and argued that the original fertilized egg with its nuclear content underwent a process of division (cleavage) until it formed the germ layers. At that time, however, the prevailing theory of fertilization still denied that spermatozoa made any material contribution to the embryo. A host of investigations of animals and plants conducted by many scholars between 1875 and 1880 led to the conclusion that fertilization consisted in the union of a part of one spermatozoon or pollen with an egg or ovule. This fusion of two cells produced the unicellular fertilized egg that only then began dividing to form the embryo. This theory aroused great excitement because it explained the continuity of life by establishing a bond between generations through the transfer of some material substance from the parents to the new individual.

Nineteenth-century embryology sought laws of development. Von Baer enumerated four laws, which account for his endorsement of epigenesis and the existence of different types of embryonic development, and therefore the organisations that he had distinguished (radiates, articulates, mollusks, and vertebrates). In post-Darwinian thought the notion of evolutionary change eroded the type concept. A major problem, therefore, was envisaging a law that considered the results obtained by descriptive embryology and simultaneously accounted for individual and ancestral development. A law, later known as the biogenetic law, formulated by Haeckel in 1866 stated that ontogeny (the development of the individual) briefly recapitulates phylogeny (the development of the organic lineage to which it belongs) determined by heredity and adaptation (*Generelle Morphologie der Organismen*, 1866). This law had considerable impact upon nonspecialists as well and acquired dogma-like status. The next generation of embryologists raised doubts about recapitulation and, in order to gain better understanding of the mechanisms of development, turned once again to problems of causation, this time however by experimenting directly on the embryo.

RENATO G. MAZZOLINI

ENCYCLOPEDIAS. We owe the word "encyclopaedia" to Quintilian's Latinized version of the Greek term denoting a circle of study or learning. This concept came to inform the notion of the seven liberal arts that passed into the medieval university curriculum. This set of favored subjects included geometry and some natural knowledge and appears in all major medieval and Renaissance encyclopedias, for example Gregor Reisch's *Margarita Philosophica* (1496) and Johann Heinrich Alsted's *Encyclopaedia* (1 vol., 1620).

During the early eighteenth century, a new encyclopedic genre, the dictionary of arts and sciences, made its appearance. It included information on the arts and crafts that had previously been excluded from liberal sciences and the universities. Antoine Furetière's *Dictionnaire Universel* (3 vols., 1690) and John Harris's *Lexicon Technicum* (2 vols., 1704, 1710) were the first examples. These works differed from the historical dictionaries of the time, such as Louis Moréri's *Grand Dictionnaire Historique* (2 vols., 1674) and Pierre Bayle's *Dictionnaire Historique et Critique* (2 vols., 1697), which covered history, geography, and biography rather than the arts and sciences. Knowledge was becoming specialized. The *Grosses vollständiges Universal Lexicon*, begun in 1732 by the Leipzig publisher Johann Zedler, which has entries on scientific topics as well as on history, theology, philosophy, and biography, reached sixty-four folio volumes by 1750. The much slimmer dictionaries of arts and sciences did not have biographical entries and treated history and geography only insofar as they were relevant to the account of technical terms.

These so-called "scientific dictionaries" focused on natural, mathematical, and craft or technical knowledge. The strength of Harris's *Lexicon* in mixed-mathematical subjects and their application in areas such as navigation, architecture, fortification, gunnery, and shipbuilding earned him the nickname "technical Harris." A member of the Royal Society (serving as its secretary in 1710), Harris incorporated substantial quotations from Isaac Newton's *Opticks* (1704), which had just come out in English translation, and inserted an unpublished paper by Newton on acids in the second volume. Ephraim Chambers's *Cyclopaedia* (2 vols., 1728) built more widely on Harris's foundations. It claimed to contain a well-rounded course of ancient and modern learning, thus justifying its use of "cyclopaedia." Like Harris, Chambers covered subjects still categorized as scientia, such as law, grammar, music, and theology. He gave more attention to crafts and trades that fell outside the area of practical mathematics treated by Harris: paper, soap- and glass-making, mining, forging, weaving, bleaching, dying, tanning, and the manufacture of cloth and pins. But Chambers distinguished between "Mechanical Arts . . . wherein the Hand, and Body are more concern'd than the Mind"

and the mechanical sciences. In keeping with the implied preference, the *Cyclopaedia* was stronger on the "sciences" than the "arts," although later editions promised to improve the coverage of trades and manufacturing arts.

The content of these dictionaries of arts and sciences gives a clue to their commercial success. They provided information on subjects, such as the mechanical arts, excluded from university education together with detailed entries on the major mathematical and physical sciences: the dictionaries of Harris and Chambers amounted to practical manuals and Newtonian textbooks. Both appeared on study guides at Cambridge, and students were directed to read particular entries. Harris and Chambers treated chemistry, medicine, and natural history less fully, possibly because specialist lexicons for these subjects already existed. They met a need not only in England but also in Europe. Chambers's *Cyclopaedia* appeared in two Italian translations (Venice, 1748–1749, and Naples, 1747–1754), and inspired the creation of the greatest of all the eighteenth-century compendia of knowledge, the *Encyclopedie, ou Dictionnaire raisonné des arts et sciences* of Denis Diderot and Jean Le Rond d'Alembert (17 vols. of text and 11 vols. of plates, 1751–1772).

Eighteenth-century encyclopedias were published and sold by subscription. This method, introduced by English booksellers early in the seventeenth century, tested the market for large and expensive works. A prospectus announcing the work gave the names of subscribers and helped recruit additional ones. The range of occupations represented in these lists—from bishops and physicians to watchmakers

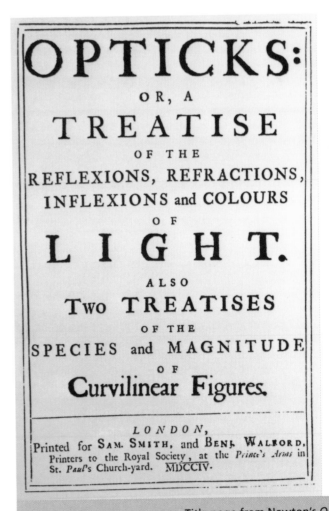

Title page from Newton's *Opticks*

and printers—indicate the breadth of the market. The first volume of Harris's *Lexicon* cost twenty-five shillings, and Chambers's two folios cost four guineas, both expensive compared with the price of monthly magazines, about six pence an issue in 1750. Subscription and serialization placed the early English scientific dictionaries within the reach of a wider group of readers than the first edition of the *Encyclopédie*, which initially cost 280 livres (around 11 guineas) and rose to 980 livres (40 guineas) by the 1770s.

Three significant changes in encyclopedias may be discerned over the course of the eighteenth century. First, the scope and importance of the nonscientific content increased: although the *Encyclopédie* did not admit biographical entries, it boasted large and sometimes controversial essays on topics in history, literature, music, art, politics, and philosophy. Perhaps its most distinguished feature, apart from its anticlericalism, was its comprehensive documentation of the arts, crafts, and trades, which it illustrated with some 2,500 engravings. In this aspect of their work, the encyclopedists claimed inspiration from the philosophy of Francis Bacon.

Second, the format shifted from relatively compressed entries on terms (the style of both Harris and Chambers) to longer essays, still arranged alphabetically. The *Encyclopaedia Britannica,* issued in one hundred installments from 1768 and published in Edinburgh in three volumes in 1771, departed from the format of the earlier dictionaries of arts and sciences, presenting the sciences as "systems" in separate treatises of at least twenty-five pages each. The *Encyclopédie Méthodique* (66 vols., 1782–1832)—the successor to the *Encyclopédie*—amounts to a set of specialist treatises, in which, in the words of a contemporary reviewer, "every science will have its dictionary, or system, apart."

The third development was the recruitment of specialists to write the articles. The *Encyclopédie* engaged some of the most distinguished natural philosophers and academicians of France, especially Gabriel François Venel in chemistry, Louis-Jean-Marie Daubenton in anatomy and zoology, Nicolas Desmarest in geology, and, of course, d'Alembert in mathematics. The third edition of the *Britannica* (10 vols., 1788–1797) followed suit. Whereas William Smellie (the main compiler of its first edition) wrote many of its treatises by collating from various books, the third edition brought in experts. For its six-volume *Supplement,* its editor, Macvey Napier, commissioned leading men of science to update articles, such as those in natural philosophy formerly done by the Edinburgh professor John Robison.

British competitors of the *Britannica* such as Abraham Rees's *New Cyclopaedia* (45 vols., 1802–1819), David Brewster's *Edinburgh Encyclopaedia* (18 vols., 1809–1830), and the *Encyclopaedia Metropolitana* (28 vols., 1829–1845) all gave science high priority and sought out leading contributors. The *Metropolitana* boasted contributions from Charles Babbage and John Herschel, who wrote extensive treatises on astronomy, light, and sound. The ninth edition of the *Britannica* (1875–1889) responded with "Physical Sciences" by James Clerk Maxwell and "Evolution in Biology" by Thomas Henry Huxley.

All but one of these nineteenth-century works abandoned the maps of knowledge that delineated the relationships between the branches of science. The exception, the *Metropolitana,* was arranged not alphabetically, but rather on a classification published in 1817 by Samuel Taylor Coleridge that placed subjects in logical or systematic order. All branches of mathematics preceded Herschel's articles on light and sound because these subjects assumed prior mathematical knowl-

edge. The *Metropolitana* did follow the nineteenth-century practice of assigning detailed articles on scientific disciplines to experts, which raised concerns about the role of encyclopedias as a medium for the public communication of knowledge. The *Britannica* eventually found a solution. Its great eleventh edition of 1911 marked the high tide of the expert article. It then floated from Cambridge University Press to the United States, at first to Sears, Roebuck and Company and later to the University of Chicago Press. From the 1930s it was sold by door-to-door salesmen as an indispensable aid to social success. The revised fifteenth edition (from 1974) of the *Encyclopaedia Britannica,* which is now published by an independent corporation, came in two versions: a "micropaedia" for quick reference and a "macropaedia" for detailed specialist articles. This division resolved the tension between the interests of most people and the scholarly imperative.

During the nineteenth and twentieth centuries, European countries and the Soviet Union created encyclopedias emphasizing their national cultures within the international circle of knowledge. The most important of these works for the history of science is the *Enciclopedia Italiana* with its collateral publications. They are the products of the Istituto della Enciclopedia Italiana, founded in 1927 by the industrialist Giovanni Treccani and directed in its scientific program by the philosopher Giovanni Gentile. The *Enciclopedia* itself, complete in thirty-six massive volumes (1929–1939), is among the world's best. When supplemented by the Istituto's *Dizionario biografico degli Italiani* (now to the letter "G" in 55 volumes, 1960 to the present) and its specialized series in art, architecture, and so on, it represents the grandest attainment of the encyclopedia as a cultural resource. The Istituto is currently publishing a *Storia della scienza,* which will extend encyclopedism with an encyclopedia of the history of science twenty times the size of this Companion.

RICHARD YEO

ENDOCRINOLOGY. The clinical specialty of endocrinology is less than a century old, but knowledge of endocrine diseases and the structures and functions of the endocrine glands has a much longer history. The physicians of antiquity described the effects of castration and diseases such as diabetes and treated simple enlargement of the thyroid (goiter) with burnt sponge or seaweed, now known to contain iodine. The anatomy of the testes, ovaries, thyroid, pituitary gland, and adrenals was long known, although as separate structures, rather than a loosely connected endocrine system. In the eighteenth century, Albrecht von Haller noted the existence of "glands without ducts," which he distinguished from ducted ones such as the salivary and sweat glands. A century later Claude Bernard crystallized the notion of "internal secretion" when he distinguished between the "external" secretion of bile by the liver and its internal one of sugar.

Despite these and many other anatomical, physiological, and pathological insights, endocrinology as a coherent body of knowledge did not emerge until the early twentieth century. It then carried with it the newsworthy but ambiguous legacy of Charles-Edouard Brown-Séquard, a serious scientific clinician who introduced in the 1880s testicular extracts as a sensational agent of rejuvenation. Brown-Séquard's death soon after his self-experimentation deflated the notion of frolicking octogenarians, but a second potent endocrine extract, from the thyroid gland, had demonstrable physiological effects. By the 1890s, the cluster of clinical conditions variously described as cretinism, myxoedema, and cachexia strumipriva had been referred to a failure of the thyroid gland. In 1891, George Murray reported the successful treatment of myxoedema with thyroid extract. That the mixture also acted as a stimulant gave it wider appeal, and it was frequently prescribed for lethargy, obesity, and general malaise.

The hormone concept appeared in 1902, when the British physiologists William Bayliss and Ernest Starling identified in the mucosa of the duodenum a substance they called "secretin." It could stimulate secretion by the pancreas even when the neurological connections were severed. This action pointed towards a chemical stimulus; three years later Starling called this class of substances "hormones," from the Greek for "to excite." The subsequent coining of the word "endocrine," from Greek words for "within" and "separate," codified the notion that hormones flow directly into the bloodstream and act on other organs or cells without the intermediating functions of the nervous system. Edward Sharpey-Schafer's monograph *The Endocrine Organs* (1916) helped define the field. He had earlier (with George Oliver) isolated a blood-pressure raising hormone of the adrenals, adrenaline. Although it took some time for the clinical specialty to rid itself of the enthusiastic claims of an earlier generation, Sharpey-Schafer's scientific synthesis firmly established its experimental roots.

The dramatic therapeutic potentials of the discipline were realized in 1921 when Frederick Grant Banting and Charles Herbert Best isolated insulin, one of the active endocrine products of the pancreas. The Nobel Prize two years later went to Banting and J. J. R. Macleod, in whose lab the work took place, but Banting shared his prize with Best and Macleod his with James Bertram Collip, the biochemist who had assisted in its purification. The relative contributions of the four men have been much debated, but insulin itself stood out as a major therapeutic breakthrough in the treatment of diabetes. The interwar period proved to be a fertile time for endocrinology, with new biochemical and bioassay techniques to identify and purify many active hormones from the ovaries, testes, adrenals, pituitary, thyroid, and parathyroids. In 1936, Edward Doisy (who shared the 1943 Nobel Prize for his work on Vitamin K) defined four criteria by which hormones could be identified. These were: 1: a gland must be identified as producing an internal secretion; 2: the substance must be detectable; 3: it must be capable of being purified; and 4: the pure substance needs to be isolated, purified, and studied chemically. This followed his research on the role of ovarian hormones on the estrus cycle, which in turn laid the foundation for the development of hormonal contraceptives as well as agents to treat menstrual and other gynecological disorders.

Research on the several endocrine glands clarified that hormones belong to various classes of bioactive substances. These include steroids (the gonads and adrenal cortex), catecholamines (adrenal medulla), iodinated amino acids (thyroid), and proteins and active peptides (anterior and posterior pituitary, pancreas, gut, parathyroids, and thyroid). Work on the pituitary by Pierre Marie, Harvey Cushing, and many others proved to be especially significant. Not only does the pituitary synthesize many of the central hormones that regulate peripheral production (through a subtle

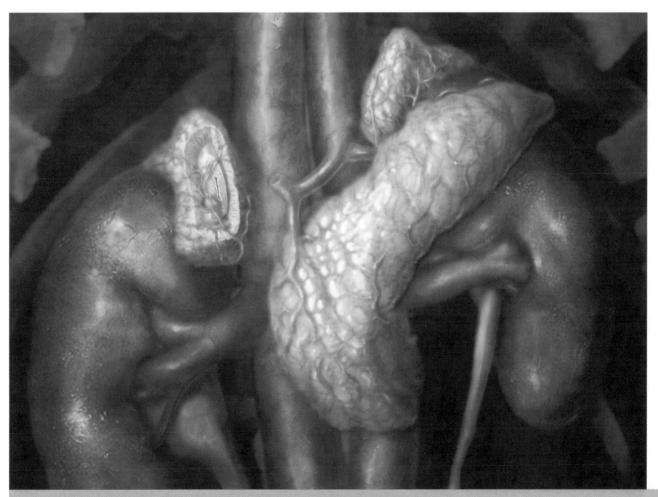

Three-dimensional visualization of endocrine glands reconstructed from scanned human data

E

system of negative feedback), it is in intimate contact with the hypothalamus, an area of the brain that also has important controlling functions on the nervous system, especially the autonomic system. The earlier notion that the endocrine system stands functionally apart from the nervous system has thus been fundamentally modified.

Research during the past half-century has been aimed primarily at clarifying the chemical structures, synthetic pathways, and molecular modes of actions of the diverse group of substances called hormones. Since these are involved in many fundamental physiological processes such as metabolism, digestion, growth, reproduction, salt-and-water maintenance, and the interaction of the organism with its environment, endocrinology has maintained its close ties with basic science, especially molecular biology. The complexity of the system allows many ways for it to go awry; the clinical discipline is now sub-specialized, with diabetes, gynecological endocrinology, and the thyroid each having its own group of specialists. Endocrinological surgery is now a recognized specialty, especially important in the treatment of tumors of the endocrine organs.

W. F. BYNUM

ENERGETICS. The great unsettled question of late-nineteenth-century physics was the status of the mechanical worldview. For more than two hundred years—from René Descartes, Christiaan Huygens, and Isaac Newton in the seventeenth century to Hermann von Helmholtz, Heinrich Hertz, and Ludwig Boltzmann at the end of the nineteenth—physicists had generally sought mechanical explanations for natural phenomena. As the nineteenth century drew to a close, Hertz reaffirmed the classical goal of physical theory: "All physicists agree," he wrote in the preface to his *Principles of Mechanics* (1894), "that the problem of physics consists in tracing the phenomena of nature back to the simple laws of mechanics." But when these words were published, physicists were no longer in general agreement about the nature of their project. Many doubted, and some explicitly denied, that mechanics was the most basic science. Other candidates contended for the honor—thermodynamics and electromagnetic theory, in particular, and several comprehensive alternatives to the mechanical worldview were proposed and vigorously debated throughout the 1890s and early 1900s.

Energetics was one of the alternatives. Tracing its origins to the founders of the law of energy conservation, especially Robert Mayer, and to the thermodynamic writings of Rudolf Clausius, William Thomson (Lord Kelvin), and Josiah Willard Gibbs, energetics attempted to unify all of natural science through the concept of energy and by laws describing energy in its various forms. The energeticists believed that scientists should abandon their efforts to understand the natural world in mechanical terms and should give up atomism as well in favor of a new worldview based entirely on relations among quantities of energy.

Energetics as a scientific project of the late 1880s and 1890s took place largely in Germany. (A prominent exception was the work of the French physicist Pierre Duhem.) Its main German proponents were Georg Helm, a Dresden mathematician and physicist, and Wilhelm Ostwald, the professor of physical chemistry at Leipzig. Helm first urged the formulation of a "general energetics" in his *Theory of Energy* (1887), which proposed an "energy principle" (a law more general than the law of energy conservation) as its basis. An essay in 1890 sought to reduce mechanics to

energetics by means of this energy principle, and another in 1892 was intended to do the same for electricity and magnetism. In 1894, Helm wrote a book on the energetic development of physical chemistry. These publications elicited an invitation to address the German Association of Scientists and Physicians at their meeting in Lübeck in 1895 on "the current state of energetics."

Ostwald's interest in energy stemmed from his reading, in mid-1886, of Dutch chemist Jacobus van't Hoff's studies in chemical dynamics and from his own efforts, in the late 1880s, to understand the thermodynamic writings of Gibbs, which Ostwald published in German translation in 1892. He was soon converted to the way of "pure energetics," the theory of which he developed in two essays published in 1891 and 1892. He then refined his theory and applied it to a variety of problems in general and physical chemistry in 1893–1894. Always the enthusiast, Ostwald traveled to the 1895 meeting in Lübeck, where he was also on the program, to demonstrate the demise of the mechanical worldview and to promote energetics as its proper replacement.

The heated debate at Lübeck turned out to be a disaster for energetics. The negative reactions of Boltzmann and Max Planck to the energeticists were taken as definitive by younger physicists such as Arnold Sommerfeld and Albert Einstein. Helm and Ostwald later replied to these criticisms, only to be rebutted again by Boltzmann (1896–1898). Ostwald published his *History of Electrochemistry* in 1896; Ernst Mach likely hurried his (incomplete) *Theory of Heat* into print in the same year to support the anti-mechanist cause; and Helm, in his history of energetics of 1898, tried to defend his own work. But the damage had been done. Ostwald continued to uphold energetics after 1900, but increasingly as a monistic worldview, not as a scientific project.

The scientific proposals of the energeticists were flawed, but the attention they received undermines the common assertion that the physical scientists of the late nineteenth century were satisfied with the state of their science. The long tradition of mechanical explanation in the natural sciences was coming to an end. The debate over energetics as a viable replacement for the mechanical worldview reflected the difficulties inherent in the mechanical view.

ROBERT J. DELTETE

ENGINEERING SCIENCE. Although the term "engineering science" first came into widespread use in the early twentieth century, "the science of the engineer" and equivalent phrases had been employed much earlier to signify parts of professional engineering transcending untutored practice, parts of science that could usefully inform innovative practice, and canonical theoretical knowledge qualified to enhance the engineer's professional status. From the mid-nineteenth century, individual engineering sciences became integrated into a systematic field of study, modeled on the physical sciences, but with a content specific to some particular engineering practice.

Recently, commentators seeking to develop an independent field of the history of technology have redefined engineering science as a "mode of knowledge" distinct, in content and style, from any physical science (David Channell, *The History of Engineering Science* [1989]). John M. Staudenmaier, S. J., writes of "engineering theory" as a "body of knowledge using experimental methods to construct a formal and mathematically structured intellectual system" *(Technology's Storytellers: Reweaving the Human Fabric* [1985]) to explain the behavior of a particular class of (idealized) artifact or of artifact-related materials. Its experimental methods involve models, testing machines, towing tanks, and wind tunnels; it is structured by the demands of practice, and thus develops ways of comparing models with full-scale apparatus, often relying on pragmatic approximation rather than rigor.

According to this model, engineering science has provided a common language through which a community of status-conscious practitioners has articulated its increasingly specialized concerns. Furthermore, a network of professional societies, schools, and laboratories, and a technical literature, existing especially in Europe and the United States from the late nineteenth century, catered to the creation, inculcation, and critical evaluation of engineering science. Those institutions acted as a cohesive and mediating force, orchestrating a transition from the scattered skills and knowledge associated with local problem-solving to the standardized, universal, and abstract theories, designs, and practices issuing from the schools.

Historical investigation reveals variations and tensions within this schematic account. From the late seventeenth century, the Royal Society of London and the Academy of Sciences in Paris gave a central role to natural philosophy in perfecting practical arts for the public good. In the aftermath of the French Revolution, plans for a reformed and centralized system of engineering training, designed to foster economic health, were implemented. The École Polytechnique (1794–1795) in Paris exemplified the militaristic

production of technocrats. Elite savants furnished bright student engineers with a core curriculum concentrating on mathematics and theoretical sciences in readiness for the traditional branches of engineering (bridges, roads, artillery, mining) taught at the *écoles d'application*. While the École Polytechnique tended to eschew practical concerns, the École Centrale celebrated its distinctive *science industrielle* as a means of producing neither savants nor artisans but men who were at once scientists, generalists, and technological problem-solvers for the new industries.

The École Polytechnique's first director, Gaspard Monge, did, however, create a science of descriptive geometry (1795) for engineering drawing; founder Gaspard de Prony published the influential *Architecture hydraulique* (1790–1796); Lazare Carnot generalized the study of machine efficiency. Subsequent engineering theorists, many of them alumni of the school, included Charles Burdin (turbines); J. V. Poncelet (author of the *Mécanique industrielle* [1829]); J. N. P. Hachette *(Traité élémentaire des machines* [1811]); and C. L. M. H. Navier (who revised Belidor's *Architecture hydraulique* [1819]). They replaced the abstraction and microscopic model-building of the physics of Pierre-Simon Laplace with a focus on macroscopic phenomena and (especially in the case of Jean Poncelet and Gaspard Coriolis) transformed engineering mechanics from an offshoot of rational mechanics into a new science of work.

If the stereotypical European engineer was scientifically schooled but industrially ineffectual, his British equivalent

The Iron Bridge spanning the River Severn at Coalbrookedale in Shropshire, England (1779). The first cast-iron bridge in the world, it has become a symbol of the Industrial Revolution.

was economically potent and scientifically illiterate. Practical apprenticeship, according to received wisdom, made the British engineer. Yet he too had at his fingertips a miscellany of "modern improvements" in handbooks, encyclopedias (such as those of Abraham Rees and, later, Andrew Ure), parliamentary reports, works of mathematical practice by men such as Charles Hutton and Olinthus Gregory (associated with the military colleges), and Thomas Tredgold's classics on carpentry (1820) and cast iron (1822). This scattered literature sat beside scientific transactions in the libraries of new engineering associations which, like the Institution of Civil Engineers (1818) in London, produced their own publications.

In Britain, the consolidation of the science of the engineer coincided with the establishment of the university-based engineering education, with one eye on European models (especially the Freiberg School of Mines) and the other on an agenda of professionalization. From the 1820s, the Mechanics Institutes (such as the Franklin Institute in the United States) targeted artisans with popular science. From the late 1830s, educators at King's College and University College in London offered mathematics, chemistry, geology, and natural philosophy to student engineers, and the Edinburgh natural philosopher James David Forbes examined "academical engineers" at the new Durham University. Low-status lecturers or demonstrators gave practical tuition (for example, in surveying), but the scientific engineer had still to complete his training with a practical apprenticeship.

From the 1840s, professors of engineering in Britain and the United States gradually articulated a corpus of unified engineering theory. Their strategies varied. Lewis Gordon in Glasgow assembled the best of collective contemporary engineering experience in a textbook keenly attuned to recent European developments (especially Benoit Fourneyron on turbines, and Gordon's mentor at Freiberg, Julius Weisbach, for hydraulics, the mechanics of machinery, and "mechanical effect"). Charles Blacker Vignoles codified railway construction in lectures reproduced in London-based newspapers. Eaton Hodgkinson collaborated with industrialist William Fairbairn and the British Association for the Advancement of Science (founded in 1831) in developing experimental regimes for the study of new engineering materials (wrought and cast iron) and innovative structures (notably the Britannia Bridge).

At the other extreme, Robert Willis's *Principles of Mechanism* (1841) mimicked the forms of deductive geometry in its kinematics, or the classification of modes of communicating motion by machinery independent of force. A standard university text, its techniques were superseded only by the work of Franz Reuleaux at the end of the century. Henry Moseley's *Mechanical Principles of Engineering and Architecture* (1843) and especially William Whewell's *Mechanics of Engineering* (1841) borrowed from French theorists of structures and work while aiming, like Willis, to place sanitized and "progressive" engineering sciences within an English liberal education.

In systematizing engineering knowledge, these author-professors acted as mediators between disembodied recent science and actual (or potential and lucrative) industrial concerns; as translators, directing the application of science to practice; or as organizers of disorganized craft practices. Such roles are consistent with Eugene Ferguson's claim that the province of the engineering sciences lay between "pure physical science" and the "empirical and intuitive knowledge of the engineer" (*Bibliography of the History of Technology* [1968]). Despite Auguste Comte's insistence that the engineer, although responsible for organizing the mediation between science and practice, was not a man of science, the École Centrale claimed that "industrial science" readied its students to mediate between a complex body of scientific knowledge and its applications to industry, and the *Engineer* insisted (1856) that the application of science to practice was itself a science.

W. J. M. Rankine's practically oriented work in thermodynamics and good relations with local industrialists secured him a chair of engineering in Glasgow (1855). From there he argued that the academically trained engineer bridged the gap between distinct worlds of natural philosophical questions (what are we to think?) and practical questions (what are we to do?). The scientific engineer worked without waste, husbanding human and natural resources, economically achieving the practical aims precisely delimited by exact theoretical science, bearing in mind the quantifiable constraints of the market. With Rankine's Certificate of Proficiency in Engineering Science (from 1862), an engineer could plan with certainty and innovate with confidence.

A forum for topical scientific engineering discourse existed in technical periodicals, including *Engineering* (1866) and the publications of the Institution of Naval Architects, the American Society of Mechanical Engineers, and many other specialist professional engineering associations. Rankine's monumental and long-lasting textbooks, especially *Applied Mechanics* (1858), defined the bedrock of the scientific engineer. The basic repertoire offered theoretical engineering sciences, including soil mechanics, hydraulics, structures and frameworks, and elasticity, but many found Rankine's works inscrutable and, ironically, divorced from practice.

Thus, Isambard Kingdom Brunel objected to the anti-progressive standardization of engineering science and the "best practices" deduced by government commissions set up to learn from railway disasters, collapsing bridges, or naval catastrophes. These commissions harbored many professorial engineering experts and academicians, such as the electrical engineer Fleeming Jenkin (Edinburgh) and the heat-engine theorist Osborne Reynolds (Manchester), who lobbied for the training of scientific engineers to ensure public safety and economic prosperity. They looked covetously to well-funded institutions, academies, and polytechnics in Europe and the United States, but generally choked at the idea of mass-produced engineers, preferring to nurture a scientifically trained, gentlemanly elite of professional leaders.

In addition to having a theoretical base, the engineering sciences developed distinctive experimental practices. For science-intensive electrical engineering companies (such as Siemens), laboratories produced reliable electrical measures in a context of international standardization. For German *Technische Hochschulen*, the research laboratory linked college technical practice with industrial production. From 1868, the Polytechnic Institute of Munich had a materials-testing laboratory. Toward the end of the nineteenth century, Robert Thurston at Cornell, Alexander Kennedy in London, James Alfred Ewing in Cambridge, and college engineering professors generally argued that purpose-built laboratories, long essentials for chemistry and physics, were now vital to engineering teaching and research, particularly as venues for precision measurement. Trinity College, Oxford, had an engineering laboratory from 1886, and the University followed suit in 1914 with its own lab—well away, however, from the "Science Area."

The engineering science laboratory also modeled practice. Schools of engineering accumulated both demonstration apparatus and experimental models. Exactly what the behavior of a small-scale experimental model or theoretical simulation revealed about its full-sized counterpart was crucial—and unclear. Benjamin Isherwood insisted that only from full-scale experimental researches like his, in steam engineering for the U.S. Navy in the 1860s, could valid general "engineering laws" emerge; the British Association accumulated vast quantities of (unreducible) data relating engine power, ship shapes, and speeds on a similar understanding (voiced by naval architect C. W. Merrifield). Economic pressures forced engineers to learn how to "scale up." In hydrodynamics, John Scott Russell's "wave-lines" and Rankine's "streamlines" pointed plausibly to low-resistance hull shapes; but from the late 1860s, William Froude turned, additionally, to experimental tanks. In aeronautical engineering, a growth area especially after World War I, wind tunnels could give workable design solutions where fluid dynamics failed. Eventually, computer simulation would complement, and in some respects supersede, those modeling techniques.

At the beginning of the twentieth century, engineering science began to appear as a named academic discipline. Charles Frewen Jenkin, son of the Edinburgh academician and himself an expert in aeronautical materials, entitled his professorial address at Oxford "Engineering Science" (1908). The following decades saw a flurry of research publications in the aeronautical, mechanical, and marine fields, now deemed branches of engineering science; textbooks in engineering science began to appear; Macmillan's *Engineering Science Series* (1922) included works on electrical engineering and telephony.

R. V. Southwell, Jenkin's successor at Oxford, launched a prestigious Oxford Engineering Science Series in 1932. Southwell's career neatly illustrates the ironies of engineering science in practice. In an anti-industrial academic environment, he offered a small group of students "essential scientific equipment" in the form of systematic theoretical knowledge of idealized engineering systems. Worried that more and more research took place in government labs or large firms, he wanted to enhance the fragile reputation of academic engineering. He taught that engineering science was not the key to industrial success; it used mathematics and physics, but unlike them, considered practical material constraints, approximate (and, increasingly, computable) solutions, matter in bulk, and visualizable models. In Oxford, at least, engineering science was a research end in itself.

BEN MARSDEN

ENGLISH-SPEAKING WORLD. Science has had several principal languages over the centuries—Greek, Latin, Italian, Arabic, Chinese, French, German, and English. During the eighteenth century, French dominated discourse about natural knowledge. During the late nineteenth century, German became the principal scientific language for a large area including, besides Germany itself, Austria-Hungary, Sweden, Denmark, the Netherlands, and parts of Switzerland. Japanese who wished to pursue a career in medicine had to know German; so did citizens of the United States and Imperial Russia. English supplanted German to become the world-wide means of communication in commerce and travel as well as in science. The so-called "English-speaking world"—Britain, the United States, Australia, New Zealand, Ireland, most of Canada, and large enclaves else-

where—has the great advantage of possessing this universal language as its mother tongue.

Britain's Legacy

Although during the nineteenth century, the British Isles produced extraordinary achievements in science—as indicated by the names Charles Darwin, Charles Lyell, James Clerk Maxwell, and William Thomson—and natural science had established a secure foothold in the other English-speaking countries, Germany was the leader in world science around 1900. Thanks in part to the work of Justus von Liebig at Giessen from the late 1820s, the Germans had become the unchallenged leaders in chemistry, both in the academy and in industrial applications. Britain's precocious William H. Perkin founded the aniline dye industry in the late 1860s, but Germany's stronger institutional base in applied science allowed it to capture the manufacture of all synthetic organic dyes. German higher education seemed equally strong. The twenty-eight German-speaking universities in central Europe, mostly located in Germany itself, had no parallel in the world in 1900. With their many distinguished professors, excellent laboratories, and easy accessibility, the German institutions drew students from all over the world, including significant numbers from the United States and Britain.

Against this array, Britain had the ancient universities of Cambridge and Oxford, the old Scottish universities, Trinity College, Dublin, and a rising number of municipal or

A far-west outpost of the English-speaking scientific enterprise: Stanford University in Palo Alto, California

105

"red brick" institutions, notably the universities of London, Manchester, and Liverpool. McGill University, the University of Toronto, three small institutions of higher learning in New Zealand, and four universities of modest size in Australia represented the higher education available in the English-speaking parts of the British Empire. The United States had begun copying the German academic model with the establishment of Johns Hopkins in the 1870s, the University of Chicago in the 1890s, and the importation of an embryonic research ethic into the older East Coast institutions. The Land Grant Act of the Civil War years had established universities that would become research centers, notably in the Middle West and California. MIT was a modest engineering school; Cal Tech did not exist.

Partly in response to the German ascendancy, England debated the mission of its established universities, the role of research, and the place of experimental science in them. Cambridge had long excelled in mathematics, but until 1851, no course of study leading to a degree in chemistry or physics existed at Cambridge or Oxford. That year, Cambridge created the Natural Science Tripos (examination), which, however, long had a second-class standing in the university. Dirtying their hands with experimental work still grated on the sensibilities of Oxford dons, who regarded chemistry as "stinks." External pressures for change from political leaders, industrialists, and British scientists with German academic degrees had aroused strong opposition. The situation for natural science was much more favorable at the red-brick universities, especially the University of London, whose BSc degree could be obtained by examination even by non-resident students.

A concerted movement for sweeping changes in the ancient universities gathered momentum after 1870. The Devonshire Commission, led by William Cavendish, Duke of Devonshire, undertook a six-year investigation (1870–1876) into the state of British science. Scottish institutions came off well; the members of the Commission praised William Thomson's program in physics at the University of Glasgow, despite his master-apprentice approach to instruction. But the Commission harshly criticized conditions in England. It recommended the enhancement of existing resources and several new initiatives: eleven new chairs for science at Oxford, a National Ministry of Science and Education, a new astronomical observatory, a redirection of collegiate fellowships away from the Classics and toward the natural sciences, and a program of grants for research by established scholars to be administered by the Royal Society.

For the rise of the English-speaking countries in science, a particularly important initiative from the 1870s was the founding of the Cavendish Laboratory at Cambridge. The Duke of Devonshire served as Chancellor of Cambridge while chairing the reform commission. A descendant of two leading physical scientists (Henry Cavendish and Robert Boyle), Devonshire had excelled in mathematics as a student and had considerable experience in the iron and steel business. His financial contribution, more than sufficient to build and equip the laboratory, set a new standard of support for science in an academic setting. The first Cavendish Professor of Experimental Physics, James Clerk Maxwell, started a tradition of excellence that under his successors made the Cavendish for half a century what Niels Bohr called the center of physics.

Lord Rayleigh, successor to Maxwell as Cavendish director, received a Nobel Prize in physics in 1904 for his discovery of argon. In 1906, Rayleigh's successor, J. J. Thomson,

received a Nobel for his discovery of the electron. Between 1895 and 1898, the New Zealand-born Ernest Rutherford worked with Thomson at the Cavendish on X-ray induced conductivity in gases. The work for which Rutherford received the Nobel Prize for chemistry in 1908—his development of a modern theory of radioactivity—took place at McGill University in Canada. Rutherford succeeded Thomson as Cavendish Professor and Laboratory Director in 1919.

Impact of World War I
When war broke out in August 1914, science and engineering students in Germany numbered about 16,000; in Britain, 4,000 at most. A 1910 estimate put the number of working British industrial chemists at one-third the number working in Germany. Germany was spending three times as much on its universities as Britain. Britain depended on Germany for imports of dyestuffs as well as tungsten for making steel, pharmaceuticals, magnetos, certain kinds of optical glass, and, to some degree, even explosives.

In the United States, surging immigration, industrialization, and economic expansion had created a favorable environment for the growth of science at the beginning of the century. John D. Rockefeller's fortune made possible the establishment of the University of Chicago in 1891; unlike the East Coast institutions, it emphasized graduate education from the start. In 1901, the United States Congress created the National Bureau of Standards and authorized it to conduct research deemed necessary to establish appropriate standards for industry; a prominent physicist was named its director. An unprecedented gift of $10 million from Andrew Carnegie resulted in the creation of the Carnegie Institution of Washington. Other industrialists founded Stanford University, Vanderbilt University, and the Rockefeller Institute for Medical Research in New York.

World War I initiated the rise to preeminence of the English-speaking countries in science, partly because the war ruined Germany's economy, but mainly because it accelerated institutional developments that might otherwise have been delayed. In 1914, Britain created the British Dyestuffs Corporation, and the following year set up what became the Department of Scientific and Industrial Research (DSIR) and encouraged the formation of Research Associations to offset deficiencies in applied science made all too apparent by the war. The DSIR survived the war to continue government support to science. In 1916, a Committee on the Neglect of Science, chaired by Lord Rayleigh, launched major initiatives directed at the creation of a scientifically more literate public. Although the United States did not enter the war until 1917, it had moved in the same direction, creating the National Research Council (NRC) in 1915, letting research contracts to twenty-one university laboratories, and undertaking research on optical glass and chemical weapons. The performance of applied science during the war caused many firms in Britain and the United States to set up or expand industrial research laboratories after the war.

Southern California first became prominent in science just after the war when George Ellery Hale, one of the creators of the NRC and director of the Mt. Wilson Observatory, persuaded local industrialists that the region should have a major research university with forward-looking programs in science. Hale's recruitment of several distinguished faculty members, together with the large endowment pledged by his business supporters, made possible the conversion of the small Throop Polytechnic Institute (founded 1891) into the California Institute of Technology in 1921, with R. A. Millikan

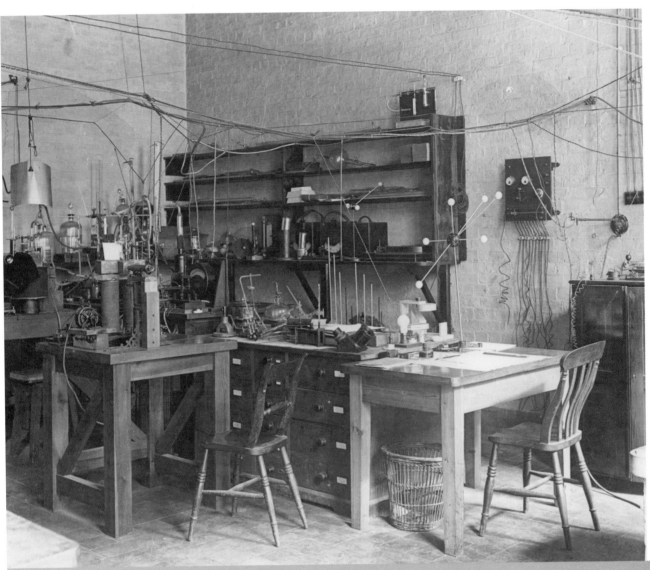

A room at the Cavendish Laboratory in Cambridge, England, where many people from around the English-speaking world studied—notably the New Zealander Ernest Rutherford (1871–1937), who became the laboratory's director in 1920

as its founding president. Science and engineering in Canada, already strong at McGill from private benefactors, gained ground and reputation at the University of Toronto. There, with the active collaboration of Charles Best and help from J. J. R. Macleod and James Collip, Frederick Banting isolated insulin from the pancreas and demonstrated its effectiveness in treating diabetes. In 1923, Banting became the first Canadian to receive a Nobel Prize in physiology or medicine.

Just before the war ended, the Allies took steps to isolate German science. Delegates meeting in London in the fall of 1918 voted to dissolve the International Association of Academies, founded in the 1890s and headquartered in Berlin, and create a new International Research Council (IRC) from which citizens of the former Central Powers were excluded. The IRC finally admitted Germany in 1926. In the interim, Germany had not ceded its leadership. Despite the policy of the IRC, able young Americans such as Linus Pauling and J. Robert Oppenheimer went to Munich and Göttingen to study quantum theory.

The English-speaking countries had three advantages that would gain them eventual leadership across the sciences: numbers, resources, and a language that enabled them to function as a single, large community of scholars. The point may best be made by pointing to migration within the com-

munity. British-style education throughout the Empire had long allowed colonials to study or work in Britain. Thus did the eminent medical clinician and researcher, William Osler, born and educated in Canada, later teach in Britain (1904–1919). Similarly, Rutherford, after taking his degree at Canterbury College in New Zealand (1894), went to study at Cambridge. The travel went both ways. In 1885, William Henry Bragg, a protégé of J. J. Thomson's at Cambridge, moved to Australia and taught physics at Adelaide until 1909, later returning to Leeds in England. His son, William Lawrence Bragg, born and educated in Australia, became Cavendish Professor of Physics at Cambridge in 1938.

The pace of these movements began to increase during and immediately following World War I, as a result of improved transportation and more opportunities in research. Born and educated at Capetown in South Africa, Max Theiler studied medicine at the London School of Tropical Medicine from 1916 to 1922; he then worked in the United States at Harvard, the Rockefeller Institute, and Yale. Also during World War I, India's great mathematician Srinivasa Ramanujan from Madras visited Britain and became a Fellow of Trinity College, Cambridge, before returning home. Frank McFarlane Burnet, born in Australia in 1899 and educated at the University of Melbourne, studied at the Lister Institute in

London, then returned home. And in the 1930s, both Subramanyan Chandrasekhar from India and John Eccles of Australia studied in England, at Cambridge and Oxford, respectively. Chandrasekhar became professor of astrophysics at the University of Chicago after his years in England.

Eccles's career shows particularly well the career possibilities available to a scientist in the English-speaking world. Born in Melbourne in 1903, he studied and taught at Oxford from 1925 to 1937, directed a research institute in Sydney from 1937 to 1943, then moved to New Zealand's University of Otago. From 1952 to 1966, Eccles served as professor of neurophysiology at the Australian National University, Canberra, after which he moved to Chicago, and later Buffalo, New York. Other colonial systems—those of the French, the Dutch, the Spanish, and the Americans—also produced patterns of this kind, though none on anything like the scale of the British.

The Migration From Germany

Adolf Hitler's accession to power in Germany in 1933 completed what World War I had begun, preparing the way for the supremacy of the English-speaking countries in science. Following the enactment of the Nuremberg Laws later that year, most Jewish scientists were forbidden to work in Germany's universities. Those who could leave gradually left Germany, more often than not for Britain (Max Born) or the United States (James Franck). Albert Einstein had left Germany in 1930; he and several other distinguished European scientists became members of the Institute for Advanced Study in Princeton, a private institution founded earlier that year by the family of Louis Bamberger, a department store magnate.

Science in the United States was deeply enriched by the European immigrants. The physicist Maria Goeppert Mayer, a protégé of Max Born's at Göttingen, came in 1930 as the wife of an American chemist, Joseph Mayer. Naturalized in 1933, Goeppert Mayer taught physics at several institutions, often without compensation. One was the University of Chicago, a leading center for physics after the arrival of Enrico Fermi and Edward Teller, themselves exiles from Fascism and Nazism. Goeppert Mayer's presence at Chicago led to a position at the nearby Argonne National Laboratory, where she noted the existence of periodic properties for nuclear isotopes and their resemblance to electron shells in atoms. This work culminated in her shell model of the nucleus, for which she shared a Nobel Prize in 1963 with Hans Jensen and Eugene Wigner. In 1935, Hans Bethe arrived from Germany by way of a two-year position at Bristol in England. From his position at Cornell as professor of physics, Bethe moved to Los Alamos, New Mexico, where he played a leading role in the Manhattan Project to develop the atomic bomb. A consummate statesman of science, as well as a brilliant researcher, Bethe received an unshared Nobel in 1967, partly for his studies of energy production in the sun and other stars.

Nor was it only physics that benefited from the influx of European scientists. Though trained originally in theoretical physics, Max Delbrück—a great-grandson of Justus von Liebig—came to the United States in 1937 on a Rockefeller Foundation fellowship, switched to viral genetics, and investigated bacteriophages at several institutions. He shared a Nobel Prize in physiology or medicine in 1969. Fritz Lipmann, a biochemist, arrived in 1939. Another Rockefeller Foundation fellow, he held positions at Cornell, Harvard, and the Rockefeller Institute (renamed Rockefeller University). Lipmann became interested in metabolism and the enzymes that aid in digestion. He shared a Nobel Prize in 1953 with another German émigré, Hans Krebs. Krebs is notable as one of a significant but smaller number of scientists fleeing Nazi persecution who found opportunity in Britain, as opposed to the United States. Others—Otto Frisch, Rudolf Peierls, and Franz Simon—made suggestions that were instrumental in committing Britain and the United States to the atomic bomb project.

Postwar Science

Despite its much smaller scientific community and more modest funding base for research, Britain continued to attract talented foreign and domestic investigators in the postwar period. In 1951, the young American biologist James. D. Watson arrived at the Cavendish Laboratory after completing his Ph.D. at Indiana University. At Cambridge, he met and began working with a somewhat older British colleague, Francis Crick. In pursuing their classic work on the structure of DNA, they took full advantage of opportunities and information produced in the English-speaking world. In 1944, Oswald Avery of Columbia University had argued that DNA was the genetic material of bacteria. Essential knowledge of amino acids came from Erwin Chargaff of Columbia, whom Watson and Crick met in Cambridge; Rosalind Franklin, Maurice Wilkins, and Raymond Gosling at the University of London supplied X-ray diffraction photographs of DNA; Linus Pauling of Cal Tech suggested a clever but mistaken model of the DNA molecule that Watson and Crick improved on. The foundation of molecular biology, like the cooperation on the atomic bomb and many other episodes in science and technology in the twentieth century, was a product of interactions in the English-speaking world.

The United States, with its large land base and growing wealth, in some ways after 1900 duplicated the institutions of the British Empire (later British Commonwealth) within its own borders. In the pursuit of science, as in the acquisition of wealth, the American academic system, and to some degree the Canadian, were founts of opportunity. These nations created effective systems of universities and government and industrial laboratories, eager for competent staff irrespective of their national origins, readily open to one another, yet intensely competitive in a national context. Innovations historically successful in one institution—especially universities—were usually copied in others. In this sense, the fifty leading research universities of North America have something in common with the German universities of 1900. The industrial research laboratories have their parallels in the old dyestuffs industries, and the national laboratories a pale antecedent in the famous German bureau of standards, the Physikalische-Technische Reichsanstalt.

Ironically, the factor that underlay the hegemony of the English-speaking countries in science—a common language—has created a more even playing field for the rest of the world. Nearly all scientists now communicate in English, except with native speakers of their own language. That makes possible large transnational collaborations and migrations for study and research. An ever more tightly knit Europe, whose scientists communicate in English and sometimes enjoy support approaching American levels, has challenged the supremacy of the English-speaking nations, or rather of the United States, since Britain sometimes belongs to Europe, and Europe sometimes speaks English. Asia should not be left out of the equation. To take one straw in the wind, in the 1990s, Ken'ichi Fukui, Japan's first Nobel laureate in chemistry, was able to attract postdoctoral fellows from the United States and other countries because all shared the common language of English.

JAMES BARTHOLOMEW

ENTOMOLOGY. Entomology (along with ornithology) was one of the first fields of natural knowledge to professionalize. Men with specialist knowledge in the area were among the earliest of scientific employees in museums. Enthusiastic input from collectors, illustrators, travelers, and specialist taxonomists buoyed interest. During the seventeenth and early eighteenth centuries, insects featured in microscopical researches like those of Marcello Malpighi and Robert Hooke. Theologians and naturalists alike praised the beauty and complexity of insects, many seeing them as evidence for the wisdom and perfect design of God's works. Religious symbolism and entomological description joined in other ways: Jan Swammerdam explained insect life cycles in *The Natural History of Insects* (1737) as signifying Christ's resurrection. At the same time, the social insects, such as ants, bees, and wasps, provided civic metaphors, as in Bernard Mandeville's *Fable of the Bees* (1714), which proposes an idealized structure for human society. Notions about the efficiency of the hierarchical castes in ants' nests or beehives, and the concept of many individuals working for the general good, appeared in many philosophical tracts and utopian fictions. Moral lessons had long been found in locust plagues and the like. Insects also had economic value, as exemplified by the cochineal beetle, which, for several centuries, provided the primary source for red dye.

Many important entomological collections were founded and expanded during the eighteenth century. New techniques and devices for catching specimens, including nets, traps, and lamps, and conventions for adequate preservation and display, were developed. Insect collections, like those of shells or minerals, amused the wealthy, intrigued the learned, and provided financial opportunities for specimen hunters, shopkeepers, and book publishers. The publication of illustrated manuals boomed, complemented by catalogues and lists of identifying names. Specialist classification schemes—especially divisions of day fliers from night fliers, and beetles and bugs from butterflies—were introduced. Carl Linnaeus identified seven insect orders (today, twenty-nine are generally recognized). Insects played a key role in systems of physicotheology, such as Linnaeus's scheme of natural economy, which adumbrated the concept of a food chain. The relative number of organisms and the balance, or harmony, between them depended on insects as an essential source of food for birds. William Paley, in his discussion of the "polity of nature" in *Natural Theology or evidences of the existence and attributes of the deity* (1807), argued that the usefulness and beauty of insects counterbalanced their stings and bites. The curious reproductive patterns of some insects such as aphids aroused great scientific and philosophical interest. For much of the century the word "insect" was applied indiscriminately to most small organisms.

In Great Britain, an Entomological Society was founded in 1833 by a small group of enthusiasts—associated with an entomological club and periodical—who broke from the Zoological Society. The new society rapidly became a locus for expert taxonomic work, publishing scientific *Transactions* from 1834. In Paris and elsewhere, specialist taxonomists were also producing many detailed studies of individual genera or families.

A number of unusual classification schemes appeared in the early nineteenth century, most notably William Macleay's quinarían system (based on grouping genera and families in fives)—a significant attempt to reveal meaningful affinities and relationships between insects. Macleay's system was developed further by William Swainson. Parasitic insects were recognized by him as either highly complex or very reduced in structure when compared to the basic type to which they were related. This recognition allowed him to classify many organisms previously difficult to place. Identification of the various stages of insect life was also a focus of research throughout the century. Concepts of host organisms for different stages of the cycle, and insects as vectors of disease, were introduced, although they were not codified until much later.

The spontaneous generation controversy—centered around the debate between Louis Pasteur and Félix-Archimède Pouchet—demonstrated the importance of distinguishing between asexual (parthenogenetic) forms of reproduction, as displayed by aphids and other organisms, and sexual reproduction; and of establishing the mechanisms that underlay fertilization and cell multiplication. In Great Britain, the natural historical approach predominated. Sir John Lubbock, the Victorian politician and banker, began his career as a talented entomologist. Aided by advances in histological techniques and microscope optics, he described several key stages of the reproductive process in insects, tracing the "germ cells" through the generations. He later observed social behavior, perhaps inventing the glass observation hive in the process, and wrote the best-selling *Ants, Bees and Wasps* (1882). In the early twentieth century, Austrian biologist Karl von Frisch went further, investigating the routes taken by bees in search of food and the "dance" by which they communicated information to others in the hive.

Charles Darwin devoted much time to studying the mutual dependency between insects and flowers, the one acquiring food or nectar and the other achieving cross-fertilization. Darwin's results on the respective adaptations developed by both sets of organisms appeared primarily in *The Effects of Cross and Self fertilisation* (1876) although he had included much original matter on the subject in his *Orchids* (1861). He based his notion of the mutual dependency of insects and flowers on a tract published by Christian Konrad Sprengel in 1793. Notwithstanding the fanfare about apes and angels following publication of Darwin's *Origin of Species* (1859), evolution was best demonstrated by the insect world. In the 1860s and 1870s, Henry Walter Bates's and Fritz Müller's demonstrations of various forms of mimicry, in which palatable insects mimic unpalatable ones or inanimate objects like leaves in order to survive, gave strong support to evolutionary theory. Henry Bernard Davis Kettlewell's study of industrial melanism in moths and their differential survival rates ultimately substantiated modern evolutionary theory. Insects also proved crucial for genetic research, especially into mutation and recombination of chromosomes. Thomas Hunt Morgan deliberately chose the fruit fly for his laboratory work because of its rapid breeding, convenient maintenance, adaptable external characteristics, and large, easily observable chromosomes. In a few years the species was acknowledged as a highly suitable organism for experimental work. Much of Morgan's achievement, in fact, rested on having chosen an appropriate organism for the job. Other insects, particularly weevils, were similarly important in early population genetics and ecological modeling in the laboratory, as in Charles Elton's seminal work *Animal Ecology* (1927).

E

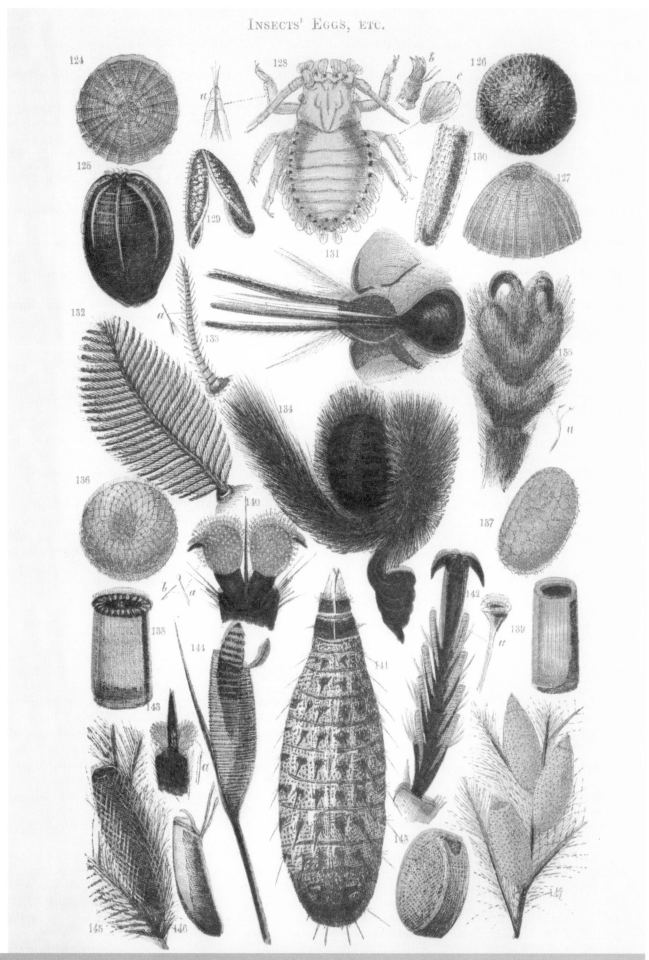

INSECTS' EGGS, ETC.

Drawings of insects as seen under a microscope. Beneath an aphid (top center) is the proboscis of a tse-tse fly. From Jabez Hogg, *The Microscope* (1883).

Insects are a significant factor in the medical health field, particularly epidemiology. Alexandre Yersin established fleas as the causative agent in plague in the 1880s. Alphonse Laveran saw the malarial parasite in human blood while working in Algeria in 1880; Patrick Manson identified the mosquito as the parasite's customary host, or vector (1894); and Ronald Ross disclosed the malarial life cycle in 1897. Throughout the twentieth century pest control—for both medical and agricultural purposes—focused on programs of insect extermination, often with powerful insecticides like DDT.

JANET BROWNE

ENTROPY. Many physicists and chemists quip that the second law of thermodynamics has as many formulations as there are physicists and chemists. Perhaps the most intriguing expression of the law is Ludwig Boltzmann's paraphrase of Willard Gibbs: "The impossibility of an uncompensated decrease in entropy seems to be reduced to improbability."

Entropy owes its birth to a paradox first pointed out by William Thomson in 1847: energy cannot be destroyed or created, yet heat energy loses its capacity to do work (for example, to raise a weight) when it is transferred from a warm body to a cold one. In 1852, he suggested that in processes like heat conduction, energy is not lost but becomes "dissipated" or unavailable. Furthermore, the dissipation, according to Thomson, amounts to a general law of nature, expressing the "directionality" of natural processes. The Scottish engineer Macquorn Rankine and Rudolf Clausius proposed a new concept, which represented the same tendency of energy towards dissipation. Initially called "thermodynamic function" by Rankine and "disgregation" by Clausius, in 1865 the latter gave the concept its definitive name, "entropy," after the Greek word for transformation. Every process that takes place in an isolated system increases the system's entropy. Clausius thus formulated the first and second laws of thermodynamics in his statement "The energy of the universe is constant, its entropy tends to a maximum." Hence, all large-scale matter will eventually reach a uniform temperature, there will be no available energy to do work, and the universe will suffer a slow "heat death."

In 1871, James Clerk Maxwell published a thought-experiment attempting to show that heat need not always flow from a warmer to a colder body. A microscopic agent ("Maxwell's demon," as Thomson latter dubbed it), controlling a diaphragm on a wall separating a hot and a cold gas, could choose to let through only molecules of the cold gas moving faster than the average speed of the molecules of the hot gas. In that way, heat would flow from the cold to the hot gas. This thought-experiment indicated that the "dissipation" of energy was not inherent in nature, but arose from human inability to control microscopic processes. The second law of thermodynamics has only statistical validity—in macroscopic regions entropy *almost* always increases.

Boltzmann attempted to resolve a serious problem pointed out by his colleague Joseph Loschmidt in 1876, and by Thomson two years earlier, that undermined the mechanical interpretation of thermodynamics and of the second law. This law suggests that an asymmetry in times dominates natural processes; the passage of time results in an irreversible change, the increase of entropy. However, if the laws of mechanics govern the constituents of thermodynamic systems, their evolution should be reversible, since the laws of mechanics are the same whether time flows forward or backward: Newton's laws retrodict the moon's position a thousand years ago as readily as they predict its position a

James Clerk Maxwell (1831–1879) with some mechanical devices in his beard. The "demon" refers to a thought experiment he devised to probe the second law of thermodynamics.

thousand years from now. Prima facie, there seems to be no mechanical counterpart to the second law of thermodynamics. In 1877, Boltzmann found a way out of this difficulty by interpreting the second law in the sense of Maxwell's demon. According to Boltzmann's calculus, to each macroscopic state of a system correspond many microstates (particular distributions of energy among the molecules of the system) that Boltzmann considered to be equally probable. Accordingly, the probability of a macroscopic state was determined by the number of microstates corresponding to it. Boltzmann then identified the entropy of a system with a logarithmic function of the probability of its macroscopic state. On that interpretation, the second law asserted that thermodynamic systems have the tendency to evolve toward more probable states. A decrease of entropy was unlikely, but not impossible.

In 1906, Walther Nernst formulated his heat theorem, which stated that if a chemical change took place between pure crystalline solids at absolute zero, there would be no change in entropy. Its more general formulation is accepted as the third law of thermodynamics: the maximum work obtainable from a process can be calculated from the heat evolved at temperatures close to absolute zero. More commonly the third law states that it is impossible to cool a body to absolute zero by any finite process and that at absolute zero all bodies tend to have the same constant entropy, which could be arbitrarily set to zero.

THEODORE ARABATZIS AND KOSTAS GAVROGLU

ENVIRONMENT. In the nineteenth century, human exploitation of the natural environment came to be recognized in the industrializing West as a threat to human welfare. Romantics deplored the destruction of forests as diminishing the world's esthetic and spiritual reserves, and scientists warned that forest depletion entailed losses in watershed and habitats for numerous plant and animal species. The outcry led the governments of Germany and France to embark on programs of forest restoration and preservation. In the United States, the concern for forests joined with the realization that the fron-

Rachel Carson (1907–1964), US biologist and writer, with her book, *Silent Spring* (1962), a classic in the environmental movement

depleting the upper atmosphere's ozone layer, which blocks the passage of cancer-causing ultraviolet light from the sun. The burning of fossil fuels was releasing enough carbon dioxide to create a greenhouse-like effect that raised average temperatures around the globe. The clearing of the tropical rain forests was destroying large fractions of the world's species of insects, birds, and animals.

In the Montreal Protocol (1987) and its toughened revision (1990), the industrial nations agreed to limit the use of ozone-depleting gases. At Rio de Janeiro in 1992, they reached an accord in principle to reduce the production of greenhouse gases below the levels of 1990; and in Kyoto in 1997, they devised tentative mechanisms for achieving that goal. However, in 2001 the United States, which produces one-quarter of the world's greenhouse gases, withdrew from the Kyoto Protocol, declaring that the required limits on the burning of fossil fuels would injure its economy. A comparable commitment to indigenous economic growth in Latin America has interfered with attempts to slow the destruction of the rain forests.

DANIEL J. KEVLES

ERROR AND THE PERSONAL EQUATION. Since Greek times astronomers have recognized that observations were afflicted by errors, that results based on them might only be approximate, and that the quality of data varied. Astronomers in early modern Europe took the first steps toward giving reliable estimates of those errors. Johannes Kepler, who used Tycho Brahe's observations to derive the elliptical shape of planetary orbits, was probably the first to construct a correction term that assigned a magnitude to error, and among the first to give a theory of an instrument (the Galilean telescope) for purposes of improving the accuracy of measurements taken with it.

During the eighteenth century, steps were taken toward standardizing the analysis of measurements and understanding the conditions under which different sets of measurements could be combined. Analysts identified two types of errors: constant (affecting the instruments or the conditions of measurement) and accidental (randomly affecting the quality of the measurements themselves). Control over instrumental errors was achieved at first by codifying the behavior and demeanor of the observer, by taking into account the limitations of the human senses (especially vision), by examining how outside sources contaminate experiments, by perfecting the construction of instruments, and by developing methods for instrument calibration.

The second type of error, the random, relates to classical probability theory. Initially the criteria for the selection of good measurements rested mainly on the notion that the median or the mean of measurements reduced the effect of errors in any of them. In 1756, the mathematician Thomas Simpson countered reports that a single well-taken measurement sufficed by demonstrating the superiority of the mean; his presentation to the Royal Society of London included a discussion of the equal probability of positive and negative errors and an argument that the mean lies closer to the true value than any random measurement. But no consensus existed about the selection or combination of measurements. The first firm parameters of an error theory emerged from the consideration of observations of the Moon's motion, especially its libration; from secular inequalities in the motions of Jupiter and Saturn; and from measurements of the shape of the earth. During the second half of the eighteenth century, Johann Tobias Mayer, Leonhard Euler,

tier was closing to create a "conservation" movement, which flourished from the 1890s through the 1910s and made its overarching goal the maintenance of the nation's natural heritage. Championed by President Theodore Roosevelt, the movement won the creation of national parks, forest preserves, and laws for the protection of wildlife.

The American environmental movement lost force during the turn towards probusiness conservatism in the 1920s, but concern for the preservation of nature revived under the reformist leadership of President Franklin Roosevelt in the 1930s and drew renewed support after World War II. Spreading affluence permitted people the time and means to visit the national parks and to find in the unspoiled beauty of nature spiritual relief from the sameness of the suburbs, television, and fast-food restaurants.

The environmental agenda was significantly enlarged when, in 1962, Rachel Carson, a trained biologist and gifted writer, published *Silent Spring,* a powerful dissection of the intricate and myriad ways that herbicides and pesticides, particularly DDT, were poisoning man and nature. Carson called the chemicals of weed and insect control "elixirs of death," explained that they killed wildlife, especially birds, as they accumulated in the wild food chain, and stressed that they threatened human health. In 1972, the federal government banned the use of DDT. In the meantime, *Silent Spring,* which was widely translated, had helped to stimulate a worldwide environmental movement with the goals of protecting nature and health against the threats of poisonous pollutants entering the air, earth, and water.

In the late 1980s, scientists warned that environmental dangers global in scope had arrived. The growing commercial and industrial use of chlorofluorocarbons (CFCs) was

Rudjer J. Boškovié, and Johann Heinrich Lambert developed ad hoc, limited, varied, but effective procedures for combining measurements made under different conditions. In 1774, Pierre-Simon Laplace deduced a rule for the combination of measurements using probability theory.

The meridian measurements made during the French Revolution to determine the new standard of length, the meter, gave the occasion to devise the first general method for establishing an equilibrium among errors of observation by determining their "center of gravity." This method, the method of least squares, was so employed in 1805 by Adrien Marie Legendre. In 1806, Carl Friedrich Gauss acknowledged Legendre's work but only to say that he had been using the method for years. A priority dispute ensued. Three years later Gauss published the first rigorous proof of the method of least squares; he demonstrated that if the mean is the most probable value, then the errors of measurement form a bell curve (Gaussian) distribution. The true value (which has the smallest error) lies at the center of the distribution, while the width of the curve determines the precision of the measurement. (Application of the method assumes the absence of constant or systematic errors.) From astronomy the method spread to chemistry, physics, mineralogy, and geodesy. It was also applied to practical projects including the reform of weights and measures, longitude determinations, triangulations, the U.S. Coastal Survey, and cadasters, where it set the boundaries within which dispute could take place. The method of least squares made large-scale projects, like Gauss's magnetic map of the earth, manageable by providing a means to combine and assess data from geographically dispersed locations. Over the course of the nineteenth century, the method dominated error analysis (especially in the German-speaking world) and shaped the development of probability theory.

The power of the method of least squares seemed to eradicate the subjective element in the treatment of measurements. But Gauss and his colleague the astronomer Wilhelm Olbers acknowledged in 1827 that sometimes measurements displayed large deviations from the mean. When was the deviation large enough to justify ignoring a measurement? Gauss could not provide an objective answer and recommended reliance on intuition. In 1852, Benjamin Peirce developed a rigorous method for rejecting outliers.

Deviations of another sort led Friedrich Wilhelm Bessel to develop the personal equation. In 1823, he noted a constant difference in the measurements taken by the former British Astronomer Royal Nevil Maskelyne and his assistant, which Bessel referred to physiological differences. With the "personal equation" Bessel calculated the average difference between two observers; he could then combine measurements taken by several observers. The personal equation created the factory-like atmosphere of nineteenth-century astronomical observatories where teams of observers were calibrated according to its principles. It was seldom used elsewhere except in psychology. Especially in Wilhelm Wundt's physiological institute at Leipzig, the personal equation became the foundation of a research program in the determination of human reaction times.

The history of error and the personal equation embraces far more than the history of rules and methods. The determination of error is always an estimate; were the true error known, perfectly accurate results could be attained. Because reliable estimates of error generate confidence in results, the history of error theory also sheds light on how trust is established in a scientific community and beyond. In the teaching laboratory, the method of least squares indicated how well student investigators performed an experiment, and thus the level of expertise they had attained. In practical fields like surveying, the introduction of the method aided professionalization. Finally, the method of least squares shaped the moral economy of the sciences by promoting honesty in the execution and reduction of observations. Proper application of the method became a sign of the investigator's integrity.

KATHRYN OLESKO

ETHER is a possibly nonexistent entity invoked from time to time to fill otherwise empty spaces in the world and in natural philosophy. Descended from the Aristotelian quintessence, which occupied the realms through which the planets wandered, and the Stoics' pneuma, which held the world together, ether characterizes theories opposed to atomism, which admits spaces void of matter. Both sorts of theories—plenary and atomistic—enjoyed vigorous revivals during the Scientific Revolution. With the invention of the barometer and air pump in the middle decades of the seventeenth century, void and ether became objects of experiment and, in practice, very much the same (no)thing.

The experimental investigation of void began above the mercury in the barometer tube. This space had the property of transmitting light and magnetic virtue, but not sound, and of allowing the free passage of bodies through it. It seemed infinitely compressible or, rather, was so subtle that it could pass right through glass. Were these the properties of a space void of all matter or of one filled with a substance different from ordinary matter? A third way, preferred by René Descartes, made the special substance and ordinary matter the same thing, except for the size and shape of their constituent parts. Isaac Newton countered with a solution as hard to grasp as ether itself. In his world system, the planets move through resistanceless spaces replete with the presence of God and perhaps also with springy ethers that mediated gravitational attraction, chemical behavior, electricity, mag-

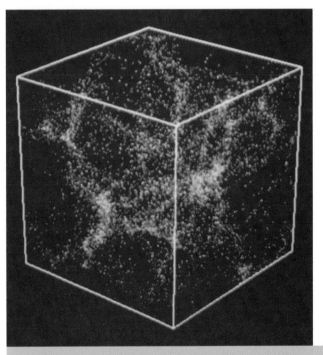

Computer simulation of a portion of the universe containing 10,000 galaxies. They tend to cluster in filaments, walls, or massive nodes, leaving large voids (or expanses of ether) where the density is virtually zero.

netism, and the interaction of light and ordinary matter. These ethers, unlike the Stoics' pneuma and Descartes' plenum, admitted voids among their particles.

With the acceptance of the wave theory of light in the nineteenth century, physicists felt obliged to suppose the existence of a subtle, imponderable medium whose undulations constituted the disturbance perceived as light. The first mathematicians to attempt a detailed picture of this "luminiferous ether" modeled it as a mechanical substance with rigidity and inertia. They managed thus to represent most of the properties of light—reflection, refraction, interference, and polarization. As William Thomson (Lord Kelvin) and the Cambridge mathematician George Gabriel Stokes explained it to other model-makers, the luminiferous ether had to combine the properties of shoemakers' wax, which allows slow bodies to pass through it under steady pressure but shatters when struck a sharp blow, with those of rigid steel, which can support transverse vibrations without suffering permanent distortion.

The ether soon became so familiar that mathematicians assimilated it to ordinary matter, or vice-versa. As latter-day Cartesians, they pictured atoms and molecules as permanent vortex rings in an all pervasive ether (Kelvin, following a hydrodynamical theory of his friend Hermann von Helmholtz, and Joesph John Thomson) or as knots or twists in it (Joseph Larmor). This sort of modeling was a specialty of physicists who had passed through the honors course in mathematics at Cambridge (the mathematical tripos). Continental physicists, especially the French, regarded it with a mixture of puzzlement and distaste. Nonetheless, James Clerk Maxwell devised an ether model for the mediation of electrical and magnetic forces that suggested that light was an electromagnetic phenomenon.

Maxwell's theory charged the ether with accounting for electricity and magnetism as well as for light. None of the several models with mechanical properties proposed to effect it succeeded. Hendrik Antoon Lorentz and others then introduced space-filling media that had nonmechanical properties in order to underpin an adequate electrodynamics of bodies moving through the suppositious ether (relativity). In 1905, Albert Einstein showed the value of discarding the ether as a substrate and reference frame for electrodynamic phenomena.

The acceptance of relativity theory, however, did not destroy the ether. Einstein himself, in his application of relativity principles to the gravitational theory (1915), supposed that a gravitating body distorts nearby space, and that these distortions determine the trajectory of a passing ponderable body. An entity that can distort its shape, deflect light, and propagate electric and magnetic disturbances can be called a void only by discourtesy. More recently, quantum electrodynamics has filled the void with a vacuum that undergoes energy fluctuations and acts as a theater for the creation and annihilation of virtual particles. One such fluctuation is said to have given rise to the present universe. Physicists appear to need an ether on which to load all the properties of the physical world they cannot otherwise explain. Ether, alias the vacuum, exists. Void is anything but nothing.

J. L. HEILBRON

ETHICS AND SCIENCE. Even if it is possible to distinguish, it is no longer possible to dissociate science from its practical applications, which often raise ethical questions. The interaction of ethics and science has always been reciprocal, but until the end of the nineteenth century, science mostly posed challenges for ethics, while in the twentieth century ethics posed new challenges for science.

"Ethics" derives from the Greek word for "character," and the Greeks and Romans assumed that if we knew the human good or could model our behavior on that of a virtuous person, ethical conduct would be natural. Christian medieval ethics added aristocratic mutual obligation and contract, the divine inspiration of natural law, and the moral fallibility of all human beings. By the seventeenth century, new knowledge was generating new forms of power, as recognized by Francis Bacon, which meant new potential for wealth, abuses, and corruption. The mechanistic division between mind and matter in the work of René Descartes, which implied irrelevance of ethical issues to natural knowledge, was denied by Baruch Spinoza's equally rationalist *Ethics*. The various scientific academies established by the early eighteenth century stressed an ethics of mutual reliability among their members as free-acting observers.

Echoing the Greco-Roman model, the story of Galileo's conflict with the church, his prosecution and recantation under duress, and the ultimate vindication of his ideas has often been taken by scientists as a parable of the need for integrity and autonomy in scientific research. Scientists have had no direct analog to the Hippocratic Oath's injunction to "do no harm," but have taken as normative Galileo's insistence on following and finding the truth about this world in the face of convention and orthodoxy. The arguments of scientists have thus been suffused with a moral subtext of struggle against entrenched authority, constructing new knowledge not only in their own interests but in the interest of humanity.

During the eighteenth and nineteenth centuries, idealizations of science became entwined with the Enlightenment promise of human progress and the norms of reason. Impressed by the success of natural philosophy, Immanuel Kant laid out ethical claims revolving around an autonomous, rational agent. His (agent-based) "categorical imperative" to treat the humanity of others not simply as a means but as an end in itself stemmed from his understanding, in contrast to his skeptical contemporary David Hume, of logically consistent thinking as essential to our human nature. In (consequence-based) utilitarian ethics, science was modeled differently, becoming the root of cost-benefit analyses that offered the greatest good for the greatest number. Since science increasingly was associated with new developments in medicine, engineering, commerce, and warfare, the ethical systems represented by Kant and the utilitarians played ever greater roles in thought about how humans should treat each other. The nineteenth-century social sciences emerged in this climate, striving to treat human relationships as objects of study in order to better them. But when George Edward Moore published his *Principia Ethica* in 1903, he cordoned off reason from moral claims on the grounds that the "good" was fundamentally indefinable in natural terms. His contemporary Max Weber also stressed the distinction between fact and value, reinforcing Hume's argument that no bridge spanned the gulf between "is" and "ought." The impact of science on ethical thought had reached an impasse.

During the twentieth century, influence shifted to the impact of ethical thought on science, particularly physics, chemistry, and the life sciences, as the sciences themselves became entrenched authority for many people. Amid the moral chaos engendered by the trauma of World War I and the world economic depression of the 1930s, scientists made themselves increasingly important for military, economic, and medical advances. Robert K. Merton noted that this fact produced among scientists renewed calls for the autonomy, integrity, and insulation of science, but at the same time brought ever more anxious and insistent demands that science incorporate the ethic of social responsibility. The demands sometimes came from scientists themselves, sometimes from citizens galvanized by specific technological developments, and sometimes from governments responding to their publics. Following World War II, demands for responsibility coalesced into movements and various professional codes of behavior. As the country with the greatest resources and influence in science, the United States was often a barometer of these developments.

With the advent of the Cold War and the nuclear arms race, physicists and other scientists in every militarily powerful nation faced tensions between pursuing new knowledge and limiting its dangers. Some scientists who helped develop nuclear weapons led efforts to limit their further use, founding journals, creating federations, informing public opinion, and advising or critiquing governments and policies. These tensions and perplexities animated the Pugwash Conferences begun in 1957 in the Nova Scotia village by that name, at which scientists from around the world met as private individuals to discuss ways to limit international strains caused by the multiplication and increasing deadliness of armaments. As the philosopher Hans Jonas has observed, the first ethical responsibility in our era is to help insure that the possibility of ethics persists, that our creations do not destroy our world.

The importance of chemistry for new materials, agriculture, pharmaceuticals, energy, and many other factors in an elevated standard of living has raised a host of ethical concerns related to social justice and the environment. The same chemical production processes that give us new materials and energy generate pollution. New herbicides and pesticides that increase food production also have negative run-off effects on the environment. Drugs such as antibiotics have undesired evolutionary impact on microbes. All of these involve financial costs beyond the reach of much of the world's population, at a human price these people often bear. Soon after the publication of Rachel Carson's book *Silent Spring* (1962), the American Chemical Society enunciated the "Chemist's Creed" (1965), pledging an ethic of responsibility to the public, science, chemical profession, employer, self, employees, clients, students, and associates. The Green Revolution in agriculture produced a backlash against monocultures in favor of biodiversity, especially in the non-Western world, and the environmental ethics movement has modified or redirected significant scientific resources and programs. Many people have argued that ethical systems may not be universally valid, but ethical concerns must be global.

World War II was also a watershed in the life and social sciences, as Nazi eugenics policies and experiments on captive human beings led to postwar trials in Nuremberg. The ten principles known as the Nuremberg Code (1947), which emphasize the informed, voluntary participation of human subjects and safeguards for their welfare, became the basis for a sequence of declarations by the World Medical Assembly and most ethical discussions of human experimentation. By 1966, in the United States, written informed consent and harm/benefit assessments had to be submitted to formal ethical review before research on human subjects could be conducted with funding from the National Institutes of Health. These considerations spread to other agencies, cre-

Antinuclear demonstration in Germany. The banner at the bottom, center left, reads, 'Break the Red Pencil / Stop the Arms Race'.

ated a demand for a new specialty of bioethics, and altered research in the social sciences.

In the late 1960s climate of distrust of the role, direction, and authority of science in human affairs, geneticists and other biologists considered whether they were confronting ethical issues analogous to those facing physicists at the dawn of the nuclear age. After a brief, voluntary moratorium on certain lines of work, biologists agreed at the Asilimar Conference of 1975 upon a set of biological and physical safeguards in research on recombinant DNA and a set of ethical guidelines for informing staff of the possible hazards involved. Soon afterward, Peter Singer's book *Animal Rights* (1975) sparked a movement to extend to animals ethical protections similar to those afforded human subjects in research, some of which the American government put into place by the end of the 1980s. Anthropologists faced intensified disputes over the norms for study and disposition of human remains.

The growth of international corporate financial interest in genetic research in the 1980s and U.S. government funding for the Human Genome Project (1991) raised new ethical issues of ownership and privacy of genetic information, as well as new clinical, public health, and civil rights concerns. The HGP therefore decided to devote some of its funding to an Ethical, Legal and Social Implications Program. At the same time, the convoluted and politically controversial charges of scientific fraud in the decade-long David Baltimore case indicated the heavy-handedness of government policing of scientific integrity. Cloning technologies, stem-cell research, defensive research on biological weapons, and programs in robotics and artificial intelligence (which has given rise to a machine-rights movement) indicate that new bioengineering and bioethical issues will continue to proliferate.

Change fostered by science has been occurring too rapidly for many people and institutions to assimilate. Science and its technologies are implicated in the tensions between Western and non-Western values. Science played its role in the colonial expansion of Europe, and is closely associated with technological and medical practices that conflict with indigenous ethical and cultural assumptions. The ethical implications of the global impact of nuclear threat, environmental degradation, and bioengineering have raised the question of whether scientists can—or should—remain individual, free-acting agents of change.

ALAN BEYERCHEN

EUROPE AND RUSSIA. The main countries of Europe (including Great Britain and European Russia from time to time) have followed a similar pattern in developing the sciences since the second half of the nineteenth century. The attitudes of the dominant churches and the rate of commercial and industrial development have variously affected the pace and intensity of the pursuit of natural knowledge in the several countries. But the ready exchange of information, people, and inventions; the similarity of institutions for the study and spread of science; and commercial competition, warfare, and colonial adventures coupled development in the main European countries. The surprising finding that in 1900 the number of academic physicists per unit of population, and the amount of investment per unit of national income, were virtually the same in Britain, France, and Germany suggests the tightness of the coupling. This equalization occurred despite considerable differences in the methods of funding and the operations of the universities in the different countries.

During the eighteenth century the chief institutions concerned with natural knowledge divided their work in the same way throughout Europe: the universities taught established science, the academies sought new knowledge. The larger observatories and botanical gardens, often associated

The teaching laboratory in chemistry set up by Justus von Liebig (1803–73) at the University of Giessen (Hesse), as it appeared around 1840, when it drew workers from all over Europe

with both universities and academies, taught, preserved, and developed their subject matters in the same way in Paris and Saint Petersburg. A flourishing book trade, expanding university libraries, and many review journals, some, like the *Göttingische gelehrte Anzeigen,* associated with universities, kept everyone interested abreast of the latest advances. European scholars saw themselves as inhabitants of a "republic of letters." The use of Latin and French as the languages of scholarly interchange, travel when war did not preclude it, the mobility of academicians (the moves of Leonhard Euler from Switzerland to Saint Petersburg to Berlin to Saint Petersburg, and of Pierre de Maupertuis from Paris to Berlin and back, exemplify the traffic), and the institution of "corresponding members" of the learned societies further enforced the notion of a pan-European communion of philosophers. Immanuel Kant's *Idea for a universal history with a cosmopolitan purpose* (1784) made a "universal cosmopolitan existence … the highest purpose of nature." Ludwig Wachler, the author of a *History of history and art from the renewal of culture in Europe* (1812), taught that the cultivation of the sciences was a peculiarly European activity.

The sciences literally helped put Europe on the map. More exacting techniques for surveying and geodesy were developed in national academies, and academy expeditions helped establish the topographic contours of Europe. European governments learned to appreciate that precision measurement increased state revenues, and they set about the laborious task of establishing common units recognized beyond provincial boundaries. Enlightened states supported natural sciences for their utility; not only technical subjects like astronomy and geodesy with obvious applications, but also natural philosophy, geography, meteorology, mining, forestry, and agriculture, whose study would prepare better civil servants and effective policing.

Science unified more than knowledge and bureaucratic process. It helped constitute modern European states. Beginning in the early 1820s the Versammlung Deutscher Naturforscher und Ärzte brought together German-speaking physicians and naturalists from the patchwork of principalities, free cities, and palatinates that made up the region. The renowned explorer Alexander von Humboldt called its meeting in Berlin in 1828 "a noble manifestation of scientific union in Germany; it presents the spectacle of a nation divided in politics and religion, revealing its nationality in the realm of intellectual progress." The German institution spread—the European system was above all one of parallel institutional forms. In 1831 "gentlemen of science" founded the British Association for the Advancement of Science, which, like its German model, had a wide membership and moved to meetings around the country. The French counterpart came into existence just after the Franco-Prussian war exposed the error of not staying closer to the practices of its rivals.

By spreading French science, which already gave the tone to European science, the French Revolution marked the acme of the Republic of Letters; by having its way by force of arms, the Revolution simultaneously disseminated a republicanism that many scholars judged to be inimical to the old cooperative scholarship. Auguste Comte may have envisioned the approach of a "scientific" stage of human civilization in which the intellectual elites of Europe would form ties across political boundaries and initiate a peaceful "European revolution" (*Cours de philosophie positive,* 1830–1842). But he was too late—and too early. From the Napoleonic wars to the unification of Germany, rivalry rather than cooperation dominated the development of

European scientific institutions. The main growth occurred in the universities and higher schools. The foundation of the University of Berlin in 1810 and the restructuring of elementary and secondary curricula in Prussia gave a strong impetus to the entire educational system. Research gradually became a responsibility of the professoriate and of their students who aimed to be secondary school teachers. The rationale became ideology: only those who had contributed to knowledge, however small the contribution might be, could transmit to others the right mixture of information and enthusiasm. The Germans invented the teaching laboratory, the research seminar, the disciplinary institute, and the Ph.D. After the middle of the nineteenth century, foreign students began to flock to the German universities, to profit from their professors and facilities and—helping to integrate the European system of science—to bring back home what they found useful and transportable. After their defeat in 1870–1871, the French sent a mission to discover what made German universities so strong. In consequence, the French strengthened their provincial faculties of science and set up new higher technical schools like the École Supérieure d'Electricité (1884) and the École Supérieure de Physique et de Chimie (1882).

The strength of the French educational system since the Revolution had been its technical schools. The École Polytechnique trained scientists and engineers in a great deal of higher mathematics combined with physics and chemistry. Its students, selected by competition, graduated to enter specialized engineering schools—for mining, civil engineering, artillery, and so on. They then practiced as state employees, civil or military. Along with the centralized École Polytechnique the Revolution created an École Normale Supérieure, which supplied the teachers for the new system of state secondary schools (the *lycées*). The excellence of the Parisian technical schools and the scientific culture they supported made France the mecca of European natural philosophers and mathematicians until the 1830s and 1840s. As late as 1845 William Thomson chose Paris as the best place to complete his education in physics.

Thomson had been educated in old British universities (Glasgow and Cambridge). By the time he went to Paris, a new sort of university, which emphasized modern languages and science, had begun to grow. The University of London was put together from University College and King's College, founded in 1826 and 1831, respectively; later other colleges were added. Provincial manufacturing centers supported the creation of "redbrick" universities, which trained practical scientists of the second industrial revolution. Beginning in the 1850s committees of Parliament forcibly brought Oxford and Cambridge into the nineteenth century by establishing professorships in science and reducing the power of the humanistic dons.

As rivalry and war propagated the stronger institutional forms from one country to another (the Germans borrowed from the École Polytechnique for their *Technische Hochschulen*), pressures from science and its applications forced the invention of new means of cooperation. Some, like the famous meeting in Karlsruhe in 1860 where chemists came to settle their differences over atomic weights, were fleeting. Others, like the International Bureau of Weights and Measures, established near Paris in 1875, have endured. The need for agreement over measures made an irresistible force for internationalism.

The push toward standardization, the increasing mobility of students, the ever more efficient distribution of scientific journals, the remarkable expansion of the applied sciences that marked the second industrial revolution—all of these factors contributed to a pan-European identity for science even as imperial rivalries reached their peak. In *A History of European Thought in the Nineteenth Century* (1896–1914), John Theodore Merz, a German with a doctorate on Hegel who ran a chemical factory in Britain, gave voice to the growing conviction that "in the course of our century Science at least has become international . . . [W]e can speak now of European thought, when at one time we should have had to distinguish between French, German, and English thought."

Around 1900, the reconstruction of the Republic of Letters was cemented by the foundation of the International Association of Academies, with headquarters in Berlin; the International Catalogue of Scientific Literature, a retrospective inventory of periodical literature run from the Royal Society of London; and, outlasting both, the Nobel Institution and its prizes. On the nationalist level, the Kaiser-Wilhem Gesellschaft (founded 1911) copied in its own way the Royal Institution of Great Britain (founded 1799) and the Carnegie Institution of Washington (founded 1902), both examples of the use of private money for scientific research, then contrary to German practice. Alarmed British scientists pointed to Germany's expenditures on higher education to try to obtain, without much luck, greater resources from a stingy government. German scientists pointed to British trade schools and to the large expenditures on big research institutions made by the United States. French scientists pointed everywhere.

World War I shattered the growing internationalism. It replaced the International Association of Academies, headquartered in Berlin, with the International Research Council (IRC), dominated by the Belgians, French, British, and Americans, which did not admit the former Central Powers until 1926. The war also led to the creation of the Soviet Union, which was to spend most of the twentieth century outside the Western concert of science, and, indirectly, Nazi Germany, which would soon be ostracized for its hounding of Jewish academics. Still, World War I consolidated parallels among the belligerents: closer cooperation between science and the military and industry in the various countries, and, among the Allies, creation of equivalent institutions for the channeling of government money into academic science. The international Rockefeller philanthropies set up to support the exchange of researchers and to help build scientific institutes in Europe (France, Germany, Denmark, and Sweden were among the recipients) also helped the advanced scientific nations progress together.

After the opening of the IRC to the former Central Powers and the foundation of various international unions for pure and applied science, cosmopolitanism had a brief renewal. Just before the Nazi takeover, for example, the staff of sixty chemists at Fritz Haber's Kaiser Wilhelm Institut für Physikalische Chemie included seven Hungarians, four Austrians, three Russians, two Czechs, two Canadians, and one each from the United States, England, France, Poland, Ireland, Lithuania, Mexico, and Japan. During the late 1920s, international meetings increased in frequency. The Nazis and fascists then promoted internationalism in their special way by forcing some of the greatest European scientists to flee, particularly to Great Britain or the United States. At the same time, the Soviet Union drew in on itself. It had recruited left-leaning European scientists regardless of passport to help build up scientific research institutes in

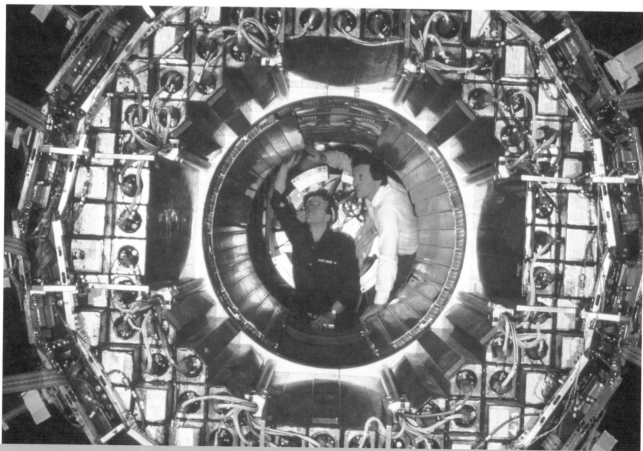

Technician working on the OPAL particle detector at CERN (Conseil Européen pour la Recherche Nucléaire), set up by a consortium of European countries

the People's Commissariat of Heavy Industry. The successive political purges of 1936–1938 expelled many visiting scientists, and the remainder left at the earliest opportunity.

World War II damaged the material infrastructure of European science and, together with the emigrations of the 1930s, made the United States by far the world's dominant scientific power. Soviet scientists who until the mid-1930s had played a lively part in multilateral European exchanges were sorely disappointed to find themselves further isolated by Cold War politics. Science remained an engine of prestige for the Soviet social experiment, however, and the growth in the Soviet Academy of Sciences in particular reflected its members' ability to turn the geopolitical insecurities of Soviet leaders into massive infusions of support for scientific research.

Two differences between Soviet and western European scientific institutions are especially notable. In Russia funding for individual programs of research did not come through formal independent peer review, but rather from large block grants to their host institutions. This practice exaggerated the discretionary powers of institute directors, who seldom resisted the temptation to cultivate huge patronage networks as the addition of classified research swelled the staffs of some institutes to a thousand or more. The Soviet Academy of Sciences also far outstripped its European counterparts in the control of institutional resources. In collective terms, it could thus dispense both resources and status, a function usually performed by separate institutions elsewhere.

Cold War rivalries and incipient European integration aided the rise of multinational laboratories. High-energy physics, with its unprecedented concentration of material and human resources on the search for the ultimate constituents of matter, took the lead. If the popular rationales for these expenditures often made reference to bilateral geopolitics, each new generation of accelerators still fostered increasingly complex multilateral collaborations. The best known institution in the western half of the continent was the European Center for Nuclear Research (CERN in its French abbreviation), founded outside Geneva in 1954 after arduous negotiations involving twelve sponsor nations. On the other side of the Iron Curtain, members of the Warsaw Pact nations joined Soviet physicists in building a rival accelerator at Dubna, outside Moscow, at an analogous institute—the Joint Institute for Nuclear Research.

Large-scale collaborations came to the life sciences with the founding of the European Molecular Biology Laboratory (EMBL) in the 1970s. Based in Heidelberg, it boasted four affiliated facilities elsewhere in Europe, and more than a dozen member nations. Where the lengthy lead times for particle experiments dictated a large permanent staff along with a steady stream of visiting researchers at CERN, EMBL had few permanent staff and visiting appointments lasting several years at most before the researcher returned to a home institution. It aimed not so much to transcend national boundaries by means of a single institution as to ensure steady cross-fertilization among the scientific communities of its member nations. Other initiatives like the European Synchrotron Radiation Facility (Grenoble), EURATOM, and the European Space Agency have been launched as well, with varying degrees of success.

The collapse of the Soviet Union and the increasing federalization of the European Union have reshaped the playing field for science in Europe. Scientists from EU nations are among the primary beneficiaries of employment mobility across borders, and continuing economic disparities have also made it attractive for Russian, Czech, or Hungarian scientific elites to pursue careers further west on the continent. Science in Russia, though financially impoverished in general, shows modest signs of stabilizing after the "brain drain" of the early 1990s, with a pronounced shift toward grant-based research funded by private (both foreign and domestic) and government foundations.

France and Germany continue to fund large systems of institutes for pure research with few rivals elsewhere in the world, but more and more of the money for academic research passes through Brussels. Since proposals seem to have a better chance of success the larger the spectrum of collaborators, EU grants make a powerful force for the integration of European science. Nonetheless, the entire enterprise maybe regarded as underfunded, particularly in Britain. Both Japan and the United States spend half again as large a percentage of their gross domestic products on research and development compared to the average EU member. The increasing autonomy of European Council members vis-à-vis their national state bureaucracies, however, offers further opportunities for the scientists of Europe to cement broader institutional alliances that constrain national policy makers. European political union remains anything but certain, yet most scientists continue to claim "Europe" as one of the surest means (whether directly or indirectly) for the local advancement of science on a global stage.

KARL HALL

EVOLUTION. What we now call evolution in biology—the notion that organisms are related by descent—was first debated within the life sciences during the second half of the eighteenth century. The word "evolution," however, had been used in the seventeenth and eighteenth centuries to denote individual, embryonic development, not descent. "Evolution" (from Latin *evolvere*, "to unroll") then meant typically the unfolding of parts preexisting in the embryo, as conceived by the supporters of "preforma-tion" in embryology. Occasionally, supporters of epigénesis used evolution to denote what they regarded instead as the successive addition of new parts in individual development.

From the mid-eighteenth century—both jointly with earlier embryological speculations and independently of them—a number of natural philosophers formulated hypotheses implying a dynamic conception of the history of the universe, the earth, and life, as opposed to a static conception of nature. Stasis was then increasingly regarded, and occasionally attacked, as typical of the major western religious traditions. The Enlightenment produced new or renewed dynamic conceptions of nature: in astronomy, by attempts aimed at extending Newtonian concepts to explain the history of the planetary system as well as its functioning (Georges-Louis de Buffon, Immanuel Kant, Pierre-Simon de Laplace); in the earth sciences, by evidence pointing at a formerly unthought of antiquity of the earth (Buffon, James Hutton); and in the life sciences, by speculations on a possible temporalization of the traditionally static system of classification of living beings (Charles Bonnet, Jean-Baptiste Robinet), by attempts at formulating materialistic explanations of the origin of life, generation, heredity, development, and change of organic structures (Benoît de Maillet, Pierre de Maupertuis, Erasmus Darwin), by the occasional observation of variability in species (Carl Linnaeus), and by the transposition of the notion of embryonic development to the entire history of life on Earth (Carl Friedrich Kielmeyer).

Charles Darwin (1809–1882) British naturalist known for his theory of natural selection

Between 1802 and 1820, Jean Baptiste Lamarck combined several of these themes to produce the first systematic, if not always clear, theory of organic change (in those years "evolution" in its present meaning is documented only in the works of Julien-Joseph Virey). Around 1830, Etienne and Isidore Geoffroy Saint-Hilaire developed and circulated Lamarck's notions further. Charles Lyell discussed Lamarck's views from a critical perspective in his authoritative geological work of the early 1830s, where he used "evolution" for the first time in its present sense in English. Lamarckian notions, combined with speculations on embryonic development and the nebular hypothesis in astronomy, figured also in the first popular book to spread an evolutionary worldview in the English-speaking countries: Robert Chambers's anonymously published *Vestiges of the Natural History of Creation* (1844).

From 1859, Charles Darwin's *Origin of Species* attracted enormous attention to the issue of the natural derivation of all species from one, or few, original living forms. In scientific as well as popular circles the question at issue was "evolution." Darwin avoided the word, however, preferring the expression "descent with modification." The philosopher Herbert Spencer and many of Darwin's own followers preferred "evolution," because of its broad implications for a view of nature—often secularized, and embracing humankind and society as well as the cosmos—that emphasized gradual, progressive change, achieved through competition.

Darwin's own explanation of evolutionary change, the theory of natural selection (Darwinism), faced strong opposition even among knowledgeable scientists. The late nineteenth century saw many attempts to fill up the gaps ("missing links") of the fossil records documenting ancestral histories, and little agreement on the causes of evolution. Around 1900, neo-Darwinism, neo-Lamarckism, and orthogenesis competed with one another and other theories of evolutionary change.

After the rediscovery of Gregor Mendel's laws in 1900, it took about four decades for biologists from various specialties to build consensus around the so-called modern synthesis, or neo-Darwinian theory of evolution, combining Darwin's notion of natural selection with the science of genetics. Since the 1940s, that has been the evolutionary theory adopted by the majority of biologists. From the mid-1960s, however, new approaches have emerged to the study of biological evolution, deploying the tools and concepts developed in the meantime by evolutionary ecology, paleontology, and, especially, molecular biology. The study of evolutionary change at the molecular level, in particular, has become a major research field, and the results achieved have led to conclusions sometimes diverging from mainstream neo-Darwinian concepts.

For example, the circumstance that genetic variation (now measured with techniques like gel electrophoresis of enzymes) is occasionally uncorrelated with reproductive success and adaptive evolution—and thus seems "neutral" with regard to natural selection—has led some biologists, notably Motoo Kimura, to develop, beginning in 1964, the neutral theory of molecular evolution. The theory asserts that much of the evolutionary change observed at the molecular level occurs via random genetic drift, unaffected by natural selection.

On another, connected front, privileging the study of fossil evidence and the process of speciation, Niles Eldredge and Stephen Jay Gould began in 1972 to develop the hypothesis of punctuated equilibria, which departs from the neo-Darwinian notion of evolutionary change as gradual and continuous. The hypothesis asserts that the history of many fossil lineages shows long periods of little morphological change (stasis) alternating with brief periods of rapid change associated with speciation.

Since the 1960s, the issue of human evolution has also aroused renewed scientific interest. The frequent harvest of ancient fossil specimens, especially from Africa; the study of mitochondrial DNA, allowing tentative dating of the more recent branches of the human family tree; and the statistical assessments of genetic variation, favoring a comprehension of how biological and cultural traits may interact in human populations through migrations; have made and continue to make dramatic news in popular as well as scientific circles.

Despite the opposition called up repeatedly by phenomena like social Darwinism and its several twentieth-century derivatives, and because of the recurrent conflicts over the religious and ideological implications of our understanding of evolution, evolutionary biology continues to carry with it today all the excitement that accompanied the publication of Darwin's *Origin* in 1859.

GIULIANO PANCALDI

EXHIBITIONS have shaped much of the cultural landscape of the modern world. Architecture and planning, mass entertainment and consumption, colonialism and imperialism, and not least, the cultures of science and technology owe much of their form and substance to the temples of modernity erected episodically throughout the world since the middle of the nineteenth century. Science suffused the very idea of exhibitions, their ideologies of progress, and the philosophies of classification that ordered displays. Exhibitions, moreover, diffused scientific ideas and introduced millions of people to scientific discoveries—radium and X rays, for example—and technological innovations—electric lighting, the telephone, plastics, and satellites. Scientists from different countries used exhibitions as a venue to meet and share their work and as a marketplace for instruments and technologies.

International exhibitions, also known as great exhibitions, universal expositions, and world's fairs, began with London's 1851 Crystal Palace Exhibition. The Great Exhibition of 1851, the brainchild of Albert, the Prince Consort, established the basic patterns of organization and display that would endure for decades without drastic modification. It built upon and to some extent supplanted traditions of local fairs and several decades of industrial displays at mechanic's institutes and national exhibitions in France and other countries. The success of the Crystal Palace Exhibition spurred other nations to follow suit, launching a veritable parade of international extravaganzas that Gustave Flaubert called

"the delirium of the nineteenth century." By World War I nearly one hundred international exhibitions had been held around the world. The largest late-nineteenth-century exhibitions frequently received visitors numbering in the tens of millions, culminating in the Paris Universal Exposition of 1900, attended by some fifty million people. In the twentieth century, international exhibitions disappeared during both world wars, only to be revived afterwards, each time with diminished status and importance.

Prince Albert promoted the Great Exhibition of 1851 as a carousel of industrial progress, a liberal and free trade antidote to the climate of unrest that haunted Europe in the years around 1848. The exhibition would provide an illustration of how "the great principle of division of labor, which may be called the moving power of civilization, is being extended to all branches of science, industry, and art." The exhibition would become a "scientific experiment," Albert announced, an attempt to reveal human progress as an unfolding of God's natural laws and to further "a naturalist's insight into trades." For Albert, a disciple of the Belgian statistician Lambert-Adolphe-Jacques Quetelet, the experimental results would show themselves

The Crystal Palace during the Grand International Exhibition in Hyde Park, London, in 1851

in the system of classification of sciences, arts, and industries. Many scientists were consulted for the classification, including the biologist Richard Owen, the German chemist Justus von Liebig, and especially, the British chemist Lyon Playfair, who presided over the final system of classes and stipulated the conditions of selection and the procedure of juries.

Classification remained an emblem of the primacy of science and a central theme of debate in major exhibitions held around the world. Several major exhibitions experimented with radically different methods of classification. For the Paris Universal Exposition of 1867, for example, the French engineer and sociologist Frédéric Le Play devised a philosophical classification system that encompassed not only industry but the whole of human activity in a didactic arrangement linked with the architecture of the exhibition palace. Also noteworthy was the attempt of Harvard psychologist Hugo Münsterberg to deepen the philosophical content of the exhibition by subsuming the classification of the world's fair held in St. Louis in 1904 to the disciplinary principles of a vast international scientific congress held at the exhibition.

Juries remained the key institution of international exhibitions. Composed of international experts, frequently scientists, their judgments set the standard for every field of endeavor. Both the selection and judgments of juries were often contested and the debates contributed greatly to the emerging concept of the scientific or technological expert. The British scientist Charles Babbage, for example, suggested that the 1851 exhibitions jury be regarded as the prototype of a professional class of scientists. In practice, juries endlessly disputed the basic principles of evaluation. As a result, exhibition juries promoted the creation of modern international institutions of standard weights and measures.

At the Paris Universal Exposition of 1855, jury members, beset with headaches over how to test, compare, and classify objects of diverse national origin, signed a document imploring the authorities of all countries to participate in international negotiations to establish coordinated meteorological standards. Several countries signaled their support, and in 1867 an international commission was established to debate and implement the metric system as the international standard for science, technology, and commerce. In the decades that followed, numerous international scientific commissions used exhibition sites to hammer out standards agreements. The most famous of these, the international agreement on standards of electrical resistance, was reached by several delegations of scientists, including William Thomson, Lord Rayleigh of Britain, and Hermann von Helmholtz, Werner von Siemens, and Rudolf Clausius of Germany, at the International Electrical Exhibition of Paris in 1881.

Several features of exhibitions attracted scientific pilgrims to the throng. Exhibitions played host to international scientific congresses, bringing scientists into direct contact with colleagues from other countries. At these meetings, as with similar gatherings of artists, industrialists, and politicians, scientists were exposed to national differences in method, apparatus, and philosophy. Exhibitions also furnished scientists with the opportunity to see and buy scientific instruments from around the world and to display and sell instruments of their own design. As in the industrial trades, early exhibition promoters expressed the hope that science would benefit from the increased contacts between instrument makers and eminent scientists. This desideratum seems to have been met frequently; for example, the Astronomer Royal George Biddell Airy visited the 1851 exhibition to examine Charles Shepard's electrically driven master clock controlling slave dials elsewhere in the building.

The optimism about this type of exchange reached its apogee in 1876, when an international exhibition devoted exclusively to scientific instruments took place at London's South Kensington museum. Scientists and instrument makers (and their apparatus) from many countries mingled profitably. After surveying what was probably the most complete spectrum of scientific instruments ever assembled, British physicist James Clerk Maxwell composed a taxonomy of scientific apparatus according to their functions and principles of construction. Arraying the different components of physical and chemical apparatus in close analytical detail, Maxwell's "General considerations concerning scientific apparatus" was a perfect example of the "naturalist's insight into trades" to which exhibitions aspired but did not always produce.

By contrast, the broader attempt at science education that was part of every exhibition's mission delivered mixed results. The early exhibitions drew on their origins in mechanic's institutes and worker education movements to promote mass education and diffusion of science and technology. The early Victorians had become adept at "learning by seeing," at understanding the principles of steam engines and related machinery, tracing with the eye the visible processes of driveshafts, gears, belts, valves, pulleys, cutoffs, and levers that drove and transmitted power. Aiming at a similar clarity and directness, exhibition displays of various scientific disciplines including the physical sciences, as well as geology, biology, and anthropology, generally eschewed the grotesque imagery of earlier curiosity cabinets in favor of lucid, analytical depictions of objects and artifacts. Statistics featured prominently in exhibits of many kinds, offering a seemingly transparent representation of the hidden facts of nature and society.

Over the course of the nineteenth century, exhibition organizers and participants gradually pulled back from the more ambitious attempts at scientific content and created exhibits that used the results of science to dazzle, inspire, and impress. The visiting public turned out to be less avid and equipped for education than promoters hoped, and new kinds of edifying entertainment gradually supplanted rigorous instruction in the majority of exhibits. Historians have attributed this transition in part to the changing nature of science and technology themselves. Late-nineteenth-century science was increasingly dominated by electricity and other phenomena (such as X rays) whose operations were invisible and whose principles proved difficult to communicate. After 1876, when the wonders of the phonograph, telephone, electric lighting, loudspeakers, and electric railways prevailed at exhibitions, entrepreneurs like Thomas Edison exploited the dazzling character of the new technologies to enhance the prestige of their business enterprises. Such developments, coupled with a growing tendency of elite professional scientists to distance themselves from applied science or technology, contributed to a growing bifurcation between pure and applied science at exhibitions. While attempts to communicate elements of applied science remained, exhibitions witnessed an increasing renunciation of attempts to communicate the content of pure science, opting instead for aestheticized displays of general convictions.

Because the diffusion of science at exhibitions overlapped with other forms of popularization, it is impossible to precisely gauge their broader cultural impact. But there can be no doubt that the ideologies and aesthetics of exhibition displays have left a legacy in many of the characteristic modes of scientific popularization, including fascination with scales of magnitude, emphasis on visual communication, and promotion of the material bounty of scientific progress.

ROBERT M. BRAIN

EXTRATERRESTRIAL LIFE. Displaced from the center of Aristotelian cosmology, the earth became one of many planets in the Copernican worldview. Galileo Galilei's telescopic observations of earthlike mountains on our moon, and of moons circling Jupiter, emphasized this displacement. The principle of plenitude, which interpreted any unrealized potential in nature as a restriction of the Creator's power, argued for inhabitants on other worlds. Although there was no evidence of lunar inhabitants, why else, asked the English clergyman John Wilkins in his 1638 *The Discovery of a World in the Moon,* would Providence have furnished the moon with all the conveniences of habitation enjoyed by the earth?

Social critics seized on lunar inhabitants either as members of a perfect society or as exemplars of all earth's vices. This literary convention furnished some defense in attacks against the establishment and helped spread the idea of a plurality of worlds. So did persistent rumors that England intended to colonize the moon.

Life spread beyond the moon in the French astronomer Bernard de Fontenelle's *Entretiens sur la pluralitè des mondes* (1686). During their evening promenades, the conversation of a beautiful marquise and her tutor turned to astronomy. On the second evening they spoke of an inhabited moon, on the third of life on the planets, and by the fifth night they had progressed to the idea of fixed stars as other suns, giving light to their own worlds. More conventional astronomy textbooks repeated these views.

Belief in extraterrestrial life permeated much of eighteenth- and nineteenth-century thought. It allowed an easy attack on Christianity, whose teachings about Adam, Eve, and Christ might appear ridiculous if the earth were not the whole of the habitable creation. Similar concerns regarding the immensity of the universe and the corresponding insignificance of humans appeared in novels.

The gullibility of a public raised on pluralist writings is illustrated by the widespread acceptance of reports in the *New York Sun* in 1835, purportedly from Sir John Herschel at the Cape of Good Hope, detailing his observations of winged quadrupeds on the moon. *The New York Times* judged these reports to be probable.

Many aspects of the extraterrestrial life debate appeared in Percival Lowell's Martian hypothesis and in reactions to it. Too modest to believe humankind the sole intelligence in the universe, Lowell, a wealthy Boston investor, announced in 1894 his intention to establish an observatory in the Arizona Territory and search for signs of intelligent life on Mars. There was already in America a lively interest in Mars, attributed by cynics to public imbecility and journalistic enterprise. Others hoped that the discovery of intelligent life elsewhere would increase reverence for the Creator. Lowell reported an amazing network of straight lines, which he interpreted as canals, and concluded that Mars was inhabited. Astronomers criticized Lowell for seeing only the evidence that supported his beliefs. Many readers, however, were persuaded by Lowell's literary skill. They also applauded the social arrangements of Mars, as elucidated by Lowell, particularly the abolition of war.

Changes in scientific knowledge in the twentieth century strengthened belief in extraterrestrial life. Larger telescopes expanded the observable universe to millions of galaxies, each containing millions of stars, all rendering it increasingly improbable that our earth alone shelters life. In 1953, Stanley Miller and Harold Urey at the University of Chicago synthesized amino acids, the building blocks of life, from a mixture of methane, ammonia, water, and hydrogen, the supposed ingredients of our primitive earth's atmosphere. Although the late astronomer Fred Hoyle attributed both the origin of life on earth and much of subsequence evolution to showers of microorganisms from space, his was a minority view, though recently resurrected. Most scientists suppose that life occurs inevitably on earthlike planets, of which they estimate that millions exist in the universe. *Star Trek,* the television series, visits some of these planets every week.

Skeptics object that, if intelligent life is inevitable and has had billions of years to evolve and travel through the universe, it should long since have reached our earth. That extraterrestrials are not known argues against their existence. Believers in UFOs (unidentified flying objects) attribute the absence of evidence of extraterrestrials to a government cover-up.

The chemical theory of the origin of life coincided with the space age and did not long remain earthbound. In 1976, in one of the greatest exploratory adventures of the twentieth century, the National Aeronautics and Space Administration (NASA) landed two Viking spacecraft on the surface of the planet Mars, at the cost of over one billion dollars. Experiments detected metabolic activity, but probably from chemical rather than biological processes.

Post-Viking, interest shifted from micro-organisms to direct communication with interstellar intelligence. Several early radio pioneers, including Guglielmo Marconi in 1920, thought they detected radio signals from Mars. The most comprehensive interstellar communication program was NASA's Search for Extraterrestrial Intelligence (SETI). From a small and inexpensive research and development project during the 1980s, SETI emerged in the early 1990s as a hundred-million-dollar program. A targeted search for radio signals focused on some thousand nearby stars, while a second element of SETI surveyed the entire sky. Ridiculed as "The Great Martian Chase," even after changing its name to "High Resolution Microwave Survey" in a vain attempt to highlight its potential for basic discoveries in astronomy, SETI lost its government funding in 1993. A scaled-back version of the original targeted search has been continued with private funding.

Would intercourse with extraterrestrials be beneficial? Suppose that they were a cancer of purposeless technological exploitation intent on enslaving us, rather than benign philosopher-kings willing to share their wisdom? Even if they should be helpful and benign, superior beings would be menacing. Anthropological studies of primitive societies confident of their place in the universe find them disintegrating upon contact with an advanced society pursuing different values and ways of life.

NORRISS S. HETHERINGTON

FIELD. The field, one of the most important concepts in modern physics, denotes the manner in which magnetic, electrical, and gravitational forces act through space. The field concept alleviated the difficulties many scientists found in assuming the existence of forces acting at a distance without the intervention of some material entity. Fields thus serve many of the functions of ether theories, which received their fullest development during the first half of the nineteenth century following the establishment of the wave theory of light by Augustin-Jean Fresnel.

Michael Faraday introduced the term "field" into natural philosophy on 7 November 1845, following his discovery of the magneto-optical effect and diamagnetism. He used the term operationally, in analogy to a field of stars seen through a telescope. During the next decade he developed the concept into a powerful explanatory framework for electromagnetic phenomena. This embodied much of his earlier thinking about the nature of magnetic action, especially his use of curved lines of force, which he had employed since the early 1830s to account for phenomena such as electromagnetic induction. It also embodied his opposition to conceptions such as atoms and the ether. As he wrote in 1846, he sought "to dismiss the aether, but not the vibrations."

Initially Faraday's contemporaries ignored his field concept, since it did not have the mathematical precision of action-at-a-distance theories such as André-Marie Ampère's electrodynamics. William Thomson (Lord Kelvin) reacted with contempt to Faraday's "way of speaking of the phenomena." However, Faraday's field theory had the great merit that in treating electrical events it took account not only of the wire carrying the electric current but also of the insulation of the wire, the surrounding medium, and so on. The notion of field made a good basis for developing a theory of long-distance telegraph signaling, which became a pressing problem in the mid-1850s with the intended construction of the transatlantic cable. Action-at-a-distance theories could not cope with this problem; Thomson, using Faraday's field concept, solved it.

This practical success prompted the adoption of the field concept in Britain. In the hands of Thomson and of James Clerk Maxwell it became a mathematical theory, much to the bemusement of the nonmathematical Faraday. However, unlike Faraday, who wished to abolish the ether from natural philosophy, both Thomson and Maxwell sought to interpret the field in terms of elaborate mechanical models (involving ethereal vortices) in an endeavor to retain the ether. This project ultimately failed. Relativity theorists such as Hendrik

Michael Faraday (1791–1867) in his laboratory in the Royal Institution in London

Antoon Lorentz and Albert Einstein replaced the ether by the nonmechanical field, a space capable of propagating forces, which is a cornerstone of modern physics.

FRANK A. J. L. JAMES

FIELD WORK. The histories and geographies of fieldwork and exploration are closely bound together in the development of modern science. During the fifteenth, sixteenth, and seventeenth centuries, both the logic of exploration and the consequences of its discoveries helped force a reconceptualization of the fundamental principles upon which scientific authority rested. Through the eighteenth, nineteenth, and twentieth centuries, exploration and fieldwork continued to be powerful forces in the shaping of science, although their main contributions had less to do with redefining principles of method than with developing substantive scientific knowledge of the world.

During the Age of Discovery (1450–1700), European nations, inspired by religious fervor and mercantile aspirations, developed a new understanding of the world beyond their own continent. Exploration in the Renaissance challenged established academic authority in three ways. First, the project of discovery, with its emphasis on the importance of experience, observation, and veracity, helped lay a new foundation for the production of knowledge about the world. This preeminently empirical form of knowledge acquisition threw into question the school philosophy with its emphasis on *a priori* reasoning, religious belief, and sedentary debate. However, this is not to say that Prince Henry the Navigator should be raised to the level of Nicholas Copernicus or Galileo Galilei as a hero of the Scientific Revolution.

Second, the objects collected during voyages of discovery and the testimonies of respected observers on board ships revealed New World civilizations seemingly incompatible with Mosaic chronicles of creation. The unfamiliar environments of the Americas also challenged the established natural histories of the Old World. The representative natural history of the sixteenth century—for example, Konrad Gesner's *Historia animalium* (1551–1558)—promoted an associative understanding of animal life in which descriptions of animals included their mythological, etymological, cosmological, and iconographic relations, as well as their habits and characteristics. Not only did the creatures of the New World undermine the supposedly comprehensive Renaissance catalogues, but attempts at their inclusion within an emblematic natural history brought existing formats and classifications into question. How could one write a natural history of an animal knowing nothing about its name, iconographic associations, roles in human culture, relations to other creatures, or place in myths and legends? By the mid-seventeenth century, natural histories included the animals of the New World and dispensed with previous classical conventions.

Thirdly, Renaissance exploration challenged classical scholarship by its emphasis on application. For instance, Prince Henry the Navigator sought geographical knowledge. However, his voyages were also commercial, colonial, and religious in motivation. As new protoscientific techniques helped merchants and rulers establish empires of trade and dominion, so Europe's more radical natural philosophers argued that science should help improve the lot of humankind. The labors of some natural historians, mathematicians, chemists, and astronomers had a direct bearing on the endeavors of those involved in oceanic exploration. For instance, John Evelyn, a founding member of the Royal Society of London, advised the English Navy about the supply of timber for their ships. Science and exploration also combined in the development of a set of technological devices that facilitated the efficient movement of people and things around the world. Practical charts of maritime navigation, the quadrant, accurate and robust timepieces, and new sorts of ships helped produce a science of exploration.

By 1650 most of the world's coastlines had been mapped, at a rudimentary level at least, and concerted efforts were underway to explore and map continental interiors. Although the majority of accounts came in the form of a topographical compendium, their geographical focus varied widely, ranging from descriptions of local areas up to continents and even the entire globe. In an attempt to make these texts useful to others, the Royal Society of London devised an agenda and method toward the standardization of exploration reports and the geographical scale of their enquiry. It preferred "regional surveys." Samuel Hartlib, the Prussian natural philosopher, promoted the use of regional surveys in the production of a "political anatomy" that organized geographical, economic, and social data. Meanwhile, Robert Boyle prepared a treatise to aid the regional surveyor, a eulogy to the inductive method, entitled *General Heads for the Natural History of a Country, Great or Small; Drawn Out for the Use of Travellers and Navigators* (1692). Boyle's text might be seen as a very early fieldwork manual.

The work of Carl Linnaeus gave a boost to international field studies, which both imitated his example and employed his classifications. Linnaeus botanized in Lapland, elsewhere in Scandinavia, Holland, France, and England. His students, or disciples as he called them, applied his binomial nomenclature to the world beyond Europe. From 1745 to 1792 nineteen of them left on voyages of discovery to, among other places, Australia and the Pacific, Siberia, Senegal, the Americas, the Arabian peninsula, the Ottoman Empire, and Africa. A series of other significant scientific expeditions of continental interiors took place during the eighteenth century. Mark Catesby and later John Bartram and his son William explored the American East Coast. Like Catesby before him, John Bartram made a good trade in supplying European natural history enthusiasts with North American specimens. Catesby and William and John Bartram, the latter acting as the King's Botanist in North America, also wrote and published influential natural histories of the Carolinas, Georgia, Florida, Pennsylvania, and the Bahamas. Many others continued to work in this tradition, culminating in the famous western territorial expedition of Meriwether Lewis and William Clark in the first decade of the nineteenth century.

Under French leadership, two international scientific teams set out in the 1730s to resolve the debate over the shape of the globe. One team, led by Pierre de Maupertuis and including Anders Celsuis, went to Lapland, the second team, led by Louis Godin and Charles Marie de Lacondamine, to Peru, to measure the length of a degree along the meridian. Their extensive collection of a wide range of measurements contributed to international scientific knowledge of the regions. At the very end of the century Alexander von Humboldt and his companion Aimé-Jacques-Alexandre Bonpland traveled through South America, accumulating enough material for thirty published volumes. Using more than four dozen measuring instruments, including chronometers, an achromatic telescope, sextants, compasses, barometers, thermometers, rain gauges, and theodolites, the two men set a new standard for regional scientific study.

Chronometer used on James Cook's second voyage, 1772

In particular, they pioneered the "isomap," the cartographic method for the delineation of comparative natural features.

Another landmark voyage of exploration was that of the HMS *Endeavour,* captained by James Cook. From 1768 to 1771 Cook traveled to the Pacific accompanied by a group of naturalists including Joseph Banks, the founder of the Royal Botanic Gardens at Kew, and Daniel Carl Solander, one of Linnaeus's foremost students. The first voyage's main objective was to observe from Tahiti the transit of Venus across the face of the sun. Although part of a broader international astronomical enterprise, the voyages played an important role in the introduction to Europe of the natural histories of New Zealand and Australia.

Cook's orders included taking possession of any new lands that might benefit the British crown. Banks and Solander's involvement in Cook's conquest of Australasia therefore enrolled naturalists as agents of the European imperial endeavor. It became commonplace for expeditions organized by the military to include men of science to assess the value of newly discovered lands and collect new species of plants and animals. These and others involved in the development of European colonial rule in the eighteenth and nineteenth centuries brought a wide array of foreign specimens back to their respective countries, feeding the growth of botanical and zoological gardens, natural history museums, and the trade in exotic plants. This association also benefited the development of the sciences. For instance, Charles Darwin's participation in the British Admiralty's hydrological survey of the waters around South America on the HMS *Beagle* was fundamental to the development of his theory of natural selection.

The study of ethnology also grew out of the close relations between science and empire in the nineteenth century. Although European traders had come into contact with different cultures for centuries, colonial expansion brought with it a heightened impetus to study aboriginal peoples, before their eradication by "civilization." The emerging sci-

ences of anthropology and ethnology developed standardized methods for the measurement of the human body, termed "anthropometry." Nineteenth-century advances in photography made further important contributions to this effort. British colonial governmental officials carried out comprehensive photographic surveys of the peoples of India in the 1860s, and in Africa in the 1890s.

The university was an important site for the furthering of fieldwork as an integral aspect of science from at least the sixteenth century. From around 1525, university physic gardens introduced medical students to herbs as living plants rather than only as dried herbarium specimens. The lack of such a garden in Bologna forced the University's instructor in *medicina practica,* Luca Ghini, to take his charges into the countryside in search of herbs. Students of Ghini later led extended expeditions during university vacations that transformed into more general lectures on natural history. This practice spread to France in the 1550s and to Sweden, Denmark, England, and Scotland by 1650. London's Society of Apothecaries was the most persistent promoter of the field excursion as a necessary aspect of medical training. Its expeditions into the English countryside occurred for 214 years without a break, stopping in the nineteenth century only because it took so long to get beyond the sprawling metropolis.

Education in field study for medical students carried over into other scientific disciplines in the eighteenth and nineteenth centuries. It became increasingly common for botany and geology students at the European universities to undertake fieldwork as part of their study. This tradition was introduced to the United States by Louis Agassiz and Spencer Fullerton Baird, who pioneered formal field teaching at Harvard University and Dickinson College, Pennsylvania, respectively. Students benefited from the proliferation of inexpensive field equipment: guidebooks with directions for taking notes, collecting and preserving specimens, and formulating a collection; tools like specially designed and reasonably priced hammers, geological maps, and "botany boxes," with tightly fitting lids and carrying straps; nets for entomologists; and guns and cameras (though these required a heavier outlay) for zoologists. Easy access to field equipment contributed greatly to the widespread enthusiasm for field study in Europe and North America in the nineteenth century. Women, children, and artisans, as much as university-educated middle-and upper-class gentleman, participated.

The establishment of anthropology and geography as discrete university disciplines at the very end of the nineteenth century extended the close connection between a scientific education and field study. Practitioners in both fields placed in situ study at the center of their disciplines. More generally, academic science began to fragment into increasingly specialized sub-disciplines, and even the largest expeditions started to limit themselves to particular tasks. For instance, while Felix Andries Vening Meinesz surveyed marine gravity on world-ranging submarines, Jacob Clay and Robert Millikan circled the globe measuring cosmic rays at various altitudes, latitudes, and depths; while Jean Abraham Chrétien Oudemans produced geographical maps of the Dutch East Indies, others made magnetic measurements and took soundings of coastal waters.

Exploration and fieldwork declined in importance during the twentieth century. Automated data-collection devices such as satellites, self-recording weather stations, and seismometers reduced the role of the human observer. Meanwhile, exploration became increasingly driven by the agendas of multinational corporations scouting for new reserves of natural resources such as oil and gas. Notable exceptions to this rule were the mapping and scientific exploration of Antarctica and the sea floor.

The high latitudes of Antarctica made it of special interest for geophysical studies. Cooperative "Polar Years" were organized by geophysicists in 1882–1883 and 1932–1933. Mapping of the continent continued after World War II by nations interested in staking claims on the landmass. However, in 1957–1958 the International Council of Scientific Unions implemented the third Polar Year, formalized as the International Geophysical Year (IGY). The success of the IGY prompted the creation of the Special (changed later to Scientific) Committee on Antarctic Research (SCAR) in 1958. This led indirectly to the signing of the 1959 Antarctic Treaty, setting the continent aside for peaceful, international, and scientific purposes. However, despite the best efforts of SCAR, Antarctica remains the one continental landmass not yet comprehensively mapped by fieldworkers working on the ground.

Simon Naylor

FOSSIL. Until the end of the eighteenth century, scholars could not decide whether fossils were the traces of dead creatures. For every fossil that clearly resembled a living animal, they found others unlike anything currently living. When minerals were believed to grow in the earth, and when spontaneous generation remained a serious hypothesis, many people assumed that fossils had grown in situ. In 1726, in a notorious example, Johann Beringer, a member of the faculty of medicine at the University of Würzburg, published a book full of illustrations of curiously shaped stones found in the region. He described them as the handiwork of God. They turned out to be the handiwork of jealous colleagues who had planted them as a hoax.

In the early nineteenth century, paleontology began to emerge as a subfield of geology. From the point of view of geologists, fossils were chiefly useful for identifying strata. Geologists concentrated on the fossils plentiful enough to serve this function, and so spent most of their time classifying marine invertebrate species. Questions that thrilled a wider public about the meaning of fossils and the history of life on earth were of limited interest to paleontologists. They have, however, loomed large in the public image of geology.

When Georges Cuvier and his followers excavated bones and reconstructed giant beasts such as the mammoth or the ichthyosaurus, they showed to almost everyone's satisfaction that some species had become extinct. While fossil marine bivalves might be thought to have living representatives in some distant ocean, no one expected to find an ichthyosaurus in a remote part of the world. How and why extinction has occurred was to generate much speculation in both scientific and religious circles.

Meanwhile, the search for fossils of extinct vertebrates had started. In 1824, the English geologist William Buckland published the first paper describing a dinosaur. In 1842, another Englishman, Richard Owen, coined the term for these creatures. Almost immediately, dinosaurs captured the place in the public imagination they retain to this day. Professional fossil collectors mounted expeditions to likely sites. At the beginning of the twentieth century, the steel magnate Andrew Carnegie, reading of a discovery of a giant dinosaur in Wyoming, dispatched a team to secure it for his new museum in Pittsburgh. After various adventures, the bones of *Diplodocus carnegii* arrived. So spectacular was

The skeleton of Diplodocus, which lived 140 million years ago, was found in Wyoming in 1902 and is now displayed at the Museum of Natural History in Houston, Texas

the creature when reconstructed that national museums throughout the world considered themselves incomplete without one. Plaster casts of Carnegie's dinosaur can now be seen in England, France, Austria, Russia, Germany, Spain, Argentina, and Mexico.

Charles Darwin admitted in his *Origin of Species* (1859) that the fossil record with its many gaps posed a severe problem for his theory. He resolved the problem by asserting that the record was incomplete. Nonetheless, his followers, including T. H. Huxley and O. C. Marsh, professor of vertebrate paleontology at Yale University, thought it important to try to trace ancestries for at least some species. They were particularly successful with the horse. For the public, though, the more important question remained the "missing link" between humans and their simian ancestors. The remains of Neanderthal man came to light in 1856, followed by Peking Man (1903) and Piltdown Man (1912), exposed as a hoax in 1953.

The ability of fossils to stimulate the imagination has not declined in recent years. In the late 1960s, a new debate started when two Americans, Robert Bakker and John Ostrom, suggested that dinosaurs were hot blooded and thus lively, not the slow-moving creatures that had been imagined. Just a little over a decade later, a group of American scientists led by Walter Alvarez suggested that dinosaurs had been killed off by an extraterrestrial object hitting the earth about sixty five million years ago. Most scientists now seem to agree. Another round of interest in fossils, sparked by the discovery that traces of DNA can be found in some fossils, inspired Stephen Spielberg's film *Jurassic Park*.

RACHEL LAUDAN

FOUNDATIONS. During the twentieth century, scientists' need for expensive experimental apparatus, large research teams, and international travel required diligent searches for funds that have been integral to setting research agendas. As Robert Kohler described the situation, "Assembling the material and human resources for doing research is no less a part of the creative process than doing experiments." Throughout the century, but particularly in the first half, foundations were central to that process.

The perpetual charitable trust as a legal entity intended to deliver a specific public benefit dates from the Elizabethan era. The general-purpose philanthropic foundation awaited the late-nineteenth-century elaboration of the nonprofit organization to give it a vehicle, and the capitalist accumulation of wealth to make it substantial. Philanthropically created foundations that support science are primarily a recent American phenomenon.

The first large foundation to support fundamental research was the Carnegie Institution of Washington, initially endowed by Andrew Carnegie with $10 million and enlarged with later gifts. The Institution hired scientists and created laboratories of its own and made numerous small grants to individual scientists and large ones to institutions, such as the Mt. Wilson Observatory and the National Research Council. Over the next three decades, American science benefited from other foundations as well: Robert Goddard's rocket experiments had support from the Carnegie Institution and the Guggenheim Foundation; Albert Einstein's visit to the United States in 1931 to collaborate with Robert Millikan was funded by the Oberlaender Trust; the China Foundation's fellowships sent Chinese geneticists and biologists abroad for advanced training. The Sauberán Foundation in Argentina helped to establish Nobel laureate Bernardo Houssay's Institute of Biology and Experimental Medicine in Buenos Aires in 1944. In the 1950s, the Nutrition Foundation provided fellowships for Central American food chemists to study in the United States.

The largest amount of money distributed in the first half of the twentieth century came from the cluster of philanthropies created by the Rockefeller fortune. Led by the Rockefeller Foundation, these philanthropies initiated programmatic giving that focused funding on particular institutions, disciplines, or problem areas, and relied heavily on knowledgeable program officers to make decisions about allocations. Rockefeller institution-building created or supported major research centers, including the Peking Union Medical College (founded in 1918), the Bohr Institute in Copenhagen (1921), the Mathematical Institute at Göttingen University (1926), the Palomar Observatory (1948), and public health institutes in Europe, the United States, and South America.

In specific fields, Rockefeller funding had significant effects. Support of physicists in the 1920s and 1930s aided in shifting the center of physics from Europe to the United States. The Rockefeller Foundation helped to create molecular biology, contributing approximately $25 million to the field from the 1930s through the 1950s.

Rockefeller philanthropies greatly expanded the role of the fellowship, both resident and traveling, as a means of shaping or even redirecting careers. In 1919, the Rockefeller Foundation began a twenty-year program run by the National Research Council, which at first supported physicists and chemists, but soon expanded to biologists and psychologists. The International Education Board (IEB), created in 1923, was the first Rockefeller philanthropy to focus on fellowships as a means of promoting science. These fellowships enabled young researchers to devote their time to their specialties during what was generally their period of greatest productivity.

After the IEB merged with the Rockefeller Foundation in 1928, the fellowship program became global, and assisted many scientists and organizations in less-developed regions. Alberto Hurtado became research director of Peru's Institute of Andean Biology in 1934 after holding a postdoctoral research fellowship from the Rockefeller Foundation at the University of Rochester. Over the next twenty years, the Foundation granted ten fellowships to Hurtado's staff to study abroad; combined with Rockefeller grants for instruments, this program made the Institute a global leader in physiology studies. Extended throughout Latin America, the fellowships of the Rockefeller Foundation, and similar fellowships offered by the John Simon Guggenheim Foundation, helped to reorient Latin American science from Europe to North America.

After World War II, the rapidly increasing scale of government-funded research induced the largest foundations, including the Rockefeller Foundation, to withdraw from general support of the natural sciences. Both the older and newer foundations turned to more specific and applied areas such as agriculture, population studies, and medicine. Particularly wealthy foundations such as the Wellcome Trust (1936) and the Nuffield Foundation (1943) in Britain, and the Howard Hughes Medical Institute (1953) in the United States, supported medicine.

Because foundations can focus on specific research areas and dispose of funds flexibly, their institutional form was adopted throughout the world in the latter part of the twentieth century, often by government initiative. The Merieux

Foundation (1967) supports research in biology and medicine in France; the Mario Negri Institute (1961) supports biomedical research in Italy; the interrelated Fundación Andes, Fundación Antorchas, and Vitae (Apoio à Cultura, Educação e Promoção Social) in Latin America (1985) and the Volkswagen Foundation (1961) in Germany give to higher education science research. A major example of government-created foundations that fund research is the Deutsche Bundesstiftung Umwelt, the largest foundation in Europe in the 1990s, established by the German government with the proceeds of the sale of a publically owned corporation. In the twentieth century, foundations became an integral element of the scientific enterprise, responsible for the founding or expansion of institutions, providing crucial support for the development of scientific careers, and aiding in the creation of new fields of science.

DARWIN STAPLETON

FRAUD. In 1981, then-Representative Albert Gore, Jr., began the hearings of the Investigations and Oversight Subcommittee of the House Science and Technology Committee. Cases of scientific misconduct had been disclosed at four major research centers in the 1980s; doubts about the integrity of American scientific research circulated. Gore wondered publicly if these cases were not "just the tip of the iceberg." Answering in the affirmative in 1982, William Broad and Nicholas Wade, well-regarded science journalists who had worked for both the *New York Times* and *Science,* published in their *Betrayers of the Truth* that scientific fraud was much commoner than anyone had believed.

Fraud is a particularly serious sin in science, whose whole purpose is supposed to be the pursuit of truth or knowledge. In the biomedical sciences in particular, a distressingly common pattern of misconduct seemed to be emerging. John Darsee, a cardiologist at Harvard Medical School, published over a hundred articles and abstracts between 1979 and 1981. After charges of fraud led to investigations in 1981, he retracted fifteen out of the twenty articles questioned. Other cases surfaced at the University of California at San Diego, the University of Pittsburgh, the Baylor College of Medicine, and the Massachusetts Institute of Technology. The latter became known as the Baltimore case because the senior author of the article allegedly containing a junior author's fraudulent data was David Baltimore, Nobel Prize winner and by then president of Rockefeller University. Although Baltimore himself was not suspected, his support of the junior author seemed ill advised. Eventually, in 1991, she was cleared of all wrongdoing, but by then the case had caused Baltimore's resignation from Rockefeller and widespread public concern.

The furor over the Baltimore case reflected growing suspicion about the practices of science. Broad and Wade had claimed that fraud was endemic to the scientific enterprise. The supposed perpetrators listed in their book included some of science's most lustrous names. Ptolemy, they charged, invented astronomical measurements; Galileo reported results too perfect to be credible; Isaac Newton fudged data; John Dalton described experiments he probably never performed; Gregor Mendel produced statistical results too good to be true; and Robert

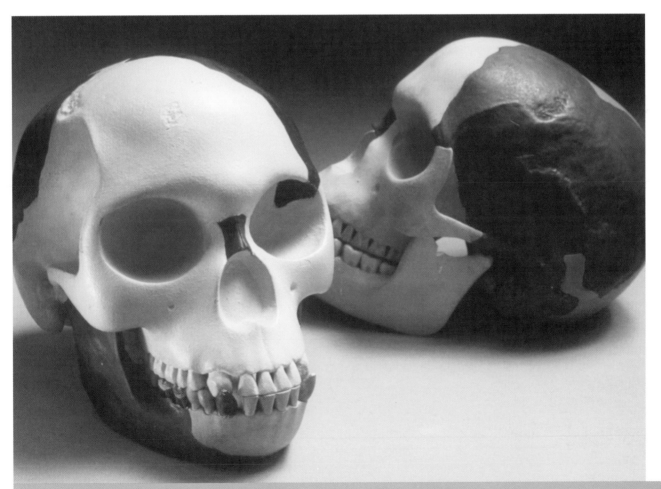

Reconstruction of Piltdown man from the jaw fragments (in brown) found in Sussex around 1912. Interpreted as the link between man and apes, in fact (as was shown in 1953), the human skull and ape jaw belonged to different individuals.

Millikan, awarded the Nobel Prize in 1923 for measuring the charge on the electron, had selected only the readings that suited him.

Far from being disinterested seekers after truth, Broad and Wade argued, scientists were as ambitious and anxious for recognition as any other professionals. They rarely replicated experiments, supposedly one of the best checks on fraud, because they received no credit for doing so. And in the face of charges of fraud or threats of regulation from outside, the scientific community drew together instead of subjecting their colleagues to investigation.

Scientists, government officials, and historians undertook serious studies of the problem. They quickly discovered the difficulty of defining fraud. Faking data with the intent to deceive others (the motive, according to most scientists, behind the planting of the Piltdown skull) was clearly wrong. But what to make of the practices identified in the nineteenth century by the computer pioneer Charles Babbage: forging (reporting observations that had never been made), trimming (working with data to make them look better), and cooking (choosing the data that best fit the theory under test)? On occasion depending on the choice of the appropriate statistical methods, trimming or cooking might be appropriate. What about thought experiments, experiments that took place only in the scientist's head? And preparing a streamlined and cleaned-up version of research for publication, although it could involve fraud, was also in most cases unproblematic scientific practice. Historians of science believed that many of the historical cases adduced by Broad and Wade fell in a benign category.

In any case, the American scientific community had not been prepared to deal with fraud. Techniques for detecting it were rudimentary. "Whistle blowers," who were as likely to suffer as the scientists they charged, brought most cases to light. Procedures for handling cases once detected did not exist. In 1985, Congress passed the Health Research Extension Act. It included important provisions concerning fraud: institutions receiving federal money had to establish administrative processes to review reports of fraud; and the National Institutes of Health had to establish a process to respond to their findings. It took five years to draft and discuss guidelines. In 1989, these were published in the Federal Register. To avoid emphasizing questions of motive, the term "fraud," defined in law as intent to deceive, did not appear. Instead misconduct was defined as "fabrication, falsification, plagiarism, or other practices that seriously deviate from those that are commonly accepted within the scientific community for proposing, conducting and reporting research."

The guidelines created considerable controversy. Many scientists wanted the ruling confined to fabrication, falsification, and plagiarism rather than opening the door to the policing of other practices that, although dubious morally (e.g., sexual harassment), were not specific to the scientific enterprise. Efforts to set up a system to deal with misconduct continued. In 1992, the Public Health Service set up the Office of Research Integrity. Over the next five years it received approximately a thousand allegations of misconduct. It investigated 150 of these and found against the researchers in about half of them. Some of its conclusions, most spectacularly in the Baltimore case, were reversed.

Although the problem of fraud emerged in the United States and seems to have been most intense there, other countries with substantial programs of scientific research, including Great Britain, Japan, Germany, France, and Australia, have all put in place procedures to detect and regulate misconduct in science. In an enterprise funded by public money, it is not surprising that governments set up systems for assuring accountability, but that they did without them for so long.

RACHEL LAUDAN

GEIGER AND ELECTRONIC COUNTERS. Twentieth-century physicists first built electronic counters to detect charged particles from radioactivity, then turned them to cosmic ray research, and later combined them in arrays for high-energy particle experiments. In 1908, Hans Geiger built a cylindrical capacitor to help Ernest Rutherford determine the charge on alpha particles. A thin wire with a high voltage ran down the center of a brass cylinder filled with carbon dioxide. A charged particle passing through the chamber would ionize some of the gas in proportion to its charge, setting up a current of ions traveling toward the wall of the tube and electrons toward the center wire; an electrometer needle registered the resultant voltage step. Increasing the voltage on the capacitor increased its sensitivity by creating an avalanche of electrons. The quantity of these secondary electrons depended on the speed and nature of the primary particles. Geiger's initial counter could count up to ten particles per minute and confirmed the double charge of the alpha particle.

Geiger subsequently refined the device by using a sharp needle instead of a coaxial wire for an anode; the additional sensitivity could detect electrons as well as alpha particles, and even photons via secondary electrons knocked out of atoms. But the Geiger counter also registered random, spontaneous counts, even with no nearby radioactive source and especially with maximum sensitivity. In 1928, Walther Müller, a postdoctoral assistant to Geiger at the University of Kiel, designed a still more sensitive counter and found that the spontaneous discharges were caused not by contamination of the gas or metal, but by cosmic rays passing through the chamber. Müller's work turned an apparent defect of the Geiger counter into an advantage, and Geiger counters (or, as they were sometimes called, Geiger-Müller counters) became a prime tool in the fruitful program of cosmic ray physics in the 1930s.

Walther Bothe soon incorporated Geiger counters into coincidence circuits, two counters wired together so as to register a particle when both counters fired together. Bothe and Werner Kolhörster at first measured counts optically, using the electronic output to nudge a mirror and photographic film to record the reflected light. Bruno Rossi, an Italian physicist visiting Bothe's institute, dispensed with the film. A simple logic circuit designed by Rossi ensured that if and only if two counters fired, then a voltage difference on the circuit would result. An experimenter could expand Rossi's circuit to more intricate arrays of counters, firing in coincidence or anticoincidence, with logic gates in the circuit to sort out the particles produced in cosmic ray showers. For example, by measuring the counting rate with and without lead blocks inserted between three Geiger counters, one could determine whether particles originated from the sky or the lead block.

The radar and atomic bomb projects in the United States in World War II developed new amplifiers, pulse-height ana-lyzers, and other electronic devices that would find use in electronic detectors. Rossi worked at Los Alamos on fast timing circuits to measure nuclear processes, such as the time between the emission of prompt and delayed neutrons from nuclear fission. Nuclear energy also provided a market for Geiger counters as radiation detectors. Following the development of vacuum tube amplifiers by the radio industry, Geiger counters were connected to audio speakers to register particle counts as clicks. A popular image of the nuclear age featured the crackle of Geiger counters betraying the presence of nuclear radiation.

After the war, electronic counters became both high art and big science in detectors for high-energy physics. Particle physicists wired new sorts of counters into electronic logic circuits: first scintillation and Cherenkov counters, which converted flashes of light into electronic pulses, and later spark chambers, a sort of flattened Geiger counter with a parallel-plate configuration, and drift chambers and multiwire proportional counters, both of which worked according to the same principle as the Geiger counter. All of these counters generally recorded electronic data instead of the visual output of cloud and bubble chambers, and used high particle counts to provide statistical evidence of phenomena instead of snapshots of individual events. By the 1970s, physicists were using computers to reconstruct particle tracks from complex collections of electronic counters.

PETER J. WESTWICK

GENETICS is grounded in the papers on inheritance in peas by the Austrian monk Gregor Mendel that he published in 1865. It emerged as a field of biology after Mendel's long-ignored work was rediscovered in 1900 by scientists concerned with what might be learned about the mechanism of evolution from hybridization experiments in plants. In the United States and England, Mendel's laws of biological inheritance were immediately embraced by a number of evolutionary biologists and plant breeders, including William Bateson at Cambridge University, who coined the term "genetics" in 1903. Yet the theory also ran into a good deal of skepticism. The mathematics of Mendelian inheritance seemed to conflict with the one-to-one male-female ratio of sexually reproducing species. Then, too, many characters varied with transmission from one generation to the next and many expressed themselves not as alternates—e.g., tall or short—but in a blended fashion, intermediate between the characters of parents.

However, in 1905, Edmund Beecher Wilson, at Columbia University, and Nettie M. Stevens, at Bryn Mawr, concluded independently that the determination of sex, including the one-to-one sex ratio, was caused in Mendelian fashion by the segregation and reunion of the X and Y chromosomes. In 1909, the Danish biologist Wilhelm Johannsen drew on his studies of heredity in selected lines of plants to propose that variation arises from two sources: one is the influence of

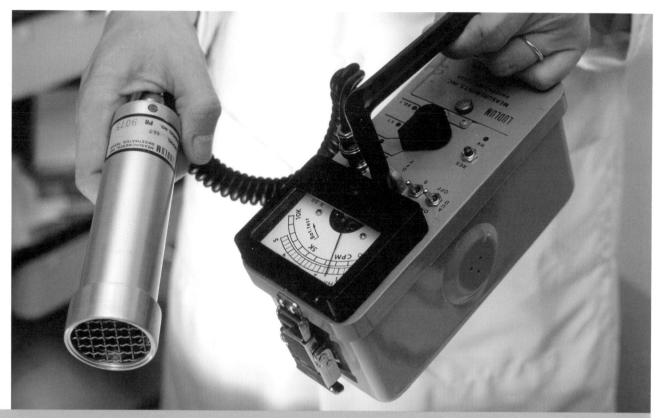

A technician holds a modern version of the Geiger counter, a detector of radiation invented by Hans Wilhelm Geiger (1882–1945) in the 1920s.

environment on the developing organism; the other is slight variation in Mendel's transmitted factors of heredity, which Johannsen called "genes." Johannsen's delineation of these shaping differences gave rise to the concepts of, respectively, "genotype" (the sum of all an organism's genes) and "phenotype" (the characters it displays, which are a product of both its genes and the environment it experiences).

Like Mendel's rediscoverers, Thomas Hunt Morgan, a biologist at Columbia University, came to the study of heredity through concern with the problem of evolution. Initially skeptical of Mendelism, he became a convert to it after 1910, when he observed a heritable mutation—the appearance of a white-eye—in the fruit fly *Drosophila melanogaster*, whose eyes were normally red. Morgan and a team of three graduate students—Calvin Bridges, Hermann Muller, and Alfred Sturtevant—proceeded to scrutinize the offspring of innumerable generations of fruit flies, finding the creatures convenient for the study of heredity because they reproduce very rapidly and in great abundance and because they are cheap to maintain, requiring only jars for housing and rotting bananas for feed.

The Morgan group demonstrated that a number of characters—not only eye color but, for example, wing shape—are transmitted by genes. They also showed that the genes reside on the flies' chromosomes and that occasionally two members of a chromosome pair exchange parts with each other. Called "crossing over," the phenomenon allows characters from genes on the same chromosome to be inherited independently. The Morgan group recognized that the frequency with which such independent inheritance occurs provides a measure of the relative physical closeness—termed "linkage"—of genes to each other. Using frequency data, they were able to draw the first genetic maps—that is, linear pictures of where in linkage units different genes are located along the chromosome. The Morgan group summarized their findings in a

highly influential book, *The Mechanism of Mendelian Heredity* (1915). By this time, studies of inheritance in a number of organisms strongly indicated that many traits, including those of an apparent blending nature, are the product of combinations of genes. In 1933, Morgan was awarded the Nobel Prize in physiology or medicine for his pioneering work.

The increasing success of Mendelism, however, was accompanied by debates among biologists about the nature of the gene. Was it a physical entity or some kind of dynamic organizing principle? Convincing evidence that genes are material entities came in 1927, when Hermann Muller, working with fruit flies at the University of Texas, showed that exposing them to X rays would induce genetic mutations. In Berlin in 1935, Max Delbrück, a physicist then turning to genetics, collaborated with two other scientists to try to ferret out information about the actual structure of the gene. Using X rays, they combined experimental data and quantum mechanical theory to account for mutations in terms of the chemical and physical behavior of atoms. Their findings indicated that genes are relatively stable macromolecules susceptible to analysis by physical and chemical methods.

In 1937, at the California Institute of Technology, where he had gone on a fellowship, Delbrück embarked on research with bacteriophage—a virus that infects bacteria and multiplies rapidly inside its host. He saw in this interaction a simple system for the study of genetics, a kind of hydrogen atom for biology. Remaining in the United States because of World War II, Delbrück worked on bacteriophage at Cold Spring Harbor, on Long Island, New York, during the summers with the Italian refugee scientist, Salvador Luria, and Alfred Hershey, a chemist on the faculty of the Washington University Medical School, in St. Louis, Missouri. Their collaboration gave rise to what came to be known as the Phage Group, a small, informal network of viral and bacterial geneticists, and it eventually brought them a Nobel Prize. The Phage Group produced relatively few experimental results of high significance in microbiological genetics, but under Delbrück's guiding influence it focused attention on the problem of self-replication in living organisms, helped recruit a number of physicists into the field, and fostered the use of physical, chemical, and statistical reasoning in microbiology.

In the early 1940s, while the Phage Group was forming, further evidence that genes are some sort of macromolecule engaged in biochemical functions came from the Nobel Prize-winning research of the Americans George Beadle, a geneticist, and Edward Tatum, a biochemist. As the result of previous work in Paris with the biologist Boris Ephrussi, Beadle thought that genes somehow shape the biochemical pathways that produce different eye colors in fruit flies. At each step along the pathway, an assist is given by an enzyme, an organic catalyst essential to the biochemical transformation in which it is involved. At Stanford in 1940, Beadle and Tatum began to pursue the hypothesis with Neurospora, an ordinary bread mold. They triggered genetic mutations in the mold with X rays and analyzed the resulting metabolic variations. They found that, with a specific gene bred into it, the mold could metabolize a given substance, while with the gene bred out, it could not—in short, that the absence of the gene forced the mold into a metabolic error. In 1945, Beadle spelled out the striking import of their research and recent related work by others: "...that to every gene it is possible to assign one primary action and that, conversely, every enzymatically controlled chemical transformation is under the immediate supervision of one gene, and in general only one." That idea was soon distilled into an apothem—the "one gene-one enzyme hypothesis," which became a guiding principle for the emerging field of biochemical genetics.

All the while, many biologists supposed that genes must be proteins, which were known to make up much of the cell and to catalyze its remarkable range of chemical synthesis. The supposition was reinforced by Beadle and Tatum's work, since it associated genes with enzymes, which are proteins. But evidence to the contrary came from a group at the Rockefeller Institute for Medical Research that was headed by Oswald T. Avery. Avery and his associates had worked for a decade to understand why an infectious form of pneumococcous could transform an uninfectious type into a similarly infectious one. In 1944 they reported that the change was caused by a transforming factor in the infectious bacteria that they identified as a deoxyribonucleic acid (DNA).

The Avery group's results suggested to some biologists that genetic material might be composed of DNA, but Avery, an older man and a retiring personality, did not push the idea and most biologists remained attached to the belief that genes are proteins. However, members of the Phage Group determined that phage consists of DNA wrapped in a protein coat. In 1952 Hershey, in collaboration with Martha Chase, showed that, when a phage infects a bacterium, it injects its DNA into the bacterial cell, leaving the protein coat on the cell surface. The clear implication of the experiment was that the injected DNA was responsible for the multiplication of the virus inside the cell. At least for members of the Phage Group, the Hershey-Chase experiment strongly argued that the phage's genetic material must be DNA.

In 1951, James D. Watson, a member of the Phage Group, arrived at Cambridge University on a postdoctoral fellowship. Convinced that DNA is the material of genes, he began collaborative work on its structure with Francis Crick, a young physicist attempting a doctorate in biology. Their partnership soon expanded to include Maurice Wilkins, another former physicist who was investigating the physical properties of DNA at Kings College, in London. A key member of his group was Rosalind Franklin, an expert in X-ray diffraction studies of biological molecules. Watson and Crick did no experiments. Rather, they devised tinkertoy models of DNA drawing on chemical and physical data about the molecule, especially some of Franklin's diffraction results with DNA. In 1953, they succeeded in determining that DNA comprises a double helix joined at regular intervals across the distance between them by one of two complementary nucleotide base pairs—adenine with thymine, or cytosine with guanine.

Watson, Crick, and Wilkins held that the structure settled the question that DNA is the genetic material. The structure immediately suggested to them how genes can replicate themselves. The two strands of the double helix would separate, each with its single string of complementary nucleotides; then each would form a template for the creation of a new double helix identical to the first. The physicist George Gamow suggested that the sequence of nucleotides must contain an organism's genetic information in the form of a code. By 1964, biologists had demonstrated experimentally that specific sequences of three base pairs code for specific amino acids. Through a complicated biochemical mechanism, a series of such triplets is translated at a cellular site into a chain of amino acids, which enfold themselves into a specific protein—for example, a constituent of the eye—involved in the organism's structure or, as in the case of an enzyme, figuring in one of its processes, like metabolism.

The working out of the genetic code enabled biologists to begin studying gene function at the molecular level. Their task was greatly facilitated by several experimental and technological innovations, including in the 1970s the technique of recombinant DNA, which allowed the removal of single genes from one organism and their insertion into another; in the 1980s, table-top machines that would determine the sequence of base pairs in a strand of DNA; and, in the 1990s, the creation of computerized databases that made available on the World Wide Web the DNA sequences in the genomes of human beings of laboratory organisms such as yeast and mice. A century after the rediscovery of Mendel's papers, genetics was a highly populated, multi-disciplinary field, wealthy in resources, and rich in promise for understanding inheritance, development, and disease.

DANIEL J. KEVLES

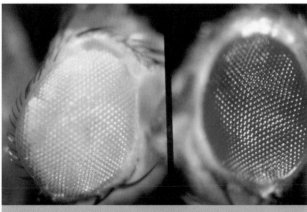

The white mutation (left) of the normal or wild fruit-fly eye (right)

GEOGRAPHY has its roots in ancient efforts to describe the surface of the earth, the form and extent of its lands and seas, and all that is observed in them. The peculiarly modern, European art of geography, as it emerged in the Renaissance, combined mathematical delineation and historical description with varying emphases. For Renaissance scholars, geography was both a body of knowledge recovered from the classical past and a newly discovered art of systematically ordering knowledge of the earth. The transmission of the *Geographia* of Claudius Ptolemy (c. 90–168) from Constantinople to Italy and its translation into Latin early in the fifteenth century was central to making the mathematical description of the earth's lands and seas the core of the new art of geography. It gave instructions for arranging geographical knowledge according to a coordinate system of parallels (latitudes) and meridians (longitudes) and for projecting those lines onto flat surfaces. Renaissance geography was closely tied to the production of maps of the earth's surface and its separate divisions, culminating in the first "atlases" of the Low-country cartographers Gerhard Mercator and Abraham Ortelius in the mid-sixteenth century.

This Renaissance "invention" of geography was sponsored by centralizing states making ever more universal claims to legitimacy. By advertising the usefulness of their art for administering and defending principalities and cities, geographers secured more or less official roles in European states from the sixteenth century. As these states began to explore and trade overseas, geographers used words and pictures to help interpret, manage, and celebrate novel discoveries and new possessions for kings, princes, and churches. Geography also carried all the prestige of humanism and the mathematical arts. Sebastian Münster, author of the *Cosmographica universalis* (Basel, 1544), was typical in advertising geography as the essential study of the active Christian prince. How could anyone understand Homer and Virgil, the campaigns of Caesar and Cato, the acts of God, the wanderings of the Jews, and the missions of the Apostles, without geography?

The Protestant Reformation gave added impetus to official patronage. As reformed and counterreformed princes and cities turned to the foundation of gymnasia and universities, geographical systems assumed a pedagogical and doctrinal function, exhibiting God's wise design of the world. The mathematical basis of geography was progressively refined as a theater for God's providence in the *Systema geographicum* (Hanover, 1611) of the theologian Bartholomäus Keckermann and the *Geographia generalis* (Amsterdam, 1650) of the Dutch physician Bernhard Varenius. Varenius's book was one of the most influential geographical systems of the seventeenth and eighteenth centuries. Isaac Newton edited the second and third editions despite Varenius's Cartesian leanings. In the work of the Jesuit Athanasius Kircher or the globe-maker Vincenzo Coronelli, who served Louis XIV at Versailles, mathematical techniques imbued geography with a renewed sense of cosmographical mission under the sponsorship of Roman Catholic Counter-Reformation and royal absolutism.

In the eighteenth century, geography flourished as a descriptive science with a mathematical foundation, often with an appeal to divine design. Enlightenment geography aligned itself programmatically, with the "systematic spirit" and against the "spirit of system," often restricting itself to positive description and tying itself ever more firmly to a technical symbolic language. Although it relied upon the observations of travelers and field surveyors, geography

was essentially a product of the cabinet. While maintaining its focus on devising critical and systematic descriptions of the earth's surface, geography expressed its cosmographical ambitions increasingly by attempts to standardize and universalize the language of geographical description—to establish uniform topographical languages and cartographic symbolism (including map scale).

These efforts reached their zenith in Enlightenment France with Cassini's trigonometric charts of France, the collection of maps for military purposes at the Dépôt de la Guerre (founded 1688), and the closely associated cabinet of J. B. B. d'Anville. Here, geography began to converge with and restrict itself to cartographical description, while occupying the center of a web of skills including the work of field surveyors, instrument makers, and engravers. Geographers such as d'Anville distinguished themselves from lesser workers by their ability to sift and compile geographical information critically and express it in ever more precise and standardized languages, especially its graphic and mathematical expression on a chart. In practice, however, the lines between positive description and philosophical speculation were ill defined. Geographers such as Philippe Buache and Nicolas Desmarest entered into debates over the nature of continents, seas, earthquakes, volcanoes, river basins, and mountain ranges—topics often labeled "physical geography" and "theory of the earth" to distinguish them from "geography" proper.

In Protestant Europe, where geography remained tied to natural philosophy and natural theology, geographers discussed such topics as the causes of the tides, the heat of the tropics, seasonal rains, the decrease of temperature with elevation, and so on. Political geography, human geography, mineral geography, plant geography, and zoogeography emerged as distinct fields, justified principally through their service to natural theology. All exposed the wise hand of Providence by revealing the diversity and distribution of created things, and the balances and economies of nature (language eschewed by French geographers). In Germany and Scotland, at Hamburg, Edinburgh, and Göttingen, in works such as A. F. Büsching's *Neue Erdbeschreibung* (11 vols., 1754–1792) and Christoph Ebeling's *Erdbeschreibung und Geschichte von Amerika* (7 vols., 1793–1816), geography took the form of theologically informed gazetteering aimed at developing industrious, purposeful citizens of the world such as great merchants and administrative officials. At Göttingen, under the auspices of Gottfried Achenwall and A. L. Schlözer, geography was closely allied with statistics and political history *(Staatenkunde)*. Immanuel Kant, who spent most of his forty years at Königsberg lecturing on "physical geography" (including physical anthropology), promoted geography's "extensive utility," supplying "the purposeful arrangement of our knowledge, our own enjoyment, and plentiful material for sociable conversation." Johann Reinhold Forster and his son Georg Forster, who together accompanied James Cook on his second expedition around the world from 1772 to 1776, similarly used geographical exploration to demonstrate the providential design of the world and to make its audience into active witnesses and instruments of providence. In his German translations of contemporary voyages and in his briefer, essayistic works, the nomadic younger Forster decisively focused geography on active exploration and the gradual emergence of underlying dynamic laws and processes.

Toward the end of the eighteenth century, the natural-historical concern with systematic collection, classification, and exposition gave way to philosophical concern with *dynamic* processes and physical causes. Taking inspiration from the Forsters' "philanthropic" approach to understanding the reciprocal influences of nature and human civilization, the Prussian mining official and naturalist Alexander von Humboldt sought physical and historical laws in systematic geographical investigations of everything from climate to language and art. Humboldt shunned the term "geography" and referred to his science as "physics of the earth." As the most renowned traveler and naturalist of the early nineteenth century, Humboldt put the systematic spatial analysis of phenomena usually left to physicists and natural historians—rocks, terrestrial magnetism, atmospheric temperature and chemistry, plant and animal species, anything open to calibrated and standardized perception—at the center of geography. He also emphasized the aesthetic and emotional responses of the traveler. And he stressed that records of medieval travel and conquest, including the works of Christopher Columbus, be preserved and rehabilitated as important geographical sources. Although Humboldt omitted God from his unfinished *Kosmos* (1845–1862, subtitled "sketch of a physical description of the world"), his dual revelation of the lawfulness of nature and the progress and limits of human knowledge of nature was implicitly congenial to a recognition of divine design.

Humboldt's contemporary Carl Ritter presented geography as a comparative study of the world's "terrestrial units" that supplied the key to a developmental understanding of the history of civilization, expressly overseen by divine providence. As delivered for three decades at the newly founded Berlin University and at the Berlin Military Academy and in his massive but unfinished *Erdkunde* (1817), Ritter's demonstration that civilization had migrated from East to West influenced generations of statesmen, soldiers, and scholars. Among them was Arnold Guyot, whose Protestant geographical theodicy found a home at Princeton University after 1848. In Britain, Mary Somerville discovered a similar providence at work in geography: both objectively, in the interaction of physical forces over the surface of the globe to produce geographical laws (*Physical Geography,* 1848), and subjectively, in the progressive interaction of the different branches of the physical sciences in geographical science (*On the Connexion of the Physical Sciences,* 1834).

Geographical societies began emerging in the late eighteenth century, imbued with a civilizing mission and informed by this sense of divine lawfulness The Association for Promoting the Discovery of the Interior Parts of Africa, founded in London in 1788, was followed by groups in Paris (1821), Berlin (1828), London (1830), Saint Petersburg (1845), and New York (1851). These metropolitan societies brought together army and navy officials, statesmen, and scholars to promote exploration and publish maps and accounts of voyages. Although membership waned in midcentury, it revived in the 1860s and 1870s with the recognition of the centrality of geography to imperial expansion and the cultivation of national identities. Between 1870 and 1890, the number of geographical societies in Europe quadrupled to over eighty, driven by the establishment of provincial geographical societies. In 1875, these societies began convening quadrennial International Congresses of the Geographical Sciences. They also encouraged the proliferation of popular geographical magazines and literature. Taking their cue from Germany, where geography was established in natural science faculties, and where academic geography and geographical societies had close ties, geographical societies urged that geography be taught in universities and secondary schools. In 1871, after the Prussian victory over France, the Paris society and the ministry of education established a Committee on the Teaching of Geography and a number of professorships at French universities. In the 1880s, the Royal Geographical Society of London succeeded in establishing chairs of geography at Oxford and Cambridge.

In the universities, geography was dominated by the prevalent enthusiasm for evolutionary theories. Friedrich Ratzel, who trained with Ernst Haeckel in Jena before settling at Munich, Halford Mackinder at Oxford, Alfred Hettner at Tübingen, and William Morris Davis at Harvard all argued that the geographical diversity of humans resulted from the variation of physical conditions over time and space. The Russian exile Peter Kropotkin and the Scottish social critic Patrick Geddes stressed the independent laws of organisms in interpreting responses to inorganic conditions. Paul Vidal de la Blache and Otto Schlüter insisted that human modes of social life (lifestyles, *Kulturformen, genres de vie*) shaped the landscape.

Regardless of their understanding of evolution, academic geographers took the region or the landscape as the fundamental unit of analysis. A few modern geographers explicitly abjured questions of evolution, and claimed that the task of the geographer was to comprehend the unique character of regions or landscapes, without attributing causality to any particular factor. For all their sometimes bitter disagreement, Carl Sauer at Berkeley and Richard Hartshorne at the University of Wisconsin agreed that regional description lay at the heart of scientific geography.

Between the 1950s and the 1970s, geographers enthusiastic about the so-called "quantitative revolution" rejected Hartshorne's strictures, and argued that by using quantification and statistics, geographers could discern the laws of social dynamics. More recently, geographers have analyzed the subjective experience of space and produced "behavioral geographies" and "mental maps."

The very ubiquity of geographical knowledge made it difficult to define the field. Since geography became an academic discipline in the late nineteenth century, its diffuseness has fueled a great deal of historical writing by academic geographers concerned with defining and defending the scientific territory and prestige of their field. This literature, rife with talk of "disciplinary crisis," is understandably preoccupied with discovering the essence of geography in past founders and precursors. Hartshorne's *The Nature of Geography* (1939) drew up a historical lineage and philosophical foundation for the discipline that established geography as a descriptive science of regional differentiation. It remains an influential interpretation of the history and philosophy of geography. Other geographers have adopted philosophies from phenomenology and logical positivism to Marxism, structuralism, and postmodernism in the search for philosophical foundations. In the 1990s, the emphasis began to shift to studying the institutional, political, and social contexts, interests, and languages of earlier geographers. The bread and butter of geography, though, has remained the training of school teachers and the preparation of regional descriptions applicable to a variety of policy needs.

MICHARL DETTELBACH

GEOLOGY. The word geology as a general term for the study of the earth was popularized in the late eighteenth century by the Swiss naturalists Jean André De Luc, who

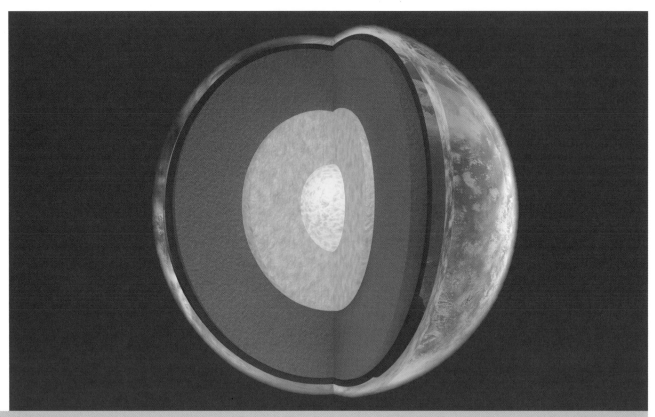

In this computer model of the earth, the core (molten iron and nickel) appears in yellow; the outer core (also molten), the seat of magnetism, in orange; the mantle (viscous), on which the crust swims, in brown.

made his career in England, and Horace Bénédict de Saussure, famous for his voyages in the Alps. Abraham Gottlob Werner disliked the term as being too suggestive of theorizing, and promoted the alternative "geognosy." But when a group of Englishmen decided in 1807 to found a society for the study of the earth that eschewed the practical, utilitarian goals of the Continental mining schools, they called it the Geological Society of London. Within two or three decades, geology had its own specialists, societies, textbooks, and journals, the Geological Society's Transactions being the first. Worldwide, the word geology (or its cognates) rapidly became the preferred term for the study of the earth.

Geologists generally divided their specialty into two parts: historical geology, which reconstructed earth history using stratigraphy and paleontology, and physical geology, which investigated the earth's structure and causal processes. The latter consisted of mineralogy, diminished from the overarching category for the study of the earth to a mere subdiscipline, petrology, and structural geology.

The successes of historical geology were manifest in the outlines of the stratigraphic column as worked out by the mid-nineteenth century. Field work with a hammer and a map was the preferred way of investigating, and the geological map an ingenious way of summarizing the results. Georges Cuvier and Alexandre Brongniart produced a pioneering map of the Paris area in 1812. The first national geological map, of England, was prepared by William Smith in 1815; the Geological Society's map followed in 1819. Although these maps were expensive and time-consuming to produce, state governments set up geological surveys to prepare them because of their economic importance for the extractive industries and agriculture. The French began fieldwork for a national geological map in 1825. The British Geological Survey was founded in 1835, followed by the Canadian (1842), the Irish (1845), and the Indian (1854).

In Europe, the Austro-Hungarian Empire and Spain created surveys in 1849, Sweden and Norway in 1858, Switzerland in 1859, Prussia and Italy in 1873, and Russia in 1882. The American states founded their surveys early: Massachusetts and Tennessee in 1831 and Maryland in 1833, but a national survey was not created until 1879.

Though the work of mineralogists and petrologists attracted less public attention than that of the historical geologists, their field rapidly moved ahead in the nineteenth century. And although they too carried out field studies, they retained their ties to chemistry and the laboratory.

Historical and physical geology supposedly worked in concert, but the results obtained in the one frequently held little interest for the other. Nonetheless, geologists sought ways of presenting a coherent picture of the earth. One possible strategy, tried by Charles Lyell in his *Principles of Geology* (1830–1833), made the study of present geological processes a necessary key to understanding earth history. Although rejected by most geologists, it provoked a useful methodological discussion.

A second strategy looked for an overarching causal process that could elucidate the details of the stratigraphic record. For most nineteenth-century geologists, the preferred hypothesis was that the earth had cooled and contracted. The nebular hypothesis proposed by Pierre Simon de Laplace and William Herschel, and the work on rates of cooling by Jean Baptiste Fourier, supported their model. In 1831, the French geologist Élie de Beaumont suggested that as the earth had cooled from a molten body, the crust at intervals had buckled under the strain, throwing up mountain chains and exterminating whole genera in the great floods that coursed down their sides. Variants of this theory, and criticisms of it, flourished for the rest of the century and culminated in the four-volume *Face of the Earth* (1883–1904) by Eduard Suess, Professor of Geology at the University of Vienna. According to Suess, the molten center of the earth had once been covered with a thin, solid crust. As the earth cooled, portions of the crust collapsed, creating ocean basins. Later, the remaining higher areas became unstable, and collapsed in turn, forming new ocean basins and leaving former ocean beds exposed as new continents.

It was a triumphant moment for geology. Two great geologists summed up the history of their science during the nineteenth century. Sir Archibald Geikie, head of the Geological Survey of Great Britain, published his *Founders of Geology* in 1905. He celebrated the achievements of British geologists, especially the Scots James Hutton and Charles Lyell. He arranged his history around battles between Neptunists and Plutonists and Uniformitarians and Catastrophists. Karl Zittel, a professor at the University of Munich and a renowned paleontologist, published a *History of Geology and Paleontology* in 1901. He gave more weight to mineralogy, petrology, and theories of mountain elevation, and praised Suess as having achieved "almost general recognition for the contraction theory."

This celebration of geology's progress was soon to seem inappropriate. The cooling earth with its foundering continents did not survive as a synthesis for more than a decade. The discovery of radioactivity revealed a heat source within the earth that counteracted the cooling from some original molten state. The discovery of isostasy made it highly improbable that continents could have foundered. Detailed studies of the Alps made it clear that simple up-down forces acting on the earth's crust could not explain the tens or even hundreds of miles of foreshortening revealed by their folded strata.

The resultant theoretical vacuum led to a proliferation of alternatives in the 1910s and 1920s. Some scientists, such as Harold Jeffreys in England and Hans Stille in Germany, attempted to revamp contraction theory in light of the criticisms. Others preferred more radical alternatives: the planetismal hypothesis advanced by Thomas Chamberlin, the radiogenic by John Joly, and the theory of continental drift of Alfred Wegener. None of these theories succeeded in garnering enough evidential support to win widespread acceptance.

For the next fifty years, geologists hunkered down and continued their map-making and surveying. Mineralogy and petrology made important advances. Underwater exploration revealed interesting gravity anomaly patterns around island arcs. Geologists found new work in the oil industry, which joined geological surveys and mining as the main sources of employment outside the universities. The American Association of Petroleum Geologists, founded in 1917, had become the world's largest professional geological society by 2000, with over 30,000 members in more than 100 countries. By this time, however, geology was no longer the umbrella discipline for the study of the earth, but just one branch of the earth sciences.

RACHEL LAUDAN

GERM. The word "germ" derives from the Latin for "seed"; it was first used in its modern sense of pathogenic microbe in the nineteenth century. The theoretical association of "seed" with disease dates from antiquity but in modern times is associated with the *De contagione* (1546) of Girolamo Fracastoro. The development of the microscope in the early seventeenth century made possible the discovery of formerly invisible living creatures. Pioneering observations by the Dutch microscopist Antoni van Leeuwenhoek later in the century disclosed identifiable "animalcules" in various waters and on human

teeth. The imperfections of most available optical instruments hindered further significant observations until critical improvements in the early 1830s. In 1835, Agostino Maria Bassi showed that a minute fungus caused muscardine disease in silkworms. Microbes soon were associated with many other diseases: Casimir Joseph Davaine, notably, repeatedly observed rod-shaped structures, which he named "bacteridia," in the blood of creatures dead of anthrax. The relationship between such structures and disease, whether cause or result, remained a matter of debate.

From the 1830s, European scientists interested in the processes of fermentation and putrefaction moved steadily towards the development of a germ theory of disease. In 1840, Jacob Henle set out the theoretical framework for such a theory, while Theodor Schwarnn demonstrated that not the air itself, but something in the air initiated putrefaction in organic substances. Louis Pasteur attracted popular and scientific attention when he announced his own germ theory of disease causation in 1864. The issue was widely debated in the following decade, until Robert Koch identified the causative organism of anthrax (1876), and later those of tuberculosis and cholera. Several recent historians have shown that several different germ theories of disease circulated in the later nineteenth century, most in a continual process of modification. Consensus was reached only around the turn of the century.

The contribution of Koch and his associates to the establishment of the germ theory extended beyond the identification of organisms. Koch drew up the program known as "Koch's postulates," which, through several subsequent revisions, continues in use as the basic tool for confirmation of an association between specific microbes and diseases. Koch and his colleagues made important contributions to the identification of bacteria by developing staining methods based on the new industrial dyes of the period, and by 1900 the bacterial causes of several dozen diseases had been established. At this time many physicians believed that every disease must have its causal bacterium. Increasingly too, they identified diseases not by symptom as in the past, but by cause, in the laboratory.

Improvements in bacterial filtration processes after 1880 led to the realization that there must be yet smaller disease-causing agents, and in 1896 Martinus Willem Beijerinck launched his controversial but valid concept of the filterable virus—possibly water-soluble microbes small enough to pass through filters and invisible to contemporary microscopes. Among the first pathogens identified as such were the agents of tobacco mosaic virus, foot and mouth disease, and yellow fever. Virology evolved rapidly as a science in the early twentieth century. The bacteriophage phenomenon was independently identified by Frederick William Twort and Félix d'Hérelle during World War I. Only with the invention of the electron microscope in the early 1930s, however, did it become possible to obtain visual impressions of viruses.

In the twentieth century, the idea of germs as disease agents became firmly established in the popular consciousness, partly through the use of the concept in advertising for domestic cleansing products. Virology remained a field of dynamic scientific interest; new or emergent virus diseases attracted attention across the twentieth century. The expansion of air travel, international trade, and global tourism alerted the medical community around 1970 to the possibilities of the diffusion of previously unrecognized and dangerous viruses.

At a more mundane level, Western countries became increasingly uneasy at an apparent upsurge in food-borne infections such as salmonellosis and listeriosis, which suggested the continuing threat to physical well-being of the endemic germs encountered in everyday life. In the last decades of the twentieth century, the discovery of prions—infectious dead proteins—forced a reassessment of the classic germ theory of disease, which was based on the belief in living disease organisms.

ANNE HARDY

GLACIOLOGY is the discipline that examines how glaciers and ice sheets behave. It studies their origin and accumulation, deformation and movement, sublimation and melting, as well as how glacial ice interacts with climate. A subdiscipline of geophysics, glaciology also has strong ties to the atmospheric sciences, particularly climatology, and to glacial geology, which analyzes the history and geological effects of glaciers, glaciation, and ice ages. The study of mountain glaciers and polar ice caps has required mountaineering skills and other high-risk tactics, so the history of glacier exploration and examination is also a history of adventure and, in some cases, tragedy.

In the late eighteenth century, Horace Bénédict de Saussure and other naturalists began studying mountain glaciers in the Alps, descriptive work that was summed up by the Swiss naturalist Louis Agassiz in his *Études sur les Glaciers* (1840). In the mid-nineteenth century, James David Forbes began systematic observations of glacial flow, using physical theory in an attempt to understand the phenomenon. In the latter part of the century, John Tyndall's publications on glaciers and glaciation influenced both scientists and the public.

The first International Polar Year (1881–1883) was largely responsible for the first studies of high-latitude glaciers and ice sheets. Expeditions to Greenland directed by Fridtjof Nansen in the 1890s and by Alfred Wegener in the early 1900s surveyed the ice sheet. Robert Scott's Antarctic expedition of 1901–1904 conducted the first studies of the southern ice sheet. The renowned valley glaciers of southeast Alaska were first examined by Grove Karl Gilbert while on the Harriman Alaska expedition in 1899.

In the early twentieth century, R. M. Deeley and P. H. Parr made the first successful mathematical models of glaciers as viscous fluids. The first professional society for glaciology was founded in the 1930. In the 1950s—recognized within the field as the beginning of its modern era—John Nye led in putting glaciology on a sound physical footing. In the same decade the International Geophysical Year (IGY) (1957–1958) sparked further studies of high-latitude phenomena.

Current glaciological investigations are interdisciplinary and international. Ice sheets preserve one of the finest records of climate change over the last hundred thousand years or more. Among the notable discoveries of recent decades is that the ice record of atmospheric carbon dioxide content shows a marked positive correlation with fluctuations in global temperature. Fears of global warming have impelled scientists also to examine short-term behavior of these large ice sheets, which hold much of the world's water and hence have an important influence on global changes in sea level. Programs are in place for drilling and examining cores from the Greenland and Antarctic ice sheets. Other glaciologists are studying the rapid surging and retreat of ice shelves and of glaciers, the basal boundary condition of glaciers, and the interaction of glaciers with their substrates. The study of ice on other planetary bodies, notably on Jupiter's moons Europa and Ganymede, on Saturn's icy satellites, and on Triton, is an emerging field. Icy outer crusts on these bodies exhibit phenomena uncommon to Earth—impact cratering preserved in ice, and ice volcanism—eruption of liquid (probably water) through the icy crust.

JOANNE BOURGEOIS

HERMETICISM. In 1462–1463, the Florentine Renaissance humanist Marsilio Ficino translated into Latin a Byzantine collection of treatises known collectively as the Hermetic Corpus. His translation, for which he interrupted his life work of translating Plato and Plotinus, introduced hermeticism, hitherto known only by a few fragmentary texts and references, to European philosophers. For two centuries, Hermetic Corpus and associated texts fascinated humanists and philosophers. They believed them to be of great antiquity, written by a younger contemporary of Moses, the Egyptian sage known as Hermes Trismegistus, an alias for the Egyptian god of wisdom and knowledge, Thoth. In 1614, the scholar Isaac Casaubon threw cold water on this reverent attitude by concluding from textual analysis that the Hermetic Corpus, far from being one of the earliest texts of revealed religion, was a much later compilation. His conclusions held up. By the end of the seventeenth century hermeticism was in precipitous decline. Today scholars believe that members of eclectic, gnostic religious groups in Egypt wrote the texts in the first and second century A.D.

The Hermetic Corpus dealt primarily with religion. It inspired the hope in Renaissance scholars that it might be a guide to the Prisca Theologica, the ancient theology, and would thus serve, depending on the point of view of the scholar, to replace Christianity or to strengthen it by extending the repertoire of revealed religion. Some texts, however, considered how the wise could come to understand and control the correspondences between the macrocosm and the microcosm. They discussed astrology, alchemy, and the signatures of plants.

Marsilio Ficino and his associate Giovanni Pico della Mirandola assimilated hermeticism to two other intellectual traditions, Neoplatonism, and natural magic. Magic has been practiced in many human societies and in broad outline everywhere depends on similar assumptions. Magicians assume that the powers by which one thing in the world affects another are hidden or occult. They can be discovered, and thus controlled, only with difficulty, usually by the magician who has special insights because of his preparation, as much spiritual as intellectual or practical.

Two kinds of magic can be distinguished: spiritual and natural. In spiritual magic, the magician prevails upon the spirits, good or bad, white or black, to set in motion these occult powers. In natural magic, the magician relies on detecting correspondences and signatures in the natural world. Renaissance humanists and philosophers distanced themselves from spiritual magic, a touchy matter that quickly led to trouble with the church. They pursued instead a dignified version of natural magic. Since both magic and Neoplatonism had contributed to the synthesis of the Hermetic Corpus, Ficino and Pico did not have far to go to assimilate it to the versions of magic and Neoplatonism current in their own time. Giambattista della Porta, the most famous exponent of natural magic, published his *Magia naturalis* (Natural Magic) in 1558. Much of it dealt with the "magic" of mechanical gadgets, secret writing, and cosmetics.

Positivist historians of science naturally viewed this amalgam of hermeticism, natural magic, and Neoplatonism as inimical to the growth of modern science. Those not wedded to that tradition thought otherwise. The distinguished American historian Lynn Thorndike wrote his monumental *History of Magic and Experimental Science* (8 vols., 1923–1958) to demonstrate that magical tradition, with its utilitarian attitude to the world that contrasted strongly with the contemplative attitude of philosophers, spawned the method of experiment. The German physician and historian Walter Pagel, in a series of scholarly studies from the 1930s through the 1960s, showed how the hermetic traditions shaped the work of chemist-physicians such as Paracelsus (c. 1493–1541) and Jean Baptiste van Helmont (1579–1644). From there, certain hermetic and Neoplatonic ideas passed into chemistry and mineralogy and were revived in the late eighteenth century by the founders of Naturphilosophie.

Hermes Trismegistus, supposed ancient Egyptian author of texts on alchemy and magic, as depicted in Zadith ben Hamuel, *De chemica senioris* (1566)

H

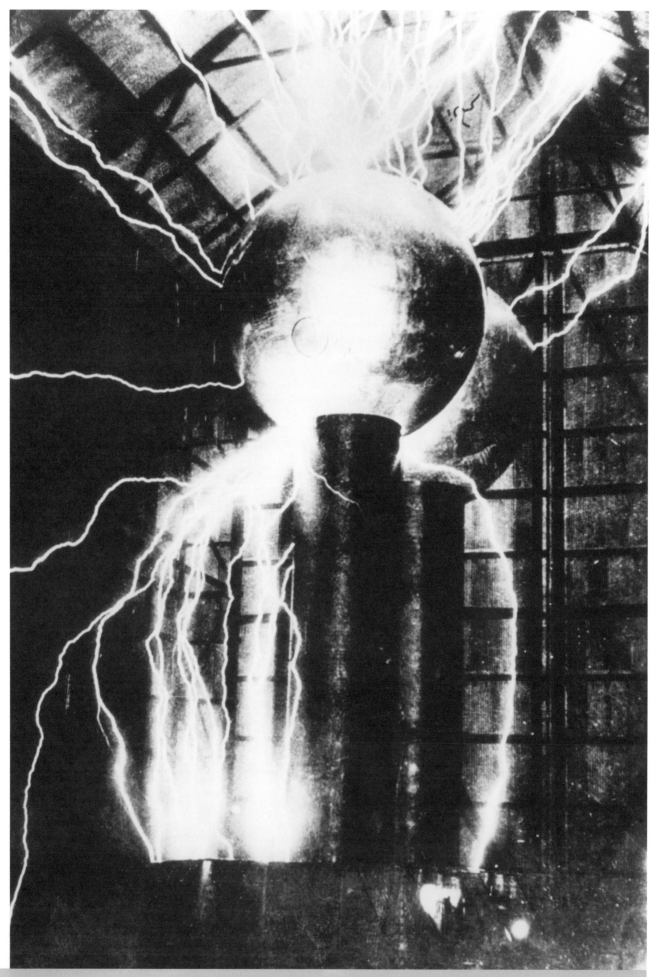

This electrostatic generator was designed and built by Robert van de Graaff (1901–1967) at MIT in the 1930s to accelerate particles in competition with the cyclotron.

In 1964 the historian Frances Yates made strong claims that hermeticism had affected not just certain methods or particular chemists but was one of the basic causes of the Scientific Revolution. Her thesis appeared when historians of science sought new interpretations of the formative period of modern science. Those who followed up her suggestions found that hermeticism in particular (as opposed to Neoplatonism) had been most influential in the theory of matter—whether in chemistry or in natural philosophy. Some historians of science continued the Pagel project. Others argued that Isaac Newton, who labored over alchemical and hermetic works for years, may have found in them support for his ideas of attraction and repulsion, traditionally regarded as occult properties. Later it was suggested that music mediated the domains of magic and experimental science and that musical practices informed natural philosophy. As the features of music thought to be occult were understood through experimentation, natural magic began to yield to science. Today few historians of science would doubt that hermeticism had an important role to play in the genesis of modern science though just what role and just how important a role have not been decided.

RACHEL LAUDAN

HIGH-ENERGY PHYSICS. The field of high-energy physics emerged after World War II out of research in nuclear physics and cosmic ray physics. Its name referred to the energies of the nuclear and subnuclear particles that physicists sought to study, and hence the field was also sometimes called elementary particle physics.

Physicists in the first decades of the twentieth century used particles emitted by radioactivity as a probe of the atomic nucleus. But many of the charged alpha and beta particles emitted in natural radioactive decay had insufficient energy to overcome the electrical barrier of the nucleus, and exist in insufficient quantities to provoke enough reactions for convenient study. Starting in the 1920s, nuclear physicists sought to increase the energy of the particles by accelerating them. Early accelerators passed electrically charged particles through a single large voltage drop (as in the Cockcroft-Walton and Van de Graaff accelerators) or multiple, smaller drops provided by high-frequency oscillators (as in the cyclotron and linear accelerator, or linac) to kick particles to higher speeds. Technical refinements and industrial-size apparatus allowed particle accelerators to produce ever higher energies through the 1930s, beyond ten million electron volts.

In the meantime, starting in about 1930, physicists began to exploit a natural source of high-energy particles in cosmic rays. A thriving field of cosmic ray research focused on sorting the nature of cosmic radiation as well as new phenomena and new particles, including the positron (detected in 1932 by Carl David A. Anderson) and a mysterious new particle with mass midway between that of the electron and proton, which was hence called the meson. Whereas nuclear physics in the 1930s emphasized the particle accelerator, cosmic ray research relied on particle detectors, especially cloud chambers and Geiger counters.

World War II interrupted the pursuit of high-energy particles but provided new resources, both technical and political, to exploit after the war. Technical resources included advances in microwave electronics and new designs for accelerators, both of which allowed physicists to push into energies of billions of electron volts. By about 1950, physicists could perceive some separation between nuclear physics

and a new subfield of particle physics, which became known as high-energy physics.

New political resources stemmed from the contributions of physicists to military technology during World War II and their continued mobilization during the Cold War. National governments supported high-energy physics as a way to train new scientists and engineers who might then work on problems of national interest; as a means to keep talented scientists on tap in national laboratories in case of military emergency; and as a hedge against scientific discoveries that might have military or industrial applications. High-energy physics also provided a surrogate arena for international competition, with American, Soviet, and European labs jockeying for the claim to high-energy hegemony. High-energy physicists accepted and encouraged such justifications of state support, in exchange for the opportunity to pursue interesting and challenging scientific problems at higher energies.

Postwar high-energy physics combined detectors and accelerators in laboratories that typified a new type of big science, characterized by large and expensive equipment, state support, cooperative team research, collaboration of scientists and engineers, and industrial-style management. American laboratories led the postwar development of big-science accelerator programs, notably at the University of California at Berkeley and Brookhaven in New York, although the Soviet Union and a new European lab at CERN soon offered strong competition. The United States in the 1960s would choose to centralize its largest accelerators in a new lab at Fermilab near Chicago, which would thereafter challenge CERN for the claim to the highest energies.

High-energy physics had theoretical and experimental components. Experimentalists pushed toward higher energies, lured by the possibility of producing previously unseen particles with masses equivalent to the energy of particle collisions. In 1955, Berkeley scientists achieved the exemplary discovery of the antiproton using the first generation of postwar accelerators. Higher energies required ever larger magnets and vacuum chambers and bigger budgets, all of which constrained the ambitions of accelerator builders. The invention of strong focusing in 1952 provided a way around the problem of magnets and vacuum volumes, both of which contributed to costs. The principle used an alternating gradient in the magnetic field to compress the beam of particles, and quickly led to proposals from Brookhaven, where the idea originated, and CERN, whose design problems had inspired the Brookhaven work, for machines in the range of 25 billion electron volts.

Physicists still needed ways to study the output of accelerators, and particle detectors grew in importance and size in the 1950s and beyond. They fell into two general categories. Image detectors, such as cloud and bubble chambers and nuclear emulsions, produced a snapshot of the tracks left by individual particles at a particular time and place. Logic devices, such as electronic counters, accumulated statistical counts of large numbers of particles. By the 1970s, physicists were combining the two types in new, even larger detectors.

Experiment led theory in high-energy physics through the 1950s, as theorists struggled to explain new resonances and particles emerging from accelerators. To make sense of the proliferating particles theorists classified them according to such properties as strangeness and isospin; then, in the 1960s, theorists developed the quark model of matter to resimplify the concept of fundamental particles and began to seek a unified theory of the four fundamental forces that would incorporate the quark model. By the 1970s, theory was driving experiment, as particle physicists directed their research to find particles predicted by the new theories. Their efforts paid off in the detection of the J/psi and W and Z particles, weak neutral currents, and several of the postulated quarks, thus confirming the so-called standard model of the theorists and encouraging speculation about a grand unified theory, or theory of everything.

The spiraling energies available in accelerators changed the definition of high energy. Accelerators that had pushed back the high-energy frontier in the late 1940s were considered medium-energy machines by the mid-1960s; succeeding generations of devices might last only a decade or so at the cutting edge. Theorists, in the meantime, extended their equations far beyond energies available in the laboratory or in nature, and particle physics began to merge with cosmology; the phenomena postulated by theorists existed only in the milliseconds after the Big Bang and disappeared as the universe expanded and cooled.

Scientific and popular attention to the quest of particle physicists made theirs the most glamorous field of physics in particular, if not science in general, in the second half of the twentieth century. High-energy physicists claimed to engage in the most fundamental research, from which all other science was derived, since they dealt with the elementary constituents of matter. Physicists in other fields, such as solid-state physics, questioned the pretensions of particle physicists and sought to divert some of their substantial government funding. The perceived fundamental nature of high-energy physics alone could not ensure continued state support, especially after the end of the Cold War. American physicists in the 1980s proposed a massive new accelerator, the Superconducting Super Collider (SSC), to pursue the Higgs boson and other exotic phenomena predicted by theory in the neighborhood of 40 trillion volts. In 1993, the U.S. Congress voted to end the multi-billion dollar project, unconvinced that the scientific results justified the social investment.

PETER J. WESTWICK

HOMEOSTASIS. The American physiologist Walter Cannon coined the word "homeostasis" in 1926 to designate the coordinated physiological reactions that maintain steady states in the body. He believed that a special term was necessary to differentiate the complex arrangements in living beings, involving the integrated coordination of a wide range of organs, from the relatively simple physico-chemical closed systems in which a balance of forces maintains an equilibrium. "Changes in the surroundings," Cannon wrote, "excite reactions in [the open system that constitutes a living being], or affect it directly, so that internal disturbances of the system are produced. Such disturbances are normally kept within narrow limits, because automatic adjustments within the system are brought into action, and thereby wide oscillations are prevented and the internal conditions are held fairly constant."

Cannon illustrated his concept by describing a variety of mechanisms that maintain constant conditions in the fluid matrix, or "internal environment," of higher animals. These included materials such as glucose and oxygen in the blood, as well as the fluid matrix's temperature, osmotic pressure, and hydrogen-ion concentration. The knowledge of the mechanisms that Cannon showed to be involved in these reactions came largely from his own previous experiments on the role of the autonomic nervous system and the adrenal secretions. The close association he established between homeostatic mechanisms and the preservation of conditions in the internal

environment, however, derived in large part from the inspiration of the nineteenth-century French physiologist Claude Bernard, whom Cannon acknowledged as the first to give a "more precise analysis" to general ideas about the stability of organisms. Cannon quoted particularly Bernard's "pregnant sentence" that "It is the fixity of the 'milieu interieur' which is the condition of free and independent life."

Originally a physiological principle, homeostasis took on broader meanings after World War II, with the recognition of the similarity of homeostatic mechanisms to feedback controls in servo-mechanisms. Biologists applied the concept at all levels—cellular, organ system, individual, and social systems. The maintenance of steady concentrations of the intermediates of a metabolic pathway despite a constant flux of matter and energy through the pathway became an example of homeostatic regulation. Cannon himself had asked in 1932 in his popular book *The Wisdom of the Body,* in an epilogue entitled "Relations of Biological and Social Homeostasis," whether it might not "be useful to examine other forms of organization—industrial, domestic, or social—in the light of the organization of the body?" His suggestion has been followed, and homeostasis in its widest sense now means the "maintenance of a dynamically stable state within a system by means of internal regulatory processes that counteract external disturbances of the equilibrium."

FREDERIC LAWRENCE HOLMES

HORTICULTURE. From the earliest times plants have been subject to utilitarian and commercial enterprise. Herbalists and apothecaries regulated the supply of medicinally useful plants to customers, while sailors and merchants took considerable risks to import valuable spices and exotics. Horticulture, however, implies the development and marketing of desirable plant commodities and as such essentially dates from the Renaissance. There are few clearer-cut examples of the long-term manipulation of natural organisms for fashion and changing human tastes.

The diversification of the eight classic florists' flowers— the auricula, polyanthus, hyacinth, anemone, ranunculus, tulip, pink, and carnation—dates from the sixteenth century. Of these, the tulip was the most important. Bulbs reached Vienna from Turkey in 1554, although they probably circulated well before that date. The plant was rapidly subjected to improvement, especially in the "breaking" or striping of the petals. Many different varieties appear in Dutch and Flemish still lifes of the seventeenth century. The production of tulip bulbs and their commerce became highly professional; monasteries provided most of the bulbs sold across Europe. In the 1630s, the Dutch suffered tulipomania, called by them the "Wind trade." The market crashed in 1637.

During the eighteenth century, the rise of botanical gardens and interest in landscape gardening and the embellishment of the great estates of Europe led to a marked increase in horticultural activities. Glasshouses and hothouses of various kinds came into use. But the real growth of commercial horticulture came in the early nineteenth century as a consequence of the industrial revolution, with easier and cheaper glass production, the repeal of glass taxes in Britain, new distribution networks like the railways, and the development of coal-fired stoves, flues, and ventilation systems. Suddenly, nursery workers could contemplate mass-production of plants. There was a marked surge in commercial nursery firms and seed producers during the nineteenth century, two of the most important being the

Vilmorin Company in Paris and James Veitch in England. Garden flowers, vegetables, vines, and fruits became highly diversified. Charles Darwin said that he grew fifty-two varieties of gooseberry alone. Public gardens began to include serried ranks of identical, brightly colored flowers laid out in formal bedding schemes. John Claudius Loudon and his wife, Jane, fuelled popular interest with gardening manuals and the first garden magazine. Flower shows and societies also played a part, such as the Horticultural Society of London (founded in 1805, later the Royal Horticultural Society) with grounds in Chiswick, London. This society began the practice of awarding medals and certificates for choice specimens at their annual show. It especially encouraged the commercial development of orchid breeding.

Diversification continued rapidly through the early twentieth century. Practical expertise inter-meshed increasingly with plant genetics, as at the John Innes Institute for Plant Breeding in Norwich, which played a central role in advancing the field. Toward the end of the century technological advances allowed highly sophisticated propagation techniques. The botanist William Stearn introduced the word "cultivar" to distinguish plants of human-made origin from real varieties.

JANET BROWNE

HOSPITAL. The traditional charitable role of the hospital was to provide shelter and food as well as spiritual salvation and bodily recovery in times of famines and epidemics. Reflecting a more positive vision of health and the new mercantile economy, young urban workers, their livelihood threatened by illness, sought hospital care during the Renaissance. By the early 1500s, this shift prompted a regular medical presence, exemplified by conditions at the Santa Maria Nuova Hospital in Florence. Physicians med-

icalized hospitals they visited, experimenting on patients with established and new remedies and preserving their newly gained experience in casebooks. They also created disease classifications, occasionally instructed medical students, and subjected deceased and unclaimed inmates to anatomical dissection. By the 1730s, European hospitals were primarily places for physical restoration of the military and civilian labor force. Providing Enlightenment physicians with greater access to wide sectors of the population, hospitals became ideal settings for an expanding medical presence. They provided the necessary context for the construction of a new medical science and improved clinical skills, nurseries capable of training better medical professionals. Some hospitals offered programs of institutional apprenticeship for surgeons (at the Hôtel Dieu of Paris) and for physicians (at British voluntary institutions such as St. George's Hospital in London and the Royal Infirmary of Edinburgh). John Aikin, who considered the hospitalized sick poor as ideally suited for "experimental practice," and John Howard, a widely traveled prison and hospital reformer, were early leaders of this hospital movement.

The conversion of hospitals into instruments of medicine acquired greater momentum in the nineteenth century. European hospitals linked to local universities such as Guys Hospital in London, the Hôpital de la Charité in Paris, and the Allgemeines Krankenhaus in Vienna became sites for comprehensive programs of education and research. Notable early proponents of hospitals as medical institutions were the French physicians Pierre J. G. Cabanis and Jacques-René Tenon. With their numerous halls filled with the sick poor, large hospitals were veritable museums of pathology. In these controlled environments, physicians took advantage of the diversity of illnesses and funneled interesting cases

A Dutch cartoon from 1637 lampooning "tulipomania," the wild speculative trade in tulips that crashed that year

The interior of the Hotel de Dieu, Paris, ca. 1500. Sewing up the shrouds of the dead within view of the dying might not have been comforting.

into special teaching units for detailed studies and experimental management.

Clinical knowledge obtained in the wards was focused overwhelmingly on acute, complex, and life-threatening conditions. This institutional environment came to shape the character of Western medicine: dramatic, disease oriented, and interventionist, in effect removing sick individuals from medical cosmology and replacing them with depersonalized disease carriers. By contrast, the largely patient-dominated context of private practice continued to shape knowledge and treatments related to more common health problems and chronic conditions. In the end, the hospital context was decisive in grounding and framing biomedical medical care.

Changes in welfare schemes and professional power relationships, educational expediency, and innovation all contributed to the reform of the traditional hospital. In the early 1800s, novel ways of practicing medicine in Paris attempted to solve the dual problems of large numbers of institutionalized sick and severe manpower shortages among attending physicians. These new techniques, pioneered by French physicians including Philippe Pinel and T. R. H. Laennec, codified the disease manifestations of individual suffering inmates, including bodily clinical signs and anatomical changes. This "medicine of observation" thus became the main tool for acquiring professional knowledge: systematic study and classification of diseases and post-mortem dissection of deceased patients. Diagnostic specificity and outcome were achieved through the establishment of clinical-anatomical correlations. A new paradigm localized all bodily suffering in organ systems. As the product of social and political factors linked to the French Revolution and its wars, this new anatomical-pathological knowledge came to characterize the Paris Medical School. Eventually it spread throughout the world. The pathological paradigm—disease

must have an identifiable anatomical seat—continues to rule biomedicine by consensus of its practitioners, and remains largely responsible for the professional solidarity among scientifically trained physicians, especially by contrast with practitioners of alternative medicine.

Sanitary considerations and medical knowledge, in turn, profoundly influenced hospital architecture and organization, the role of caregivers, and patient management. Hospital space was divided into separate pavilions and provided with improved heating and ventilation, practices pioneered in the 1880s by John Shaw Billings during the construction of the Johns Hopkins Hospital in Baltimore. Also in the United States, Edward S. Stevens and Isadore Rosenfield were among influential twentieth-century architects whose designs facilitated internal hospital circulation and greater patient privacy.

By the late nineteenth century, the strict separation between administration and caregivers, including physicians and nurses, remained. Physicians had the power to admit and discharge patients, substituting criteria based on medical needs for previous religious and charitable yardsticks. The work of nurses, professionally trained on the model established by Florence Nightingale, became an able extension of medical management. Total immersion, peer control, and behavioral guidelines were demanded of all institutional caregivers, forging stronger professional bonds through the creation of hospital instruction programs such as internships and residencies.

For the past two centuries, hospitals have remained ideal locations for the most advanced clinical research, teaching, and patient management of acute medical conditions. Hospitals also function as testing grounds for new technological devices, starting with instruments such as the stethoscope, ophthalmoscope, and laryngoscope, and continuing with forms of imaging from X rays to body scans. Beginning in the 1820s, many of the clinical characteristics observed in particular groups of patients underwent quantification and statistical manipulation, thereby exposing the probabilistic nature of clinical diagnosis and prognosis. The growing body of knowledge of patient outcomes became an increasingly valuable tool for judging the efficacy of medical treatments, especially after the employment of random clinical trials following World War II. And most of the therapeutic revolution of the last half-century took place in hospital settings affiliated with academic medical centers.

GUENTER B. RISSE

HUMAN GENOME PROJECT. The human genome project originated in the latter half of the 1980s in the United States. Its goal was to map the location of the 80,000 to 100,000 genes that human beings were thought to possess and to sequence the three billion base pairs that human DNA was estimated to contain. Recent technical developments had encouraged biologists to consider the mapping and sequencing effort a practical possibility. Human DNA had been found to include numerous restriction fragment length polymorphisms (RFLPs), so called because they were snipped from DNA by restriction enzymes and varied in length. Seemingly ubiquitous in the genome, they could provide numerous points of reference for gene mapping. Moreover, techniques for rapidly sequencing DNA had been incorporated into commercially available machines. At the then-current sequencing price of about one dollar per base pair, the cost of sequencing the entire human genome would come to three billion dollars. Enthusiasts of the human genome project needed government funding.

In the United States, they found it initially in the Department of Energy (DOE), which had a long-standing interest in the mutational impact of nuclear radiation on genomes. In 1987, DOE initiated an ambitious five-year human genome program that would comprise among other activities the development of automated high-speed sequencing technologies and research into the computer analysis of sequence data. The National Institutes of Health (NIH) quickly joined the genome game, if only to take principal control of it away from the big science—oriented Department of Energy. However, the increasing NIH commitment to the genome project stimulated opposition within the biomedical scientific community. The dissenters feared that the genome project would be a three-billion-dollar big science crash program, built around a few large bureaucratized centers that would be given over to DNA sequencing. The project would be tedious, routinized, and likely to sap resources from meritorious areas of biology.

A coalition of genome enthusiasts and skeptics nevertheless found common ground in a genome project that would be spread over fifteen years and would serve a broad biological interest by sponsoring genomic investigations of nonhuman organisms such as mice and yeast. The project would speed the search for genes related to disease (a type of research that many biologists wanted to pursue anyway). Part of the money would be invested in the development of technologies that would make sequencing rapid and cheap enough to be accomplished in many ordinary-sized laboratories rather than in just a few large facilities.

Biomedical scientists and industrial representatives stressed to Congress that the project promised high medical payoffs and would be essential to national prowess in world biotechnology, especially if the United States expected to remain competitive with the Japanese. In October 1988,

James D. Watson, the codiscoverer of the structure of DNA, was appointed head of what soon came to be called the National Center for Human Genome Research in NIH. The move effectively decided in favor of NIH the nagging issue of the lead federal agency in the biological side of the project; DOE would deal primarily with technology.

Following the United States, Britain, France, Italy, several other nations, and the European Community established projects to map and sequence at least parts of the human genome. In 1988, the Human Genome Organization was established as an international body—a "U.N. for the genome," one biologist remarked—intended to foster collaborative efforts and the exchange of information. Both the NIH, at Watson's initiative, and the European Community, at the behest of the European Parliament, incorporated into their respective genome projects investigations of the ethical, legal, and social issues in human genetics—for example, eugenics and the privacy of genetic information. The project was the first in the history of science with a mandate to deal with such matters.

Through the 1990s, genomic data poured out of laboratories on both sides of the Atlantic and into centralized databases, including one at the European Molecular Biology Laboratory, another at the Los Alamos National Laboratory, and still another at NIH's genome center in Washington. Late in the decade, the databases were made easily and freely accessible on the new World Wide Web.

Profit-making competition entered genomics in 1992 when Craig Venter, a specialist in gene sequencing at NIH, left to head a new private center called The Institute for Genomic Research (TIGR). Although TIGR would be nonprofit, it was funded by a venture capital group that established Human Genome Sciences Inc. to develop and market

Dr. Craig Venter, president of Celera Genomics, with machines for sequencing DNA

Alexander von Humboldt (1769–1859), German naturalist, traveler, and statesman, in his library

products resulting from TIGR's research. Venter predicted that TIGR would track down one thousand genes daily and would identify the majority of human genes within three to five years. In 1998, Venter moved to a new, for-profit company called Celera that aimed to sequence the entire human genome by 2001 using rapid new automated machines supplied by its principal owner, the Perkin-Elmer Corporation. Goaded by Celera, the NIH genome center picked up its sequencing pace. In June 2000, at a White House ceremony presided over by President Bill Clinton, Venter and Francis Collins, the head of the NIH project, announced that they had both completed a full draft of the human genome.

Despite the triumph, the entrance of profit-making companies into wholesale gene-sequencing worried leading biomedical scientists. The companies, led by Celera, have proposed to patent large fractions of the human genome without knowing much more about them than their base-pair sequences. Their strategy stimulated a forceful statement in 2000 by the presidents of the Royal Society of London and the National Academy of Sciences in the United States stressing that "the human genome itself must be freely available to all humankind." Offsetting the drive to privatize the genome are the freely accessible databases to which the public projects and their grantees in the United States and Europe are steadily contributing, but how much of the genome will be locked up by private corporations depends on the policies of the world's patent offices.

DANIEL J. KEVLES

HUMBOLDTIAN SCIENCE. Historians use the term "Humboldtian science" to describe a type of scientific practice during the nineteenth century that resembled the work of Alexander von Humboldt, whether or not it resulted from Humboldt's direct influence. Susan Faye Cannon coined the term in 1978 to signify a scientific style that conducted observations with the latest instruments, corrected measurements for errors, and linked these to mathematical laws; constructed maps of isolines connecting points with the same average values; identified large, even global, units of investigation; and used nature rather than the laboratory as a site of investigation. The term, as applied to nineteenth-century science, has since acquired other connotations, including connecting different types of large-scale phenomena, demonstrating their interdependencies, seeking a universal science of nature, and using large-scale international organizational structures to execute local readings as part of a global effort.

Scholars since Cannon have been careful to differentiate what Humboldt did from Humboldtian science. Humboldt deliberately avoided speculation and description as was found in natural history and natural philosophy. The major theme of his master science of terrestrial physics was the equilibrium of the earth's forces. For Humboldt, isolines represented not merely average values, but also a natural aesthetic order (as they did in patterns of maximum areas of concentration in the regional distribution of plants) and even political stability. This aesthetic sensibility rarely appears in Humboldtian science despite its importance to Humboldt, who in many ways incorporated the Romantic emphasis on aesthetics, the imagination, and the picturesque in image and word. Nature was to Humboldt not only the assemblage of averages and the balance of forces, but also an aesthetic composition. The language of his travel books projected strange worlds in living color, a literary quality with great public appeal. He also wanted to retain in nature study the morally didactic qualities that eighteenth-century aesthetic theory had valued. In this sense, Humboldt's science, in contrast to Humboldtian science, was not merely knowledge to be learned, but to be lived. Hence some of the social values associated with the "European tour" in the nineteenth century came from their association with Humboldt's science.

Humboldtian science, as it has been used, also does not include two diametrically opposed directions in which Humboldt's work was taken: popular science and disciplinary specialization. The aesthetic image of the unity and balance of nature's forces particularly appealed to the public. The theme of harmony in Humboldt's work acquired political, social, and religious connotations, and helped to make nature study a part of liberal culture in Germany. The image of nature's order became an antidote to social and political disarray after the European revolutions of 1848. Immediately following Humboldt's death in 1859, Humboldt Associations, and later Humboldt Festivals, were established throughout the German states. They promoted interest in nature through public participation in nature walks and specimen collecting. More focused disciplinary uses of Humboldt's work appeared after industrialization exuded pollution, damaged forests, and in other ways highlighted the interconnectedness of environmental conditions. August Grisebach published in 1872 the first comprehensive classification of the earth's vegetation according to climatic conditions in which he adopted Humboldt's techniques in plant geography, especially Humboldt's notion of "social plants" (plant species in a regional environment forming special communities, such as heaths, savannahs, and bogs, that excluded the germination of other species).

Humboldtian science differed markedly from the institutionalized, disciplinary-based sciences that took shape in the nineteenth century. Although Humboldtian science shared the methodological rigor of nineteenth-century scholarship *(Wissenschaft)*, it eschewed the intellectual specialization of, and sharp divisions between, scientific disciplines. For example, Humboldt and his Berlin colleague the physicist Heinrich Wilhelm Dove took meteorological measurements, but Dove's meteorology never reached out to other scientific disciplines like botany and never included naturalistic drawings in color. Dove also conducted some of his experiments in a laboratory; a Humboldtian scientist worked only in nature. The laboratory scientist posed detailed, particular questions in a contrived environment where certain variables could be held constant. Practitioners of Humboldtian science viewed nature as an ensemble, an organic whole whose interrelatedness could be captured in a geography broadly defined and keenly sensitive to large-scale issues. British natural philosophers especially viewed Humboldtian science as a rigorous counterbalance to the specialization and professionalization then shaping the content and practice of science.

Despite its marginal institutional position, Humboldtian science had a powerful effect on certain areas of science in the nineteenth century, especially geomagnetism, as well as on the development of certain scientific communities. Historians have found Humboldtian science more in evidence in Anglo-Saxon regions than elsewhere. Humboldtian science appeared most frequently in Victorian Britain with its vast empire over which scientists could collect data on the scale advocated by Humboldt. The best example of Humboldtian science is the British Magnetic Crusade, an effort dedicated to measuring the magnetic features of the earth in the British empire and beyond. Humboldt himself had proposed to the Royal Society of London that its members undertake global geomagnetic observations; in the 1830s the British government donated over £100,000 to the enterprise. Directed by Humphrey Lloyd of Trinity College, Dublin, the Magnetic Crusade consisted of a chain of fixed magnetic observatories with standardized instruments whose measurements—magnetic declination and the horizontal and vertical components of magnetic intensity—were sent to England where Edward Sabine reduced them. Methods of observation were printed on instruction sheets and distributed; adherence to the rules of observation was upheld by naval officers who conducted many of the observations. Through these observations Sabine could correlate deviations in Earth's magnetic phenomena to the action of sunspots and demonstrate the eleven-year cycle in sunspots.

The British viewed Humboldt as writing within their tradition of providential design in nature, and were annoyed that he did not specify the design's spiritual agency. Yet they believed that Humboldt's measuring methods were suited for shaping character and tempering laziness in young men. Humboldtian science defined the work of two leading British scientific organizations, the Royal Society of London during the 1820s and the British Association for the Advancement of Science in the 1830s. British imperial activity also bore the mark of Humboldtian science. Charles Darwin carried a copy of Humboldt's *Personal Narrative* aboard the voyage of HMS *Beagle* from 1831 to 1836. Humboldt's aesthetic image of nature recurs in the paragraphs on the tangled bank near the end of Darwin's *Origin of Species* (1859). In Australia magnetic observations at the Rossbank Magnetic Observatory between 1840 and 1854 and astronomical ones at Melbourne's Flagstaff Observatory (founded 1857) were further examples of Humboldtian science. The Ross-bank data became Australia's first project in physics, inspiring a younger generation, including Georg Neumayer, the German scientist who founded the Flagstaff Observatory. In characteristic Humboldtian fashion, Neumayer gathered data from remote locations for map construction by means of the telegraph. British colonial administrators believed Humboldtian science was a part of their "civilizing mission." Even British imperial literature captured its importance. Rudyard Kipling's *Kim* (1901) not only immortalized the empire's penchant for gathering data on natural and human activity (Colonel Creighton was an ethnographer, Kim a surveyor), but also took place during the period of political unrest when natural and social data about India became a form of surveillance deployed to hold the empire together.

Elsewhere, Humboldt directly influenced the Berlin geographer Carl Ritter, but he, like other Humboldt-inspired German scientists, directed no large-scale projects. When Humboldt proposed to the British that they inaugurate global geomagnetic observations, he did not know that Carl Friedrich Gauss had already published a mathematical theory of magnetic intensity in 1833. Working with the physicist Wilhelm Weber, Gauss nonetheless made the Magnetic Observatory at the University of Göttingen (then a part of the British empire) the center of the British Magnetic Crusade. Gauss and Weber designed the instruments for the project, all chronometers were calculated, and all observations were reduced, according to Göttingen mean time. Neither Gauss nor Weber, however, held up Humboldt's work as a model; both continued to work within the framework of laboratory- or observatory-based disciplinary sciences.

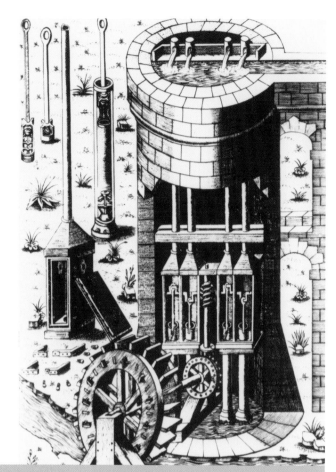

An undershot water wheel driving water pumps via a worm gear and other machinery from Antonio Ramelli's *Le diverse et artificiose macchine* (1588)

Many other scientists, even among the British, felt that Humboldt's science led to writing in outmoded traditions of travel literature and that the integration it claimed was rarely achieved. In the context of discipline-building and professionalization in Germany, Humboldt's science came to be viewed as amateurish, a throwback to an earlier era. Humboldtian science of a sort did promote scientific internationalism, but to what degree is still disputed. Although a concept constructed by historians rather than by historical actors to explain their own actions, Humboldtian science seems to capture the sciences of empire.

KATHRYN OLESKO

HYDRODYNAMICS AND HYDRAULICS. From at least the third millennium B.C., canals, dams, and reservoirs were used for irrigation in Egypt, in Mesopotamia, and probably also in Asia. The building of these constructions and contemporary techniques of navigation imply some practical understanding of fluid motion. A greater theoretical knowledge and more elaborate apparatus appeared in Alexandria in the third and second centuries B.C. Archimedes established the laws of equilibrium of immersed solids, and Hero discussed pneumatic and hydraulic devices and the connection between efflux rate and water head (depth of the mouth). The word "hydraulic" was originally used to describe an Alexandrian invention, the water-powered organ.

The tremendous growth of hydraulic construction during the Roman Empire and the medieval period led to important innovations, such as aqueducts and waterwheels, but added little to the Greeks' understanding of fluid equilibrium and motion. A Renaissance man, Leonardo da Vinci,

brought late-medieval mechanics and the emerging experimental trend to bear on these questions. His insights into the pressure-head relation, eddy formation, flux conservation, and open-channel dynamics probably aided Galileo's disciple Evangelista Torricelli, who in 1644 established the proportionality between the efflux velocity and the square root of the water head. Torricelli also explained the principle of the Florentine barometric tube by the balance between the weight of supported mercury and atmospheric pressure.

In seventeenth-century France, Blaise Pascal formulated the law of isotropic pressure, and persuaded his brother-in-law to verify the altitude-dependence of barometric pressure, which in Pascal's view excluded the Aristotelian *horror vacui*. Hydrostatics thus reached maturity. Fluid motion still challenged the new mechanical philosophy. In his *Principia mathematica* of 1687, Isaac Newton discussed fluid resistance in order to show, contra Aristotle and René Descartes, that matter could not fill interplanetary space. By theory and experiment, he established that the resistance of a fluid to motion through it was proportional to the cross section of the moving object, to the fluid density, and to the squared velocity.

Newton's reasoning used the balance between the momentum lost by the object and that acquired by the fluid and a drastic simplification of the flow pattern. In contrast, the Swiss geometer Daniel Bernoulli based his *Hydrodynamica* of 1738 on Leibnizian *vis viva* (kinetic energy) conservation, thus obtaining the relation between wall pressure, velocity, and height (Bernoulli's law). His word "hydrodynamica" expressed the synthesis between conceptions of hydrostatics and hydraulics. Only after suitable extensions of Newtonian dynamics and differential calculus did "hydrodynamics" come to mean a general theory of fluid motion. In 1744 and 1752, Jean Le Rond d'Alembert published two treatises in which he applied his general principle of dynamics to fluid motion and established the paradoxical lack of resistance to the motion of a solid through a perfect fluid. Probably motivated by this breakthrough, in 1755 the Swiss geometer Leonhard Euler obtained the partial-differential equation for the motion of a perfect fluid by equating the forces acting on a fluid element to the product of its acceleration and mass. He also showed how to derive Bernoulli's law from this equation. In his *Méchanique analitique* of 1788, Joseph Louis Lagrange solved Euler's equation for simple cases of two-dimensional fluid motion and proved a few important theorems.

D'Alembert's paradox and the nonlinear structure of Euler's equation deterred geometers and engineers from applying the new fluid mechanics to concrete problems. The French masters of late eighteenth-century hydraulics, Jean-Charles Borda, Charles Bossut, and Pierre-Louis-Georges Du Buat, combined experiment, global balance of momentum or *vis viva*, and physical intuition. Borda and Du Buat corrected Newton's misconceptions about fluid resistance; Borda completed Bernoulli's ideas on efflux and on head loss in a suddenly expanding pipe; Bossut and Du Buat established the proportionality between the loss of head in a long pipe or channel and the squared velocity; Du Buat formulated the general condition of permanent (constant velocity) flow as the balance between wall friction, pressure gradient, and weight.

The scope and accuracy of this semi-empirical approach grew considerably in the nineteenth century with the work of French, British, and German engineers. In the 1830s, the increased interest in canal building and river navigability led

Jean-Baptiste Bélanger and Gaspard Gustave de Coriolis to compute the backwater caused by weirs. Between 1850 and 1870, Henri-Philibert-Gaspard Darcy and Henri-Émile Bazin made extensive measurements of flow in pipes and channels. In Britain, John Scott Russell, William Rankine, and William Froude studied how wave formation, streamlining, and a vessel's skin friction affected ship resistance. Most influential were Froude's model-towing experiments and his formulation of the laws that relate small-scale data to true-scale resistance.

Fundamental hydrodynamics also progressed. The mathematical physicists Simeon-Denis Poisson, Augustin-Louis Cauchy, George Biddell Airy, George Gabriel Stokes, William Thomson (Lord Kelvin), Joseph Boussinesq, and John William Strutt (Lord Rayleigh) provided solutions of Euler's equation for ocean waves, ship waves, canal waves, and solitary waves. In 1858, while studying the aerial motion in organ pipes, Hermann Helmholtz discovered that rotational motion in a perfect, incompressible fluid obeyed remarkably simple conservation laws. Ten years later, Thomson exploited the resultant steadiness of annular vortices to represent atoms of matter. Meanwhile, von Helmholtz and Rayleigh argued that the formation of highly unstable vortex sheets (thin layers of uniformly rotating fluid) behind solid obstacles provided a solution to d'Alembert's paradox.

In 1822, the French engineer-mathematician Claude-Louis Navier inserted a viscosity-dependent term in Euler's equation. As Stokes demonstrated in his memoir on pendulums of 1850, the equation correctly described the regular flows observed for small characteristic lengths and velocities (e.g., the diameter of the bulb and its velocity in the pendulum case), but it seemed useless for the irregular flows observed in hydraulic cases. In the 1840s, Navier's disciple Adhémar Barré de Saint-Venant suggested that a variable effective viscosity (viscosity depending on local agitation) could be used to describe the average large-scale motion in pipes and channels. Saint-Venant's protégé Boussinesq successfully implemented this approach in the 1870s.

Whereas the French separately studied the two kinds of flow—laminar and turbulent, in Thomson's parlance—in 1883 the British engineer Osborne Reynolds studied the transition between them. He found it to occur very suddenly (as had been observed by Gotthilf Hagen in 1839) for a given value of the number LUD/η, where L and U are the characteristic length and velocity of the flow, D the fluid's density, and η the fluid's viscosity. By astute experiments and by analogy with the kinetic theory of gases, Reynolds shed light on the implied instability. Thomson and Rayleigh then pioneered the mathematical study of this question.

Despite the practical orientation of some of its theorists, nineteenth-century hydrodynamics failed to meet hydraulic and other engineering needs. It did produce, however, some of the key concepts that permitted the success of applied fluid mechanics in the twentieth century. Helmholtz's theorems on vortex motion and his concept of surfaces of discontinuity (or vortex sheets) served Ludwig Prandtl's and Theodore von Kármán's theories of fluid resistance, Frederick Lanchester's, Martin William Kutta's, and Nikolai Joukowski's theories of the airfoil, and Vilhelm Bjerknes's theory of meteorological fronts. Reynolds's and Boussinesq's theories inspired Geoffrey Taylor's, Johannes Burgers's, Prandtl's, and Kármán's statistical approaches to turbulence.

The newer fluid mechanics bridged fields as diverse as hydraulics, marine architecture, meteorology, and aeronautics. Large laboratories were built to combine model measurements, theoretical analysis, and technical forecast. Prandtl's Göttingen institute set the trend early in the twentieth century; similar institutes were created in other industrializing countries. The United States and the Soviet Union became leaders in theoretical and applied fluid mechanics.

OLIVIER DARRIGOL

ICE AGE. The *Etudes sur les glaciers* by the Swiss botanist and geologist Louis Agassiz (1840) opened the eyes of geologists to the possibility that a great ice age had occurred in the recent geological past. The evidence for the hypothesis was already well known. In northwestern Europe, the location of almost all early geological research, a thick layer of boulder clay covered the bedrock, huge stones (erratics) turned up far from their mother strata, bare rocks showed long, parallel scratches, and the remains of earlier beaches appeared well above existing sea levels. Until Agassiz, though, these manifestations had been put down to a vast flood. Since most naturalists still believed in the relative youth of the earth, they relied on written testimony as much as on field evidence. An ancient flood figured prominently in Greek authors such as Ovid as well as in Genesis. Moreover, from the early nineteenth century, most geologists held that the earth had cooled from an originally hot state, making it difficult to contemplate a past ice age.

Louis Agassiz drew on work by earlier Swiss geologists to reinterpret the phenomena and argue that most of Europe had been covered by an ice sheet. By the early 1860s, even the most reluctant geologists, such as Charles Lyell, had grudgingly come to agree. What caused the ice age, Agassiz never explained. In the nineteenth century, a Scottish autodidact, James Croll, set forth the most satisfactory attempt in his book, *Climate and Time* (1875). He suggested that as the shape of the earth's orbit slowly changed

Jean Louis Rodolphe Agassiz (1807–1873), Swiss-born American paleontologist, zoologist, and geologist

as a result of gravitational interactions with other planets, the variations in ellipticity caused occasional ice ages. One of the consequences of his theory was that glacial conditions in one hemisphere would be opposed by interglacials in the other hemisphere.

Scientists soon invoked ice ages to solve other problems. They explained the well-known changes in sea level around the Baltic by the locking up of sea water as ice or by the depression of the crust under the weight of the ice. They suggested that humans had reached North America by crossing from Eurasia on a bridge of ice. They told the story of much of human pre-history as a series of adaptations to life on the southern edge of the Eurasian ice cap.

By the 1920s, using fieldwork by the United States Geological Survey and studies on gravel river terraces by German geologists, scientists had decided that Agassiz's great ice age had in fact consisted of four different stages of advance and retreat. Since these stages occurred in the southern hemisphere as well as in the northern, geologists dropped Croll's theory. Following suggestions that radiation was the decisive cause of glaciation, Milutin Milankovich, a Serbian mathematician, calculated the radiation received in the two hemispheres at various times in the last half million years. At the time, these calculations did not seem to offer the needed support for the four-stage theory.

Following World War II, scientists abandoned the four stage theory as inconsistent with their findings from deep-sea cores. Correlations between the ages of the cores, their paleomag-netism, and their temperature at the time of formation (using oxygen isotopic ratios) revealed a more complicated story that seemed to fit better with information about radiation cycles. As regards the cause of ice ages, though, the verdict is still out.

RACHEL LAUDAN

IMMUNOLOGY as science dates from the 1880s, although inoculation against smallpox goes back many centuries. The history of immunology falls into two periods, before and after World War II. It begins with serology: identification of bacteria, clinical application of vaccines and sera to infectious diseases, and the chemical problem of specificity. After the war, transplantation and grafting rather than infectious disease led immunological work. Unlike other biosciences, immunology was not reductionist: newer work concentrated on the activities of cells rather than on chemistry. The field grew rapidly in the 1960s and 1970s as the new cellular immunology developed; many of those who participated wrote accounts of the period. The historiography of the subject developed in the 1990s and deals with social, scientific, and business history. French writing on the subject has an epistemological twist.

Smallpox inoculation originated in Asia and the Middle East, came west in the 1700s, and may be responsible for the decline in smallpox deaths by about 1790. Vaccinia (cowpox) as inoculum was suggested several times in the late 1700s, most famously by Edward Jenner, a country doctor (though it is unclear if the material he used for vaccination was actually *Vaccinia*). Production was unregulated, and the operation painful and sometimes ineffective; nonetheless health authorities enforced inoculation through such measures as the British Compulsory Vaccination Act of 1853. Compulsion led to worldwide antivaccination movements with strong political and anticolonial overtones.

The Age of Serology, 1890 to 1950

In the 1880s, evidence for germ theory began to mount. Louis Pasteur announced his rabies vaccine and the Russian zoologist Elie Metchnikoff suggested that white blood cells defended the body against invaders. Pasteur liked Metchnikoff's idea and invited him to Paris. But the Franco-Prussian war of 1870 was still being waged on the intellectual front and a rush of publications from Robert Koch and his Berlin colleagues overtook Metchnikoff's work. As bacteriologists, the German scientists were more interested in immune serum, which could be used to identify bacteria, and ignored cells. Animals could be immunized not only with bacteria, but also with bacterial toxins, and immunity transferred passively to another animal via serum. In 1891, antiserum against the toxin of diphtheria proved to be effective in treating the disease. Serum manufacture using horses began at the Institut Pasteur; a global network of serum institutes followed. In Germany, the state guaranteed production and standardization. On the battlefields of World War I, tetanus antitoxin strikingly reduced the incidence of tetanus. At war's end, the victorious Allies through the League of Nations and its Health Organisation set up their own standardization project at the Statens Seruminstitut Copenhagen, bypassing German laboratories, but still using German techniques.

Standardization was central to serology. Paul Ehrlich's standardization in 1894 of diphtheria antitoxin provided a starting point for theory and research. According to his side-chain theory, cells had receptors (the side-chains) that normally functioned to capture nutrients. The receptors could be blocked by toxin, which caused the cell to repair itself by producing an excess of new side-chains, which were shed into the serum and formed serum antitoxin. Toxin and antitoxin bound irreversibly on contact. Specificity was absolute. Ehrlich called this a pluralistic view; receptors for every possible antigen were already present in the normal animal. His critics objected that the theory required far too many specific substances.

The alternative, propounded by Karl Land-steiner of Vienna, gained currency after 1900. Specificity became approximate, a matter of the closeness of fit, determined by the charge outline of antigens. The antigen-antibody reaction became reversible as in colloid chemistry. On this view, antibody might be formed by assembling protein molecules on antigen as template, as the Prague chemist Felix Haurowitz suggested in 1928; unlike Ehrlich's theory, Landsteiner's required no preformed antibody. But Ehrlich's vocabulary and his cartoon-like pictures of the union of antigen and antibody outlived his chemistry. A century later, we still speak of receptors. In the mid-1920s, Swedish chemists began differentiating serum proteins, first by molecular size in the ultracentrifuge, then by charge and then by both together. Antibody activity was found to lie in the globulin fraction of the serum protein. This work led to Rodney Porter's elucidation of the four-chain structure of antibody globulin (1962), the definition of a family of

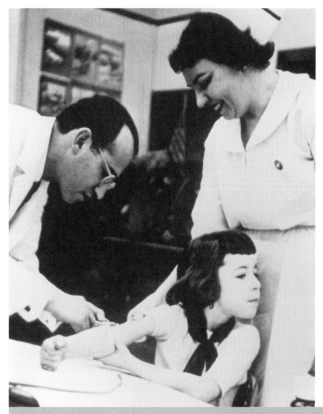

American microbiologist Jonas Salk (1914–1995) runs tests on his vaccine against polio.

different immunoglobulins each with a different immunological function, and to the sequencing of the amino acids making up the chains.

Cellular Immunology, 1950s to 1980s

Antibiotics came in with World War II and although new vaccines still appeared, notably Jonas Salk's polio vaccine (along with antivac-cinationism), serological treatment of disease declined. Thinking became more biological, dealing with reactions in animals and cells rather than serological chemistry. The key problem was graft rejection, important in wartime along with blood transfusion. Discussion centered on tolerance: Peter B. Medawar in London, arguing on the model of the blood groups, suggested that graft intolerance was immunological, while Frank Macfarlane Burnet in Australia taught that tolerance of self developed in fetal life. Various theories appeared bringing antibody-producing cells to the fore: selection theories of antibody production reappeared. Burnet's fruitful clonal selection theory proposed that immunocompetent cells carried a range of natural antibodies as receptors. Antigen triggered multiplication of a clone of cells, and each clone produced one specific antibody. Clones that recognized foreign (that is, nonidiopathic) material survived the fetal period, self-clones being eliminated. This view overtook the template theory about 1967. Burnet linked immunology to modern biology through Darwinian selection and the population genetics of clones, and to current thinking on protein genetics.

An avalanche of new work focused on populations of lymphocytes—then cells with no known function, now seen as mediating the immune response, including immune recognition and memory. Immunological experimentation turned to the reactions of animals, usually inbred mice. Old cells-versus-serum controversies were resolved as it appeared T lymphocytes, developing in the neonatal thymus, mediate cellular immunity and interact with B lymphocytes from the bone marrow, producers of serum antibody; the cells cooperate via messenger molecules named lymphokines. At this point, Anne-Marie Moulin suggests, researchers began to recognize an "immune system." Clinical applications of cellular immunology included autoimmunity, hypersensitivity, and transplantation surgery. Pharmaceutical companies patented immunosuppressants and, later, perfectly specific monoclonal antibodies originally derived from cultured myeloma, a cancer of lymphocytes.

In the 1970s, with increased funding especially in the United States, the profession expanded: journals proliferated, congresses national and international were initiated, symposia and courses organized.

Acquired immune deficiency syndrome (AIDS) appeared in 1982; human immunodeficiency virus (HIV), isolated in 1984, was found to affect a particular subpopulation of lymphocytes, the T4 cells, key to the immune response. T4 cells became part of popular discourse and historians too became interested in immunology.

PAULINE M. H. MAZUMDAR

IMPONDERABLES. Around 1800 physical science enjoyed a fleeting unification under a scheme that developed from study of the phenomena of heat and electricity. The discovery of the conduction of electricity down damp threads by Stephen Gray in 1729 prompted the assimilation of the agent of electrical attraction to water running through a pipe, an analogy strengthened by Benjamin Franklin's comparison (1751) of the machines used for generating electricity (globes or cylinders of glass spun against the hand) to pumps, and Leyden jars (condensers) to reservoirs. For those who accepted Robert Symmer's version of Franklin's theory (1759), which made negative charge as real as positive, electricity was served by two fluids, which, since ordinary bodies appeared to weigh no more when electrified than when not, were taken to be imponderable.

In order to explain the most evident electrical phenomena, natural philosophers ascribed repulsive and attractive forces to the droplets of the electrical fluids: repulsive between droplets of the same fluid, attractive between those of different fluids and between the fluid(s) and ordinary matter. To account for the differences in the degree of electrification or tension exhibited by insulated conductors of different shapes and sizes electrified in the same way by the same machine, philosophers ascribed a pressure to the electrical fluid(s) and specific electrical capacities to the conductors. Johan Carl Wilcke and Alessandro Volta developed these concepts in the 1770s.

Most chemists and natural philosophers of the eighteenth century traced the action of heat to a special substance, which, like electricity, was understood to be an expansive fluid because of its spontaneous "flow" from hot to cold bodies. Also like electricity, its parts were taken to be self-repellent in order to explain the expansion of bodies when heated. Within the Newtonian philosophy the self-repellency of heat arose from a repulsive force acting between the particles of the heat fluid. With the discoveries of latent and specific heats by Wilcke and Joseph Black in the 1770s and 1780s, the parallels between the heat fluid and the agent of electricity broadened: latency could be regarded as a bonding between heat and matter; specificity indicated an analogy between temperature and heat capacity, on the one hand, and tension and electrical capacity, on the other.

The standard representations of magnetism and visible light easily fit the imponderable model. By analogy to electricity, magnetism came to be regarded as a distance force arising from magnetic fluid(s) whose particles obeyed the same rules of attraction and repulsion that regulated the traffic of the electrical fluids. The main distinction—that nothing comparable to conductors of electricity existed for magnetism—was regarded as a question of degree not kind. The magnetic fluid(s) stayed in magnetic substances as electrical fluid(s) did in strong insulators. Franz Aepinus worked out these parallels in detail in 1759. As for light, its particulate nature was assured by the widely held optical theories of Isaac Newton, which endowed light particles with short-range forces by which they interacted with matter to produce the phenomena of reflection, refraction, and inflection (diffraction). The capstone of the arch of imponderables was the discovery by William Herschel in 1800 of radiant heat beyond the red end of the visible spectrum. Infrared light connected heat and ordinary light and, via the analogies between heat and electricity, light with magnetism. More speculative philosophers added fire, flame, phlogiston, and what-not to the generally accepted five (or seven) imponderables.

The scheme, which functioned as a standard model for physical science around 1800, had two important assets. For one, it immediately explained the existence of the phenomena it covered by the mere presence of the relevant agent. For another, it lent itself to the fashion of science of the time, quantification. In 1785, Charles Augustin Coulomb established to the satisfaction of the members of the Paris Académie des Sciences (and few others) that the interfluid forces in electricity and magnetism declined, as did the force of gravity, with the square of the distance between interacting elements. Pierre-Simon Laplace and his school pursued the program of quantifying the distance forces that are supposed to act between elements of the heat fluid (which they called caloric) and between light particles and matter. Laplace and Jean-Baptiste Biot managed to give detailed accounts of refraction, both single and double; polarization; and other optical phenomena in these terms. By taking literally the concept of heat as a conserved fluid, Laplace created a brilliant theory of adiabatic processes that resolved the longstanding and scandalous discrepancy between theoretical treatments and measurements of the speed of sound in air. Although it did not appeal to the notion of distance forces, the adiabatic theory encouraged belief in the existence of caloric.

A serious fault with the scheme of imponderables, apart from its multiplication of weightless fluids at a time when chemistry was learning to live strictly by the balance, was the ontological independence of the several fluids. The unification the scheme brought rested on parallel treatment of diverse phenomena, not on connections among their agents. This weakness was partially overcome by the linking of electricity and magnetism beginning with the discovery of the action of a current-carrying wire on a magnet by Hans Christian Oersted in 1819. But the replacement of the particulate by the undulatory theory of light in the early nineteenth century, and the annihilation of caloric by the kinetic theory of heat in its middle decades, destroyed the old standard model. A new synthesis seemed imminent and immanent in James Clerk Maxwell's unification of electricity, magnetism, light, and radiant heat, and the program pursued around 1900 to reduce ponderable matter to electromagnetism. That program failed, leaving the electron, the electric current, and the flow of heat as residues and reminders of the first standard model in physics.

J. L. HEILBRON

INORGANIC CHEMISTRY. Traditionally, chemical substances were classified on the basis of their origins, the most general distinctions being between the mineral kingdom and the animal or vegetable kingdoms. After the demonstration in 1828 that urea, a compound produced by living things, could be synthesized from inorganic chemicals, the discipline of organic chemistry developed as a distinct area of study—the chemistry of compounds of carbon and the elements with which it readily combines (hydrogen, oxygen, nitrogen). Inorganic chemistry then became the chemistry of compounds of all the elements other than carbon. This early distinction based on origin accounts for the peculiarity that a few carbon compounds—such as the oxides, carbonates, and cyanides—are still generally regarded as inorganic. As a recognized area of study, inorganic chemistry dates from the nineteenth century, but as a practical interest in substances from inanimate sources, it is rooted in alchemy and it stretches back centuries to mining, metallurgy, medicine, dyeing, glassmaking, and gunpowder production.

Among the numerous problems facing nineteenth-century chemists, many revolved around the lack of agreement over standards, such as chemical notation and an atomic-weight scale. Two chemistries seemed to exist, organic and inorganic, each with its own set of atomic weights. At the International Chemical Congress at Karlsruhe, Germany, in 1860, the Italian chemist Stanislao Cannizzaro circulated a short paper on the problems associated with atomic weights

and ways of resolving them. During the next decade chemists succeeded in clearly distinguishing between atoms and molecules, reforming and standardizing atomic weights, and reuniting the two chemistries with a single set of conventions.

While catalyzing reform, Cannizzaro's paper also had a profound effect on the thinking of many chemists, including Dmitrii Mendeleev and Lothar Meyer, both of whom organized the elements on the basis of increasing atomic weight (Mendeleev in 1869 and Meyer in 1870). The modern periodic table, the eventual outcome of this organization, is more closely associated with Mendeleev, who was by far the bolder of the two. He not only organized the elements into a table based on his periodic law, but also predicted the existence of several elements that were unknown at that time, as well as their properties. These represent one of the first instances of successful prediction in chemistry. Mendeleev's table assumed its modern form in 1914 when the English physicist Henry G. J. Moseley organized the elements on the basis of increasing charge in the atomic nucleus, i.e., increasing number of protons.

In 1858, the German chemist August Kekulé advanced his theory that the atoms in molecules are arranged in specific ways relative to one another. These structural formulas, along with the idea that the valence or "combining power" of an atom is constant, worked very well for organic compounds and fueled the dramatic growth in this area of chemistry after 1860. Kekulé tried to extend these ideas to inorganic compounds, but they failed even in simple cases. More complicated molecules—like those of the coordination compounds first synthesized during the nineteenth century—were particularly problematic.

The enduring apparatus of inorganic chemistry: clamp and trivet stands, Bunsen burner, various flasks including one for titration, and a test tube

While an assistant to Robert Bunsen in Marburg, Germany, Frederick Augustus Genth synthesized several ammonia-cobalt compounds in 1847. He published this work in 1851 after emigrating to the United States. The following year the American chemist Wolcott Gibbs also began investigating these compounds, and in 1856 he and Genth jointly described the synthesis and analysis of thirty-five ammonia-cobalt compounds. Their report of the properties and striking colors of these unusual compounds presented a challenge to theorists.

In 1869, the Swedish chemist Christian Wilhelm Blomstrand made the first attempt to describe the structures of the compounds synthesized by Genth and Gibbs. Making use of the variable valence of nitrogen, he proposed a chain theory, which the Danish chemist Sophus Jørgensen subsequently adopted and modified. This model linked ammonia molecules (NH_3) in an ammonia-cobalt complex together in a chain like the CH_2 groups in an organic hydrocarbon compound. More importantly, Jørgensen prepared and examined many new complex compounds, including some with chromium, rhodium, and platinum, as well as cobalt. He also determined many of their physical properties. The vast amount of experimental data collected by Jørgensen, Gibbs, and Genth was essential to the subsequent development of the revolutionary coordination theory.

The theory, a foundation-pillar of inorganic chemistry proposed by Alfred Werner, represented a new way of describing inorganic compounds and was not merely a modification of organic structural theory. Werner obtained his doctorate from the University of Zurich in 1890 with a dissertation on the spatial arrangement of atoms in molecules containing nitrogen. In 1893, the year he began teaching at the University of Zurich, he published the first of his papers on his theory of variable valence. He described molecular inorganic compounds as having a central (metal) atom surrounded by a definite number of other atoms, molecules, ions, or radicals in a three-dimensional arrangement. The number of such groups around the central atom was termed the coordination number. The ammonia-cobalt compounds have a coordination number of six, the six ammonia molecules being arranged at the vertices of an octahedron (8 faces defined by 6 vertices—two square pyramids sharing a common square base) centered at the cobalt. Werner's coordination theory provided a tool for understanding not only inorganic compounds and reactions, but also many organic and biochemical reactions, such as those involving Grignard reagents in which a central magnesium ion is coordinated with both halide ions and organic groups. Werner received the Nobel Prize in 1913.

Since many chemists regarded Werner's monumental work as having completed inorganic chemistry, the subject generated little interest during the early part of the twentieth century. The American Chemical Society further marginalized the field by making it an area within physical chemistry. Not until the Manhattan Project in the early 1940s and the need to separate uranium isotopes did the field of inorganic chemistry began to flourish again. A group of chemists organized a separate Division of Inorganic Chemistry within the American Chemical Society and began the journal *Inorganic Chemistry.*

The 1950s mark the reemergence of inorganic chemistry. Although the first organometallic compound was synthesized in 1827, chemists could not devise an adequate description of its structure and bonding until the early 1950s when they prepared and studied many other such compounds. The structure of one of these novel molecules, ferrocene, was elucidated by two Harvard chemists and subsequent Nobel laureates, Robert Woodward and Geoffrey Wilkinson. The ferrocene "sandwich" has an iron(II) ion as the bonding center between two parallel, aromatic, five-member carbon rings. The development of quantum mechanics and significantly improved understanding of atomic structure led to new bonding theories that can interpret these novel structures satisfactorily.

Another pivotal figure in inorganic chemistry of the second half of the twentieth century is F. Albert Cotton, a former student of Wilkinson's. His textbook, *Advanced Inorganic Chemistry,* written with Wilkinson and currently in its sixth edition (1999), has trained several generations of chemists since its first edition in 1962. Cotton's 1963 textbook, *Chemical Applications of Group Theory,* which appeared in its third edition in 1994, has provided chemists with an extremely powerful tool for understanding, explaining, and modeling the structure and reactivity of inorganic compounds.

The resurgent inorganic chemistry originating in Werner's "completed masterpiece" is an essential component of materials science, an interdisciplinary field that blends chemistry and engineering. Thin films, industrial diamonds, ceramics, superconductors, semiconductors (both traditional and organic/organometallic), LEDs (light-emitting diodes), and lasers are a few of the materials and devices that will continue to be improved through advances in inorganic chemistry. Current trends that should have significant results in the twenty-first century include greater theoretical understanding of the formation of ceramics, leading to improved materials for engineering; synthesis, development, and manufacture of organometallic LEDs; synthesis of diamond and other commercially important films; detailed computer models of every element in the periodic table and three-dimensional visualization tools accelerating growth in all aspects of inorganic chemistry; and a more powerful understanding of quantum mechanics, leading to improved communication and computational devices.

RICHARD E. RICE AND FRANK A. PALOCSAY

INSTITUTE. The university-based institute was the instrument and symbol of Germany's dominance of natural science at the end of the nineteenth century. In its spatial isolation from the rest of its university, the institute represented and enforced the division of the sciences by discipline and of the professoriate by research accomplishment.

Institutes evolved from two university practices. The earliest, dating from the eighteenth century, was the cabinet for instruments or other materials used for demonstration in teaching and to a limited degree, for research. Their maintenance required workrooms; their use for instructional demonstrations, lecture rooms. Initially privately owned, cabinets were placed on the university (state) budget by 1850. The evolution of cabinet to institute depended upon the establishment of university laboratories and the inauguration of the professorial research ethos in the early nineteenth century. Institutes were thus the principal venue through which the manual practices associated with experimental research became a regular part of university instruction in the sciences. An early example is Justus von Liebig's chemistry laboratory at Giessen, founded in 1826.

The second university practice that gave rise to institutes dates from the early nineteenth century. The emphasis German elites placed on *Bildung* (the formation of mind and character)—based in study of ancient languages, philosophy, history, and later theoretical natural science and taken as the key to advancement at higher levels of government service—was a central impetus in the development of new methods of instruction based on learning the principles of research. To prepare secondary teachers capable of imparting proper *Bildung,* professors of philology created special seminars in which students were systematically taught disciplinary knowledge and research methods that could in principle lead to the production of original research. This model entered the natural sciences in 1825 in the Bonn seminar for the natural sciences, followed in 1835–1836 by the establishment of the Königsberg seminar for physics and mathematics, directed by Carl Gustav Jacobi, a classicist turned mathematician, and the mineralogist turned physicist Franz Ernst Neumann. Like the university cabinet, the seminar required a dedicated budget, director, and space. Before 1850, when laboratories began to appear alongside cabinets, they also were found associated with seminars in either the natural sciences or physics and mathematics combined. Managing and maintaining the cabinet, laboratory, and seminar required increasingly greater financial resources and support services, adding to the administrative complexity of these units. As the professorial research ethos took hold and instructional techniques for transmitting it to students were developed, the nature of instruction became ever more complex.

In the second half of the nineteenth century, the institute emerged as the principal site in the university of original research, both professorial and student. The institute by then was an amalgamation of physical space, financial resources, material supplies and equipment, student clientele, support staff, and professorial leadership. The longstanding German tradition of having a single full professor (*Ordinarius*) per discipline stamped the organizational structure of the institute as one run by a director who had near total control over all persons in the institute's sphere, including assistant and associate professors (*Privatdozenten* and *Ausserordinarien*).

The success of the instructional mission of institutes beyond the production of scientific practitioners (where success was uneven) can be measured by the demographics of their student clientele. Chemical institutes, like Liebig's, included students who wished to become physicians, pharmacists, agriculturalists, and future secondary teachers. Similarly and simultaneously physics institutes furthered the careers of physicians and secondary teachers. Seminars in all the natural sciences, which generally had poorer resources than full-fledged institutes, catered in addition to geographers, technicians, astronomers, businessmen, and civil servants. Students interested in technology and engineering found places in institutes in the Technical High Schools (Technische Hochschulen), which began to multiply after 1870. Institutes thus spread through the educated male elite in Germany an outlook not only familiar with the techniques of research, but one highly appreciative of its social and cultural values as well.

The institute phenomenon eventually took over the entire university system in Germany. Resources devoted to teacher (and research) training grew faster than resources devoted exclusively to service teaching. For example, in 1873 the University of Leipzig replaced an old physics cabinet, built in 1835, with an institute four times as large. This, in turn, was replaced by one three times larger still in 1904. Laboratory facilities occupied 12 percent of the cabinet, 46 percent of the first institute (1873), and 60 percent of the second—

A physics institute, Scottish style, in the later nineteenth century: William Thomson (1824–1907), later Lord Kelvin, lecturing in his basement laboratory at the University of Glasgow.

if the thirteen rooms and veranda of its baronial quarters are deducted, 75 percent. Most of the increase came in small rooms for individual research rather than in teaching laboratories and lecture halls.

The system was in principle continuously renewed by the "call"—the invitation of a professor in one state to take over an institute in another. The invitee would negotiate with both, for equipment and space as well as salary. A man in demand might leave a string of new buildings in his wake. Hermann von Helmholtz received a new institute of physiology as a dowry when he moved from Bonn to Heidelberg in 1858, and a new physics institute when he moved on to Berlin in 1871.

The institute spread throughout Europe, including Britain, and, with an important exception, the United States. Although American university departments provided disciplinary separation, teaching facilities, and, in time, a research ethic, their more democratic organization thwarted any pretensions of their chairs to papal authority and perquisites, as was the custom in Germany. The long-term historical consequences of the fluidly democratic structure of the department versus the rigidly hierarchical structure of the institute were crucial for the future development of the scientific community in both countries. Whereas American universities have been receptive to interdisciplinary cooperation, German universities have been less so due to the persistence of the rigid administrative practices of the institute. Consequently at the end of the twentieth century, Germany's educational ministers favored interdisciplinarity by encouraging innovation outside the outmoded institute structure and by offering pathways for career advancement for younger scholars that did not rest on permanent appointments in institutes.

By the beginning of the twentieth century competition among the European nations in natural science and its applications prompted the formation of institutes with few if any teaching functions. Among them, the Carnegie Institution of Washington (founded in 1902 with a gift larger than Harvard's endowment), the research departments of the national bureaus of science, and the Nobel institutes for physics and chemistry are prominent international examples, alongside the many institutes of the Kaiser Wilhelm Gesellschaft and the Soviet Academy of Sciences.

KATHRYN OLESKO

INSTRUMENTS AND INSTRUMENT MAKING. Although the concept of a scientific instrument may seem clear, the historian is bound to find it problematic, not least because the term did not come into common use until the second half of the nineteenth century. The present usage, in its application to the past, comes partly from a projection of current scientific practice onto earlier activities and partly from choices made by collectors, curators, and dealers as they constructed a specialist interest in material culture that would guide their activities in museums and salesrooms.

An important function of contemporary scientific instruments is to investigate the natural world, to discover new truths about nature. But until the beginning of the seventeenth century instruments had no such role. In the terminology of the time, some "mathematical instruments" played an integral part in certain mathematical arts or sciences, but had no place in the science that dealt with causes and explanations in the material world, natural philosophy. Practitioners used these to solve problems and produce practical results, such as casting a horoscope, telling the time, finding the latitude, or drawing a map.

Astronomy provides the earliest record of the use of mathematical instruments and through astronomy many of the technical characteristics of mathematical instruments developed. This precedence might be seen as the outcome of a Platonic belief in a geometrical cosmos. But an alternative view is just as plausible. The regulation of time and calendar by the changing appearance of the sky required measurement and invited instrumentation; a Platonic concept of geometrical astronomy may have been a theoretical formulation of an existing operational practice in observing the heavens.

Astronomical instruments fixed in observatories were generally made by bringing together local resources such as woodwork, metalwork, and masonry, whereas personal portable instruments like astrolabes and sundials came from mathematical instrument makers, and specialist workshops in recognized centers of production. One of the earliest makers on whom we have much biographical information was Jean Fusoris, university educated and a church canon, who set up a workshop in Paris and produced astrolabes and clocks in the early fifteenth century.

Other early makers or founders of workshops were leading mathematicians and astronomers. Johannes Regiomontanus established a workshop in Nuremberg in the 1470s; several surviving instruments are attributed to him. Scholarly mathematicians from the sixteenth century with a strong commitment to the development of instrumentation include Peter Apian in Ingolstadt and Gemma Reines (called Frisius) in Louvain. Gemma worked in association first with Gerardus Mercator and later with his nephew Gualterus Arsenius to produce a great many instruments and a variety of new designs. An international trade developed. The Louvain workshop benefited from an understanding with Christophe Plantin whose printing house in Antwerp was used for their ordering and distribution. This arrangement represented a wider association between instrument production and other mathematical commerce, such as mapmaking and book publishing.

The sixteenth century saw a remarkable development in instrumentation as part of a general flourishing of practical mathematics. The development of navigation and commerce and changes in the conduct of warfare inspired new ways of harnessing geometry to more effective action. This activity tended to take place at court or in the city rather than in the university. Mathematics occupied an inferior position in the university hierarchy to medicine, law, and natural philosophy, but at court it could be used as a tool for political and territorial advance, and instruments were used for persuasion as well as action. The appearance of many surviving instruments from this period indicate that their role was partly rhetorical.

Among many new designs from the sixteenth century were different types of sundials, quadrants, and nocturnals for finding the time, universal astrolabes, theodolites, and other surveying instruments, the cross-staff and back-staff for astronomical navigation, and the sector for a wide range of calculations. The publication of many books on instrumentation and the spread of centers of production, notably to Florence, Venice, Nuremburg, Augsburg, Ingolstadt, Louvain, Paris, Antwerp, London, and Prague, accompanied and supported the development in the range of designs.

Because these mathematical instruments did not engage with natural philosophy, they did not have to respect the received account of the natural world. Terrestrial globes rotated on polar axes in advance of the publication of the Copernican theory simply for convenience. Different projections of the celestial sphere could be used on the two sides of a single astrolabe according to their intended applications, a freedom that reflected the variety of projections used in contemporary cartography. In both fields, convenience and efficiency were the criteria of success, not fidelity to nature. At the same time, the status enjoyed by practical mathematicians in nonacademic contexts for work, and their freedom from the disciplinary restrictions of the university, gave them a relative confidence and autonomy that would eventually facilitate the application of their practices to the reform of a demoralized natural philosophy.

The application of instruments to discovering the truths of nature began in the late sixteenth and early seventeenth centuries, most significantly in the use of the telescope in astronomy. Instrumentation had always been part of astronomical practice, of course, but it had been applied to mathematical astronomy, not the natural philosophy of the heavens, which was treated as a separate discipline. Galileo insisted that his telescopic discoveries from 1609 onwards gave evidence for the Copernican cosmology and so thrust the telescope into the forefront of a dispute in natural philosophy, where its reliability as a tool of discovery would be a critical issue.

The telescope and the microscope created a new domain of instrumentation separate from the established trade of mathematical instruments. A different category of artisan, the more able and enterprising among the spectacle makers, produced the new optical instruments. Like the telescope, the microscope first arose in a commercial rather than a learned context. It was an optical toy with no agenda for use in natural philosophy until the mid-seventeenth century.

Then an increasing interest in explaining natural phenomena through the interaction of invisible particles acting as tiny machines made the microscope a likely arbitrator of the claims of the mechanical philosophy. Through the development of the microscope and telescope a new trade was born. By the late seventeenth century, although they included spectacles among their stock, some specialists had become "optical instrument makers."

The natural philosophers involved themselves closely in this development. Johannes Kepler and René Descartes had been concerned with the true form of an aplanatic lens, one that did not suffer from spherical aberration. Christopher Wren designed an unsuccessful machine for grinding hyperbolic lenses to remove the defect, while other early fellows of the Royal Society ground telescope objectives, as did Christiaan Huygens in the Netherlands. In the case of microscopes, Robert Hooke associated with the London makers and frequented their workshops, while in Delft Antoni van Leeuwenhoek made his own extraordinary microscopes with their single, tiny, spherical lenses. The best optical glass came from Italy, where Eustachio Divini in Rome and Giuseppe Campani in Bologna led the field. Italian natural philosophers, such as Gian Domenico Cassini for the telescope or Marcello Malpighi for the microscope, could rely on the products of the best commercial workshops. Leeuwenhoek had to make everything himself.

By the late seventeenth century, the commercial trade in optical instruments was particularly vigorous in London, where visitors to the shops of Christopher Cox, John Yarwell, or Richard Reeves might expect to buy a fine telescope or a microscope equivalent to the one illustrated in Hooke's *Micrographia* (1665). But the early promise of microscopes as arbitrator of philosophy proved hollow. If fleas and other tiny things were as complicated as they appeared to be, the fundamental mechanical corpuscles lay far beyond the instrument's reach. Microscopy declined in natural philosophy. Nonetheless Hooke's astonishing illustrations had made their mark: through much of the eighteenth century a widespread interest in natural history would supply the makers with a ready clientele for microscopes.

A third category of instrument with which the natural philosophers had an even stronger engagement than with optical instruments emerged in the later seventeenth century. These "instruments of natural philosophy," unlike the mathematical and optical ones, had no location of their own within the trade. Natural philosophers themselves designed the instruments and contracted assembly to artisans. Philosophical instruments included air pumps and electrical machines, which, unlike the passive telescopes and microscopes for observing, intervened and interfered with nature. They literally implemented the collaborative, public, and institutionalized experimental philosophy practiced in the Royal Society of London and other societies that cultivated natural knowledge. Experimental demonstrations were to be performed in public before witnesses and repeated at will: they created a need for instruments of natural philosophy.

Practical applications continued to drive improvements in mathematical instruments even while optical and philosophical instruments began to capture attention. Edmund Gunter in Gresham College, London devised a quadrant for telling the time and performing other astronomical calculations, a sector for navigating by the Mercator chart, and a rule for achieving the same end with logarithmic scales. The ubiquity and longevity of the "sliding Gunter" or logarithmic slide rule testify to the sophistication of mathematical instrumentation in the early-modern period.

As instruments changed over the seventeenth century so did their provenance and markets. London grew into a major center for instrument making and, in the eighteenth century, dominated the trade. Makers in London could belong to any guild or company—they could nominally be grocers, or haberdashers, or fishmongers—and the companies did not restrict the production methods, designs, or materials. This freedom, which contrasted with the centralized and regimented situation in Paris, suited a trade that needed to combine disparate materials, adopt new designs, adapt working practices, and merge artisanal skills. New configurations in the trade began to emerge, as certain London makers at the turn of the century, notably Edmund Culpeper and John Rowley, traded across the traditional boundaries by offering both mathematical and optical instruments.

During the eighteenth century, the most ambitious makers dealt in "mathematical, optical and natural philosophical instruments." Demonstration apparatus became fully commercial under the stimulus of subscription courses in experimental natural philosophy, such as those given by Francis Hauksbee in London and the abbé Jean-Antoine Nollet in Paris. Makers offered books (often written by themselves, in the cases of George Adams or Benjamin Martin), demonstrations, and courses of lectures in addition to instruments. Shops presented their wares within the context of the regu-

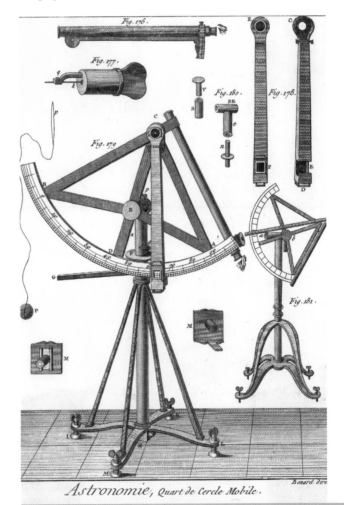

Astronomical and geodetic instruments of the 17th and 18th century

lar trade in luxury goods, intriguing foreign visitors. The growth of material consumption within the middle classes benefited the makers and natural philosophy had a fashionable following, encouraged by entertaining lecture courses or domestic demonstration from itinerant lecturers. The formation of instrument collections spread from institutions, universities, and the aristocracy to the homes of the bourgeoisie—a development encouraged by entrepreneurial traders in a buoyant market.

The rise of a consumer market directed the production of instruments toward the elegant, such as barometers, globes, and orreries, and the spectacular, such as air pumps and electrical machines. Telescopes, particularly the Gregorian reflector, and microscopes multiplied in the same context, and their designs reflected their intended station in a library or a drawing room. The solar microscope was developed to project large images of microscopic subjects onto a wall to entertain a group. At the same time, however, London manufacturers consolidated a leading position in the most exacting part of the trade: measuring instruments for astronomers, navigators, and surveyors.

A succession of outstanding makers of precision instruments in eighteenth-century London, beginning with George Graham and continuing through Jonathan and Jeremiah Sisson, John Bird, Jesse Ramsden, and John and Edward Troughton, raised the status of makers among the community of mathematicians and natural philosophers to an unprecedented level. These makers produced observatory instruments for fundamental measurement in astronomy—at first mural quadrants, transit instrument, and zenith and equatorial sectors, and later meridian circles—and sextants, theodolites, and other precision measuring instruments for everyday professional use. Their work was complemented by that of several outstanding optical instrument makers, John and Peter Dollond for lenses and James Short for telescope mirrors.

While individual skills must figure in the explanation of this development, certain institutional factors also played an important part—commissions from the Royal Observatory and later the Ordnance Survey, and the liberality of the Royal Society, which elected the leading makers as fellows, awarded them medals, and published their papers in the *Philosophical Transactions*. The activities of the Board of Longitude charged with administering the longitude prize established in 1714 were also influential. One of the contending methods, that of lunar distances, demanded exact and robust instruments. The board publicized methods it rewarded, for example, Bird's prescriptions for making quadrants.

At the end of the eighteenth century, makers began to move away from a concentration on handwork in small workshops. Jesse Ramsden employed some fifty men in his premises in Piccadilly; the Board of Longitude published his description of the dividing engine he built for the mechanical graduation of scales on sextants and other instruments. Hand division had previously been the most prized skill in the precision trade; it was now mechanized and, comparatively speaking, deskilled. Subcontracting, buying in parts, even buying whole instruments and adding the retailer's name, became common in the eighteenth century as the trade grew and its organization became more complex. These trends accelerated during the nineteenth century.

The acceleration proved costly to the London workshops. They lost their dominance, partly through complacency, partly through loss of status in the community of learning, partly through the vigorous rise of other centers of innovation. The downgrading of manual skill in the social changes brought by the industrial revolution may have been a factor in the loss of status, but the makers as individuals never regained their positions of respect. Even in astronomy, scientists with mechanical flair like George Biddell Airy designed the major instruments and commissioned components from different makers, adopting the division of labor from contemporary industry. Germany and France became increasingly competitive.

Munich was the center of the resurgent German industry. The able makers there included Georg von Reichenbach, Joseph Liebherr, Joseph von Utzschneider, Joseph Fraunhofer, Traugott Lebrecht Ertel, Georg Merz and Carl August, Ritter von Steinheil. They focused on precision instrumentation, which they pursued in partnerships of opticians and mechanicians. Thus they benefited from research-based improvements in glass quality as well as from innovative designs in structures and mountings. The workshop of the Repsold family formed another center in Hamburg, while Karl Philipp Heinrich Pistor and Johann August Daniel Oertling were active in Berlin from 1813 and 1826, respectively. Observatories, other than British ones, equipped in the nineteenth century usually had German instruments, whereas the many eighteenth-century foundations, including French ones, had been supplied from London.

The French Revolution swept away the old restrictive practices of the guilds and put in place reforms, such as the metric system of weights and measures, that would create work for instrument makers and encourage innovation. Étienne Lenoir, Jean Nicolas Fortin, and François-Antoine Jecker seized the new opportunities, supplied standards of length, weight, and capacity throughout the country, and met the renewed demand for portable instruments from mathematical professionals. Prominent and successful workshops in nineteenth-century France included Gambey, Lerebours and Secretan, Gautier, Morin, and others. The French developed a particular expertise in physical optics, led by Jules Duboscq and later by the aptly named Jean-Baptiste-François Soleil.

From 1851 onwards, international exhibitions furthered the international character of the instrument trade. The exhibitions' reports give a good indication of the relative strengths of the contributing nations. The British were taken aback at the success of their rivals at the Great Exhibition in London (1851). Microscopes, largely through the introduction of the achromatic objective, had again become serious tools of scientific research, and here London makers continued to shine; but elsewhere they had lost much ground. By the end of the century, the German workshops of Zeiss and Leitz had seized the lead in microscopy.

By 1900 the "scientific instrument" in the modern sense of the term had arrived. As makers sought to respond flexibly to rapid innovation, the old characterizations and distinctions became irrelevant. Spectroscopy opened up a vast new area of instrumentation for chemistry and astronomy. Industrial instruments greatly expanded the market open to instrument entrepreneurs, while the coming of the electrical industry and the spread of power supply, of the electric telegraph, and then of radio, opened up a large field for collaboration between scientists and manufacturers. Techniques of detection and measurement had not only to work on the laboratory bench, they had to be standardized and made sufficiently robust to travel successfully to distant stations.

The twentieth century was characterized by ever larger manufacturing units, close liaison with research laboratories in universities, in institutions, or in-house, a bewildering array of new techniques and instruments, and the growing irrelevance of regional contexts other than as economic determinants. This flexibility has been particularly marked as electronic technologies have increasingly displaced mechanical ones. Instrument making has become difficult to isolate from science itself. That may always have been the case. The ubiquity of instrumentation in today's science makes the relation obvious.

A further feature of the twentieth century was the rise of collecting, both institutional and private. Museums now have large collections of instruments—transferred to them from societies, universities, manufacturers, industries, collectors, dealers, and salesrooms. Historians have not realized the potential of this resource fully. Instruments have been integral to the story of science. Although material evidence may be more intractable and awkward to use than written sources, historians of science can scarcely afford to neglect it.

JIM BENNETT

INSTRUMENTS, BIOLOGICAL. The fine woodcut representing a few dozen anatomy instruments—from the most delicate lancet to rough saw and hammer—included in Andreas Vesalius's epoch-making *On the Fabric of the Human Body* (1543) is an icon of the then new regard for instruments in the pursuit of natural knowledge. So too were the balance for measuring variations in weight owing to ingestion, excretion, and perspiration, discussed in Santorio Santorio's On *Static Medicine* (1614), and the diagrams describing simple loop and palpation experiments performed on the human body in William Harvey's *Movement of the Heart and Blood in Animals* (1628).

Many of the instruments represented by Vesalius, Santorio, and Harvey derived from established techniques in medicine, surgery, natural philosophy, alchemy, or chemistry. The same applied to several instruments used by early modern naturalists, which came from pharmacy, agriculture, hunting, breeding, and the multifaceted know-how of merchants and travelers. The emphasis on instruments, however, was new, and it affected the study of living things just as it did astronomy and other sciences infused with the "new philosophy." The positive evaluation of artisanal skills extended to cooperation with printers to employ the latest advances in the art to represent and spread knowledge and achievements—a trend from which anatomy, natural history, and printing itself benefited in turn.

From the 1620s, a genuinely new instrument became an icon of what later would be called the life or biological sciences. This was the optical microscope, put to good use after 1660 by Robert Hooke, Marcello Malpighi, and Nehemiah Grew. Meanwhile the "mechanical philosophy" penetrated the study of plant and animal life. The air pump played a role when Robert Boyle showed that plants produce air (1680–1682). John Mayow and others used simple cupping glasses and siphon arrangements for similar purposes. But perhaps no one better than Stephen Hales, with his *Vegetable Staticks* (1728) and *Haemastaticks* (1733), conveyed Europe-wide the notion that organisms could be included in experimental apparatus that could measure the movements and pressure of blood or sap, and the quantification of the airs inspired, expired, and transpired.

The study of the chemistry of life throughout the eighteenth century continued to demand new instrumentation. Apparatus developed by chemists became basic tools for investigators exploring animal heat and respiration. The thermometer and the calorimeter have remained fundamental for physiology to the present. The stethoscope came in 1816.

Electrical machines were adapted to the investigation and possible improvement of living organisms after the invention of the Leyden jar. With the rise of Galvanism and the invention of the voltaic battery in 1799, electric currents became available. From the 1840s, galvanometers—based on the deflection of a compass needle by a wire carrying a current, and developed mainly in connection with telegraphy—allowed scientists like Emil du Bois-Reymond to carry out new measurements of the small quantities of electricity involved in physiological processes.

The family of electrical measuring devices used in physiology expanded quickly after 1850. In 1855 Rudolf Albert von Koelliker and Heinrich Müller argued that electrical activity must accompany the functioning of the vertebrate

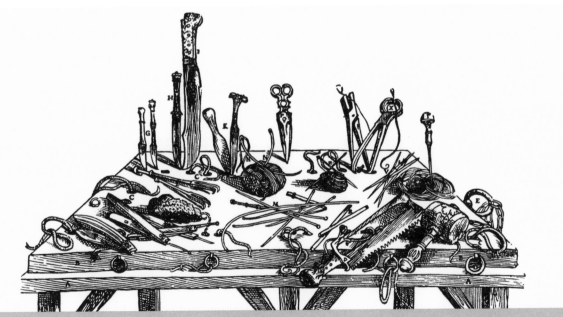

Dissecting tools pictured in Andreas Vesalius, *De humani corporis fabrica* (1543)

heart. In 1874, physicist Gabriel Jonas Lippmann introduced the capillary electrometer based on the response of the surface tension and thus the shape of the meniscus of mercury to a change in electromotive force of as little as 0.0001 volt. Étienne-Jules Marey applied the instrument to the study of muscles, where the quick reactions of the new electrometer made it possible to distinguish individual muscle-action potentials, which the galvanometer did not. Photographic recording devices adapted to the electrometer allowed Lippmann and Marey, in 1876, to record the changes of the electromotive force in the contracting heart of a tortoise and a frog, producing the first electrocardiograms. Further improvements enabled Augustus D. Waller, in 1887, to obtain the first human electrocardiogram.

In the 1840s, another new family of apparatus had been introduced—pneumatic and mechanical instruments used to study the combined action of respiration and the systolic and diastolic rhythms of the heart. The first such device, Carl Ludwig's kymograph (from the Greek *kyma*, "wave"), combined a manometer connected to the artery and clockwork moving a recording cylinder (1846). The self-registering apparatus was inspired by the indicators that James Watt used to chart pressure variations in a steam engine. The myograph (for taking tracings of muscular contractions and relaxation), the sphygmograph (for recording the movements of the pulse), and the cardiograph followed soon.

Important improvements introduced after 1830 in microscopes (correction of spherical aberration), the preparation of specimens (better microtomes and staining techniques), and microsurgery facilitated an unprecedented flow of microscopic observations that molded the content, laboratory set-up, and teaching habits in cytology, histology, embryology, and neurology through the mid-twentieth century. Similar effects on research, training, and manipulative skills were produced after the mid-nineteenth century in botany, entomology, zoology, paleontology, and anthropology by the creation of natural history museums, agricultural experiment stations, and oceanographic institutes.

Physiology and clinical medicine found new opportunities for instrumental developments after 1900 with the introduction of new electromagnetic apparatus. Willem Einthoven's string galvanometer (1903) made possible the first complete electrocardiograph, produced by Cambridge Scientific Instruments in 1908. Einthoven's machine, filling two rooms, evidently was big science. Soon, however, the introduction of vacuum-tube amplifiers developed for radio communications allowed the production of more practical, and less expensive electrophysiological and medical apparatus based on electronic technology, setting a pattern of exchange that has continued to the present.

Also in the 1920s, the ultracentrifuge—in which an oil-turbine generated gravitational fields reaching 400,000 *g* by the 1940s—was developed by The Svedberg. Meant to determine the size of colloidal particles, the ultracentrifuge proved essential for the study of hemoglobin and proteins. Later versions have become popular instruments in biochemical laboratories. So have electrophoresis machines, beginning with those produced by Arne Tiselius in the 1930s. Since World War II these machines—together with X-ray diffraction installations, electron microscopes, electronic cell counters, flow cytometers, fluorescent-activated cell sorters, radioactive tracers, and peptide synthesizers—have reshaped life science laboratories. The new physical apparatus and some old and new laboratory animals, such as the mouse (*Mus musculus*), the fruit fly (*Drosophila melanogaster*), the bacterium *Escherichia coli*, and the fungus *Neurospora crassa*, have changed the sociology as well as the layout of the laboratory.

The development of biotechnologies since the 1960s and genomics in the 1990s have brought an impressive host of new instruments: protein sequencers, peptide synthesizers, gene or DNA sequencers, biolistic apparatus (or "gene guns," using microprojectiles to inject DNA into cells), patch clamp amplifiers (measuring minute membrane cell currents), and polymerase chain reaction machines (to identify and reproduce a gene or a segment of DNA). Concomitantly, information technology has come to play an increasingly important role in biology. Magnetic resonance imaging, and computerized tomography scanners have reshaped hospital, clinical, and patient practice.

With U.S. industry analysts expecting a 12 percent per year increase in the market for life science instrumentation in universities and other schools between 1998 and 2003, and with the related market in hospital and clinical research instrumentation expected to grow at 48 percent per year, biological instruments are more than ever industrial, as well as research, assets.

GIULIANO PANCALDI

INSTRUMENTS, ELECTRICAL MEASURING

Electrometers

Until the invention of the electric cell by Alessandro Volta in 1800, studies of electricity concerned only electrostatics. The first electrical measuring devices quantified the amount of electricity produced by a frictional machine or stored in a Leyden jar. Although various electroscopes and electrometers had been in use since the 1740s, electricians (as they called themselves) lacked fundamental concepts of charge, tension, and capacity, and had not defined their units of measurement. The first instruments divide into three main groups in accordance with their principle of operation: electrostatic attraction and repulsion, spark length, and heating effects of discharges. The first group includes all the electroscopes with suspended balls, metallic strips, or movable pointers. Of the many types proposed during the later eighteenth century, those of John Canton (pith balls), Abraham Bennet (gold leaves), and Volta (straws) deserve special mention. These instruments were neither comparable nor absolute. The other groups include Timothy Lane's discharging electroscope (spark length) and Ebenezer Kinnersley's "electrical thermometer" (heating effect).

In the last quarter of the eighteenth century, electrostatics became increasingly quantitative. Volta managed to make his straw electrometers comparable to one another and almost proportional to the intensity measured. By adding a condenser to his electroscopes Volta increased their sensitivity and detected the weak contact potential between two metals. It was a fundamental step leading to his discovery of the electrochemical pile.

Between the end of the eighteenth century and the first decades of the nineteenth century electrostatics became highly mathematized by Simeon-Denis Poisson and others who built on the laws of force demonstrated by Charles Augustin Coulomb. New types of electroscopes were introduced. The most important later models derived from the absolute galvanometer (and its reduced form, the portable electrometer) developed by William Thomson, Lord Kelvin, after 1850. It used the attraction of two metallic disks. Thomson also designed a quadrant electrometer in which a large suspended aluminum needle moved between four insulated brass quadrants. This instrument, often modified and improved, remained in use well into the twentieth century.

Galvanometers

In 1820, the Danish natural philosopher Hans Christian Oersted published the description of his experiments demonstrating that an electric current can deflect a magnetic needle. Johann S. Schweigger, Johann Poggendorff, and James Cumming soon introduced current multipliers, essentially copper wires coiled around a magnetic needle. The coil increased the action of the current on the magnet. These simple galvanoscopes were followed by "astatic" ones designed by Leopoldo Nobili around 1823. Nobili suspended a pair of identical and parallel needles with like poles pointing in opposite directions. He inserted the lower needle into the multiplying coil and used the upper one as an indicating pointer on a circular scale. Thanks to this system, Nobili's galvanometers did not respond to the earth's magnetism. They underwent many important improvements during the nineteenth century.

In 1837, the French physicist Claude Pouillet invented the tangent and sine galvanometers, the first devices for measuring absolute current. Here the action of a current flowing in a circular coil around a magnetic needle counterbalances the action of the earth's magnetism. Owing to their simple geometry, Pouillet's galvanometers allowed the measurement of a current in terms of the dimensions of the coil, the intensity of the earth's magnetic field, and the deflection of the needle. The absolute electrodynamometer of Wilhelm Weber (1845) had a movable coil in the center of a larger, fixed one. This instrument does not require one to know the value of the earth's magnetism and can also measure alternating currents.

The development of telegraphy, the laying of the first transatlantic cable in 1858, and the need to define electric standards produced great advances in galvanometry. Detecting the weak and damped signal transmitted by the cable engineers needed a very sensitive, quick, and robust instrument. William Thomson designed a moving magnet galvanometer that met all these requirements. He suspended a tiny magnet with a small mirror attached and magnified its deflections by reflecting a ray of light onto a scale. Thomson subsequently introduced a multiple magnet astatic version of his instrument.

Moving coil galvanometers had been in use since the 1820s, but Thomson's telegraphic siphon recorder of 1867 was the first commercial instrument of this type. In 1885, the French physicist and physiologist Arsène d'Arsonval together with the electrician Marcel Deprez, designed a galvanometer of the same type that found widespread use. It employed a light rectangular coil hanging between the poles of a powerful permanent magnet as the current detector.

Another popular late revival was the string galvanometer with a light, current-carrying metallic wire as the detector. First proposed in 1827, greatly improved by Willem Einthoven around 1900, and used in the first electrocardiographs, the string galvanometer, duly modified, figured in the oscillographs invented by William du Bois Duddell at the end of the nineteenth century.

Sophisticated current balances, based on electrodynamic action between movable and fixed coils, were used for high precision laboratory measurements. The indefatigable Thomson devised a series of such instruments in the 1880s for use as secondary standards for calibrating others' instruments. Additional clever nineteenth-century instruments included the "Wheatstone bridge," invented in 1843 by the English physicist Charles Wheatstone, who developed the idea from Samuel H. Christie. This bridge amounts to a circuit including a sensitive galvanometer. It enables one to determine the value of unknown resistances by balancing currents to sire a zero reading on the galvanometer.

Industrial Instruments: Ammeters, Voltmeters, and Supply Meters

The rise of the electrical industry required new and robust measurement instruments that would be easy to operate. In the early 1880s, the English physicists William Ayrton and John Perry produced a moving iron ammeter, which sucked a piece of iron, connected to a helical spring, into a current-carrying solenoid. When the iron was attracted in the solenoid, the spring uncoiled and moved a pointer which was fixed to it. Similar apparatus with a much higher internal resistance absorbed a very small amount of current and served as voltmeters. In 1888, instruments patented by the British engineer Edward Weston began to supersede these instruments. Weston's ammeters and voltmeters had a pivoted moving coil between the poles of a strong permanent magnet. The instrument maker Robert Paul at the beginning of the twentieth century introduced the low-friction moving coil unipivot meter, which did not require accurate leveling. Although these instruments only measured direct current (DC), they continued to be widely used in the twentieth century.

For alternating current (AC), the German firm Simens and Halske, and then Weston and others, introduced compact electrodynamometers. A small moveable coil was inserted in a larger fixed coil. The coils were connected in series, and a current flowing through them produced a deflection of the moveable one. Thermal (hot wire) instruments became essential for measuring high-frequency currents, when solenoids and coils present high inductances. Philip Cardew patented the first practical apparatus of this kind in 1883; Hartmann and Braun produced a more compact and successful design in the 1890s. Voltage could be measured with a galvanometric voltmeter (fundamentally an ammeter with a very high internal resistance) or with an electrostatic voltmeter of the types invented by Thomson.

Dial of a voltmeter manufactured by the Schuckert firm ca. 1890

The Sputnik satellite, launched during the International Geophysical Year, began the space race.

The use of shunts made possible measurement of currents of widely differing magnitudes.

The introduction of electric light in the 1880s and the distribution of electricity to private customers required apparatus for measuring and recording the amount of electric energy supplied to the users. Thomas Edison patented the first electrolytic supply meter and Hermann Aaron invented an electricity-driven pendulum clock system, while others introduced electric motor meters operating against an electromagnetic brake. With the increasing use of AC, the induction-motor meters became standard for measuring domestic electricity consumption. Electronic supply meters, introduced in the 1980s, are now used for industrial applications.

The invention of the thermoionic valve revolutionized the technology of electrical measurement. In the 1920s, the first meters using thermoionic elements were introduced. Electronic oscilloscopes replaced electromechanical models, DC amplifiers increased sensitivity, and copper oxide rectifiers and diodes adjusted DC instruments for AC. In the second half of the twentieth century, solid-state transistors and miniaturized circuits created the possibility of a new generation of instruments. Voltage could be converted into time intervals and measured with a quartz-controlled clock. Today cheap electronic multimeters with digital displays can measure voltages, resistances, capacities, and so on in DC or AC.

PAOLO BRENNT

INTERNATIONAL GEOPHYSICAL YEAR. The International Geophysical Year (IGY) was an ambitious international scientific project that ran from July 1957 to December 1958. In 1950, American geophysicists had proposed a Third International Polar Year that would make significant advances on the earlier ones of 1882–1883 and 1932–1933 by using the rocketry, information processing, and other instrumentation developed during World War II. The project quickly widened to geophysics as a whole. Sanctioned by the International Council of Scientific Unions—the parent body of international scientific organizations—and implemented by national committees in participating countries, it involved some eight thousand scientists from about sixty different nations. It was timed to coincide with the twenty-fifth anniversary of the Second International Polar Year and with a peak in the sunspot cycle.

The IGY Special Committee decided to concentrate on the topics most likely to benefit from a global approach: aurora and airglow, cosmic rays, geomagnetism, glaciology, gravity, ionospheric physics, longitude and latitude determinations, meteorology, oceanography, seismology, and solar activity. The project produced an unparalleled database as well as a number of major discoveries. Oceanographers confirmed the existence of a continuous worldwide system of submarine midocean ridges (actually huge mountain chains), one piece of evidence that contributed to plate tectonics in the mid–1970s. Satellites launched by the United States detected belts of radiation around the earth (named the Van Allen belts) and the influx of charged solar particles believed to be responsible for the auroras. Scientists in Antarctica determined the size and shape of the land mass underlying the ice and discovered a jet stream circling the continent.

The IGY was a prime example of "big science." Governments contributed major funding. Scientists participated in much larger numbers than had been normal in peacetime. International cooperation led to the invention and dissemination of new, intricate, and very expensive instruments. Scientists became more involved in and gained new standing in politics and international law. IGY's success encouraged the United States to commit to Skylab; it led to more intense Antarctic exploration; and it prompted further international cooperation in the International Year of the Quiet Sun (1964–1965), the International Hydro-logical Decade (1965–1975), and the International Decade of Ocean Exploration (1970–1980).

The two-China problem, competition in Antarctica, and the space race exemplify relations between politics and the IGY. In 1955, the People's Republic of China agreed to join the IGY. Two years later, on learning that the Nationalist Chinese of Taiwan had belatedly signed on, the communist government backed out. Scientists on the mainland decided to go ahead with the research even though they could not do so under the umbrella of the IGY. In the case of Antarctica, seven countries that had been asserting territorial claims agreed to set them aside for the duration of the IGY. Eleven nations cooperated in establishing fifty-five research stations. The nations shared logistical support, which their militaries often provided. Although these complex arrangements caused some tensions, the experiment succeeded sufficiently that in December 1959 the Antarctic Treaty was signed preserving the continent for the purposes of peaceful scientific research.

The space race dates from 4 October 1957 when the Soviets successfully launched *Sputnik,* the first artificial satellite to circle the Earth, and part of the IGY. From then on scientists used data gathered by both Soviet and U.S. satellites, supposedly freely circulated through three centers, one in Moscow, one in Washington, and one divided among several other nations. The Soviets, however, who used military rockets to launch satellites, did not release data about their launch vehicles, and the U.S. government suppressed information about their bomb tests, even as IGY scientists detected the effects. In China, Antarctica, and during the space race, scientists had to learn to cope with a world in which science was no ivory tower activity but deeply enmeshed in politics. The history of the IGY is ripe with implications for the politics and sociology of science as well as information about the postwar explosion in earth and planetary sciences.

RACHEL LAUDAN

INTERNATIONAL ORGANIZATIONS. International science organizations are ideologically motivated by belief in the unity of nature, the universe, and scientific laws. Despite criticisms from social constructivists, universalism motivates internationalism. While coexisting with other knowledge forms, modern science was founded on ideas coming from several cultures and traditions, being thus international at its inception. Early examples include the international meteorological project started by James Jurin, secretary of the Royal Society of London in 1723. Observations of the transits of Venus in 1761 and 1769, coordinated by the Frenchman Joseph Delisle, involved Italians, Portuguese, Spaniards, Russians, Danes, and Swedes as well as the French and English, who happened then to be at war.

During the nineteenth century science took on a more national cast, with attendant glories and declines. National scientific associations emerged. The British Association for the Advancement of Science was founded in 1831, its German counterpoint in 1822, its American in 1848, and the Indian Association of Cultivation of Science in 1876. Scientific rivalries mirrored diplomatic relations. Internationalist impulses balanced these nationalist trends as even national efforts could contribute to international science. The met-

ric system, invented and promoted by the French, prevailed throughout Europe. The Conférence Diplomatique du Mètre (1875) resulted in the creation of the International Bureau of Weights and Measures located at Sèvres.

International meetings sought to transcend national borders. International congresses of chemists met in 1860, of geologists in 1875, and of physicists in 1900. Universal exhibitions, such as Paris 1889 and 1900, included scientific sessions. International committees deliberated standards and nomenclature (for example, electrical units and atomic weights). Reacting to the growing nationalist sentiments of the time, many scientists adopted internationalist ideals by the end of the nineteenth century, culminating in the foundation of the International Association of Academies (IAA) in 1899. However, most of these early international associations succumbed in World War I. Science became a war instrument, and scientists national propagandists, as in the "Appeal of the 93 Intellectuals" defending German war aims (October 1914) and counter-manifestos issued by the Allies. Similarly, the Allied position against Germany in 1918 led in 1919 to the formation of the International Research Council (IRC) from which the former Central Powers were excluded until 1926. The coming to power of the Nazis in 1933 and rearmament snuffed out the brief interwar interlude of renewed internationalist impulses.

Twentieth-century scientific internationalism, however, worked to counterbalance the destructive association of science and the state. The number of international scientific meetings is revealing: 20 between 1870 and 1900,14 between 1901 and 1914, 7 during the war, 15 between 1918 and 1923, and 45 in the early 1930s. Similarly, international organizations proliferated after 1918, fostering research and the free mobility of scientists. The International Union of Pure and Applied Chemistry (IUPAC), the International Union of Biological Sciences (IUBS), and the International Astronomical Union (IAU) were founded in 1919; the physicists followed with the International Union of Pure and Applied Physics (IUPAP) in 1922. The International Council of Scientific Unions (ICSU) replaced the IRC in 1931; its founders insisted that science was nonpolitical and universal. Scientists set the basis for the internationalism of UNESCO and other UN organizations after World War II. The experiences of UNESCO and the United Nations Atomic Energy Commission (UNAEC) indicate the opportunities and perils of international organizations during the later twentieth century.

The UN General Assembly created the UNAEC as its exclusive agent in the field, with a mandate to create mechanisms for research and control of atomic energy and for the elimination of nuclear armaments. UNAEC's initiatives, however, were curtailed by the Security Council's veto power and it became a venue for nationalism. At the first UNAEC meetings, held in June 1946, the U.S. representative, Bernard Baruch, insisted on the veto, controls, and sanctions. The Soviets asked for the destruction of nuclear weapons. The French argued that it was necessary to determine the limits of the scientifically possible.

To complicate UNAEC activities, in July 1946 the United States tested improved nuclear devices at Bikini and in August passed the Atomic Energy Act imposing rigid controls on nuclear material. Despite a growing air of futility, the commission announced that international controls were still possible given enough safeguards. In November, the UNAEC presented a progress report to the Security Council. Despite French protests, armaments debate focussed on atomic weapons. The General Assembly demanded an atomic control convention from the Security Council. In December the UNAEC approved Baruch's proposal calling for a system to outlaw atomic weapons and instruments to enforce the system. The report was approved, Poland and the USSR abstaining. The commission submitted Baruch's recommendations to the Security Council.

Considering his job done, Baruch resigned in January 1947. His plan got nowhere. In February Andrey Gromyko proposed a convention prohibiting atomic weapons, the destruction of existing stockpiles, an international control system, and an international organization for atomic energy research. The Cold War gave little chance for an agreement. The UNAEC assembled for the last time on 29 July 1949. On 23 August the Soviet Union detonated its first atomic bomb.

The short lived and nearly forgotten UNAEC was superseded by the International Atomic Energy Agency. However, the United Nations now operates on atomic energy matters along the lines UNAEC discussed. No "illegal" atomic operations are allowed, and no atomic wars have occurred. By denying their national affiliation and working directly within the structure of the UNAEC, scientists reinforced the highest internationalist ideals and achieved long-term results. Despite this success, the story of UNAEC-IAEC shows that science can easily become a theater for international conflict. The history of UNESCO illustrates the point from a different perspective.

UNESCO was preceded by the International Committee of Intellectual Co-operation, founded in 1922 and based in Geneva, and its executive agency, the International Institute of Intellectual Co-operation, founded in 1925 and based in Paris. Both existed until 1946. UNESCO had another precursor in the International Bureau of Education (IBE)

founded in 1925 and based in Geneva. IBE became part of UNESCO in 1969. In November 1945, the London Conference of Allied Ministers of Education approved UNESCO's constitution. It entered into effect in November 1946. One of UNESCO's five main functions is the advancement, transfer, and sharing of knowledge.

UNESCO comprises three bodies. The General Conference, composed of member states, approves the biannual program and budget. The Executive Board, composed of fifty-eight representatives, meets twice a year and functions as an administrative council, supervising the program's execution. The Secretariat is appointed every six years. UNESCO is supported by national commissions, nearly seven thousand schools, and over six thousand clubs and associations.

UNESCO's impressive achievements include a vast publishing program, over ten thousand titles between 1946 and 2000, among them the *World Science Report* and the *UNESCO Courier,* issued in twenty-seven languages. Membership increased steadily until 1980, when a crisis of credibility hit. The United States, Great Britain, and Singapore left in 1984 and 1985 (membership nonetheless rose from 153 in 1980 to 159 in 1990). When the crisis ended, numbers again increased rapidly, reaching 188 in 2000.

The Americans and the British quit UNESCO because they thought that its programs threatened their national interests. For them, UNESCO did not use its resources neutrally. Unable to convince the majority of the UNESCO assembly, they withdrew, thereby creating a stronger and more internationalist organization. Politically motivated projects declined, efficiency improved, and hiring processes became visible as other nations moved in to keep the dream of international science and education alive. Federico Mayor (Spain) returned UNESCO to political neutrality during

High over Earth, the International Space Station moves away from Space Shuttle Endeavor on August 19, 2007

his term (1987–1999). Improvements continued, made easier by the dissolution of the Soviet Union.

In the early twenty-first century the excessive emphasis on applications and financial gains may be more threatening to internationalism than nationalism. The problem obtrudes in the two great human adventures that survived the Cold War, polar research and the International Space Station. Polar research must be international because of the nature of the problems and demands on resources. Nationalistic positions are irrelevant in conflicts between different disciplines over the uses of research vessels, logistics, and instruments. Like polar research, national competition marked the early history of space exploration. Space research has always been very close to military applications. Nevertheless, most regard Yuri Gagarin and Neil Armstrong as individual astronauts, not as flag carriers. They have been taken out of their nationalist contexts to become international symbols. The International Space Station (ISS) may open a new chapter in the history of humanity. By confronting research issues above the planet, ISS reinforces the unity of human society and raises interesting possibilities for a reinterpretation of history.

REGIS CABRAL

IRRITABILITY. Physiologists and biologists have used the term "irritability" to denote the property of organs, tissues, living matter, and protoplasm that allows their stimulation or excitation. According to ancient physiological doctrines, the irritated part must be able to recognize being irritated in order to respond. Hence Galen (129/130–199/200) assigned a kind of "perception" not only to the nervous system, but also to organs like the stomach, uterus, and bladder, and why the notion of irritability was often associated with that of sensation, perception, and sensibility during the seventeenth and eighteenth centuries.

Building upon ancient doctrines and contemporary experiments, both William Harvey and Frances Glisson put forward doctrines of irritation. In his early work *Anatomia hepatis* (1654), Glisson maintained that the stomach and intestines expelled harmful agents because these organs were "capable of irritation." In his *Tractatus de ventriculo et intestinis* (1672) he shifted from a doctrine of irritation to one of irritability by assigning to fibers a "natural perception" independent of nerves, so that they could be irritated and respond to such irritation. This property he called irritability.

Glisson's doctrine lapsed into oblivion, until its partial revival by Albrecht von Haller in a paper published in Göttingen in 1753 ("De partibus corporis humani sensilibus et irritabilibus"). Haller suggested "a new division of the parts of the human body" based on experiments carried out mainly on living animals and consisting in diversified stimulation of different parts of the animal body. Haller named irritable any part that contracted when touched, and sensible any part that evidenced signs of pain. Since all parts displaying irritability were muscular, and those displaying sensibility were nervous, Haller stated that both properties depended "on the original fabric of the parts." In so doing

Albrecht von Haller (1708–1777), Swiss anatomist and polymath

he correlated a specific physiological behavior with a specific tissue structure.

Haller's doctrine aroused blazing controversy for over twenty years. Robert Whytt contested Haller's clear-cut distinction between irritability and sensibility in his *Physiological Essays* (1755), maintaining that muscular contractions arise from their sensibility and "are no more than an effort of nature to throw off what is hurtful." Felice Fontana investigated the laws of irritability, or muscular contraction, and discovered that the heart loses irritability during contraction, a phenomenon later named the refractory period of the heart (*De irritabilitatis legibus*, 1767).

By the early nineteenth century, the notions of irritability and sensibility had been incorporated into most physiological systems. Some authors applied them also to plant physiology. However, while contractility replaced irritability in Haller's sense, biologists like Jean Baptiste Lamarck considered irritability to be the fundamental property that distinguished animals from vegetables. During the second half of the nineteenth century, irritability was assigned to the protoplasm of cells. By the early twentieth century, it concerned the response of all living cells and organisms to change in their environment, and was increasingly replaced by the term "excitability."

RENATO G. MAZZOLINI

J

JOURNAL. The scientific journal and its essential companion, the journal article, have continuously grown in importance since their debut in the mid-seventeenth century. As the word "journal"—and its substitute, "periodical"—suggest, this medium is characterized by currency and regularity of publication. Correspondence, appendices or revisions of books, and even manuscripts predated the journal as methods for communicating scientific news, but none of these formats could match the stability of the journal as a repository for the rapidly growing scientific literature.

The first regularly published periodical to include scientific essays and reviews was the *Journal des Sçavans,* which began publication on 5 January 1665. It was followed later that year by the first journal to specialize in experimental science and natural philosophy, the *Philosophical Transactions* of the Royal Society of London. Its articles generally reported briefly on experiments or observations, fresh and accessible material appropriate for prompt publication. Founded in 1682, the *Acta Eruditorum* of the Academia Naturae Curiosorum, by publishing in Latin, attracted articles in academic fields such as mathematics.

During the eighteenth century, the founding of hundreds of new scientific academies and societies paced the proliferation of scientific journals and concentrated the control of the scientific community over its burgeoning literature. One of the most tangible steps taken by these institutions was to provide opportunities for the dissemination of knowledge. The Paris Academy of Sciences, after reorganizing in 1699, established a record of its accomplishments through the *Histoire,* an annual publication required by the Crown, and the *Mémoires* written by individual members, reviewed by the assembly, and issued with the *Histoire* beginning in 1701. Societies sought to stimulate discoveries, inventions, and improvements through open communication of results; the successful ones created a readership of correspondents, professors, officials, agronomists, physicians, and others who consumed and contributed to their programs. Most smaller societies and academies in the eighteenth century, especially those in the German states, adhered more closely to the Royal Society's model of prompt publication than the Paris Academy's deliberate transactions, but not without borrowing from the Paris model the practice of explicit institutional affiliation with their journals.

This same period witnessed two more trends in journal publishing: the proliferation of privately published journals and specialization. The two trends were linked, if only because academies and societies with their learned memberships usually supported journals covering the whole of science, while independent publishers often followed more narrowly defined interests. Journals setting the latter trend were the Abbé Rozier's *Introduction aux observations sur la physique* (later the *Journal de physique),* founded in 1771; *Der Naturforscher,* founded in 1774 and edited by J. E. I. Walch; and William Nicholson's *Journal of Natural Philosophy, Chemistry, and the Arts,* founded in 1797 and more commonly known as "Nicholson's Journal." While these viewed all of experimental science as their domain, other journals in chemistry, forestry, natural history, mining, medicine, and additional fields sharpened the focus more narrowly. Private journals covering general science reached their high point by the mid-nineteenth century, then were overwhelmed by institutionally sponsored and single-discipline journals. The *Philosophical Magazine,* founded by Alexander Tilloch in 1798, exemplified this pattern by reducing its coverage gradually to physics research and by swallowing Nicholson's Journal. While the publications of academies continued to cover the sciences generally, a parallel trend toward the division of transactions along disciplinary lines emerged, led by the voluminous *Comptes Rendus* of the Paris Academy. Conferences became an important means of semiformal communication among scientists, and their proceedings joined journals in the publication of contributions. By the early twentieth century, the article and conference paper dominated formal scientific communication.

The growth of the journal literature encouraged innovations in bibliographic control of these publications. By the end of the eighteenth century, the expense and number of periodicals made it difficult for any individual to survey the literature, let alone acquire it. Annual and multiyear indexes for periodicals and review journals such as Lorenz Crell's *Chemisches Journal* (1778–1781) covered the literature and followed the example of the *Allgemeine Deutsche Bibliothek* (1765–1792) by providing intellectual access in the form of indexes. By the end of the century, review journals and analytical bibliographies of periodical literature began to appear, culminating in the *Allgemeines Repertorium der Literatur* of Johann Samuel Ersch, published between 1793 and 1807 to cover publications from 1785 to 1800. Indexes, bibliographies, and biobibliographies edited by Ersch, Johann Poggendorff, Georg Christoph Hamberger, and others prepared the way for comprehensive indexes to the scientific literature such as the *Royal Society Catalogue of Scientific Papers,* covering the entire nineteenth century; its successor, the *International Catalogue of Scientific Literature,* continuing to the beginning of World War I; *Science Abstracts,* which began publication in 1898; *Chemical Abstracts,* founded in 1907; and dozens of others. By 1960, *Science Abstracts* alone generated about 21,000 citations with abstracts annually, and *Chemical Abstracts* occupied roughly 3,000 abstractors. With the rise of bibliometrics, new forms of bibliographic control such as citation indexes, offered in Eugene Garfield's *Sci-*

ence Citation Index since 1961, navigated a vast sea of citations. As the literature grew, abstracting and bibliographic services such as the INSPEC (Information Service in Physics, Electrotechnology, and Control) database *(Science Abstracts)* began to depend on computers to deliver searchable bibliographic databases. By the beginning of the twentieth century, printed books had yielded their central position in scientific communication to the journal, conference paper, and preprint. Issues of quality control, economics, and technology shaped the journal in this century. The system of peer review that evolved over the course of the century gave intellectual control of journal contents to editors and reviewers representing the ranks of scientists. The challenge of managing the expense of publication proved more difficult as the size of the published literature grew. One solution, represented by the founding of the American Institute of Physics in 1932, was to concentrate nonprofit publishing by member societies. But since the 1950s consolidation has favored private publishers such as Reed Elsevier and Springer Verlag, who are able to purchase stables of specialized journals and to profit from expensive subscriptions placed by research institutions and libraries, rather than individuals. In the 1980s and 1990s, the reduction of library budgets and ceaseless growth of the printed journal literature precipitated a crisis. Computer technology and the Internet led to innovations such as online refereed publications, introduced by the *Online Journal of Current Clinical Trials* in 1992, or informal preprint servers and ftp sites; they offer the possibility of accelerating the pace of scientific publication while challenging the role of for-profit publishers by reducing the cost of disseminating results.

HENRY LOWOOD

J

LABORATORY, INDUSTRIAL RESEARCH. The industrial research laboratory first appeared in commercial enterprises around 1860. Previously, research related to industrial processes took place in universities, academies, and private laboratories. Sometimes inventors set up their own enterprises with which they associated their laboratories. But after 1860, companies began establishing in-house research facilities.

The industrial research laboratory as an organizational entity has several typical features. It is generally separated from production facilities and not subject to immediate demands from production or production managers. Industrial research is a continuous activity; scientific investigations and their extension to new products become routine operations of the firm. Industrial research also features cooperation of scientists from different disciplines, engineers, technicians, and craftsmen, working in an interdisciplinary manner. Since interdisciplinary activities of people with different backgrounds and tasks make coordination and hierarchy necessary, a coordinating institution at the top of the research structure is often created for the purpose—either a central research laboratory or a responsible member of a board of directors. Those conditions of routine activity, novelty, interdisciplinarity, and coordinated hierarchy confirm a company's engagement in industrial research. The same features characterize the work carried out in industrial research laboratories.

Beginning in the late 1850s a considerable number of chemists began working in industry for iron foundries. After Henry Bessemer had announced his revolutionary process for converting iron into steel in 1856, German foundries quickly implemented his invention and employed chemists to develop and refine it, and to look for new alloys. Afred Krupp in 1863 established what was probably Germany's first industrial research laboratory at his crucible steel foundry in Essen; and in 1883 he created a second laboratory with the special mission of finding new alloys, improving existing steels, and investigating the properties of iron and steel. About one hundred foundries around Sheffield in England also set up chemical testing sites by 1900. In the United States, the Pennsylvania Railroad Company established a chemical laboratory in 1876, probably becoming the first American enterprise to do so in pursuit of technological innovations.

The emerging organic-chemical and electrical industries gave rise to a great number of industrial research laboratories from the 1870s onwards. Following the discovery in 1856 of synthetic aniline dyes derived from coal tar by William Henry Perkin and August Wilhelm von Hofmann in London, many firms were established in Britain, France, Switzerland, and Germany to develop it. These firms, synthesizing great numbers of dyes, grew rapidly. By 1880, however, advancing scientific progress, increasingly complex production processes, lawsuits over patents, and fierce

A machine hall in the Krupp works, Essen, Germany, in 1911

competition had driven many European companies out of business. Apart from a handful of British enterprises, some ten German firms continued to grow and provided 80 to 90 percent of the world production of synthetic dyes by 1913. All the surviving companies had developed particularly strong industrial research laboratories.

The firms first sought enduring connections with university researchers to supplement and later replace the scientific knowledge of the aging company founders. Moreover, the first all-German Patent Law of 1877 made copying of other companies' inventions and production processes illegal. Companies had now to file their own patents, check their claims of novelty, screen competitors' patents, and evaluate inventions and discoveries offered to them from university professors. All these were the duties of the newly established industrial research laboratories, which emerged between 1877 and 1886 in the leading German dye companies. With rapid scientific progress in new fields like pharmaceuticals, photographic chemicals, artificial fibers, and synthetic rubber, and with a continuous stream of young chemists leaving German universities, the biggest German chemical companies—BASF, Hoechst, and Bayer—each employed around 300 chemists in their large research laboratories and testing stations by 1912.

In the United States, DuPont de Nemours started the investment in industrial research by creating research laboratories from 1902 on, after it had been threatened with antitrust suits for misusing its market power in explosives. Here, industrial research, embodied in industrial research laboratories, had the function of deliberately broadening and widening the enterprise's activities.

In the electrical industry, after the introduction of the telegraph in the 1840s and 1850s, a number of firms in the United States, Germany, Italy, and Britain, and some independent inventors, notably Thomas Edison, started to work on the telephone, high voltage systems, and—in the 1870s—the incandescent light bulb. Rapid scientific and technical progress, competition for market domination influenced by national patent laws and corporate acquisitions, and, in the case of Siemens, the death of the company founder and main inventor (Ernst Werner von Siemens), prompted Siemens and Halske (Germany), General Electric (United States), and Philips (Netherlands) to set up research laboratories around 1900. They were to safeguard a constant stream of marketable new inventions and technologies. Their main activity in the first years centered on the incandescent light and lighting technologies. But with the arrival of the telephone, X rays, and new theories in physics, the scope of the research laboratories in the electrical industries widened to include vacuum tubes and X-ray machinery, and then, more generally, to encompass theoretical physics, physical chemistry, chemistry, acoustics, and mechanical technologies. Inspired by the success of others, the American Telegraph and Telephone Co. (AT&T) and Eastman Kodak (photographic equipment) also began to pursue industrial research in newly created laboratories. Despite different aims and business strategies, at the onset of World War I most large industrial enterprises in the United States, Great Britain, and Germany had departments for pursuing industrial research. Usually a centralized main laboratory directed several dispersed laboratories and testing stations while maintaining close long-term relationships with nearby universities.

Drawing on war profits, a return to peacetime conditions, and a postwar economic boom, the years from 1919 to 1926 saw unprecedented growth in the number of new

Left to right, John Bardeen (1908–1991), William Shockley (1910–1989), and Walter Brattain (1902–1987) shared the Nobel Prize for Physics in 1956 for their invention of the transistor.

industrial research laboratories and the expansion of existing ones. Also, as companies grew during the war years and mergers became common, huge industrial complexes with several thousands of workers and large research facilities were established. By 1925, AT&T employed about 3,600 staff members in their "Bell Laboratories," a company it set up for the sole purpose of pursuing industrial research. The same year DuPont had a research staff of around 300 in the same year, which rose to about 700 by 1930. In automobiles, General Motors created probably the largest infrastructure for research and development. In Europe, the biggest spender on research and development was I. G. Farben, a chemical trust stemming from the merger of six German dye companies (including Bayer, BASF, and Hoechst) in 1925; it employed about 1,100 research chemists in at least sixty laboratories by 1930. Imperial Chemical Industries (ICI) in Britain, which also resulted from a merger of six chemical companies, had a research staff of around 400 chemists. In other sectors such as textiles and branded goods, British companies saw great investment in industrial research in the interwar years. In the electrical industries, Siemens and Halske employed roughly 900 chemists, physicists, and engineers in more than seventy laboratories. By 1934 Philips had a corps of 370 researchers. In steel, Germany was the home of probably the biggest industrial enterprise of the interwar years, the Vereinigte Stahlwerke AG (United Steel); it combined the research efforts of several firms, with a research staff of at least 400 people.

During World War II, each belligerent nation made use of the knowledge, technologies, and manpower of giant industrial enterprises for their war efforts. In the United States, DuPont was heavily involved in the Manhattan Project leading to the atomic bomb; in Britain, ICI also participated in a nuclear power project. In Germany, I. G. Farben supplied synthetic fuel and rubber for the war effort. All required substantial investment in science and technology to produce nuclear power, radar, antibiotics, jet engines, and early computers. The Cold War resulted in a continuation of large research efforts by both government and industry. Many companies established new industrial research laboratories.

The organization and management of industrial research laboratories have changed over time. Their number, location, administration, and coordination altered frequently as companies grew, diversified, closed, or sold production lines, or merged with other firms. Some companies found it useful to centralize all research efforts in one big department for research and development; others continued to decentralize research along product lines.

A typical modern industrial research laboratory has a managing director, group leaders, team heads, and scientists. The director reports to the company's board. An experienced scientist supervises the laboratory work of interdisciplinary groups of scientists and engineers. A large and diversified company may maintain many testing and investigating stations organized along the companies' different lines. But only the centralized, main industrial research laboratory with direct access to a company's top management enjoys the status of the scientific and technological heart of the enterprise.

Companies have tried various means of financing their industrial research laboratories. Until World War II, the divisions at Siemens had to pay for scientific investigations and tests done by its main industrial research laboratory, while DuPont allowed their laboratories to spend substantial amounts before evaluating their output. In contrast, Bayer and BASF for many decades permitted their laboratories, which produced new inventions and discoveries regularly, to function without regular evaluation. Researchers in testing stations could not choose their projects, whereas outstanding scientists in the centralized main laboratory might enjoy great freedom in deciding their agendas. Sometimes, large enterprises distanced their creative scientists from the immediate concerns of manufacturing by founding new companies or divisions only for the purpose of conducting industrial research, as AT&T did with Bell Laboratories in 1925 and Vereinigte Stahlwerke AG did with a new subsidiary in 1926. IBM located research divisions in a foreign country (Zurich, Switzerland) to safeguard academic freedom and benefit from the stimulation of a famous nearby technical university. Some companies, like DuPont during the 1930s, allowed fundamental research in their laboratories but abandoned the initiative when it gave no greater returns than earlier approaches.

Despite secrecy's importance in industrial research, especially for patentable discoveries, industrial scientists need intellectual exchange with colleagues and ways to discuss their theories and inventions. Beginning in the 1920s, after decades of secrecy, many enterprises set up their own journals to publish recent results or allowed their researchers to publish freely in academic journals. This relaxation aided recruitment of young scientists since they did not have to abandon academic standards and ambitions on entering industrial research laboratories. They could thus enhance their own and their company's reputations, build a record for transfer to a university, and earn a chance at a Nobel Prize. Winners include Irving Langmuir and Horst Störmer at Bell Laboratories in 1932 and 1998, respectively, and Gerhard Domagk at Bayer/IG Farben in 1939.

ULRICH MARSCH

LAMARCKISM became a critical term in biology in the 1880s and 1890s within the debate over evolution theories that developed during the temporary eclipse of Darwinism.

Given the time and context, Lamarckism, "neo-Lamarckism" (introduced by the American entomologist Alpheus Packard in 1884), and "neo-Lamarckian" (attached to the doctrines of some evolutionists active around 1900) had little to do with the theory of evolution advanced by Jean Baptiste de Lamarck almost a century earlier.

In the later context, Lamarckism designated above all the doctrines that characteristics acquired through use during the life of an organism could be transmitted to its offspring and that the environment played a direct role in the modification of living beings. Many regarded the "Lamarckian" inheritance of acquired characters as an appropriate complement, or even a necessary alternative, to Charles Darwin's notion of natural selection, which seemed unable to sustain the broad evolutionary theory and world-view that Darwin himself had advocated. The experimental evidence brought to support the inheritance of acquired characters by authors like Charles-Édouard Brown-Séquard, Paul Kammerer, Ivan Pavlov, and William McDougall, however, proved insubstantial, and the notion fell by the wayside after the severe criticism of August Weismann.

"Lamarckism" as used in biology today retains its late-nineteenth-century significance. It also evokes memories of the Lysenko affair, the dramatic confrontation in the 1930s and 1940s between a Soviet version of the doctrine of the inheritance of acquired characters, supported by Stalin's head biologist and agriculturalist Trofim Denisovich Lysenko, and Western, neo-Darwinian geneticists.

In recent decades historians of biology have unearthed evidence revealing other important, but relatively unknown chapters in the history of Lamarckism. It is now agreed that Lamarck's own works and ideas circulated more widely than previously suspected in several European countries before the publication of Darwin's *Origin of Species* in 1859. Thus, Lamarck's important legacy, and the controversial reception accorded to it in scientific and popular circles from the 1830s through the 1850s, merged in depth with the assessments of Darwin's own work. Darwin engaged in frequent dialogue with Lamarck's views and concepts while refining his own theory and presentation strategies, and subscribed to the then-popular notion of use-inheritance. Many who joined in support of evolution after 1859, including prominent defenders of Darwin's like Thomas Henry Huxley and Ernst Haeckel, and successful propagandists of evolutionism like Herbert Spencer endorsed Lamarckian, rather than properly Darwinian views. The histories of Lamarckism and Darwinism appear now more closely intertwined than was allowed by mid-twentieth-century biologists in the wake of the triumphs of the neo-Darwinian theory of evolution.

GIULIANO PANCALDI

LASER AND MASER. MASERs (microwave amplification by stimulated emission of radiation) produce coherent microwave radiation with very low noise. LASERs (light amplification by stimulated emission of radiation) emit infrared-visible radiation of very high coherence. Although the idea of using stimulated emission to produce coherent radiation dates from the 1930s, the first maser, built by Charles Hard Townes at Columbia University, did not materialize until 1954. The basic idea was that if more particles of a medium can be placed in an excited rather than in an unexcited state, then a radiation interacting with the particles is amplified rather than absorbed because stimulated emission prevails over the absorption. The presence of a resonant cavity enhances the interaction of the particles with the radiation and allows the formation of an electro-magnetic vibratory mode.

In his first maser, Townes used a microwave transition at 23.870 GHz (= 1.25 cm) in ammonia molecules. He employed a microwave cavity with an inverted population obtained by using a quadrupole electric field to separate the excited ammonia molecules from the unexcited ammonia molecules in a beam emerging from an oven. The excited ammonia molecules enter a cavity capable of resonating at around 1.25 cm. Here they may amplify a low signal at the resonant frequency or, if sufficiently plentiful, may generate a signal. Nicolai Gennadievich Basov and Aleksandr Mikhailovich Prokhorov in Moscow arrived at the same idea as Townes at about the same time. They wanted to improve the characteristics of microwave spectroscopes. They had noticed that a medium with an inverted population had a stronger signal to noise ratio than a normal medium.

The first ammonia maser produced very monochromatic radiation with extremely low noise. In 1956, Nicolaas Bloembergen pointed out that solid state masers might be tuned and suggested a system whose energy levels depend on the strength of an imposed magnetic field, so as to permit tuning over a considerable frequency range. The system was soon put into operation by H. E. Derrick Scovil, George Feher, and Harold Seidel at Bell Telephone Laboratories.

Although the maser represented the first application of stimulated emission, and a revolutionary way to consider microwave sources, it did not have a dramatic technological application because less expensive, smaller, and simpler semiconductor devices also could emit or amplify microwave radiation with very low noise. However, Arno Penzias and Robert Wilson used a maser when they discovered the black-body cosmic background.

Lasers extend the use of stimulated emission into the visible and infrared. Townes and Arthur Schawlow gave the first thorough discussion of their operation and properties in 1958. Two years later Theodore Harold Maiman developed the first working laser by placing a rod of ruby in the center of a helical flash lamp. The two end faces of the rod were parallel to each other and silvered so as to create an optical cavity. Pulsed radiation at 6943 Å (0.69 μm) traveling along the axis of the rod was obtained by pumping with light from the flash lamp.

Soon Ali Javan and his associates at Bell Labs developed the first continuous gas laser utilizing a mixture of helium and neon. They obtained several inverted levels in neon by collision with helium atoms excited in a radiofrequency discharge. This laser emitted continuously at 3.95 μm, 1.1 μm, or 0.63 μm. It appeared that almost every substance can lase (serve as the medium of a laser). Helium-neon and ruby lasers were joined by neodymium lasers, which emit usually pulsed radiation of moderate coherence and high power at 1.06 μm, tunable lasers operable both continuously or with very short pulses, and tiny diode lasers stimulated directly by an electric current. The market now offers a hundred different lasers, some of which emit pulses as short as a few femtoseconds.

Even before lasers became practical, their possible applications were discussed. The military dreamed of secure communication channels, radar with great resolution, death rays to destroy enemy targets, and so on. Many applications of lasers have been found in medicine, chemistry, and spectroscopy. Today, lasers read and write compact discs, control mechanical processing and measurements, and send signals down optical fibers. Nonlinear optics was born with lasers. And in physics itself, lasers have been used to demonstrate Bose-Einstein condensation, the movement of molecules during chemical reactions, and other exotic phenomena. Lasers also had a profound influence on quantum mechanics with the development of quantum optics and the creation of coherent and nonclassical states.

MARIO BERTOLOTTI

LATIN AMERICA. The European invasion of the Americas produced a knowledge holocaust. We know little or nothing about the local institutions and artifacts that were destroyed. We eat tomatoes, corn, beans, and potatoes without understanding how they were developed. We have limited knowledge about the ways in which the indigenous peoples of what is now referred to as Latin America came to have zero, decimal positional numerical systems, books, accurate calendars, and an accounting for the motions of Venus. Although the pre-Columbian world possessed a rich network of knowledge-producing institutions, it would be anachronistic to call this knowledge science in the modern sense. The conquest, which brought with it the Inquisition and later legalized slavery, also brought conquerors who rejected "unscientific" knowledge.

The colonial period (roughly 1500 to 1800) saw some investigations of natural knowledge and some relevant institutional development. Gonzalo Fernández de Oviedo wrote his *Historia Natural y General de las Indias* describing the flora, fauna, and peoples known to the Spanish at that time. The Spanish founded institutions such as Cordoba University in Argentina in 1613. (The Portuguese did not create institutions at this level.) The region continued to draw European naturalists. Pehr Löfling, a disciple of Linnaeus, described the Orinoco flora. José Celestino Bruno Mutis, a Spaniard established in Colombia, continued Löfling's work. Mutis mobilized intellectuals in Nueva Granada in an Expedición Botanica. His disciples, Clement Ruiz Pabon and Juan José d'Elhuyar, visited Sweden in 1781.

Charles Townes (born 1915), inventor of the MASER, forerunner of the LASER

José Bonifácio de Andrada e Silva, a Brazilian elected to the Portuguese Academy of Sciences, worked in Europe from 1790 to 1799. Andrada e Silva carried Antoine-Laurent Lavoisier's ideas to Scandinavia. There he collected some 3500 minerals and fossils, which today are housed in the Brazilian Imperial Collection, Petrópolis. For a while he held the chair of metallurgy at Coimbra in Portugal. After Brazil became independent from Portugal in 1821, Andrada e Silva struggled to end slavery. Failing, he moved to France in 1823 and returned to science. Like Andrade e Silva, the naturalist Alexander von Humboldt had an interest in mineralogy. He stayed in Caracas in 1799 and 1800 and collected materials in Cuba, Mexico, Bolivia, Colombia, Ecuador, and Peru. He expanded the horizons of European scholars with his descriptions of the New World, in which he did not always fully acknowledge Mutis's contributions.

In the half-century following the independence of Latin American nations from Spain and Portugal (roughly 1820 to 1870), several important Europeans and North American naturalists visited the region. Alfred Russel Wallace went to the Amazon; Charles Darwin visited many parts of South America including Argentina and the Galapagos Islands; Eugenio Warming and Peter Wilhelm Lund carried out biological and paleontological studies in Lagoa Santa, central Brazil. Some of the stream of visitors stayed and contributed to the scientific and institutional growth of Latin America. An outstanding example, Fritz Müller, a Ph.D. from the University of Berlin and an M.D. from the University of Greifswald, moved to Blumenau in Brazil in 1852. He corresponded with Louis Agassiz, Max Schultze, Ernst Haeckel, and Charles Darwin. His book *Für Darwin* appeared in Leipzig in 1864 and, in an augmented English version, *Facts and Arguments for Darwin*, in London in 1869. His work on the evolution of Brazilian crustaceans provided solid support for Darwin's theory and won Müller an honorary doctorate from the University of Bonn. Nearly all of Müller's 248 published scientific works were written in Brazil.

While positivism did not receive support from European natural scientists, it had a profound impact in Latin America. Auguste Comte, positivism's founder, maintained that humanity evolved according to a law of the three stages. The most primitive of these, the theological stage, was characterized by a belief in supernatural forces. Positivists regarded Catholic Latin American countries as theological states dependent intellectually on Europe. In Argentina, President Domingo Faustino Sarmiento, who greatly contributed to the country's development, believed—under the inspiration of Comte's theory of stages modified by a Romantic evolutionary theory—that civilization was urban and European. The doctrine made it difficult for Argentinian scientists to obtain local patronage. The director of the Buenos Aires Natural History Museum, zoologist Hermann C. C. Burmeister, refused to support Florentino Ameghino, a local genius whose biological and paleontological work was known in Europe. Europeans and North Americans occupied many important posts; Benjamin A. Gould at the Cordoba Astronomical Observatory and Emil Bose at the La Plata physics institute are examples.

In Brazil, Emperor Pedro II promoted science and letters. Nevertheless, the establishment in 1889 of a positivist republic by the military left the country without universities. Military schools taught from positivist writings and fostered applied research. The Campinas Agricultural Institute, the Butantã Biological Institute, and the Institute for Technological Research (IPT) exemplify the sorts of institutions then founded. The IPT, a test center for industry and civil engineering, was founded in 1899 by Antonio Francisco Paula Souza, one of the first ministers of the Brazilian positivist republic. Medical science made outstanding advances. Oswaldo Cruz, founder of Brazilian experimental medicine, eradicated yellow fever, bubonic plague, and smallpox from Rio de Janeiro despite positivist opposition. One of the major biomedical research institutions of Latin America, the Oswaldo Cruz Foundation, bears his name.

After 1914, the influence of positivism declined throughout Latin America. This decline had many benefits. Distorting Comte's work and accepting it as absolute truth, the Latin American positivists not only had opposed the teaching of most post-Newtonian physics, including the concept of electromagnetic field and non-Euclidean geometry, but also governmental engagement in the institutional development of science and education, including the creation of universities. Their position in technical and military schools made it all the more difficult for scientific advance.

As a new way of thinking emerged, Argentine science flourished. With a per capita income greater than that of Italy or Sweden, Argentina attracted the European powers. Both the French and the Spanish promoted their own institutes and lectures in Argentina. The Germans supported physics at Emil Bose's La Plata physics institute. Bose hired Einstein's former assistant Johann Laub, the engineer Konrad Simons, and some brilliant Argentineans. Richard Gans, who had studied with Ferdinand Braun at Strasbourg, succeeded Bose in 1911. Niels Bohr noticed Gans's application of H. A. Lorentz's theory of magnetic fields to free electrons. Between 1925 and 1945 Gans taught in Germany, which gave Argentineans, including Gans's student Enrique Gaviola, who received his doctorate from Berlin in 1926, opportunities to study there. Unfortunately this flowering of Argentinean science did not last.

In Brazil, the antipositivist reaction resulted in the foundation of the Brazilian Academy of Sciences (ABC) in May 1916, supported by the Associação Brasileira de Educação (Brazilian Association for Education) and the Instituto Franco-Brasileiro de Alta Cultura (French-Brazilian Institute for Advanced Studies). ABC had its own periodical, renamed in 1929 the *Anais da Academia Brasileira de Ciências*. Its leaders included naval officer Álvaro Alberto da Mota e Silva, its president from 1935 to 1937. The opposition to positivism became public during Einstein's visit in 1925 on his way to Argentina. At Sobral, in the northeast of Brazil, the expedition coordinated by Arthur Eddington photographed the eclipse of 1919, validating the general theory of relativity. The Brazilian positivists had opposed Einstein's ideas in newspaper articles but suffered ridicule after the eclipse findings became known.

Brazilian and American agriculture prospered from international connections. In 1925 Iwar Beck-man from Sweden developed the wheat hybrid Frontana at the Alfredo Chaves experimental station in Vereanópolis, Rio Grande do Sul. This variety saved North American wheat growers after the problems caused by leaf rust in the 1940s and 1950s.

In the 1930s, after a failed revolution against the central government, the São Paulo elite created the Universidade de São Paulo (USP) as an instrument for social and economic development. A number of European researchers, including Fernand Braudel and Claude Lévi-Strauss, became USP professors. Physicist Gleb Wataghin, a Ph.D. from Turin University, also joined USP. He discovered cosmic-ray showers and developed the theory of the multiple production of cosmic rays. He trained a number of students and his group actively cooperated with Arthur Holly Compton during his cosmic-ray expedition in the 1930s.

Mexicans also participated in Compton's project. Manuel Sandoval Vallarta, who graduated from MIT in 1921 and joined its faculty, became interested in Compton's discovery of charged particles in cosmic rays. Vallarta demonstrated experimentally Oliver Heaviside's formulas for the electromagnetic propagation in conductors as well as his operational calculus.

Vallarta and his colleague at MIT, Georges Lemaître, followed up Comptons's experimental results on the effect of the earth's magnetic field on cosmic rays. Lemaître had suggested that the universe originated from one primitive atom or "cosmic egg." His work with Vallarta, which concluded that charged particles made one component of primary cosmic rays, supported the cosmic-egg theory. In 1943 Vallarta became professor of physics at the National Autonomous University of Mexico (UNAM). He had a profound influence on Mexican physics. His students include Alfredo Baños, Carlos Graef Fernandez, Luis Enrique Erro, and Marcos Moshinsky. Outside Mexico, Vallarta's most famous student was Richard Feynman.

Between 1945 and 1990, science and the state had a love-hate relationship in Latin America. On several occasions, states exiled their brightest while trying to foster science that might aid development. Under the regime of President Juan Perón, Argentina missed many opportunities to build. Immediately after World War II, Gaviola planned an atomic research institute and invited Werner Heisenberg, who accepted but never came. The international press, fearing atomic weapons in the hands of a totalitarian regime, attacked the plan. When the United States announced at the United Nations Atomic Energy Commission (UNAEC) that it was ready to retaliate against what it considered "illegal" atomic programs, and a U.S. Air Force B-29 squadron flew over Montevideo, the Perón regime dropped Gaviola's project.

This incident, combined with conflicts between Perón and the universities, made the Richter adventure possible. Austrian chemist Ronald Richter arrived in Argentina in August 1948 and convinced Perón to build laboratories at Bariloche. In March 1951, Perón announced that Richter had discovered how to control nuclear fusion. Ridiculed by the scientific community, Perón ended the project in November 1952. The nuclear field, under the leadership of Gaviola, Jorge Sabato, and José Antonio Balseiro, flourished. The Atucha 1 nuclear reactor went critical in 1967. Argentina has sold nuclear knowledge to Peru, Algeria, Turkey, Iran, and Australia.

The sort of support given nuclear physics did not recur in other areas of knowledge. Normally scientists and professors worked under pressure and even persecution. Expelled from his university, the Argentinian physiologist Bernardo Alberto Houssay went on to receive a Nobel Prize in 1947. By the mid-1970s, the universities were completely dysfunctional, 547,000 Argentineans had left the country, and an unknown number of students had disappeared.

In Brazil, constant tension existed between the government and the scientists even though both sides believed that science should contribute to development. Gradually, thanks to the Brazilian National Research Council (CNPq), research centers such as the Brazilian Center for Physics Research (CBPF) were founded according to a plan outlined at the ABC meetings in 1945. Alvaro Alberto described the requirements for the atomic age: research, mineral pros-

pecting, and proper industrial facilities for isotope production and assembly of instruments. The ABC requested that the government invest in research centers, send Brazilians abroad for training, and invite foreign scientists to visit Brazil. Nuclear relations between Brazil and the United States turned on Brazil's possession of monazite, a major source of thorium, cerium, and other rare earth metals and compounds. Brazil wanted to exchange monazite for nuclear technology. The United States responded with a systematic smuggling of the ore.

Getúlio Vargas, elected president in 1951, supported the Brazilian program of science for development. Like President Truman, Vargas considered nuclear energy an important component of industrialization. Nevertheless, the United States opposed the Brazilian program. Brazil started an independent program that included a secret agreement with occupied Germany. It collapsed in 1955, but the institutions it created became the basis of Brazilian scientific growth. In 1975, a new agreement was reached between Brazil and Germany, but Germany failed at transferring nuclear technology to Brazil.

After 1955, international cooperation in physics grew. One example is the partnership between Nordita, the Nordic Institute for Theoretical Physics headed by Bohr, and the Porto Alegre Physics Institute. In the late 1950s and early 1960s, Theodor A. J. Maris and Gerhard Jacob (president of CNPq in the 1990s) visited Nordita. Their leadership transformed Porto Alegre into a center for research on the Mössbauer effect and gamma ray correlation, two major research methods in nuclear physics. The application of these methods to solid state physics catapulted graduates from Porto Alegre into leading positions elsewhere. Other Latin Americans visited Nordita, for instance Argentinean solid-state physicist Leo Falicov, a link between Latin America and Berkeley. His best-known Porto Alegre student, Cylon E. T. Gonçalves da Silva, founded the Brazilian synchrocyclotron accelerator at Campinas.

In Mexico, President Aleman heeded the warning of Vallarta, Graef Fernandez, and others. In August 1945 he made science-for-development one of his main policies. In 1949, Vallarta moved to Mexico as full professor. Thanks to many like him, Mexico developed a unique nuclear policy that reflected views popular at the time. Many Mexicans believed that the United States's atomic monopoly increased injustice, poverty, and violation of rights. This perception led to the Tlatelolco Treaty of 1994, which renounced all military nuclear programs. Science-for-development became the enduring center of Mexican research, notably in agriculture. Supported by the Rockefeller Foundation and the Mexican Ministry of Agriculture, CIMMYT, the International Maize and Wheat Improvement Center, produced high-yield corn varieties. The Green Revolution, despite downplaying local varieties and increasing petroleum dependency, did achieve its goal of increasing global food production. Institutions modeled after CIMMYT were created in other parts of the world.

The difficulties of practicing science on the periphery may be indicated by the nominations of Latin American scientists for Nobel Prizes. In the 1920s and 1930s the Brazilian Carlos Chagas was nominated four times for the prize in medicine. In 1909 he discovered Tripanossomiase americana, identifying the disease parasite and vector. Known today as Chagas disease, it plagues over twenty million persons in at least eighteen countries. International recognition of his achievement would have translated into visibility and power at home. Envious, Afrânio Peixoto, rector of Rio de Janeiro University, mobilized attacks on Chagas. At the National Academy of Medicine, Chagas faced criticism from influential persons, and his work was not incorporated into medical education. In 1912, he received the Schaudinn Prize, awarded by the Hamburg Institute for Tropical Diseases. Yet when the Nobel Prize secretariat approached Brazilian authorities about the nomination, neither the medical community nor the politicians recommended Chagas. Other potential Brazilian Nobel candidates were Leite Lopes and Cesar Lattes.

In 1947, Bernardo Houssay was awarded the Nobel Prize for medicine (along with Carl Ferdinand and Gerty Cori). As a student, Houssay had developed a method to investigate pituitary gland hormones. He became professor of physiology in 1909, a year before receiving his degree with an award-winning dissertation. In 1943, the Peronists, in a crackdown of potential opposition, evicted him from the University of Buenos Aires. Supported by the Rockefeller Foundation and a local entrepreneur, Juan Bautista Sauberan, Houssay founded the Institute of Experimental Biology and Medicine. He continued his research on the pituitary, insulin, and diabetes; trained over 250 doctoral students; and published over two thousand scientific papers.

In 1970, Luis Federico Leloir from the Institute for Biochemical Research, Buenos Aires, received a Nobel Prize for his research on sugar nucleotides. Leloir took his M.D. in Buenos Aires in 1932 and worked in Houssay's institute until interrupted by Peronism. He moved to the Corises' biochemical laboratory at Washington University and then to David Green's experimental medicine institute at Columbia. On his return to Argentina, Leloir, like Houssay before him, founded his own institution, the Fundación Campomar (1947). The award of the Nobel Prize sheltered him

from the vicissitudes of politics and military persecution. Leloir is a role model for Argentinean scientists.

In 1984, Niels Jerne, Georges Köhler, and Cesar Milstein shared the Nobel Prize for medicine or Physiology for their work on the immune system and the production of monoclonal antibodies. Born at Bahia Blanca, Argentina, Milstein was a graduate in chemistry from the University of Buenos Aires. In 1952, he completed a Ph.D. on aldehyde dehydrogenase at the Institute of Biological Chemistry. With a fellowship from the British Council, he received a second doctorate for work on enzyme active sites with Frederick Sanger at Cambridge in 1960. In 1961, Milstein became the head of the Division of Molecular Biology at the National Institute of Microbiology, Buenos Aires. In 1963 he resigned when the military began to persecute intellectuals and scientists. Milstein returned to Cambridge and to a Nobel Prize trajectory.

As can be seen from these cases, the lack of recognition for Latin American science can have as much to do with internal factors as with external ones. Historians of science, most but not all of them from Latin America, are trying to record the rich history of which only a few examples from Mexico, Brazil, and Argentina have been presented here. Further information about these and many other cases may be found in *QUIPU*, the main Latin American journal for the history of science, founded in 1984.

REGIS CABRAL

LAW AND SCIENCE are central establishments of modern Western culture. Law directs our action in the world; science our knowledge of the world. Scientific knowledge and techniques have played an ever-increasing role in the spreading of justice in modern society. Institutions of the law have helped to clarify the character of legitimate scientific knowl-

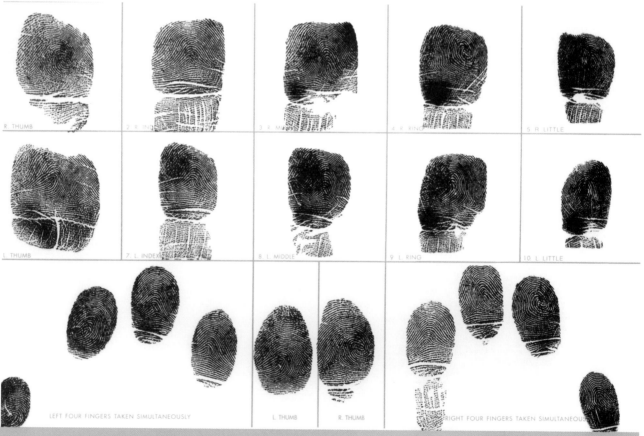

An FBI form completed with all ten fingerprints

edge and practices, and to readjust the social and institutional relations that their application required.

The law was a major patron of nineteenth-century science. Men of science served as representatives, consultants, and witnesses for the courts and the interested parties in the rising tide of litigation on matters of energy (first gas and oil, and later electricity), environment (pollution and contamination), public health (food and drug adulteration, water supply, sewage treatment), transportation, communication, mining, industry, agriculture, insurance, patents, and, of course, forensics. At the beginning of the nineteenth century, forensic experts employed only basic microscopy and toxicology; by its end, they detected stains and forgeries using infrared and ultraviolet light, differentiated human from animal blood, identified people by body shape, traced minute quantities of inorganic substances by their line spectra, reconstructed important characteristics of a corpse from partial clusters of its bones, and photographed the insides of items with X rays.

Early in the twentieth century, experts learned to identify people by their fingerprints and firearms by their ballistic prints, and to determine genetic relations by blood groups. By the end of the century, toxicology broadened to evaluate occupational exposures, public health hazards, and toxic wastes. Epidemiology grew from the study of disease transmission to accidents, birth defects, and mental illnesses. X-ray technology was joined by other medical imaging techniques, such as computerized tomography (CT), positron emission tomography (PET), and magnetic resonance imaging (MRI). Electron microscopes detected the tiniest clues of crime, and molecular biology identified people and determined their genetic relations. The twentieth century also saw a growing involvement of social scientists expert on the qualities of parenting, the causes of violence, and the validity of eyewitness testimony and repressed memories. Social scientists likewise provided statistical and methodological arguments vital for the resolution of disputes such as antitrust litigation and employment discrimination.

The criminal justice system was but one of the modes of interaction of science and law. During the nineteenth century patent law became a major mediator between the producers of scientific knowledge and those who adapted it to the various wants of society. Late in the century, the legal domain of regulation evolved to control the risks scientific knowledge and its technological products created for public safety and the environment. The twentieth century saw the continual intensification of this regulatory effort and the growth of governmental agencies to protect public health, the environment, workers, and consumers. Meanwhile, private tort law evolved to provide individuals with a way to seek compensation for scientific-technological breakdowns. In recent decades, massive legal controversies in which hundreds of thousands of claimants sought compensation for industrial accidents, polluted environments, workplace hazards, and defective products, have clogged the courts.

Twentieth-century developments in medical research, genetics, molecular biology, and their associated biotechnologies presented new legal challenges. Expanded options for contraception and abortion created one set of legal conflicts within changing public expectations about women's sexuality and liberty and the legal rights of the human fetus. Reproductive technologies such as artificial insemination, in vitro fertilization, and embryo implantation created a second set of legal conflicts for family and parenthood. Dramatic advances in surgery, organ transplantation, drug therapy, and resuscitation created a third set of legal conflicts around the questions of patients' rights and the responsibilities of the state and the medical community. Public fears and distrust of biotechnology created a fourth set of legal disputes, which have resulted more often than not in decisions favoring the interests of science and industry. The most notable instances were the patentability of genetically engineered life forms in the 1980s and their release into the environment.

The law typically refrained from intruding upon the practice, management, and dissemination of basic science. The processes of peer review, funding, teaching, publication, and laboratory and research administration ordinarily remained outside the purview of the courts. Still, in the late twentieth century courts were asked to clarify the boundaries of acceptable behavior by scientists and scientific institutions, and to adjudicate claims of fraud, misrepresentation, and misappropriation of research results; bias in peer review; and mistreatment of experimental subjects. A second avenue by which the courts became involved in the activities of basic science was litigation arising from moral and religious opposition to the purposes of modern science and challenges to the privileged status the scientific enterprise enjoys in modern culture. The attacks on nuclear energy and biotechnology by social critics are a case in point. So are the assaults on science by animal rights activists, conservationists, antiabortion groups, and creationists. In some of these cases the law cast its regulatory net over scientific practices. On the whole, though, the law continued to defer to science and has been reluctant to participate in assaults upon the scientific enterprise, or to adjudicate between science and other belief systems in ways that could obstruct the advance of science and its values.

TAL GOLAN

LIGHT, SPEED OF. Several investigators tried to measure the speed of light in the seventeenth and eighteenth centuries. Galileo, or perhaps later his followers, flashed light to an assistant, but the speed was too great to measure. In 1675, the Danish astronomer Ole Rømer noticed that intervals between eclipses of Jupiter's moons are less when Jupiter and the Earth approach each other; he correctly attributed the phenomenon to the time it takes light from Jupiter to reach the Earth. Using contemporary estimates of satellite periods and distances, Roemer calculated a velocity of 214,000 kilometers per second (k/s). James Bradley's discovery of the aberration of starlight provided a second means of estimating the speed of light, since the aberration angle depends upon the ratio of the speeds of the observer and of light. If extended to the speed of light, Bradley's calculations would have produced about 264,000 k/s.

In the nineteenth century, French physicists Armand-Hippolyte-Louis Fizeau and Jean Bernard Léon Foucault made terrestrial measurements of the speed of light by passing a beam through the gaps in a rapidly spinning toothed wheel. They obtained values of 315,300 and 298,000 k/s. The American physicist Albert A. Michelson improved on their experiments by measuring the interference fringes produced by a light beam split up in his "interferometer" and made to traverse slightly different paths through it. That raised the light velocity to 299,910 k/s (1879). Next Michelson attempted to detect the expected change in the speed of light caused by its motion through the hypothetical luminiferous ether. The surprising null result of the 1887 ether-drift experiment suggested that the speed of light is constant, independent of the speed of the emitting body. This result became a crucial element in the pedagogy, and perhaps in the discov-

The Marine Timekeeper no. 1, (1735) invented and built by John Harrison (1693–1776)

ery, of Einstein's relativity theory. Subsequent measurements of the speed of light over precisely measured distances and timed electrically ended in the spurious agreement of several sets of pre-1941 measures at 299,776 k/s. Holding Michelson in awe, followers ended their searches for flaws in their experimental apparatus when their measures agreed with his. New technologies later increased the accepted speed by nearly 17 k/s, more than four times Michelson's purported 4 k/s margin of error, to 299,792.5 k/s. Newer technology, including radiotelemetry, also improved the determination of planetary distances and the astronomical unit.

NORRISS S. HETHERINGTON

LONGITUDE is the angular distance east or west of a standard meridian, the complementary coordinate to latitude (the angular distance north or south of the equator), both used in expressing geographical location. It has been important in science because of its significance for astronomical observation and because of the influence of attempts to devise a method for finding longitude when at sea.

Various standard meridians have been determined by the position of an important observatory, a large port, or a significant geographical feature such as the Canary Islands, as used by Gerardus Mercator. The international agreement of 1884 to accept the line of longitude through Greenwich as the world's prime meridian owed much to the diligent work of astronomers at the Royal Observatory, but also reflected Britain's imperial dominance and the quality of its official sea charts.

Difference in longitude amounts to difference in local time (places distant by fifteen degrees differ by one hour). The time at a distant meridian can be found in a number of ways and compared with local time determined astronomically. A lunar eclipse, for example, might be timed, and its occurrence compared with the time given in ephemerides calculated for a standard meridian, making allowance for a variety of factors such as parallax. Galileo suggested that Jupiter's four moons, which he discovered, offered a handy celestial clock, with numerous moments of coincidence with the limb of the planet and between the moons themselves. Simultaneous timing of explosions of rockets, or direct connection by geodetic survey, provided other methods in favorable circumstances.

Methods viable on land were rarely useful at sea, where the problem of finding longitude, made acute by voyages of discovery into the Atlantic and Indian Oceans, became a synonym for the impossible. Three influential methods were proposed in the sixteenth century. The chronometer method involved the apparently simple expedient of carrying a portable watch set to standard time. Suggested by Gemma Reiner (called Frisius) in 1530, much mechanical ingenuity would be required to bring timekeepers up to the level of seagoing robustness and accuracy necessary to make this method useful. The lunar-distance method, proposed by Johann Werner in 1514, involved the measurement of the moon's position with respect to certain stars, and the calculation of standard time from the measurement via tables prepared by astronomers. At this stage, the lunar theory, the stellar positions, and the seagoing instrument to make the measurement did not exist. A third method did not depend on timekeeping but on global accounts of the distribution of magnetic variation with latitude (which could be measured directly) and longitude (which could not). Martin Cortes maintained the currency of this idea through his much-translated and republished textbook, *The Arte of Navigation* (1561).

Attempts to effect these methods led to many significant developments—from the beginnings of state-sponsored observatories in Europe to the invention of the spring-regulated watch. The most famous of the rewards offered for a solution to the longitude problem—the £20,000 prize established in Britain in 1714 to be administered by a Board of Longitude—resulted in enormous interest in the problem in the eighteenth century, and eventually the completion of both the chronometer and lunar-distance methods, seen as rivals throughout their development but used in complementary ways in the navigational practices of the nineteenth century. Both Johann Tobias Meyer (posthumously), for lunar work, and John Harrison, for a chronometer, received part rewards from the Board, Harrison's being later made up to the maximum amount by the British Parliament.

JIM BENNETT

LOW-TEMPERATURE PHYSICS. The field of low-temperature physics, or cryogenics, emerged in the late nineteenth century. In 1877, two researchers succeeded in liquefying oxygen independently within days of each other. Raoul-Pierre Pictet, a Swiss physicist, and Louis Paul Cailletet, a French mining engineer, both cooled oxygen gas under pressure, then rapidly expanded the volume to condense the gas. Cailletet soon reproduced the feat with nitrogen. In 1895, Carl von Linde in Germany and William Hampson in England developed a method for industrial-scale production of liquid air, which aided subsequent cryogenics research. The three leading low-temperature laboratories—at the University of Leiden (under Heike Kamerlingh Onnes), the University in Cracow (Karol Olszewski), and the Royal Institution in London james Dewar)—engaged in a race to lower temperatures and the liquefaction of hydrogen and, after its discovery on Earth in 1895, helium. In 1898, Dewar won the race for hydrogen, using a variation on Linde's technique to reach about 20° Kelvin. In 1908, Kamerlingh Onnes used liquid hydrogen to cool helium enough to condense it at low pressure, at around 5° K. The Leiden laboratory thereafter enjoyed a fifteen-year monopoly in the production of liquid helium.

The early history of cryogenics illustrates the proliferation of academic research laboratories in the late nineteenth century, and their move into fields requiring such relatively expensive apparatus. The work involved chemists, engineers, skilled glassblowers, and instrument makers as well as physicists. Kamerlingh Onnes's success with liquid helium owed as much to his ability to form a team with physical, mechanical, and chemical expertise as to his high standards of experimental precision and keen grasp of thermodynamic and electromagnetic theory.

Cryogenics demonstrates the interpenetration of industry and science in the second industrial revolution—in particular, the budding refrigeration industry, which had emerged as a rival to natural ice in the late nineteenth century, especially for brewing lager beer and shipping meat to Europe from Argentina and New Zealand. Industrial uses of liquid air and its components, such as liquid oxygen for oxyacetylene blowtorches, spurred the formation of firms such as Linde Air (founded by von Linde), British Oxygen Company, and L'Air Liquide. Dewar's development of a silvered, double-walled flask with an intervening vacuum led quickly to a commercial market in thermos bottles (although Dewar failed to patent his flask). Kamerlingh Onnes had ties to Dutch industry. The industrial relevance of low-temperature research induced national governments to sponsor it in their standards laboratories such as the U.S. National Bureau of Standards and the German Physikalisch-Technische Reichsanstalt (PTR).

Academic physicists instigated their own low-temperature programs. The elucidation of specific heats at low temperatures, explored by Dewar and extended by Walther Nernst and F. A. Lindemann, provided important evidence for the fledgling quantum theory before World War I and helped establish low-temperature research as a fruitful field of physics. Pyotr Kapitsa's investigation of magnetic effects at low temperatures in Cambridge, which he continued in Moscow, and William Giauque's work on magnetic cooling and specific heats in Berkeley illustrate the spread of low-temperature physics in the 1930s. Cryogenic techniques would find application after World War II in the production of the first thermonuclear fusion weapons, in rocket propellants, and in bubble chambers for particle physics experiments. The volatile liquids and high pressures of cryogenics required elaborate safety precautions, although they did not always prevent catastrophic explosions.

Two important lines of research emerged from peculiar phenomena observed at low temperatures. In 1911, Kamerlingh Onnes and his collaborators found that electrical resistance in mercury suddenly vanished at 4° K. This "superconductivity," as Kamerlingh Onnes called it, puzzled theorists for decades. In 1933, Walther Meissner and Robert Ochsenfeld at the PTR in Berlin found that magnetic induction as well as electrical resistance disappears in a superconductor, and hence showed that superconductivity included more than its name indicated. In 1957, John Bardeen, Leon Cooper, and John Schrieffer of the University of Illinois produced a satisfactory microscopic explanation of superconductivity, based on quantum mechanical coupling of electrons with opposite spin.

Superconductivity promised spectacular technological applications in low-loss electrical power transmission and high-power superconducting electromagnets. But known materials that exhibited superconductivity proved too fragile for power transmission; and, like heat, high magnetic fields, as in electromagnets, destroy the superconductive state. Hopes for new technologies rekindled with the discovery of so-called type II superconductivity in 1961, which persevered in the presence of magnetic fields, and then flared anew with the announcement in the mid-1980s of a class of ceramic materials that stayed superconductive at temperatures up to 100° K.

The second peculiar phenomenon that stemmed from observations by Kamerlingh Onnes was a drop of density in liquid helium below about 2° K. With the spread of low-temperature physics, unexpected results with liquid helium began to accumulate, suggesting two different states of helium: normal helium I and low-temperature helium II. In 1937 and 1938 several physicists established that the viscosity as well as the density of helium II seemed to vanish, and that it could form a thin film that swept up the sides of vessels; Kapitza termed the effect "superfluidity." In 1955 Richard Feynman arrived at a microscopic theory of superfluidity based on quantization of vortices in the fluid. The theories of both superconductivity and superfluidity rely on interactions among individual particles or atoms; Pauli's exclusion principle does not apply, and Bose-Einstein statistics instead of Fermi-Dirac statistics govern the behavior. In other words, superconductivity and superfluidity are macroscopic quan-

L

Heike Kamerlingh Onnes (1853–1926), Dutch physicist, was the first man to liquefy helium.

tum phenomena; hence their novelty and interest, and the difficulty in accommodating them within physical theory.

PETER J. WESTWICK

LYSENKO AFFAIR. Lysenkoism was a doctrine of heredity espoused by the Soviet agronomist Trofim Denisovich Lysenko that contradicted modern genetics. Lysenko began propagating his views in the 1930s, gradually winning the support of many journalists, educators, administrators, and officials of the secret police. In 1940, Lysenko's most prominent opponent, the internationally known geneticist Nikolai Vavilov, was arrested; he died three years later in prison. In 1948, Lysenko won a complete victory by gaining the backing of Stalin and the Soviet government. Departments of genetics in universities and research institutes were forced to follow the new official view. Lysenko became the autocrat of Soviet biology, often casting his critics as traitors to the Soviet Union. Several thousand Soviet biologists opposing him were arrested. Not until 1965, after the fall of his supporter Nikita Khrushchev, was Lysenko finally overthrown.

Commentators in the West commonly explain Lysenko's influence by a consonance between his support for the doctrine of the inheritance of acquired characteristics and Soviet ideological desires to "create a new Soviet man." If people can inherit improvements acquired from the social environment, so the argument goes, then revolutionary changes in society can quickly result in the improvement of human beings. This explanation cannot stand. Lysenko believed in the inheritance of acquired characteristics in plants and animals, but he opposed applying his views to humans; he regarded attempts to alter human heredity as examples of bourgeois influence on science. All of Lysenko's work concerned plants and animals of agricultural value, including wheat, tomatoes, potatoes, corn, chickens, and dairy cows. His rise to prominence was linked to his efforts to aid Soviet agriculture at a time when forced collectivization had lowered productivity. None of his nostrums led to genuine improvement of agriculture. Rather, his monopoly of Soviet biology for several decades prevented the Soviet Union from receiving the agricultural benefits of modern genetics.

Lysenko's unsophisticated biological views were embodied in a vague "theory of nutrients" that assigned primary importance to the environment in the determination of heredity. He denied the existence of genes and disputed the importance of DNA. He regarded heredity as a property of the "entire organism." He claimed to have changed several species of plants into new ones by manipulating environmental conditions, claims that many biologists at the time recognized as false. Most of his methods, however, were less ambitious; for example, his attempt to accelerate the maturation of crops by soaking seeds before planting. Soviet administrators liked this approach because, if successful, it might allow harvesting before the fall frosts that plagued Soviet agriculture. Lysenko's most costly, even disastrous, biological experiments came toward the end of his career, when he caused severe damage to the dairy industry by breeding pedigreed cows with less valuable bulls, canceling the results of generations of careful animal husbandry.

China developed a Lysenkoist movement in the early phases of Mao Tse-Tung's rule. Between 1949 and 1956, a period in which Chinese leaders copied Soviet policies, Lysenkoism was the only officially sanctioned approach to genetics. Led by Luo Tianyu, a plant breeder in the Beijing area, Chinese Lysenkoism stressed populist and nativist themes, ascendant since the 1949 revolution, and won political favor more for these reasons that for any imagined contribution to agricultural technology. Mao's brief "Hundred Flowers" campaign of relative intellectual openness in 1956 sent Lysenkoism into permanent eclipse. The cost of Chinese Lysenkoism was delay in the deployment of orthodox genetics in agriculture rather than destruction of the sort wrought by the parent movement in the USSR.

LOREN R. GRAHAM

L

MAD COW DISEASE. In 1986, Bovine Spongiform Encephalopathy (BSE) was described in the United Kingdom and dubbed "Mad Cow Disease" because the infectious agent caused brain tissue to become sponge-like and make the animal "mad." Ten years later, after thousands of cows had been infected and prematurely slaughtered so that they would not enter the human food chain, a new human disease appeared. Fifteen young U.K. residents were diagnosed with a similar brain-wasting condition, variant Creutzfeldt-Jakob disease (vCJD). CJD had been known for some time.

During its first five years of named existence, vCJD had struck ninety-six people in the United Kingdom as of June 2001, and perhaps two or three elsewhere. Ninety percent of the world's 180,900 cases of BSE had occurred in the UK. That prompted the scientific community to conclude that "the most likely way people got vCJD was from eating tainted beef."

BSE aroused scientific and policy debate for some years. In 1996, some warned that the Mad Cow crisis would be the AIDS epidemic the UK never had. In 2000, when the disease migrated to continental Europe, the *Frankfurter Allgemeine* compared it to Europe's Black Death of the fourteenth century.

Mad Cow Disease became a continuing problem not only because of the threat to animal health—a real threat that claimed the lives of thousands of cattle—but also because of the scientific uncertainty of the length of incubation, the presence of the infective agent, and the actual vector of transmission. Scientists still do not know how people get vCJD in the first place. A recent report of the House of Lords again pointed to eating beef as the most probable assumption.

United Nations agencies responded to the challenge through the Office of International Epizootes (OIE), the Food and Agriculture Organization (FAO), and the World Health Organization (WHO), which created policies to eliminate the threat to animal and human health. Since the consensus held that the disease originated from feeding infectious animal products to cattle, the practice was stopped, surveillance implemented, and certain beef and beef products banned.

The infectious agent responsible for the disease could be a self-replicating protein called a prion. Or, what many believe more likely, it could be viral-like, with nucleic acids carrying genetic information. The agent cannot be identified easily in live animals or humans since it resides mainly in the central nervous system. Science has hedged its bets about the risk of BSE to humans: "theoretical," "hypothetical," "negligible," "remote," and "incalculably small" were the terms used to describe the risk to humans. But the loss to agriculture, trade, and other industries has been almost incalculably large, some $20 billion according to recent estimates. Some believe the response has extended well beyond the threat to human health.

The case of Mad Cow Disease illustrates how modern society blurs facts and fears. Fears generated by the BSE crisis spilled over to genetically modified foods, biomedical research, and other scientific programs. The episode also highlights some of the challenges of globalization. Multilateral organizations and multinational companies provide the resources for protecting public health, but public fear and emotion often impede reason and appropriate policy responses.

SCOTT C. RATZAN

MAGNETO-OPTICS. The effects of magnetic fields on light have had an importance for physical theory far beyond their significance in nature since their first detection in 1845. That occurred because William Thomson, Lord Kelvin, inferred from Michael Faraday's ideas about electricity and his own ideas about light that glass stressed by an electric field should rotate the plane of polarized light passing through it. Faraday looked, found nothing, and substituted a magnetic field, which worked. Success prompted a characteristic leap; Faraday inferred that magnetism could be concentrated, as it had been in the experiment, by materials other than ferromagnetics. This insight, the first spin-off from a magneto-optical effect, led him to the discoveries of para- and diamagnetism.

In 1862, Faraday sought to change the spectrum of a light source by placing it in a magnetic field. No luck. But the fact that he had tried encouraged a repetition some thirty years later. Pieter Zeeman had just obtained his doctorate from the University of Leyden with a prize-winning thesis on a second magneto-optic effect, the change in polarization of plane-polarized light reflected from an electromagnet. In 1896, Zeeman saw the bright yellow lines of sodium broaden when he placed their source in a magnetic field. He brought this news to his professor, Hendrik Antoon Lorentz. From his own model for the emission of light, in which the radiator is an "ion" of unknown charge e and mass m, Lorentz predicted that the broadened lines should be resolvable into triplets polarized in certain ways and separated by a distance proportional to e/m. Zeeman confirmed the prediction and deduced the value of e/m. It came out close to the number that Joseph John Thomson had found for the ratio of charge to mass of cathode-ray particles. The "Zeeman effect" played a major part in the establishment of the electron as a building block of matter. Zeeman and Lorentz shared the Nobel Prize for physics in 1902.

Most Zeeman patterns differ from Lorentz's triplet. Explaining quartets, quintets, and so on proved too much for both classical and early quantum theories of atomic structure and spectral emission. After World War I, demobilizing physicists found the "anomalous Zeeman effect," which most of them had ignored, high among the outstanding problems of atomic physics as described in Arnold Sommerfeld's comprehensive survey, *Atombau and Spektrallinien* (1919).

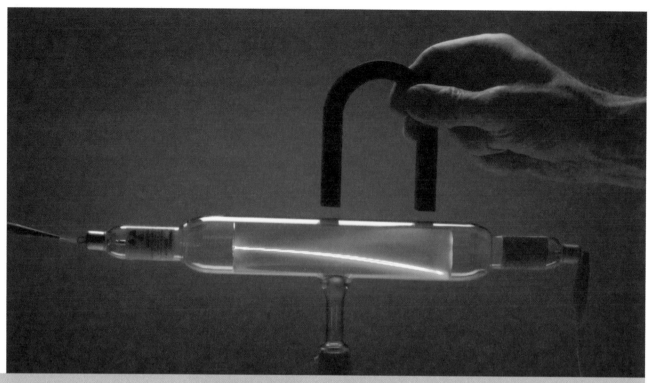

A magnet appears to bend light in a cathode ray tube.

Lorentz's theory derived the magnitude of the line splitting from *g*, the ratio of the magnetic moment to the orbital angular momentum of the radiating electron. Alfred Landé, a young Jewish theorist at the University of Frankfurt am Main, managed to refer the refractory splitting to an anomalous value of *g* and to accepted rules for quantum transitions. Attempts to derive the anomalous *g* from an atomic model failed until the introduction of electron spin in 1925

Claude-Louis Berthollet (1748–1822), French doctor and chemist

by Samuel Goudsmit and George Uhlenbeck, young Dutch physicists who, like Landé, made their careers in the United States. Meanwhile, analysis of the systematics of quantum transitions in the anomalous effect helped to guide Wolfgang Pauli to the most striking of all the discoveries prompted by magneto-optical phenomena: the "Exclusion Principle," which ascribes four quantum numbers to each electron in an atom and prohibits any two electrons from having the same values for all their quantum numbers. Pauli's fourth quantum number was soon associated with Goudsmit and Uhlenbeck's spin. Particles that, like electrons, are exclusive, divide the universe with particles that, like photons, are gregarious. Both sorts have revealed much when under the influence of a magnetic field.

J. L. HEILBRON

MASS ACTION. The law of mass action expresses the mathematical relationship between the quantities of the substances present at the beginning of a chemical reaction in which they participate and the quantities of both reactants and products present when the reaction has reached an equilibrium. Although formulated in essentially its present form as an equation during the late nineteenth century, its underlying concept goes back to around 1800 and the French chemist Claude Louis Berthollet.

Eighteenth-century chemists organized much of their cumulative knowledge of the chemical operations they could carry out in their laboratories in the form of tables of "rapports" or "affinities" which they also sometimes called "elective attractions." These tables expressed in highly compressed form the order in which substances would replace each other in combination with a third substance. In the case of interactions or "double decompositions" between two neutral salts, the affinity tables expressed the direction in which this exchange took place. The Swedish chemist Torbern Bergman published the most complete affinity table of the century in 1778. He performed thousands of experiments to gather the information arranged in it. In some cases, the exchange seemed to go in the opposite direction from the expected order. Heating the substances, for example, disrupted the order established by operations carried out in solution at room temperature; but Bergman believed that more careful control and further experimentation would suffice to eliminate these apparent inconsistencies.

Berthollet encountered similar anomalies, some of which referred to the insolubility or volatility of a product, which removed it from the solution. Moreover, the normal direction of a chemical change could often be overcome by adding much greater amounts of one of the products. Berthollet concluded that chemical changes do not go to completion except when one or more of the products is removed; otherwise the proportion between the initial and final products depends on their relative masses as well as their affinities.

Berthollet connected these views with a belief that chemical compounds exist in indefinite proportions in solution. When the acceptance of John Dalton's atomic theory discredited this belief, some of Berthollet's contemporaries inferred that his views on mass action were untenable; others, however, including the influential Jöns Jacob Berzelius, could separate these ideas. For several decades chemists regarded Berthollet's mass action as a competitor to Bergman's affinities. The issue appeared chemically insoluble, because the relative quantities of each substance present in a solution could not be determined without applying reagents that themselves disturbed the equilibrium.

In 1862, Marcellin Berthelot and Péan de Saint-Gilles devised an effective way to test Berthollet's concept of mass action by studying the very slow chemical reaction between an alcohol and an organic acid to form an ester and water. At intervals they removed small portions of the solution and titrated the acid with a base without affecting the reaction sensibly. Their results strongly confirmed Berthollet's mass action and stimulated two Norwegian chemists, Cato Guldberg and Peter Waage, to make similar determinations using particularly sluggish inorganic reactions. Guldberg and Waage obtained results analogous to those of the French team and in 1864 published a mathematical law of mass action, which they subsequently simplified. By 1879, they had arrived at the form of the law that has been used ever since.

FREDERIC LAWRENCE HOLMES

MASS SPECTROGRAPH. The mass spectrograph is an electromagnetic instrument for separating ions on the basis of their charge to mass ratio (e/m), and hence for studying their mass and chemical nature. In 1912, Joseph John Thomson and his assistant Francis Aston, analyzing positive rays (ions that stream through a hole in the cathode of a gas-discharge tube), discovered an ion closely associated with that of neon, atomic mass 20, but corresponding to mass 22. For several years identification of this ion as a compound, a new element, or an isotope of neon remained uncertain, but from 1913, Frederick Soddy actively promoted it as evidence of isotopes in nonradioactive substances.

The subsequent development of the mass spectrograph is intimately connected with Soddy's concept of isotopes and the Rutherford-Bohr atom. The first instruments, invented by Arthur Dempster in Chicago in 1918 and Aston in Cambridge in 1919, both attempted to separate isotopes unambiguously using variations on Thomson's positive-ray apparatus. But it was Aston, working in the Cavendish Laboratory at Cambridge under Ernest Rutherford, whose name became linked with the mass spectrograph.

The two instruments relied on different focusing techniques and produced different types of results. In Aston's mass spectrograph perpendicular electric and magnetic fields focused ions with different masses at different points on a photographic plate. Aston identified and measured the atomic weights of a large number of isotopes; established the "whole number rule" for atomic weights (that isotopic masses are integral multiples of that of hydrogen, then known only as a single isotope of mass 1); and, with his second instrument of 1925, measured deviations from this rule, the "packing fraction" of nuclei (a measure of the mass equivalent of the energy binding the constituents of a nucleus together). He received the Nobel Prize for chemistry in 1922 for his work. Mass spectrographs are used extensively for accurate atomic weight determination.

Dempster's instrument, which Aston refused to call a "mass spectrograph" because it provided a momentum rather than mass spectrum, established a tradition of "mass spectrometers." In this design, a magnetic field perpendicular to the plane of a beam of ions causes them to move in a circle whose radius depends on the mass and velocity of the particles. In half a turn around a narrow vacuum chamber, ions of the same mass and velocity can be caught in a cup, the others having ended in the walls of the chamber. Dempster used a quadrant electrometer to detect them in the cup quantitatively. By varying the accelerating potential he selected different ions and measured their relative abundance. Although he failed to distinguish unambiguously between the hypothetical isotopes of magnesium and chlorine, Dempster opened the way for accurate abundance determinations and subsequently discovered many isotopes.

From the mid-1920s on several different types of mass spectrograph have been developed to meet the needs of spectroscopists, atomic-weight chemists, and radioactivists. The most important of these instruments were those of Kenneth Bainbridge (1933), who provided the first experimental proof of the Einstein mass-energy relationship, and Alfred Neir, who introduced a 60-degree (rather than 180-degree) analyzer in 1940. In the 1930s and 1940s physicists invented other electromagnetic means of separating ions: time-of-flight, radio-frequency, and cyclotron-resonance instruments in particular. By this time isotopes had become fundamental to many physical sciences, commercial instruments were available, and the earlier distinction between mass spectrographs and spectrometers had been lost as mass spectrometry became established as a central technique in an era of increasing reliance on instrumentation.

ISOBEL FALCONER

MATERIALS SCIENCE. Although materials have long been objects of scientific inquiry—Galileo discussed the strength of beams in his *Two New Sciences* (1638)—the academic discipline of materials science appeared only recently. The mechanics of elastic bodies, which developed as a kind of mixed science, became an integral part of the program of experimental philosophy developed by Robert Hooke at the Royal Society, by Edmé Mariotte in France, and by Jakob Bernoulli in Switzerland. Only in retrospect, however, can we identify these studies of the mechanical properties of wood or iron as a protoscience of materials. The generic notion of materials is a fairly recent invention. The new discipline emerged around 1960 when the departments of metallurgy of a number of academic institutions were renamed "metallurgy and materials science" and a few years later materials science emerged as an autonomous entity.

This linguistic change reflected an inner evolution of metallurgy toward the determination of crystalline structures.

Beginning with the study of crystals by X-ray diffraction (1913), the determination of microstructure became the prime concern of physical metallurgy. The notions of crystal lattices, dislocation, and defect proved key to understanding the macroscopic behavior of metals. The connections between microstructure and mechanical properties were probed, and the models and theories elaborated by physicists put to work for designing new materials.

X-ray diffraction techniques gave precise atomic pictures of solids, and quantum mechanics provided the theoretical foundations for their further description. The solid state became an object of investigation in itself. Solid-state physicists discriminated between properties depending on the idealized crystal pattern and properties dependent on "accidents" of the inner arrangement or of the surface of the solid. This stress on structure-sensitive properties in the study of crystals turned the subject toward materials science.

A solid is not a material, however. The notion of materials combines physical and chemical properties with social needs and industrial or military interests. This hybrid concept implies that knowing and producing cannot be separated. Significantly, the discipline that emerged in the 1960s has been named "materials science and engineering" (MSE).

The generic notion of materials first appeared in the language of policy makers and referred to a bottleneck holding up advances in space and military technologies. The idea that all materials were strategic emerged during the Cold War in the United States in response to *Sputnik*. Designers sought high-performance materials with previously unknown properties for use in extreme circumstances. The Department of Defense's Advanced Research Project Agency (ARPA) invested heavily in academic research on materials and created interdisciplinary laboratories equipped with expensive instruments to prompt joint research involving metallurgists; chemical, electrical, and mechanical engineers; chemists; solid-state physicists; and electronics specialists. This program created the research field of MSE, at this stage mainly an American science. In Europe, a number of materials science centers grew out of former metallurgy departments, but materials did not become a political concern and solid-state chemistry emerged more prominently.

In the 1970s, new social priorities reoriented academic research from military to civilian goals. Environmental and safety legislation, together with economic competition with Japan, put new demands on material scientists. Materials science was now conceived as a response to "man's needs." While the U.S. federal budget for research and development stagnated, industrial companies became more engaged and

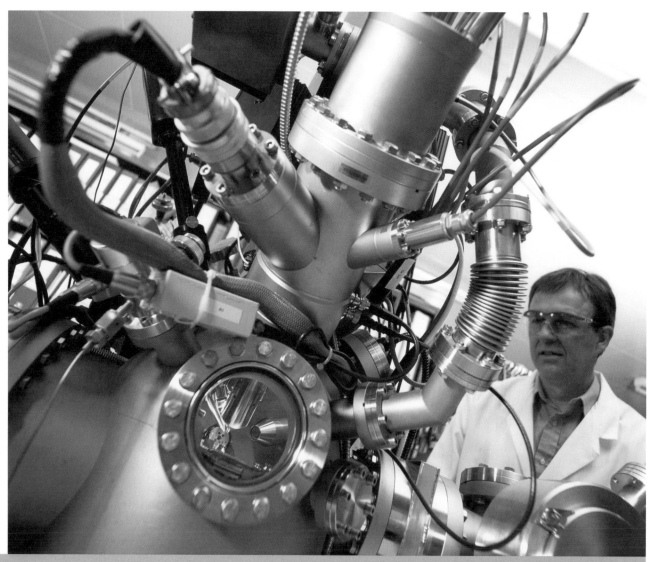

A secondary ion mass spectrometer, subjects ionized molecules abraded from a surface to a time-of-flight measurement, which determines their acceleration and thence their mass.

research became more concerned with process. The interrelation of structures and properties with functions and processes, visually represented by a tetrahedron in many textbooks, provided the conceptual framework for MSE and helped to make it an established, teachable discipline. Courses in MSE proliferated in engineering schools, an annual review of materials science started (1971), and a Materials Research Society (1973) and a European Materials Research Society (1983) appeared.

At the same time the leadership that physicists and metallurgists had exerted passed to chemists. Development of composite materials made of a matrix reinforced with fibers acted as a driving force in the formation of the discipline. Unlike conventional mass-produced plastics, composite materials are shaped to achieve specific functions and respond to specific demands. They offer the paradigm of "materials by design," a product of science and technology working together. Composites technology reinforced thinking in terms of four variables—structure, properties, performance, and processes; changes made in any of them can have a significant effect on the performance of the whole system and require a rethinking of the entire device. The traditional linear approach—given a set of functions find the properties required and design the structure combining them—gave way to a systems approach aided by computer simulation. The synergy between the four composite material variables called for a synergy between various specialists and a new organization of labor in project teams.

In the 1990s, academic research regained dominance. Following a drastic reduction of technical staff at most industrial companies, many industrial researchers joined university laboratories. MSE continued to diversify. Part of the materials science community shifted from microscale to nanoscale analysis. Instruments, which had already played a decisive role in the emergence of MSE with X-ray diffraction in the 1920s and the transmission electron microscope in the 1950s, once again proved crucial: the scanning tunneling microscope and the atomic force microscope allow not only the visualization but also the manipulation of individual atoms. With nanotechnology, materials are no longer carved like a statue out of a block of marble but by bonding atoms or groups of atoms. The key step becomes the assembly of building blocks.

In the 1990s, materials scientists suddenly became interested in mollusk shells, insect cuticles, algae, and spider silk. These composite structures, associating the hard and the soft, combining inorganic and organic components, capable of high performance, appeared as models for human technology in three respects. They are models of functional materials, optimally performing several functions including growth, repair, and recycling. They are models of structure: the remarkable properties of bulk materials such as bone or wood result from a complex arrangement at different levels, each controlling the next; the hierarchy of structures from the molecular to the macroscopic appears as a mark of the superiority of nature's design over human engineering. Finally nature assembles components at low energy cost, teaching lessons in processing. Biomimetics thus became a fashionable topic covering projects ranging from the design of a shield inspired by the layered structure of the abalone shell to the development of genetically engineered materials such as artificial spider silk. More importantly, biomaterials inspired the emergence of a new style of chemistry, *chimie douce,* concerned with reactions at ambient temperature in open reactors resembling reactions occurring in biological systems.

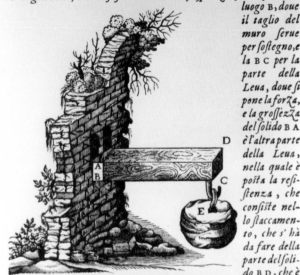

A diagram illustrating Galileo's theory of the strength of beams, from his *Two New Sciences* (1638)

Nanotechnology and biomimetics disrupt rather than reinforce the fragile coherence of the mixed discipline of MSE. The field is imploding. Its territory is dismembered into many research areas concerned with different scales and kinds of structures. The frontiers of MSE border bio-engineering and artificial intelligence. Materials scientists follow divergent epistemic practices. Some advocate rational design by computer simulation. They want to build up a material by computer calculations *ab initio,* starting with the most fundamental information about the atoms and using the most basic rules of physics. Others apply a combinatorial approach, developed initially in the pharmaceutical industry. It calls for the simultaneous synthesis of a large array of compounds at once, screened to detect and select interesting structures. Despite their differences, both strategies look exceedingly systematic when compared with the semiempirical methods chosen by scientists who encourage new materials to assemble themselves. Again two different pathways may be distinguished. Some scientists engineer bacteria, while others try the chemical route. Whether materials science will split into branches integrated into established disciplines or become a discipline of its own, pioneering a new style of science, the future will tell. Meanwhile MSE functions as a laboratory to test new frontiers in science.

BERNADETTE BENSAUDE-VINCENT

MECHANICAL PHILOSOPHY. Many seventeenth-century natural philosophers sought to explain all physical properties and processes in terms of the motion of the least parts of

DISCOURS

DE LA METHODE

Pour bien conduire fa raifon, & chercher
la verité dans les fciences.

PLUS

LA DIOPTRIQVE.

LES METEORES.

ET

LA GEOMETRIE.

Qui font des effais de cete METHODE.

A LEYDE
De l'Imprimerie de IAN MAIRE.
cI) I) c XXXVII.
Avec Privilege.

Title page of the *Discourse on Method* (1637) and its illustrative essays by René Descartes. The essays sketch out a mechanical and mathematical world view.

matter of which physical bodies are composed. They usually referred to these least parts as corpuscles so as not to confuse the mechanical position with the type of ancient atomism that Pierre Gassendi had tried to revive early in the century. Although the mechanical philosophers (or corpuscularians) agreed in rejecting Aristotelian philosophy and most of the mystical elements associated with Renaissance naturalism, they divided over the positive formulation of their position. "Mechanical philosophy" is a cover term for a continuum of positions from a pure kinetic theory of motion on one end to a robust matter theory on the other. These variations can be seen in the works of René Descartes, Francis Bacon, Galileo, Robert Boyle, and Isaac Newton.

Descartes maintained in his *Discourse on Method* (1637) that matter is pure extension, from which it followed that there could be no empty space; that all motion must result from direct contact; and that all change must be change of place (local motion). Descartes concluded that any property possessed by a material body had to arise from the motion imposed on the matter it contained by an external source. All physical processes, therefore, were to be explained by the laws of motion that the least parts of matter obey. Only the human soul escaped mechanical explanation. The world was a vast machine made up of smaller machines (including human and animal bodies) consisting of inert particles moved by physical necessity. Although Descartes located the origin of motion in God, his principles of inertia and the plenum allowed him to describe a deterministic system where, on impact, motion is transferred but not destroyed.

Cartesianism dominated corpuscularism throughout the seventeenth and into the eighteenth centuries, but it had several strong competitors. In his *Novum organum* (1620),

Bacon advocated explanations in terms of the motion of matter. In his investigation of heat, for example, he concluded that bodies feel warm when the particles of matter that compose them move rapidly. Unlike the later Cartesians, however, Bacon insisted that experimental and observational techniques had to be developed to discover the true nature of the particles responsible for such qualities. Galileo's *Assayer* (1623) offered a similar account of motion as the cause of heat, and his *Discourse on the Two New Sciences* (1638) presented detailed experimental studies of mechanical subjects. Both Bacon and Galileo brought the practices of craftsmen and mechanics to bear on natural philosophical issues. In this tradition, the mechanical philosophy helped to elevate the intellectual, social, and economic status of the technical arts.

Many natural philosophers in England in the generation after Bacon took his works as their model. Boyle followed Bacon's experimental program and believed in the Baconian ideal of useful knowledge. Writing in the 1660s, Boyle was also influenced by the works of Descartes, Gassendi, and Galileo, and introduced the term "mechanical philosophy" in 1674 to refer to all explanations of physical phenomena in terms of matter and motion. Unlike philosophers before him, however, Boyle tried to use chemical analysis to turn the mechanical philosophy into an experimentally based theory of matter. He also elaborated upon the distinction, first introduced by Galileo, of the primary and secondary qualities of bodies. In *The Origin of Forms and Qualities* (1666), Boyle maintained that quantifiable properties, such as size and shape, are primary because all material bodies possess them. Other qualities, such as color or texture, arise in us in consequence of the particular configurations of corpuscles in the bodies that we see or touch.

Newtonian or classical mechanics is often taken as the paradigm of mechanical explanation. Yet in his *Principia mathematica* (1687), Newton upset the mechanical philosophy by introducing the concept of force. Unlike Descartes and Boyle, for whom force amounted to the pressure of one body on another, Newton's force was the measure of the change in motion of a moving body. Thus he added a third element to the original principles of matter and motion. At first mechanical philosophers, especially Cartesians, rejected Newtonian forces as a throwback to sympathies and antipathies. But his scheme gradually gained acceptance as mathematicians succeeded in deploying gravitational force to ever finer phenomena and other examples of distance forces turned up in electricity and magnetism.

Following Newton's achievements, mechanical conceptions came to be applied to all areas of learning, not always with advantage. Ernst Mayr, for example, in *The Growth of Biological Thought* (1982), argued that reliance upon mechanics advanced physical sciences but led to the neglect of the biological ones. This assessment can of course be extended to the human sciences as well. Sociologists and psychologists in the nineteenth and twentieth centuries often attempted to find deterministic laws covering the behavior of groups and of individuals.

At a more global level, some have argued that ecological disaster can be attributed, at least in part, to mechanistic ideas of nature. In *The Death of Nature* (1980), Carolyn Merchant put forward the still controversial thesis that with the mechanical philosophy scientific inquiry became a masculine activity imposed upon a passive, feminine nature. According to Merchant, this attitude set the stage for, and ultimately justified, the "rape" of nature.

ROSE-MARY SARGENT

M

MECHANICS. If bodies move, forces move them; if they are in equilibrium, opposing forces hold them at rest; for mechanical devices to work, there must be forces of both sorts. Motion, forces, and machines have been the subject of two distinct sciences: the science of motion, and mechanics. In the Aristotelian tradition, the science of motion belonged to physics, or natural philosophy, the science of natural bodies "insofar as they are natural." Aristotle opposed natural motion (a falling rock) to violent motion (a weight raised by a pulley). Violent motions and the machines that created them were the concern of the mechanical arts—acting *against* nature for practical ends—and of mechanics, or the science of weights. The division of mechanics into manual or practical, and rational or theoretical, goes back to Pappus of Alexandria in the early fourth century A.D. and was current thirteen hundred years later.

The Renaissance inherited many important achievements in rational mechanics, including the parallelogram rule for the composition and resolution of motions, early forms of the principles of virtual work and of virtual velocities, demonstrations of the law of the straight and angular lever, an embryonic notion of moment (torque), and determination of centers of gravity. Equally important was the understanding that geometrical demonstration was essential to mechanical theory. This legacy underpinned the evolution of mechanics in the early modern period. Simon Stevin and Galileo simplified Archimedes' proof of the law of the lever; Christiaan Huygens devised a more rigorous proof (1693). Galileo used the angular lever and the notion of moment to determine equilibrium conditions on the inclined plane (*Le meccaniche*, c. 1593).

The parallelogram rule for motions uses geometrical displacements straightforwardly. Not so the corresponding rule for forces, because it is not obvious what their "composition" and "resolution" mean. Following the work of Stevin and others, Pierre Varignon based his theory of equilibrium on the rule for forces (*Projet de la nouvelle mécanique*, 1687). Isaac Newton recognized its indispensability, and cannily prepared for his own proof of the rule in the *Philosophiae naturalis principia mathematica* (1687) by stipulating in his second Law of Motion that every change in motion caused by an impressed force takes place "along the straight line in which the force is impressed." This ensured *by definition* the geometrical equivalence of the rules for forces and motions. As for the principle of work, Newton claimed that it depends on the equality of action and reaction (Law III). In René Descartes's formulation of the principle of mechanical work, the same force that raises one hundred pounds through two feet will raise two hundred pounds through one foot (and so on). This he used effectively in short treatises on machines he sent in 1637 to Marin Mersenne and Constantijn Huygens.

These examples belong to "rational mechanics" as understood by Pappus. They remind us that the major figures, better known for their contributions to the science of motion, also contributed to mechanics, though their thinking in these areas revealed the conceptual fluidity characteristic of pivotal transformations in the development of science. Two contrasting signs of this fluidity were the creative coupling of principles from both sciences, and indecisiveness about the relations between mechanics and physics. Galileo corroborated his law of free fall through experiments on the inclined plane, and the equilibrium conditions on the inclined plane played key roles in the formal demonstration of the law in the Third Day (or part) of his *Discourses concerning Two New Sciences* (1638). In the fourth part, Galileo used the law of fall and the composition rule to demonstrate the parabolic path of projectiles, a result he obtained and confirmed experimentally around 1608. Apart from certain medieval innovations in the geometrization of natural motion, natural philosophy had not been mathematical, whereas mechanics had never been anything else. Galileo decisively blurred that dichotomy by showing that natural motions could be given mathematical descriptions in accord with experiment and mechanical principles. Still, he would have agreed that *Le meccaniche* belonged in a different disciplinary pigeonhole from the third and fourth part of his *Discourses*.

In *Principia philosophiae* (1644), Descartes set out his pioneering three "Laws of Nature," according to which a bodily state persists until forced to change by external causes, a moving body endeavors to move always in a straight line, and exchanges of motion (size × speed) between colliding bodies are determined by the contests between their forces of persistence and by Descartes's conservation law. Descartes claimed that his laws and the collision theory derived from them could explain the whole physical universe, including machines. Yet there is nothing on mechanics in his *Principia*, nothing that explains the work principle of 1637. Christiaan Huygens's masterly solution to the problem of centre of oscillation (*Horologium oscillatorium*, 1673) required an insight from Galileo's *Discourses* (third part) enunciated as a principle by Evangelista Torricelli (1644): a system of heavy bodies cannot move of its own accord unless the common center of gravity descends. Torricelli's principle also played a crucial role in Christiaan Huygens's collision theory, out of which tumbled the result that in perfectly elastic collisions the quantity mv^2 remains constant. Huygens regarded this result as a notable corollary of his collision rules; to Gottfried Wilhelm von Leibniz it suggested the universal conservation of *vis viva*, a force measured by mv^2, to add to the already

M

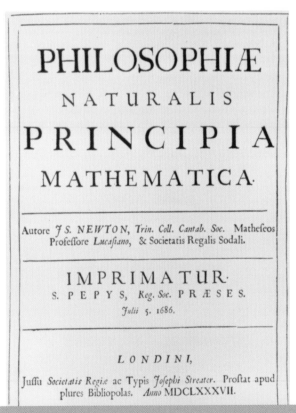

PHILOSOPHIÆ

NATURALIS

PRINCIPIA

MATHEMATICA.

Autore *J S. NEWTON*, *Trin. Coll. Cantab. Soc.* Matheseos Professore *Lucasiano*, & Societatis Regalis Sodali.

IMPRIMATUR·

S. PEPYS, *Reg. Soc.* PRÆSES.

Julii 5. 1686.

LONDINI,

Jussu *Societatis Regiæ* ac Typis *Josephi Streater*. Prostat apud plures Bibliopolas. *Anno* MDCLXXXVII.

Title page of Isaac Newton's *Principia* (1687), which laid down the laws of mechanics and applied them to various problems of motion, from bullets to planets

known conservation of "directed motion." This confirmation of force as a metaphysical reality led Leibniz to the creation in 1691 of a new science of force, which he baptized *dynamics*. It led in turn to a protracted argument in the early decades of the eighteenth century about whether motive force should be *mv*, the Cartesian and Newtonian measure, or mv^2, the Leibnizian measure.

Newton transformed Descartes's "Laws of Nature" into three "Axioms" or "Laws of Motion" according to which a body persists in its state of rest or straight-line motion (Law I), the force impressed on a body is proportional to its change of motion (Law II), and action and reaction are equal and opposite (Law III). From these laws Newton demonstrated the mutual dependence of his inverse-square law of universal gravitation and Johannes Kepler's first and third laws of planetary motion—the second law being a consequence of inertial motion under any central force. The basic problem—to determine the central force given the planet's deviations from inertial motion summed as an orbit, and conversely—was quite foreign to traditional mechanics. Although in the *Principia* Newton links Law III to the work principle and proves the parallelogram rule for forces (which is "abundantly confirmed from mechanics"), the *Principia* is not a treatise on mechanics, but on "the mathematical principles of natural philosophy."

However, Newton's *Principia* was a major exercise in rational mechanics in a new sense that emerged in the work of Isaac Barrow and John Wallis. Barrow had argued (1664–1666) that geometrical theorems apply to all of physics, so that the principles of mechanics and of physics become identical. For Wallis, mechanics was "the part of geometry that deals with motion, and investigates, apodictically and using geometrical reasoning, the force with which such and such a motion takes place" (*Mechanica*, 1670–1671). Similarly, for Newton rational mechanics was "the science, set out in exact propositions and demonstrations, of the motions that result from any forces whatever and of the forces that are required for any motions whatever" (*Principia*, "Preface"), and natural philosophy was basically the problem of "finding the forces of nature from the phenomena of motions and then to demonstrate other phenomena from these forces." The same ideas were to inform Leonhard Euler's *Mechanica* (1736), significantly subtitled *The Science of Motion Expounded Analytically*.

"Rational" or "theoretical" mechanics in the older sense should be distinguished from the post-Newtonian sense of "rational mechanics," which comprised dynamics and stat-

ics. Mechanics in its golden age (the eighteenth century) was not merely a set of variations on the principles and methods of Newton's *Principia*. Among additional ingredients were the concepts and symbolism of Leibnizian differential and integral calculus, which became standard in treatises on analytical mechanics of the period, and the new mathematics, particularly the calculus of variations, which made it possible to formulate new principles that solved new problems.

To take some notable examples, a general theory of rigid-body motion became a desideratum following the work on centers of oscillation of Huygens, Jakob Bernoulli (1703), and Jean d'Alembert (*Traité de dynamique*, 1743), and the researches on lunar libration and equinoctial precession by Newton (*Principia*), d'Alembert, and Joseph Louis Lagrange. Here the principal figure was Leonhard Euler (memoirs of 1750, 1758), whose *Theoria motus corporum solidorum seu rigidorum* (1760) provided a general theory of rigid-body motion. Euler's researches depended on a "new principle of mechanics" (1750), his recasting of Newton's Law II in the analytic form $mdv_{x,y,z} \propto f_{x,y,z}\, dt$. Euler introduced moment of inertia (1749) and principal axes of rotation (suggested by the rolling of ships about three orthogonal axes), which he applied in his theory of the spinning top, an exceptionally difficult problem that had not even been recognized as a problem since the early seventeenth century.

Suppose in a system of bodies in mutual constraint the motion applied to each body a_i resolves into the motion actually acquired v_i and another motion V_i. That is the same as if the v_i and V_i had initially been communicated together, so that the system would have been in equilibrium had the V_i alone been present. That is "d'Alembert's Principle," the centrepiece of his *Traité de dynamique*, which allowed the methodological reduction of dynamics to statics. Lagrange reformulated the principle and coupled it with the principle of virtual velocities to obtain the first formulation of what became "Lagrange's Equations" (*Mécanique analytique*, 1788). Lagrange showed that the conservation of linear and angular momentum, and of *vis viva*, and the principle of least action, follow from his equations, rather than being foundational principles in their own right.

Pierre de Maupertuis's principle of least action had sounded a new note. Reflecting on the controversy of the 1660s over Fermat's least-time optical principle, Maupertuis argued (1744) that in all bodily changes, the "action" (Σ mass $\times$ speed $\times$ distance) is the least possible, a principle that for Maupertuis and Euler—though not for d'Alembert and Lagrange—pointed to the gover-

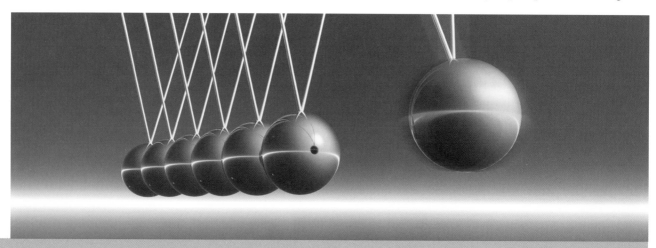

"Newton's cradle," a standard teaching apparatus of the 18th century, illustrates the conservation of momentum.

nance of all things by a Supreme Being. (Σ signifies a sum over all particles in the system under consideration.) Given the principle of virtual velocities, Σ force $\times$ ds $= 0$, which means, by the principles of the integral calculus, that the integral of this sum is a maximum or minimum. Euler developed the least action principle clearly and rigorously for a single particle (1744), and, in a memoir on lunar libration (1763), Lagrange extended Euler's result to an arbitrary system of bodies and derived a general procedure for solving dynamical problems.

The nineteenth century saw new departures in the application of principles established in the preceding two centuries. The relativity of motion, a central theme since the work of Galileo and Huygens, became the object of further study in the work of Alexis-Claude Clairaut, who asked how a system of moving bodies would behave if the system moved along noninertial curves (1742). Gaspard Gustave de Coriolis showed (1835) that the Newtonian laws of motion apply in a rotating reference frame if the equations of motion include a "Coriolis acceleration" in a plane perpendicular to the axis of rotation, a kinematic acceleration which Coriolis interpreted as an extra force (the "Coriolis force") and which became important in ballistics and meteorology. An important step in the formalization of mechanics was Heinrich Hertz's attempt to remove inconsistencies arising from the assumption within traditional classical mechanics that forces are ontologically prior to the motions they cause. He treated forces as "sleeping partners" in a formalized mechanics that depended on the operationally understood notions of time, space, and mass, and when necessary on linkages to hidden masses with hidden motions with respect to hidden coordinates (*Die Prinzipien der Mechanik*, 1894).

Maupertuis's variational principle enjoyed an improved mathematical treatment by William Rowan Hamilton (1834,1835), whose transformation of Lagrange's equations was modified and generalized by Carl Gustav Jacobi in the form now known as the Hamilton-Jacobi Equation (1837). In turn, the Hamilton-Jacobi Equation found fruitful application in the establishment of the quantum mechanics of Louis de Broglie (1923) and Erwin Schrödinger (1926).

ALAN GABBEY

MESMERISM AND ANIMAL MAGNETISM. Mesmerism was the creation of the Viennese physician Franz Mesmer, who regarded his technique of "animal magnetism" as an application of Newtonian principles to physiology. His doctoral dissertation at the University of Vienna concerned the influence of the Moon and planets on the human body, the idea being that the movement of the universal ether had an effect on health. He argued that the body required a certain quantity and rhythm of ethereal motion; disorders arose through an imbalance or incorrect type of motion.

Mesmer tried out this "tidal" theory of physiology in his medical practice in 1773–1774. He found that the application of magnets established an "artificial tide" in a patient. She initially reacted with pain, then improved dramatically. After this first therapeutic success Mesmer extended the practice to patients of all kinds. He could treat several at once by using a structure called a "bacquet," a circular tub studded round the edges with metal rods. Patients held fast to the rods, from which the magnetic influence supposedly flowed.

Mesmer's hometown of Vienna proved less receptive to his ideas than Paris. There his practice drew crowds of patients from the nobility. Magnetic clinics sprung up throughout France, although orthodox doctors and natural philosophers

The French-Italian mathematician Joseph-Louis Lagrange (1736–1813), author of *Mécanique analytique* (1788), a formulation of mechanics of very wide application

M

remained skeptical. Several of his pupils became prominent magnetists in their own right—Charles d'Eslon, Nicolas Bergasse, and Guillaume Kornmann among them—and mesmeric societies sprang up across the country. The success of Mesmer and his protégés drew the attention of the Paris Faculty of Medicine and the Royal Academy of Sciences, each of which appointed a commission to investigate. The commissioners attended magnetic clinics and tried the bacquet. Some of them experienced strong effects; others, nothing. Some of

The Austrian doctor Franz Mesmer (1734–1815) professed to be able cure people of most diseases by stimulating their animal magnetism. The experience sometimes sent patients, usually women, into a trance. The illustration dates from 1785.

the commissioners suspected that imagination might play a role in the phenomena. To test this, they persuaded a number of patients to believe they were being magnetized when in fact they were not (and vice versa). The magnetized patients exhibited no effects, while the unmagnetized patients experienced the expected "crisis." The commissioners concluded that although the phenomena were real, no physical agency caused them. Since the imagination was not then considered a legitimate cause of natural phenomena, attributing to it the mesmeric phenomena amounted to a form of dismissal. Mesmer lost control of the movement after this point, and several historians have suggested that he went mad.

Initiative passed to the marquis de Puysegur, who transformed mesmeric phenomena in one crucial respect. Before his time, mesmeric effects had been brief and violent, followed by a transformation in the patient's physical comfort. Puysegur produced a different phenomenon: an altered state of mind. In this lucid trance the patient said and acted in ways that seemed to indicate the presence of new mental powers. Subjects displayed signs of clairvoyance, foretold the future, diagnosed their own and other peoples' diseases, and spoke languages they had never learned. This new form of the mesmeric state could be used as a flexible tool for psychic and medical experimentation.

Mesmerism spread and diversified throughout Europe in the early nineteenth century, and many mesmeric societies and clinics were founded. In France, it again became a serious contender for scientific and medical respect, based on the work of Puysegur and of other major advocates such as Joseph Philippe François Deleuze and, from the 1830s, Charles Dupotet. In the 1820s, another royal commission investigat-

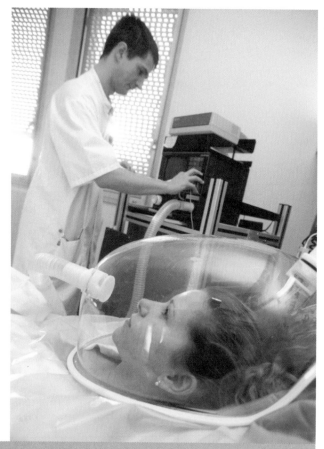

A calorimeter is used to measure oxygen consumption, and thus resting metabolic rate, the number of calories a person burns per day at rest.

ed the practice, with mixed results—validating some effects, failing to reach consensus on others. Meanwhile mesmerism became well established in Germany and Switzerland; its more influential advocates included Johann Kaspar Lavater, Christoph Wilhelm Hufeland, and Carl Kluge. It took hold in Britain in the 1830s, a little later than on the Continent. Throughout the 1840s and 1850s it remained prominent in British public and medical discussion, and in 1842 its advocates could claim that they had used the mesmeric trance to create the first widespread surgical anesthetic (the first operation using ether anesthesia took place in 1846).

Medical mesmerism declined as an organized and prominent force in the second half of the nineteenth century, partly because of the proliferation of related sciences of mind. Hypnotism, for instance, was created as an alternative to mesmerism in 1842 and the spiritualist movement, which began in the 1850s, included many mesmeric elements. By the twentieth century the practice had been entirely subsumed within hypnotism, leaving only its terminology in popular usage. At that stage the terminology came to refer to fascination, charisma, and sex appeal rather than to a formal state of altered consciousness.

ALISON WINTER

METABOLISM designates the totality of the chemical changes that take place among the constituents of living organisms.

The Hippocratic physicians called the conversion of food to the humors of the body "coction" by analogy with cooking. The analogy served as the basis for imagining the underlying process until the seventeenth century. As Greek anatomists from Aristotle to Galen described the internal organs of the body in increasing detail, they came to see nutrition as a sequence of similar transformations taking place from the mouth, through the stomach and intestines, and into the blood vessels, progressively changing into blood, the final nutritive fluid. The old anatomists also knew that the body continuously lost matter, not only through excretions, but also through "invisible transpiration." One of the earliest recorded experiments was an effort to measure the loss by comparing the quantity of food taken in by a bird with that accounted for in its solid excretions.

The systematic study of these exchanges goes back to the experiments of the Venetian physician Santorio Santorio, who, in the early seventeenth century, weighed himself on a large scale together with his food and excretions. From the differences measured daily over a very long time, he determined the quantity of matter lost through his skin and lungs in "insensible perspiration" and its variation according to internal and external factors.

During the seventeenth and eighteenth centuries, the nutritional exchanges of the body began to be explained by analogy with acid-alkali reactions, or fermentations, studied by the emerging science of chemistry. Often such transformations were referred to as composing the "animal economy," a phrase derived originally from analogy with the management of a household. A wholly new understanding of the overall significance of these exchanges came with the theory of Antoine-Laurent Lavoisier that respiration is a slow combustion yielding heat and work. Lavoisier thus explained the continuous food supply as a replenishment of carbon and hydrogen continuously consumed.

The rapid development of "plant" and "animal" chemistry in the early nineteenth century, and their fusion into the emerging field of organic chemistry, provided more robust foundations for investigating the chemical changes in living organisms. By the 1840s, the term "Stoffwechsel" had emerged as the preferred designation of these processes in German literature; its most common English translation, "metamorphosis," had previously been used both in German and English to describe the multiple chemical reactions, mainly partial decompositions, that organic compounds can undergo in the laboratory.

In his well-known treatise on the cell theory, Theodor Schwann introduced the adjective *metabolische* to signify the phenomena of chemical change that cells can produce either on molecules within themselves or in the surrounding fluids. French texts began in the 1860s to translate *Stoffwechsel* as *le métabolisme*. Michael Foster adopted the word "metabolism" in his textbook of physiology in 1878, and it soon afterward became the standard term in English.

Throughout most of the nineteenth century, efforts to define the intermediate chemical reactions that connect the foodstuffs entering the body with final decomposition products amounted to conjectures based on knowledge of the chemical properties of the substances involved. The experimental study of the *Stoffwechsel* consisted of quantitative measurements of the intake of carbohydrates, fats, proteins, and oxygen, and of the excretions in the form of urea, carbon dioxide, and water, according to different dietary regimens in health and disease. In 1904, Franz Knoop fed dogs a diet of phenyl-substituted fatty acids. The animals metabolized these compounds only with difficulty, with the result that they excreted some intermediate breakdown products. In this way, Knoop established that fatty acids are decomposed by a succession of "β-oxidations," each shortening the carbon chain by two atoms. This was the first experimentally established sequence of intermediate reactions; unfortunately, Knoop's method did not work for other reactions. During the next three decades, Knoop insistently advocated the view that the goal of biochemistry was to establish the complete sequences of decomposition reactions connecting foodstuffs to final end-products and the synthetic reactions producing body constituents.

During the first decade of the twentieth century, investigators found more direct methods of studying the chemical changes that take place between the beginning and end points of metabolism, and a new subspecialty, increasingly called "intermediary metabolism," began to take form. Federico Batelli and Linda Stern in Italy, and Thorsten Thunberg in Sweden, independently devised manometric methods to examine the phenomena in isolated tissues by testing the effects on their rate of respiration of adding substances suspected of being intermediates. Gustav Embden in Germany and others studied similar problems by means of perfused isolated organs. They identified a number of substances, such as pyruvic acid, acetic acid, and several dicar-boxylic acids, that must take part, but could not connect them and other suspected intermediates into well-demonstrated reaction sequences. Meanwhile, the achievement of cell-free fermentation by Eduard Buchner stimulated the study of the intermediate phenomena in yeast, which were more accessible to direct examination than animal tissues. A series of partially speculative fermentation schemes culminated in a sequence proposed by Carl Neuberg in 1913 in which hexose sugars broke down into methylglyoxal. The proposal guided investigators for more than a decade, until they showed that methylglyoxal played no part at all. By 1935, a modified sequence of reactions, resulting in particular from the work of Embden

and Otto Meyerhof, defined the pathway of anaerobic carbohydrate metabolism.

In 1930, a young physician named Hans Adolf Krebs entered the field of intermediate metabolism, bringing with him methods that he had learned from Otto Warburg. Krebs discovered a cyclic process in 1932 through which urea is synthesized in mammals. He went on to discover several other pathways, including most notably the citric-acid cycle of carbohydrate metabolism in 1937. By then, individual pathways were beginning to link up in extended networks. The introduction of radioactive isotope tracers after 1940 accelerated progress in their identification. By mid-century, "metabolic maps" were complicated enough to fill large charts on biochemistry laboratory walls, and the main routes in the decomposition and synthesis of the amino acids, sugars, fatty acids, nucleic acids, and their many derivatives seemed nearly complete. Investigators began turning their attention to the question of the regulation of the pathways to maintain steady states while responding to the changing energy and other requirements of the organism, a quest that occupies metabolic biochemists to the present day.

Frederic Lawrence Holmes

METALLURGY may be defined as the extraction of metals from their ores, their working and processing, the study of their structure and the development of alloys.

Although metals had been extracted and shaped for thousands of years, it was not until the sixteenth century that Georgius Agricola, a physician working in a German mining district, codified known metallurgical processes. His posthumous publication, *De re metallica* (1556), became an important text for later metallurgists, although it was based on theory and observation rather than on practical experience. Agricola's contemporary, Vannoccio Biringuccio, who was the chief armorer of Siena, produced a practical guide to metallurgical techniques, *Pirotechnia* (1540), based on his own practical experience.

René de Réaumur published an account of the French iron and steel industry in the 1720s based on his own observations and experimental work. His memoirs on the art of converting iron into steel had a mixed reception. Some critics believed that he had little understanding of metallurgy, while others viewed him as one of its pioneers.

During the eighteenth century, major developments in iron and steel manufacture occurred in Britain. In 1709, Abraham Darby successfully used coke instead of charcoal to smelt iron ore. This made possible the production of cast iron in great quantities and the construction of major cast-iron structures such as the first iron bridge in the world, a 100-foot span across the River Severn (1779). Benjamin Huntsman invented the crucible process for making steel in 1740, and Henry Cort developed the puddling process for the conversion of pig iron into wrought iron in 1784.

Sir Henry Bessemer's patented process of 1856 made possible the bulk production of cheap steel. A decade later, the German engineer Carl Wilhelm Siemens introduced the open-hearth furnace into Britain, while Emile Martin and his son Pierre did the same in France. This process could melt scrap steel, leading to the production of large quantities of high-quality structural steel, fundamental to the worldwide expansion of the railways and mass transportation.

In 1854, Henri-Étienne Sainte-Claire Deville introduced a method for the commercial extraction of aluminum from bauxite. At first, aluminum was a luxury metal, and Napoléon III had a banqueting set made from it. In 1886,

M

Bessemer converter in the Longwy steelworks in France, 1930

M

the American Charles Hall and the Frenchman Paul Héroult, working independently, found that aluminum oxide could be dissolved in molten cryolite and the aluminum extracted by electrolysis. This method is still in use today.

Metallography, the study of metal surfaces, has proved particularly important to metallurgy's development. Between 1863 and 1865, Henry Clifton Sorby examined the surfaces of polished and etched specimens of steel under the microscope, the results being referred to as microstructures.

Steel is a complex alloy, based on iron with varying amounts of carbon. Steel has a number of phases which are visible in the various microstructures and which possess different physical and mechanical properties. Sorby's micrographic work on the structure of steel was confirmed by X-ray diffraction. An analytical technique that provides clues to the internal structure of a material, it helped to confirm the atomic structure of metals and other materials.

The American physical chemist Willard Gibbs proposed the phase rule in 1876 in a maze of mathematics and using a terse style difficult for most of his readers to understand. This rule defined and classified phase changes in metals and metal mixtures using the then new techniques of thermodynamics. A phase may be defined as a distinct homogenous material that can be physically separated from other parts of the system. This work prompted the development of phase diagrams that visually illustrate these changes.

By using metallography and phase diagrams, metallurgists could predict the phases present in alloys at different temperatures. This led to the development and understanding of the heat treatment of alloys—for example, the quenching and tempering of steels and the age-hardening of aluminium alloys, introduced by the German Alfred Wilm in 1906.

Subsequent advances in the theory of solids gave rise to the concept, associated with Geoffrey Ingram Taylor, that deformation in metals takes place by the movement of dislocations (defects in the atomic arrangement) through the crystalline matrix. This concept led in turn to an understanding of failure through creep, fatigue, and brittle fracture, and to the development of strengthening mechanisms in modern alloys. The movement of dislocations was later confirmed with the aid of the electron microscope. Subsequently, more powerful field-ion microscopes, and high-resolution electron and atomic-force microscopes, have enabled metallurgists to specify the position of individual atoms.

Willliam Hume-Rothery carried out definitive work on intermetallic phases, electron compounds, and metallic structures, and proposed rules regarding the solid solubility of metals. The development of solid state physics, quantum theory, and the theory of the periodic table have increased our understanding of the atomic structure of metals and their behavior.

In the late twentieth century, the development of the jet engine led to the demand for higher performance metals. A variety of light alloys, such as those based on aluminum and titanium, as well as superalloys (complex alloys that perform well at high temperatures), have been created for use in aerospace. Nanotechnology, the study and manufacture of materials and structures on the nanometer scale, and metal matrix composites are emerging as significant areas of metallurgical development in the twenty-first century.

SUSAN T. I. MOSSMAN

METEOROLOGY. The history of modern meteorology begins with the Scientific Revolution. The late sixteenth and first half of the seventeenth century saw the invention of the meteorological instruments—thermometer, barometer, hygrometer, wind and rain gauges—and around 1650 natural philosophers began using them to record weather observations. They immediately understood the importance of coordinating observations over as wide a space as possible. Scientific academies solicited weather diaries and organized observational networks; Leopold de' Medici, Grand Duke of Tuscany, founder of the Accademia del Cimento, and Robert Hooke of the Royal Society of London both sponsored networks of observers in the 1650s and 1660s. They were motivated in part by theories deriving from the Hippocratic treatise *Airs, Waters, and Places* that related the weather to disease; for two and a half centuries meteorologists attempted to correlate weather patterns with epidemic outbreaks and climate with public health. The application of meteorology to agriculture provided further motivation. In addition, Enlightenment meteorology attempted to rationalize traditional weather lore, including astrological meteorology, searching through recorded observations for patterns confirming traditional wisdom.

Among the few attempts at a theoretical understanding of weather phenomena were explanations of the trade winds by Edmond Halley and George Hadley. According to them, the rising mass of heated equatorial air is replaced by an inflow of cooler air from higher latitudes. This north-south circulation is deflected, according to Halley, by the movement of the subsolar point with the earth's diurnal motion, or, in Hadley's theory, by the acceleration we now call Coriolis. A flow of warm air at high altitude from equator to poles completes these early pictures of the general cir-

Weather station at the Royal Observatory, Greenwich, in 1880

M

culation. They illustrate the role of oceangoing commerce both as a source of data and incentive for meteorology.

Early modern meteorologists were frustrated by observers' lack of discipline and by the poor quality of instruments, which rendered observations nearly useless. The late Enlightenment resolved these problems. Emerging modern states organized large networks of disciplined observers, instrument makers developed precise instruments of all types, and natural philosophers devised methods of systematic measurement. By the end of the eighteenth century meteorologists had access to large quantities of reliable weather data for the first time.

Enlightenment meteorologists, seeking weather patterns and correlations with agricultural harvests or outbreaks of disease, lacked a sense of the geographical expanse of weather events and of their development over time. Romantic natural philosophers worked out geographical and temporal syntheses. Alexander von Humboldt's famous isothermal lines synthesized temperature observations over the globe; Humboldt integrated all the factors of climate into a unified science of the earth that he called "physique générale." Heinrich Wilhelm Brandes drew (or perhaps proposed to draw) synoptic maps of the weather over Europe for every day of 1783, tracing the progress of temperature changes across the Continent, uncovering the geographic distribution of barometric pressure, and relating wind direction to barometric differences. In the 1830s meteorologists took up the kinetics of storms. Heinrich Wilhelm Dove's "Law of Gyration" described the veering of storm winds resulting, he argued, from the conflict of equatorial and polar air currents; William C. Redfield insisted on the rotary motion of storms. James Espy introduced thermodynamic considerations, pointing to the adiabatic cooling of rising moist air and the energy of latent heat released in precipitation as the "motive" force of tropical storms.

The advent of the telegraph around midcentury made possible the nearly immediate collection of meteorological data on a continental basis; at the same time, the growing importance of meteorology for agriculture and oceangoing commerce led governments to establish national weather services to coordinate observation, particularly for storm warning. The resulting inflow of data fed the systematic production of synoptic weather charts, which became

important research tools. A community of meteorologists evolved, its members more consistently trained in physics and mathematics, while the discipline acquired journals and professional societies. These factors, along with the emergence of thermodynamics after midcentury, led to quantitative treatment of Espy's supposition. A consistent body of work emerged, known as the "thermal" or "convective" theory of cyclones, that derived the kinetic energy of storms from the release of latent heat and the adiabatic cooling of rising currents of air. William Ferrel applied hydrodynamics to the process, showing that air movement caused by any chance pressure gradient will be bent into a spiral by the earth's motion, generating a barometric low and the beginnings of a storm system. Hermann von Helmholtz and Vilhelm Bjerknes were the best known among scientists applying hydrodynamics to meteorology.

Around the turn of the twentieth century, balloons, kites, and airplanes made available observations of the upper atmosphere, while aviation generated demand for detailed forecasts in three dimensions. World War I sharpened these requirements. Discrepancies in the temperature distribution above storms had led meteorologists around the beginning of the century to consider the role of air masses of differing temperatures and geographic origin in the formation of storms. The polar front theory, developed immediately after the war by Bjerknes and his Bergen (Norway) school of meteorologists, demonstrated the origin of cyclones in the encounter of cool, polar air masses with warmer air. In the 1920s, the Bergen school extended the air-mass approach to weather not associated with storms.

Around the same time, Lewis Richardson succeeded in computing (after the fact) a six-hour advance in the weather using numerical algorithms. The effort consumed six weeks, generated disappointing results, and convinced meteorologists of the uselessness of a computational approach. The advent of the electronic computer during World War II encouraged a new attempt at computational forecasting. John von Neumann, who selected meteorology to demonstrate the computer's usefulness, had by 1956 shown that it could generate accurate forecasts. The computer has enabled meteorologists to exploit the immense quantities of data arriving from weather satellites and a greatly increased number of observational sources in the atmosphere and at

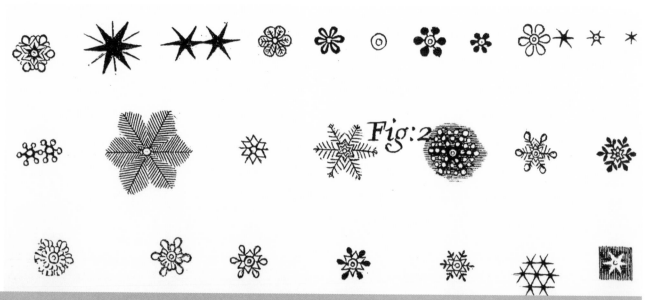

Snow flakes, as depicted by Robert Hooke in *Micrographia* (1665)

the earth's surface. Computational models of the atmosphere have since blurred the distinctions among observation, experiment, and theory.

THEODORE S. FELDMAN

MICROSCOPE. The microscope is an instrument for obtaining an enlarged image of an object, which may be viewed directly, photographed, or recorded electronically. The number of times the investigated object appears enlarged determines the magnification of the instrument, and the resolving power specifies its capacity to distinguish clearly between two points.

The earliest simple light microscope consisted of a single lens framed by a ring, plate, or cylinder, combined with a device for holding the object and a focusing mechanism. The compound microscope consisted of a movable tube containing two lenses or lens systems, the objective forming an enlarged image of the object and the ocular or eyepiece magnifying it; a stand; and a specimen stage. Illumination was provided either by a mirror placed under the stage to reflect light into the instrument or by a lamp built into the stand.

The microscope probably was invented during the second decade of the seventeenth century since the earliest printed descriptions and illustrations of a microscopically observed object, the bee, appeared in 1625, in the *Melissographia* and the *Apiarium* published by members of the Accademia dei Lincei. Robert Hooke's enthusiastically received *Micrographia* of 1665 presented a lavishly illustrated survey of "minute bodies" ranging from the point of a needle and the pores of cork to bookworms and fleas. It also contained an analysis of methods of microscopy and a description of Hooke's compound microscope, an instrument with a single-pillar stand on a solid base and a tiltable tube. Other seventeenth-century microscopists, notably Antoni van Leeuwenhoek, Marcello Malpighi, and Jan Swammerdam, used simple microscopes. Leeuwenhoek made more than three hundred of them, small plates of metal encasing a lens with provisions for focusing, the majority magnifying between 75 and 150 times. Communicating his findings largely through letters to the Royal Society of London, he became known particularly for his observations of "animalcules" in sperm.

In the eighteenth century, investigators throughout Europe continued to use both simple and compound microscopes. Spherical and chromatic aberrations, however, impaired the performance of these instruments. Objects appeared blurred and surrounded by colored fringes, because a spherical lens surface brings the light rays passing through different parts of the lens to a focus at different points, and light rays of different colors are refracted differently. Reducing the aperture with a diaphragm could lessen the spherical aberration, but at the cost of dimming the image. The aberrations affect the compound microscope more strongly than the simple microscope.

Achromatic telescope objectives consisting of lenses combining crown and flint glass were first made in the later eighteenth century. Although manufacturing the smaller lenses of microscopes proved much more difficult, Joseph Fraunhofer and other instrument makers produced achromatic microscope objectives of low magnification by the early nineteenth century. After Joseph Jackson Lister showed in 1830 how to construct aplanatic objectives (achromats with minimal spherical aberration), achromatic instruments of higher magnification became widely available. Together with advancing preparation techniques, they greatly enlarged the scope of microscopy. Microscopists examining

Microscope designed and employed by Robert Hooke (1635–1703), as depicted in his *Micrographia* (1665)

plant and animal tissue established the cell as the unit of life, thus transforming histology and pathology and massively stimulating microscopical investigation. Facilitated by the expansion of laboratory and academic science, microscopy became an integral part of medical education, diagnosis, and research, as well as a tool for organic chemistry and the physical sciences.

In 1873, Ernst Abbe published a theory of image formation that enabled the design of optically improved instruments. In the early 1880s, Abbe and Otto Friedrich Schott produced apochromatic objectives, which eliminated the residual secondary spectrum of the achromat and almost completely corrected both chromatic and spherical aberration. At that time, novel techniques

A technician demonstrates a scanning electron microscope at the University of California at Berkeley.

M

of staining and cultivation allowed the identification of pathogenic bacteria, which offered a potent new explanation of diseases.

In the late 1930s, the development of phase contrast microscopy, which utilizes the principles of diffraction to convert variations in optical paths into intensity variation, allowed the direct study of unstained transparent biological specimens. The illumination system improved with the incorporation of electric lamps in the 1930s, and again with the introduction of low-voltage tungsten-halogen lamps in the 1960s, which are now the norm. The light microscope has become ubiquitous. Current applications include routine medical tests and examinations of the surface quality of materials.

The twentieth century introduced new kinds of microscopes that utilize rays other than light. The electron microscope contains a source supplying a high-voltage electron beam, an evacuated column with electromagnetic fields along its length that act as a lens, a specimen stage, and an imaging system. In the transmission electron microscope (TEM), an electron beam passes through the object. In the scanning electron microscope (SEM), a comparatively small electron beam scans the object to produce an image of its surface.

The electronic engineers Max Knoll and Ernst Ruska constructed the first electron microscope in the early 1930s, utilizing contemporary cathode-ray technology, improved electronic tubes, and vacuum technology, as well as the quantum mechanical principle that the electron can be regarded as a wave. Ruska developed an instrument for commercial manufacture in association with a group of engineers at the electrical firm of Siemens in Germany. Their TEM entered the market in 1939, one year earlier than the TEM constructed by the physicist James Hillier and his group at the Radio Corporation of America (RCA). In 1948, Charles William Oatley at the University of Cambridge launched a research project to construct an SEM, which led to commercial production in 1965.

Both the biomedical and physical sciences use the TEM and SEM. The TEM requires elaborate preparation techniques. To maintain the vacuum, the specimens must be dehydrated; since electrons interfere strongly with matter, the sections must be extremely thin; and chemical fixation is needed to prevent alterations under the electron beam. The introduction of the ultramicrotome and plastic embedding material in the late 1940s facilitated preparation of delicate biological specimens, and rapid freezing has supplemented chemical fixation since the late 1960s. Preparation for the SEM, which can accommodate large specimens, is easier. Biological specimens are rendered conductive by metal coating; other specimens can frequently be investigated without preparation.

Current applications of the electron microscope include virus biophysics, polymer morphology, and materials characterization and inspection in semiconductor technology.

JUTTA SCHICKORE

MILITARY INSTITUTIONS. The contributions of science to warfare, especially to the wars of the twentieth century, are familiar to students of history. Not so well understood is the equal and opposite action: the influence of military institutions on science and technology. Although interest in the subject has mushroomed over the last decade, historians have not yet forged an overall synthesis. Recent research has focused on U.S. science during the Cold War, but older judgments regarding the two world wars need revisiting. Because the line separating science from technology has remained shifting and indistinct—thanks in part to military influence—"science" here stands for science and technology.

The early modern constellation of the sciences reflects a military influence. Early modern mathematics included disci-

Not long after the invention of the hot-air and hydrogen balloons in the 1780s, they were adapted for military purposes and served as observation posts in the wars of the French Revolution. A 19th-century print of an 18th-century illustration of the launching of a montgolfière.

plines directly applicable to military affairs: fortification or military architecture, naval architecture, ballistics, cartography, and navigation. Early modern natural philosophy, on the other hand, included a broad range of nonquantitative subjects, from physics to botany and psychology; these pursuits offered little to the practice of warfare. Galileo Galilei consulted for the Venetian Arsenal, a naval institution, as a mathematician and courted the Medici family with a military compass. But when the telescope brought in his own ship he abandoned his career as a mathematician for the higher-status occupation of court philosopher.

Because mathematics was essential to the education of its military officers, the early modern state became an important patron of the subject. In France during the Ancien Régime, military and naval academies employed the top mathematicians of the age, including Gaspard Monge, who trained Charles Augustin Coulomb and Lazare Carnot. Carnot's technical contributions to French arms earned him the title "father of victories." Natural philosophy also received support as part of the cadets' general education. The Ecole Polytechnique, revolutionary successor of these institutions, produced much of the most important physics, mathematics, and engineering of the early nineteenth century. In the United States the Ecole's sister school, Thomas Jefferson's Military Academy at West Point, served as the only source of trained civil engineers for several decades and graduated military men who achieved international stature as scientists. In an era when military officers were broadly educated and mathematics included so much military content, mathematicians and engineers naturally found a home in military institutions.

Military support, intensifying after the Seven Years War, helped transform mathematics and natural philosophy. In France and England, national cartographic projects originated in military campaigns. These projects developed advanced methods of triangulation and measurement; along with other military and naval requirements, they generated intense demand for precise instruments. Profits from the sale of these instruments to armies and navies supported instrument makers' research and development and helped industrialize the scientific instrument trade; Jesse Ramsden's revolutionary instruments and his innovations in the organization and technology of instrument manufacture depended on his sale of sextants to the British Navy. At the same time, military engineers like Coulomb and England's William Roy crossed over into natural philosophy, applying mathematical techniques to fields like electricity, magnetism, and the study of gases, contributing to their quantification. Military needs and military engineers thus played an important role in the emergence of precise scientific instrumentation and in the quantification of physics in the late Enlightenment.

The early modern state also experimented with the mobilization of civilian scientists for military research. In France the monarchy employed members of the Royal Academy of Sciences in the reform of the manufacturing sector. Antoine-Laurent Lavoisier took on the gunpowder industry. Setting up a laboratory at the Arsenal in Paris—where he also carried out his more famous chemical researches—he developed methods of gunpowder manufacture that made France an exporter of high-quality gunpowder and laid the foundations of industrial chemistry. The Revolutionary government employed a number of Lavoisier's colleagues at a weapons laboratory at Meudon, where Claude

Leslie Groves (1896–1970), head of the Manhattan Engineer District, with (on the right) J. Robert Oppenheimer (1904–1967), the director of the Project's Los Alamos laboratory, where the atomic bombs were designed

Louis Berthollet and others developed incendiary weapons, explosive shells, and new types of gunpowder. The rediscovery of these explosive shells in the late 1830s revolutionized naval warfare.

In the United States the army revolutionized manufacturing in the first half of the nineteenth century, developing at its national armories the so-called "American System": machine manufacture of weapons with interchangeable parts. Besides introducing modern methods of gauging and pattern replication, the army developed advanced business and accounting practices to manage its inventory and distribution requirements. The American System eventually took over much of American manufacturing and was eagerly received in Europe. Both the British Navy—in the case of the scientific instrument trade—and the American Army provided markets without which it would have been more difficult, if not impossible, to develop these technologies. No private arms manufacturer of the early nineteenth century would have undertaken as risky and pointless a venture as attempting to make weapons with interchangeable parts.

Closely related to military cartography was exploration, also often a military venture. James Cook earned his reputation charting the Saint Lawrence River for the Battle of Quebec. On his Pacific voyages he applied the most advanced techniques of land-based cartography to hydrography and contributed to the solution of the problem of longitude, which had long preoccupied the British Navy. Cook's voyages, part of a series of naval expeditions to the Pacific, set a precedent for the union of scientific and naval operations. The published goal of Cook's first voyage was the observation of the Transit of Venus—a purely scientific activity. But secret instructions charged Cook with establishing a foothold on the reputed Southern Continent and with surveying resources for naval stations and colonization. Cook carried with him civilian naturalists and artists who made important contributions to geography, botany, ethnography, and other sciences. Charles Darwin's *Beagle* voyage belongs to this

M

same series of imperial hydrographical expeditions. In the United States the army, beginning with the expedition of Meriwether Lewis and George Rogers Clark (1803–1806), played a leading role in the exploration and conquest of North America. The expeditions of its topographical engineers, from the Revolution until their dissolution in 1853, ranged broadly through cartography, anthropology, geology, survey of natural resources, and diplomacy.

Notwithstanding its nurturing of manufacturing technology, the nineteenth-century U.S. military generally failed to appreciate the larger potential of science and technology for warfare. The navy dragged its feet on steam power and propellers in the first half of the nineteenth century; the army notoriously resisted new technology during the Civil War. Nor were rank-and-file scientists, jealous of their independence, anxious for close relations with the military. But the scientific leadership grasped the technological character of modern war and perceived that solutions to technological problems required not only engineering but also basic scientific research. During the Civil War they urgently lobbied for an agency to direct military research and development. The navy responded with a permanent commission that enjoyed civilian status, no funding, no research capabilities, no power, and little meaningful activity. The National Academy of Sciences (NAS), born in 1863, likewise contributed little to the war effort.

Much seemed the same when World War I began. In Europe and the United States the military misapprehended the character of technological warfare, but the stalemate rendered the military more receptive to new ideas. Fritz Haber convinced a skeptical German headquarters in 1915 to experiment with poison gas. A gas arms race ensued, which mobilized scientists on both sides; England's Porton Down occupied 7,000 acres, with a breeding colony for animal and human experimentation. Its scientists were better paid than those in other scientific occupations. In the United States, Edgewood Arsenal in Maryland, employing 2,000 people and turning out 200,000 bombs and shells per day, had no rival in size until the Manhattan Project.

The U.S. scientific leadership tried several approaches to mobilizing science for war. The Naval Consulting Board, Thomas Edison's child, applied methods of invention and engineering to problems of military technology and made little use of academic scientists. The National Research Council (NRC, a creation of the NAS) took a different approach, organizing basic research for war and uniting both academic and nonacademic scientists with engineers. Its leaders recognized not only what science could do for the war, but also what war could do for science.

By war's end, the NRC's success had demonstrated the need for fundamental scientific research in modern warfare. Academic science won greatly increased status. "Those who shared in the consciousness of the University's power and resourcefulness," remarked one dean, "can never be fully content to return to the old routine of the days before the war." Private foundations poured money into research projects. Industry, impressed with scientists' practical and managerial skills, welcomed them. The war introduced team-based research to American science, and, as it crippled European science, the war made the United States a world scientific power. But the military-scientific alliance was not perfect. The NRC could only coordinate projects; it had little money and could not contract out research. The military feared that academics would exploit its sponsorship for their own purposes. The National Advisory Committee on Aeronautics

(NACA) offered a third, more promising approach to war-related research. Well funded and with authority to maintain its own laboratories, NACA forged strong ties among academics, government scientists, and the military. This model would shape the organization of science in the next war.

In 1941, the scientific rank and file again showed little interest in military work. Scientists who had served in World War I favored preparedness. Vannevar Bush had worked at the NRC's submarine detection facility and had served as chair of the NACA, as well as dean of engineering and vice president at the Massachusetts Institute for Technology (MIT), uniting, in his person, the historical precedents for a scientific-military alliance. Under his leadership the Office for Scientific Research and Development (OSRD) organized most scientific work for the war. Patterned after the NACA, the OSRD contracted out research and development to universities and industry, allowing scientists to work on military projects in civilian and academic settings. Huge projects at the nation's top universities and engineering schools—MIT's Radiation Laboratory employed 4,500, for instance—made essential contributions to the war effort. The Manhattan Project, an exception to this pattern, fell to the army under conditions that academic scientists were glad to escape at war's end.

World War II taught the nation that its security depended on technological superiority; that new military technology demanded fundamental research not tied to immediate needs; that big projects and lots of money produced great results; that the nation required scientists, who alone understood the new weapons, at the highest levels of strategic planning; and that an unfailing supply of them must be guaranteed through the cultivation of science education. These lessons shaped the institutional structure and the content of Cold War science. National laboratories at Argonne, Berkeley, Oak Ridge, Brookhaven, and later Livermore took up where the Manhattan Project left off, while universities and engineering schools carried on the approach of the OSRD. Wartime projects had built Stanford and MIT into great schools. Scientists from these and other select institutions favored by the OSRD had foreseen and jockeyed for greatly increased postwar support. Interdisciplinary departments in military-related fields like microwave electronics proved highly successful, as did quasi-independent laboratories managed by academic institutions, such as Johns Hopkins University's Applied Physics Laboratory and Charles Stark Draper's Instrumentation Laboratory at MIT. Besides microwave electronics, crucial to radar and communications, favored subject areas included materials science for semiconductor research, automated systems, and nuclear science.

Through these institutions military relations helped to direct the orientation and shape the content of science. Military officers populated graduate programs, which in the immediate postwar years might include classified courses among their offerings. Graduate students wrote theses on military topics, then filled the ranks of the next cohort of professors. In subjects like quantum electrodynamics—the applications of which include lasers and semiconductors—theoretical approaches and results might respond to military requirements. Semi-military agencies like the RAND Corporation, applying the social sciences to military purposes, fostered pervasive quantification in these fields. The Korean War intensified the military influence in science. By late 1951, the Department of Defense and the Atomic Energy Commission (AEC) funded 40 percent of all academic and industrial research, while defense-related research occupied two-thirds of the nation's scientists and engineers. Through panels and summer study groups scientists advised the government on issues of technology and strategy. The General Advisory Committee to the AEC, for example, contributed to the decision to create the hydrogen bomb; it directly succeeded the Manhattan Project's Scientific Panel, which had advised the War Department on targeting and deployment of the atomic bomb. In all these ways American scientists helped the United States win the arms races of World War II and the Cold War.

THEODORE S. FELDMAN

MINERALOGY AND PETROLOGY. Mineralogy's disciplinary status has undergone three distinct shifts. From the sixteenth through the early nineteenth century, it bridged chemistry and natural history. It used the laboratory techniques of the former and the principles of classification of the latter to study the whole of the mineral kingdom. During the nineteenth century, mineralogy lost this commanding position and became a subdiscipline of geology. The study of minerals (chemicals that occur naturally in the earth's crust) separated from that of rocks (distinctive assemblages of minerals), leading to a distinction between mineralogy and petrology in the latter part of the century. Following World War II, geology came under the earth sciences, and mineralogy and petrology were transformed by the theory of plate tectonics and by new instrumentation.

In spite of changes in disciplinary status, from the eighteenth century to the present, mineralogists have concentrated on two problems. The first, classification, has been essential for geological theory and practical applications in mining. It has also been a scientific nightmare. Classifying depends on being able to make clear distinctions at various levels of organization. In the case of animals and plants, individuals can usually be distinguished easily and most of the time species too by the test of reproductive capability. Although in the eighteenth century, Carl Linnaeus made a gallant attempt to extend these methods to minerals, it was a doomed strategy. Over the centuries, mineralogists have oscillated between using chemical composition and crystal form. Unfortunately, these do not map onto each other. Two minerals of the same composition can have different forms, and vice versa. Adding to the difficulties, the chemical composition of many of the commonest minerals is not fixed but allows a range of variation. Formal classifications have always been supplemented by keys to field identification using a variety of visible characters.

The second key mineralogical problem is how minerals and rocks originated. Since they occur interlocked with one another, mineralogists from the seventeenth century on have assumed that they originated as fluids and subsequently hardened in their present positions. The fluidity could have been caused by heat, water, or some combination of the two. Mineralogists have fought recurrent battles over the relative importance of these factors. In either case, they have always hoped they would be able to use their knowledge of chemical reactions to reconstruct a genetic account of rock history—a geogony based on an invariable sequence of chemical reactions following from some initial state.

M

A false-color image taken (on January 12, 2006) by Spirit Rover; the minerals (colored white) may indicate that water once was present on Mars. The minerals do not make a mountain range: the main trench is 30 cm wide.

Mineralogy differed greatly from the historical geology better known to the public and more thoroughly studied by historians. Mineralogists have always focused their attention on the hard rocks (igneous and metamorphic). The sedimentary rocks so dear to historical geologists because of their embedded fossils have taken second place, even though mineralogists have attended to clay mineralogy and sedimentary petrology. Mineralogists have always worked closely with chemists and with crystallographers. They have found experiments and microscope work as important as fieldwork. Germans and Scandinavians dominated mineralogy partly because of the abundance of hard rocks in those countries, but also because of their distinguished traditions in chemistry and crystallography. Only in the twentieth century did they begin yielding to Canadians and Americans.

From the Renaissance through the eighteenth century, mineralogists produced one classification of rocks and minerals after another. Among the more important were Georg Bauer, better known as Agricola, the Swedish chemist Johan G. Wallerius, and Abraham Gottlob Werner. All distinguished four major groups with different chemistries: earths, metals, salts and combustibles. Earths resisted heat and water, metals became fluid on heating, salts dissolved in liquids, and the combustible substances (coal, for example) burned. Because chemistry formed the basis for classifying rocks, the students spent as much time in the cabinet or laboratory working with chemicals and blowpipes as they did in the field. Werner drew the pessimistic conclusion that no theoretically sound principles of mineral classification were to be found. Hence he instructed his students to begin dividing up rocks by the time of their formation.

Employed by European states as mining inspectors or surveyors, mineralogists left their laboratories to climb mountains and descend mine shafts. By the second half of the eighteenth century, these men—including Lazzaro Moro and Giovanni Arduino in Italy, Johann Lehmann in Germany, and Guillaume-François Rouelle in France—opted for an alternative approach to rock classification. They divided rocks into two main kinds: primary and secondary. Primary rocks were hard, often crystalline and the matrix in which metals and precious minerals were to be found. They made up the core of mountain chains. Secondary rocks were relatively soft and granular, layered or stratified and banked up against the primary rocks that formed the mountain cores. Often, secondary rocks contained fossils, which by then most mineralogists agreed were the indurated remains of animals and plants.

In seeking the causes for this twofold division of rocks, mineralogists found common ground with cosmogony, the study of the development of the globe. Since the seventeenth century, cosmogonists had argued from the earth's globular figure that at some time in the past it had been fluid. Fluidity could have been caused by heat, as a minority of cosmogonists had argued. Mineralogists, though, preferred water, as suggested by the chemist Johann Joachim Becher in his *Physica subterranea* (1669). They believed that a thick, chemical laden ocean had once covered the earth's surface. The primary rocks crystallized out of the ocean as the high mountain chains, a conclusion supported by the chemists' belief that crystals could be deposited only from watery solutions and not from hot melts. As the water became less saturated, and as waves and rivers wore away the mountains, the ocean began depositing the silt that solidified as the secondary, stratified rocks. This theory, Neptunism, was most fully developed by Werner at Freiberg.

From about 1830 to 1880, mineralogists looked to new developments in chemistry to aid them with mineral classifications. Jöns Jacob Berzelius, the Swedish chemist, distinguished the silicates and aluminates—the classes of chemicals most abundant in the earth's crust for the first time. Gustav Rose offered the most comprehensive classification of minerals to date in his *Mineralsystem* (1852). For practical purposes, mineralogists continued to use external features. Friedrich Mohs, best known for developing a hardness scale for minerals, developed one of these. James Dwight Dana adapted it for an American audience. His *System of Mineralogy* published in 1837 must be one of the most enduring of textbooks in the history of modern science. In modified form, it was still in use in the 1960s.

In 1860, Henry Clifton Sorby invented the polarizing microscope, transforming the process of identifying minerals. Thin sections of minerals or rocks were placed on slides that could be rotated beneath polarizing lens. The characteristic color changes that were observed on rotating the slide served to identify the mineral. This new technique allowed mineralogists for the first time to see and identify mineral assemblages formerly invisible to the naked eye. It gave an enormous boost to petrology. Karl Rosenbusch used it to particularly good effect, summarizing the new results in his classic textbook, *Mikroskopische Physiographie der petrographisch wichtigen Mineralien* (1873).

In the nineteenth century, theories of the origin of rocks and minerals also became more sophisticated. Charles Lyell suggested that besides volcanic, plutonic, and sedimentary rocks, geologists needed a fourth category, which he called metamorphic. These arose through transformation of the other classes by heat and pressure. While agreeing that gneisses, schists, and perhaps granite might be problematic, continental mineralogists continued to believe that water, perhaps under heat and pressure, perhaps containing many strong chemicals, was crucial to petrographic change. Carl Gustav Christoph Bischof summed up the state of the argument in what became the standard geochemical text, *Lehrbuch der chemischen and physikalischen Geologie* (1848). In Canada, Thomas Sterry Hunt made another stab at a chemical geogony. His theory was rejected.

At the end of the nineteenth century, mineralogists and petrologists found that new research in thermodynamics, particularly that of J. Willard Gibbs on the phase rule, offered an alternative way to think about mineral and rock origins. They began constructing phase diagrams for certain common rocks to clarify the sequence and manner in which the different crystals had formed. The founding of the Carnegie Institute of Washington in 1902, and the construction of a lavishly equipped laboratory there, aided this program of research. The United States could now compete with Germany. In 1928, Norman Bowen summed up then recent developments in his classic, *The Evolution of the Igneous Rocks* (1928).

The question of the origin of the rocks was pursued in the field as well as in the laboratory by two opposing camps that frequently compared themselves to the Neptunists and Plutonists of a century earlier. The minority camp, the migmatists, believed that migmatites (as they called the puzzling hard rocks of varied composition) were formed in place as circulating fluids converted extant rocks into something completely different. The majority camp, the magmatists, led by the Canadians Norman Bowen at the Carnegie Institute and Reginald Daly at Harvard, argued that they were intruded from reservoirs of molten magma beneath the earth's crust.

M

Within this camp, heated debates raged about whether there was one magma or many, and whether magmas were homogenous or differentiated. There the matter stood at the beginning of World War II. Following the war, novel techniques in the laboratory and the field, including deep sea drilling, suggested new directions for mineralogical research.

RACHEL LAUDAN

MOHOLE PROJECT AND MOHOROVIČIĆ DISCONTINUITY.

The purpose of the Mohole Project (1957–1966) was to drill through the earth's crust to the Mohorovičić discontinuity, the seismic interface between the earth's crust and mantle. This boundary was discovered in 1909 by Yugoslav geophysicist Andrija Mohorovičić who noted that seismic waves returning from depth indicated there was a zone of abrupt change in the speed of seismic waves some kilometers below the earth's surface. Called Moho for short, this zone defines the base of the earth's crust and marks a change in composition. The depth of Moho varies from about 25–40 km (15–25 mi) beneath the continents, to 5–10 km (3–6 mi) beneath the ocean floor. Recently, following the acceptance of plate tectonic theory, geoscientists have decided that changes in deformational behavior are a more significant aspect of the earth's structure than changes in composition. They divide the outer earth into the rigid lithosphere (crust and upper mantle) overlying the more deformable asthenosphere.

Project Mohole was the brainchild of AMSOC, the American Miscellaneous Society, an informal group of geoscientists formed in the 1950s. Prior to this, crustal drilling was primarily undertaken to explore for oil and gas and had been limited to land and shallow water. Drilling for scientific purposes was much less common. It had begun with efforts to determine the structure, composition, and history of coral islands. In 1877, the Royal Society of London sponsored a borehole that went down 350 m (1,140 ft) on Funafuti in the South Pacific. In 1947, pre-bomb-test drilling of Bikini reached 780 m (2,556 ft). In 1952, drilling on Eniwetak finally reached basaltic crust beneath coralline rock at a depth of over 1,200 m (4,000 ft), still well short of the Moho. In the 1950s, some countries, including Canada and the Soviet Union, proposed drilling deep holes in continental crust.

Project Mohole, funded by the U.S. National Science Foundation, was designed to drill in the deep sea. The technological challenge was to drill the deep-ocean floor in water depths of thousands of meters. Although Mohole successfully drilled cores in water depths of 950 and 3,560 m (3,111 and 11,672 ft), it did not come close to reaching the Moho. Mohole, commonly seen as one of the first big-science projects in the United States, was terminated by Congress in 1966 and widely considered to have been a failure.

Nonetheless the project demonstrated that ship-based ocean drilling was feasible. It helped spawn the highly successful Deep Sea Drilling Project, begun in 1968, to drill through cover sediments on the ocean floor. Since then scientific deep-ocean drilling has become an international endeavor. Oil companies are reaching deeper and deeper objectives. Moreover, a number of countries and consortia have developed continental deep-drilling projects. None of this drilling has reached the Mohorovičić discontinuity, however.

Even so, scientists now believe that we can observe the Moho on land. By the late nineteenth century, a number of European scientists had recognized that in the Alps uplifted oceanic crust was represented by layered chert (lithified deep-sea sediments) overlying basalt (oceanic crust) over-

lying ultramafic rocks (high-density rocks rich in iron and magnesium), the so-called Steinmann trinity, after Gustav Steinmann. This package of rocks is called an ophiolite, and the transition from basalt to ultramafic rocks is believed to be the crust-mantle boundary—the Mohorovicic discontinuity.

JOANNE BOURGEOIS

MOLECULAR BIOLOGY.

The second half of the twentieth century witnessed a transformation in our understanding of certain key mechanisms fundamental to life. These mechanisms concern the biological phenomena of heredity and development and the chemical processes of the synthesis of proteins and nucleic acids. The techniques developed to investigate these phenomena and the conceptual structure into which they have been fitted constitute the subject known as molecular biology. The former can be likened to a toolkit and the latter to a manual. They have been put to work in numerous areas of biology from phylogeny and population genetics to immunology and neuroscience. With advances in these techniques have come applications to pharmacology (designer drugs), in agriculture (recombinant strains of crop plants), and in forensic science (DNA fingerprinting).

More than a toolkit and manual, molecular biology represents a combination of approaches of the chemist, biochemist, geneticist, and microbiologist, and offers a unifying conceptual structure provided by the mechanism and genetic determinants of protein synthesis. It can hardly be called a discipline, however, because its techniques have been absorbed by biochemists and geneticists, by embryologists, immunologists, and ecologists, and their disciplines have not blended. The practice of molecular biological techniques in so many areas of biology has made it a common currency in the many areas of the science of life.

Since all living things are constituted of molecules, and biochemists have always studied the behavior of molecules, why has molecular biology stirred up so much adverse comment? As Erwin Chargaff once quipped, a molecular biologist is a biochemist practicing without a license. Molecular biology is interdisciplinary to an extent that biochemistry never was before biochemists faced those who were to call themselves molecular biologists. The approach of the biochemists, dominated by their concern to unravel the nature of metabolism, its pathways and energetics, rarely included genetics, and paid only occasional attention to structural crystallography. And among chemists, those studying natural products concentrated on the proteins and the carbohydrates, leaving the nucleic acids to a mere handful of researchers. The change in biochemistry came when scientists accepted the notion that the genetic material consists of nucleic acid, not protein, and that the nature of a protein depends on the nature of the nucleic acid in the presence of which it is formed.

But again, had not biophysics a long history before 1950? Biophysicists had been very active in the study of the nerve impulse, the behavior of membranes, and the effects of ionizing radiations, and, in conjunction with physical chemists, they had investigated large molecules by ultracentrifugation and electrophoresis. But as a group, biophysicists concentrated on technique and did not immerse themselves in the conceptual problems of biology. Thus, when deoxyribonucleic acid (DNA) rose to prominence as the stuff of the genes, those involved gave their work a new title to distinguish it from that of the biochemists and biophysicists around them. This they achieved through such instruments as the *The*

M

Journal of Molecular Biology published by Academic Press beginning in 1959, the renaming of the Medical Research Council Unit for the study of the Molecular Structure of Biological Systems in Cambridge as the MRC Laboratory of Molecular Biology (1956), and the publication of James D. Watson's *The Molecular Biology of the Gene* (1965).

The Festschrift to the German physicist-turned-biologist, Max Delbrück, *Phage and the Origins of Molecular Biology* (1967), pointed to the work of the group formed around Delbrück to study the process of replication in bacterial viruses as the source of molecular biology. This book provoked a response from John Kendrew in *Scientific American* pointing out that the phage group was one source, but not the only one. Structural X-ray crystallography of the proteins was the other. He dubbed the former the "Informational School" and the latter the "Structural School," using the term school in a loose sense to refer to a network of researchers who, though scattered, constitute specialist communities. By the time Watson's enormously influential fragment of autobiography, *The Double Helix,* appeared in 1968, the three elements—phage, structural chemistry, and the addition of physics to biology—had become the distinguishing features of the popular history of molecular biology.

This historiography has been criticized. The salience given to the physicists, it is argued, exemplifies the construction of history by the actors to legitimize their importance. True, the search for a parallel to the physicists' complemen-

tarity principle in biology led nowhere, and the solution to the mysteries of the gene—how it duplicates, maintains its constancy, mutates, and is expressed—came from a combination of chemistry, genetics, and cytology, not physics. But indirectly, physics informed the disciplines of X-ray crystallography and physical chemistry by establishing the nature of the chemical bond, and offered a model in Delbrück's career for collaborative research among the phage workers. Also, physicists helped with funding; for example, Sir John Randall used the influential position he had gained for his war work to mastermind the establishment of the first research unit of the UK's MRC given to the biophysical study of the cell. Revisionist histories also complain that too much emphasis has been placed on the influence of the Austrian physicist Erwin Schrödinger's book, *What Is Life?* (1944) in drawing physicists and chemists to biology; but it is difficult not to accept the testimony of Francis Crick and Maurice Wilkins who were inspired by the eloquent appeal of *What Is Life?* to explore the remarkable properties of the gene, which, like an aperiodic crystal, so faithfully replicates its structure.

The conceptual structure that constitutes molecular biology consists first of the assertion that proteins arise through an interaction between certain proteins and certain nucleic acids. They owe their shape, long held to determine their specificity, to the folding of the long polypeptide chains that compose them. The manner of folding is determined by the specific sequence of the building blocks or "residues" (amino acids) along the chains, not, as formerly suggested, by the presence of another molecule to which they adopt a complementary shape. The sequence does not arise, as many had assumed, from the sequential action of a battery of proteolytic enzymes, but to the sequence of residues or bases on the polynucleotide chain of a nucleic acid (DNA) in the cell's nucleus acting as a template. The sequence represents a code or cipher for the amino acids of the protein being synthesized. It is copied from the DNA of the chromosome in the nucleus onto a "messenger" ribonucleic acid (mRNA). Passing out into the cytoplasm, the mRNA determines the sequence of amino acids in the protein being synthesized. DNA makes RNA make protein.

In 1957, Crick codified this picture in an address to biologists

James Watson (b. 1928) and Francis Crick (1916–2004), with their model of the structure of DNA they worked out in 1953

entitled "On Protein Synthesis." He stated two general principles: *the sequence hypothesis,* "the specificity of a piece of nucleic acid is expressed solely by the sequence of its bases . . . this sequence is a (simple) code for the amino acid sequence of a particular protein," and the *central dogma,* "once information has passed into protein *it cannot get out again* . . . the transfer of information from nucleic acid to protein may be possible, but transfer from protein to protein, or from protein to nucleic acid is impossible" (Crick, 1958). Crick defined carefully his use of the term "information": "the *precise* determination of sequence, either of bases in the nucleic acid or of amino acid residues in the protein." This understanding of the term implied a functional meaning in contrast to the purely syntactic meaning found in information theory.

In the decade following Crick's address, molecular biologists addressed the major features of protein synthesis and discovered all parts of the code relating nucleic acid and protein sequences. A sense of triumph marked the completion of this first phase of molecular biology extending from the 1950s to the mid-1960s. The emerging picture was simple. The information in DNA determines the information in the proteins according to a universal code. Since all that remained was filling in the details, many of the leaders among the molecular biologists began to look elsewhere for fresh problems to solve. Those who stayed the course engaged in a surprising and revealing task.

Exceptions were soon reported, both real and apparent, to the universality of the genetic code, to the sequence hypothesis, and to the central dogma. The concept of the gene, once unambiguous, became a term with multiple meanings as molecular tools dissected it in varied ways. With the introduction of the techniques of recombinant DNA in the 1970s came novel methods to manipulate the genetic material and to reveal the multiple levels of control of gene expression possessed by the cell. The discovery in 1970 of enzymes (reverse transcriptases) that copy RNA base sequences back into DNA upset the complacent assumption that information only flows from DNA to RNA—a direction allowed for in Crick's statement of the *central dogma,* but widely assumed not to be possible. The revelation in 1977 that often only parts of the message (mRNA) from the DNA is translated into protein destroyed the simple one-to-one relationship between a DNA sequence and a polypeptide chain. Other discoveries revealed that much of the chromosomal DNA of higher organisms does not carry the information to determine a given polypeptide chain, but has some other function, gene regulation being one.

This second phase of molecular biology lasted from the 1970s to the present. In several respects it is a transformed version of the first phase. In the past, critics accused molecular biologists of adopting a too-reductionist approach, but the multi-level picture of the system of gene expression that has emerged in the second phase of the subject makes this accusation hard to justify. The most significant intellectual outcomes of the current phase of the subject relate to evolution and development. On the one hand, the extent to which the molecular machinery of the cell has been conserved in evolution has surprised everyone. On the other, the attribution of so much of biological diversity to the variety of ways in which the same genetic equipment is expressed has directed increasing attention to the genetic control of development. The recent success in sequencing the human genome, and those of several model organisms, has strikingly emphasized these points.

This more sophisticated molecular biological science has in the last three decades of the twentieth century been put to work in many fields, in none more dramatically than embryology. By 1980, all knowledgeable people recognized that the tools of recombinant DNA technology were opening up methods for the manipulation of genetic material of considerable commercial promise to industry. With these techniques, organisms and their products could be designed for specific purposes. No longer did humans have to wait for nature to turn up the right genetic combination through long, continued breeding. Parasexual processes came to complement or replace sexual processes and to bridge the chasm separating genera. Such power to produce trans-genic organisms has led to accusations that molecular biologists are "playing God" and endangering nature. The development in 1985 of the polymerase chain reaction (PCR) has made possible the amplification of minute quantities of DNA—even a single copy—a technique of great versatility for medicine and science. Thus, from an esoteric exploration of the nature of the gene, its message, and its product, molecular biology has moved into the marketplace, and now plays *a* significant part in the economic and social culture of the twenty-first century.

ROBERT OLBY

MULTINATIONAL LABORATORIES.

During the Cold War, few nations outside the two superpowers had the resources to drive big science. Countries wishing to compete with them had to pool resources. The pooling worked particularly well in Europe and in the physical sciences. Reconstruction requirements, Cold War dilemmas, the threat of Stalinism, competition from the United States, support from international organizations, and an understanding of limitations combined with the politics of European unification to provide the setting for the emergence of European multinational laboratories. The Soviet bloc and other regions also housed multinational projects, which remained, however, under national control.

Several overarching political institutions assisted the development of European multinational laboratories: the Organization for European Economic Cooperation (OEEC) formed in April 1948 to manage the Marshall Plan and transformed in 1960 into the Organization for Economic Cooperation and Development (OECD); the North Atlantic Treaty Organization (NATO), created in April 1949; and the European Coal and Steel Community (ECSC), agreed to by France, the Federal Republic of Germany, Belgium, the Netherlands, Luxembourg, and Italy in April 1951. In 1957, Belgium, France, the Federal Republic of Germany, Italy, Luxembourg, and the Netherlands signed treaties setting up the European Economic Community (EEC) and European Atomic Energy Community (EURATOM), both of which merged with the ECSC in 1967. The High Authority established to supervise the ECSC treaty became the European Commission. The EEC made explicit its European Community Research, Technology, and Development policy in 1974, the same year that the first elections to the European Parliament were held. The first laboratory created within this broad political context was the European Organization for Nuclear Research (CERN), which gained broad support.

Louis de Broglie issued the first high-level call for a multinational laboratory as an instrument to revive Euro-

Louis de Broglie (1892–1987), French physicist, the prime mover in the invention of wave mechanics, and, though he almost never left France, a proponent of international laboratories.

pean science at the Lausanne European Cultural Conference in 1949. Supporters of the call included Raoul Dautry, administrator-general of the French Atomic Energy Commission; Pierre Auger, director of UNESCO's Department of Exact and Natural Sciences from 1948 to 1959; and Edoardo Amaldi, one of the founders of Italy's National Institute for Nuclear Physics. UNESCO provided the institutional framework for CERN. In 1951, Cornelis Jan Bakker and other UNESCO consultants presented their recommendations. They called for a temporary organization, $200,000 in funding, and eigh-

The BepiColombo Mercury Planetary Orbiter of the European Space Agency

teen months to prepare an administrative, financial, and technical program.

Niels Bohr offered his institute as a home for CERN; the offer was accepted, but only for the theoretical group. The representatives of the eleven countries that set up CERN in February 1952 chose Amaldi as secretary general of the new laboratory, and in October decided to build it near Geneva. The formal founding of CERN by the Federal Republic of Germany, Belgium, Denmark, France, Greece, Italy, Norway, the Netherlands, the United Kingdom, Sweden, Switzerland, and Yugoslavia took place in 1954. In October 1954, Felix Bloch succeeded Amaldi and became CERN's first permanent director general. Though motivated by American competition, the CERN management did not reject Ford Foundation funding. The Soviet inauguration of the Dubna 10 GeV protonsynchrotron in 1957 introduced a second major competitor. CERN's first accelerator, a 600 MeV proton synchrocyclotron, was inaugurated in 1957, coordinated by Bakker. The CERN proton-synchrotron, whose development was led by Odd Dahl, began operating in November 1959 at 28 GeV.

Nearly half of the particle physicists in the world work at CERN, supported by a staff of three thousand. The size of the operation and the number of researchers complicate relations among project managers. Traditional European disciplinary divisions created more problems than did national differences. In contrast to the American tradition, CERN at first kept science apart from engineering and performed poorly in comparison to the Brookhaven laboratory. European scientists had to learn how to do big science.

Good management and a research focus on reproducible results raised CERN gradually from an institution that missed opportunities in the 1960s and that still had a low reputation in the mid-1970s, to the renowned producer of W and Z boson results and Nobel Prizes.

The failure to establish CERN in Copenhagen—the theoretical group moved out in 1957—motivated the creation in its place of the Nordisk Institut for Theoretisk Atomfysik (Nordita). Bohr and his colleagues recognized that none of the Nordic countries alone commanded sufficient resources to compete in nuclear and elementary particle physics—despite the Norwegians' success in operating JEEP, the first nuclear reactor outside the sphere of the major powers in 1951. Moreover, experience with the UNAEC revealed some of the barriers that the Cold War introduced into nuclear science.

In January 1953, Bohr from Denmark, Torsten Gustafson from Sweden, and Egil Hylleraas from Norway met at Gothenburg to organize an atomic committee. The timing was politically appropriate: the following month, the Nordic Council had its first meeting in Copenhagen. Finland joined the Nordita project in November 1955 and Iceland in January 1956. Bohr gained the Nordic Council's approval for Nordita in February 1957. Nordita started operations on 1 September 1957, within a month of the departure of CERN's theoretical group from Copenhagen.

In the same year, EURATOM set up its Joint Research Center (JRC) at Ispra, near Lago Maggiore in the north of Italy. Centers at Karlsruhe (1960), Geel (1961), and Petten (1961) followed. Until 1973 JRC focused on nuclear energy. After that, it diversified into other fields. During its first decade EURATOM hesitated over its goals, which made the management of the JRC very difficult. Should it be an instrument for industrial or energy policy, or a nuclear research organization? JRC's functions varied from selling nuclear energy to advocating its peaceful uses.

The U.S. Atoms for Peace policy had motivated the creation of EURATOM; Europeans wanted nuclear independence. The Germans had experienced U.S. restrictions since an American intervention had stopped a joint project with Brazil in the early 1950s. The French supported EURATOM and the JRC only on condition that they could develop nuclear weapons. Nothing in the EURATOM charter appeared to prevent it. EURATOM also permitted the free movement of nuclear raw materials.

The JRC employed the concept of the five-year research program now a cornerstone of the European Commission's research policy. The first program, 1958–1962, divided the tasks into in-house or direct research and external contracts or indirect research. In 1959, thanks to Francesco Giordani, head of the Italian National Research Council, the nuclear research center at Ispra was transferred to EURATOM. The second program, 1963–1967, continued this trend, putting more weight on direct research.

A crisis ensued in 1968, when it became clear that EURATOM did not synchronize with national programs. A European atomic consensus did not exist. Most of EURATOM's projects stagnated or stopped, notable exceptions being the biological program and the fusion research project, the Joint European Torus (JET). The crisis was linked to tensions between Great Britain and France. The JET lab ended up near London.

Support for the JRC returned once it became clear that a growing scientific gap existed between Europe and America, and that European scientists were emigrating to the United States. In 1974, the Europeans decided on a common science and technology policy and chose in 1977 six areas of action for the JRC: energy; raw materials; environment; living and working conditions; the network for the exchange of technical information (Euronet); information science, telecommunications, and transport. The JRC became a research infrastructure for these areas. In December 1982 the European Strategic Program for Research and Development in Information Technology (ESPRIT) was approved. It engaged European information technology industry in JRC projects.

The reorganization of the JRC in 1988 brought further diversification: a headquarters in Brussels, the Institute for Reference Materials and Measurements (IRMM) in Geel, the Institute for Transuranium Elements (ITU) in Karlsruhe, the Institute for Advanced Materials (IAM) in Petten, the Institute for Systems, Informatics and Safety (ISIS), the Environment Institute (EI), the Space Applications Institute (SAI), and the Institute for Health and Consumer Protection (IHCP) in Ispra, and the Institute for Prospective Technological Studies (IPTS) in Seville. The JRC acquired a staff of nearly 2,500, of which 1,600 were researchers. After 1998, the JRC became not only the scientific and technical support for implementation of the European Union's policies but also its reference center for science and technology. Nearly 30 percent of the JRC's total budget of approximately 300 million euros now goes to nuclear activities. The JRC competes increasingly for funding from private as well as public sources.

Another important European multinational science institution is the European Space Agency (ESA). Again a unifying theme facilitated the alliances between scientists. ESA evolved from the European Space Research Organization (ESRO) and the European Launcher Development Organization (ELDO), which had confronted gigantic political and economic difficulties. As at CERN, Auger was a central figure. His years, from 1959 to 1967, were learning years. But they were also years when several European countries tried to develop their own space programs. Under Auger's inspiration, ESRO and ELDO achieved some successes, for instance launching fifty-six sounding rockets, but fell short of expectations.

From 1969 to 1973, under Hermann Bondi, ESRO evolved into ESA. Research fields comprised fundamental physics, plasma physics, high-energy X-ray and gamma-ray astrophysics, and special cosmic-ray studies and measurements of solar neutrons and charged particles. The Bondi era began optimistically, but the agency soon confronted the realities of costs and the need to accept cooperation with the Americans and the Soviets. Cooperation collapsed under the strains of the Skylab project, forcing a search for alternatives. The deployment of Ariane in December 1979 gave the Europeans autonomy. Despite substantial scientific achievements, ESA's budget is no larger than ESRO's in real terms. ESA has achieved cooperation (and competition) with the United States on equal terms, which none of the European nations alone could have done.

There is a difference between integrated and interdependent multinational organizations. An integrated laboratory like the JRC has a supranational organization behind it, like the ECSC treaty of 1951 and the EEC treaty of 1957. CERN does not have such a structure and, therefore, its members have an interdependent relationship. That the JRC carried the main burden of integration may have allowed CERN the institutional space to pursue pure science. Historians of science have not yet evaluated the contributions of key JRC actors such as David Wilkinson, Marc Cuypers, and, especially, Hans Jörgen Helms, a former JRC director and one of the key institutional builders of European science. Indeed, the history of European big science in general has yet to receive the attention it deserves. When the overdue examination comes, it will find a clear temporal marker: in a single year, 1957, Nordita started operations, CERN's synchrocyclotron came on line, the JRC was created and, on the other side of the Berlin wall, the first *Sputnik* flew.

REGIS CABRAL

MUSIC AND SCIENCE. In the early twenty-first century, the relationship between science and music is typically understood in terms of particular specialties within the natural and human sciences (e.g., architectural acoustics, the physics of musical instruments, neurosciences), and what these can reveal about music's physical and cognitive effects. A longer historical perspective, however, shows that the disciplines of both science and music have altered dramatically over the last few hundred years. New technologies have transformed musical as well as scientific practice, and through their use of instruments and shared understanding of measure and time, the two domains have been closely intertwined. Before Isaac Newton transformed the mathematics of physics, the paradigm was "nature is musical"; thereafter the formula became "music is natural."

Since the Enlightenment music has been classified among the fine and performing arts; consequently, its role in the Scientific Revolution of the seventeenth century has generally been overlooked. Until around 1700, however, music was considered to be a science as well as an art, that is, a body of systematic theory including both practical and speculative aspects. It was also an academic discipline: music, astronomy,

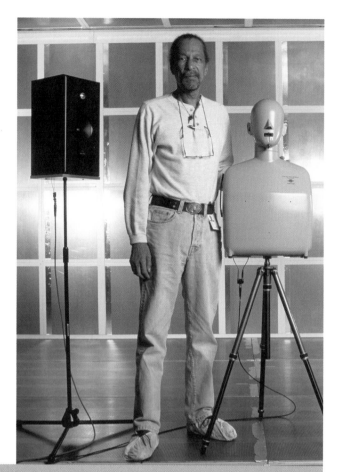

American acoustic engineer James Edward West (b. 1931) in his laboratory at Bell Labs. West is perhaps best known for his microphones.

M

geometry, and arithmetic made up the mathematical sciences of the quadrivium, which, together with the trivium (grammar, rhetoric, and logic), formed the core of the medieval arts degree course. Up to the sixteenth century the most authoritative source on musical science was Boethius's *De musica* (sixth century A.D.), which promoted the Pythagorean harmonic doctrine that audible music is a tangible expression of the underlying mathematical principles (harmonia) governing the relations between the elements of all significant structures in the cosmos.

Some musicians were already declaring this harmonic tradition irrelevant to their art in the early sixteenth century. Practitioners who played instruments with fixed pitches like keyboard and lutes realized that polyphonic music composed for two or more parts did not agree with the Pythagorean scale defined by the ratios of small integers. This conflict between musical practice and theory played a significant part in the emergence of experimental science as the physical properties of musical instruments, especially the vibration of strings, increasingly became the subject of philosophical enquiry. In his *Istitutioni harmoniche* (1558), the Venetian composer and music theorist Gioseffo Zarlino presented a new theory of consonance, which he claimed had been tested experimentally. The lutenist Vincenzio Galilei disputed Zarlino's scenario, and in the process became the first person to check the results of Pythagoras's legendary experiments with hammers, strings, and other sounding bodies. He proved that most of them were wrong. Galileo Galilei—an accomplished lutenist like his father—further investigated the properties of vibrating strings and announced his findings in the *Discourses Concerning Two*

New Sciences (1638). Although Galileo understood the relationship between pitch and frequency, credit for the discovery of the physical variables governing the pitch of musical strings goes to Marin Mersenne, whose *Harmonie universelle* (1636) contained the first published account of "Mersenne's laws." These boil down to the formula that frequency is proportional to the square root of string tension, and inversely proportional to string length as well as to the square root of the string's thickness.

The universal harmony of Mersenne's title indicates that although musicians rejected Pythagorean intonation on empirical grounds, early modern mathematicians continued to find the tradition of speculative harmonics inspiring. Johannes Kepler saw his search for universal mathematical laws as an extension of Ptolemy's *Harmonics* (second century A.D.), which assumes that sounding music *(musica instrumentalis)* embodies the harmonic principles governing human and also cosmic bodies *(musica humana et mundana)*. Kepler's *Harmonices mundi* (1619) builds on the concept that God created the world in accordance with geometric archetypes reflecting musical consonances. Kepler calculated the "harmony of the spheres" derived from the maximum and minimum angular velocities of the planets measured from the sun. The musical ratios that express these intervals are not Pythagorean, however, but those shown by Zarlino to be the basis of modern polyphonic practice.

The relationship between music and science thus developed in two complementary directions during the seventeenth century. First, musical phenomena continued to be investigated in their own right, most notably in the new field of acoustics. Joseph Sauveur claimed to have established this discipline in 1701, but Francis Bacon had already identified the "Acoustique Art" in his *Advancement of Learning* (1605) as exemplifying his new scientific method. Mersenne's systematic investigation of the properties of musical sound was taken up in the Royal Society of London and the Paris Académie Royale des Sciences. At the same time, however, musical/harmonic models continued to be fruitfully applied to other branches of the physical sciences. Robert Hooke, for example, postulated a unified theory of matter in which all particles act like musical strings vibrating sympathetically. Mersenne's laws similarly provided Newton with the basis for his analogy between colors and musical tones in the *Opticks* (1704), as well as his wave theory of sounds presented in the *Principia mathematica* (1687).

The success of the Newtonian synthesis brought the study of the relationship between music and science during the eighteenth century almost entirely within the framework of mechanics. In his *Traité de l'harmonie* (1722) the composer and theorist Jean-Philippe Rameau reduced the rules of harmony to a single principle of fundamental bass, which he compared to Newton's gravitational laws. Musical phenomena such as resonance and the overtone series appeared in popular texts of experimental physics, and were a staple of lecture demonstrations of natural philosophy. Meanwhile, leading European mathematicians like Jean Le Rond d'Alembert, Daniel Bernoulli, and Leonhard Euler disputed the mathematics of vibrating strings, a debate that contributed to the development of a viable theory of sound propagation. Pierre-Simon de Laplace's employment of the caloric theory of heat to resolve discrepancies between calculated and observed velocities of sound was a centerpiece of the physical science of the early eighteenth century. Enlightenment medical theorists also sought to explain music's effects in terms of vibration. Richard Browne's *Medicina musica;*

or, A Mechanical Essay on the Effects of Music, Singing and Dancing (1729) was one of the earliest treatises to address the physiological and psychological mechanisms governing human responses to music.

The nineteenth century marked a new, instrumental phase, which coincided with the shift to laboratory science as the dominant model of scientific practice. Ernst Chaldini's *Die Akustik* (1802) showed that most complex musical phenomena could not be explained by prevailing theory. Charles Wheatstone, Félix Savart, and other nineteenth-century physicists relied on new acoustical instruments (tonometer, siren, resonator, kaleidophone, speaking machine, etc.) in their quest to analyze and synthesize musical sounds and human speech. These acoustical experiments had important consequences for the scientific analysis of music. They provided the essential background for *Die Lehre von den Tonempfindungen als physiologische Grundlage für die Theorie der Musik* (1863), in which Hermann von Helmoltz established his new discipline of physiological acoustics. They also contributed to the invention of Alexander Graham Bell's telephone (1876) and Thomas Edison's phonograph (1877), technologies where parallel research into acoustical and electromagnetic phenomena converged for the first time. These inventions signaled a long-term shift from mechanical to electrical forms of sound production. In the short term, they had immediate application in the emerging field of psychological acoustics. Wilhelm Wundt and Carl Stumpf investigated the perception and judgment of musical tones, while Lord Rayleigh, whose *Theory of Sound* (1877) set the research agenda for the next fifty years, consolidated Hermann von Helmholtz's advances in physical acoustics. On the basis of Rayleigh's work and new materials for the absorption of sound, the Harvard physicist Wallace Sabine developed a new applied science of architectural acoustics.

During the twentieth century, the ability to record and reproduce sounds electronically had an enormous impact on the production and consumption of music. For the first time (except for barrel organs and other musical automata) it became possible to hear music without requiring live musicians. The music industry expanded in the wake of demand stimulated by the gramophone, radio, and movies. Experiments with electric pianos, guitars, and other amplified instruments in the 1920s and 1930s led to their commercial manufacture in the 1950s and 1960s and the creation of a distinctive pop and rock musical culture. Electroacoustic and computer-generated music, in which "sound objects" abstracted from their acoustic and notated sources could be manipulated in new ways, made their appearance. Pierre Schaeffer, who invented *musique concrète* in 1948, and Iannis Xenakis, whose stochastic compositions of the 1950s and 1960s were based on the applicability of the kinetic theory of gases to music, exemplify this genre of modern composition stimulated by new electronic and digital technologies.

Laboratories continued to be important sites for exploring and reconfiguring relationships between music and science throughout the late twentieth century, especially in the recording and telecommunications industries. In 1957, the first experiments in digital sound synthesis took place at the Bell Telephone Laboratories. They led not only to new musical applications but also to new research in the psychophysics of music. Since the 1960s advances in computer technologies and research into artificial intelligence have strongly dominated approaches to music analysis and music psychology, which in keeping with the increase in passive listening by mass audiences has concentrated more on studying responses to music than on analyzing the skills necessary for performance. The computational methods used by cognitive psychologists to investigate the processes of hearing, perception, and memory have also been complemented by neurophysiologists' studying music's effects on brain activity by means of PET (positron emission tomography) scans, which permit real-time observations of variations in blood flow across the brain. More recently, scientists have raised questions about a genetic basis for musical ability as the human genome project nears completion, but have found no definitive evidence.

The close relationship between Western science and Western music that persisted into the seventeenth century has continued. Yet once harmonic motion became expressible in a mathematical equation rather than vibrating strings, the importance of musical models for the natural and human sciences diminished. Although the string theory currently fascinating physicists resembles Hooke's concept of universal vibrating matter, modern cosmologists have not come to strings via music. And as the sciences become ever more specialized—acoustics itself being divided into numerous subdisciplines—the connection between music and any single science has fragmented. Nevertheless, some consistent patterns have emerged, especially the role of instruments in generating scientific knowledge about music. New instruments and techniques have been created to investigate the changes effected on human nature by music. These musical and scientific experiments have typically been linked through a shared reliance on mechanical, electrical, and, most recently, digital technologies.

PENELOPE GOUK

M

NATURAL HISTORY. Originally, natural history was the study of the natural world in all its observable diversity, embracing animals, plants, minerals, and aspects of what now fall under archaeology, anthropology, geography, meteorology, and geology. The objects of study were not always of living origin, as in the observation of weather patterns; nor were they always of natural origin, as in the collection of ancient coins or man-made artifacts such as prehistoric pottery. The term "natural history" perhaps ought to be regarded as a designating technique rather than as a subject area. To conduct a natural historical study was to collect, describe, classify, and from the seventeenth century onward, to perform minor experimental investigations into observable phenomena. At heart, it was descriptive, depending on a large variety of examples collected and arranged for edification, inclusive rather than exclusive, and rarely reductive in the form otherwise developed by Western natu-

The Swedish botanist Carl von Linné (1707–1778) in Lapp clothes. During his expedition to Lapland in 1732, he covered over 7300 km.

ral philosophers. In this sense, natural history takes its origin in the encyclopedic endeavors of authors such as Pliny the Elder. Pliny's *Natural History* in thirty-seven books dealt with cosmology, geography, anthropology, zoology, botany, medicine, chemical recipes, mineralogy, magic, and human industry and art, a miscellany of information for the most part comprising extracts from other authors.

The ancient and medieval scholar described living things by particular properties, uses, or wonders so that others might use or wonder at them. Moral and didactic themes were overwhelmingly important. Manuscripts and early printed books included references to fables, astrological correspondences, religious symbolism, and what are now considered imaginary beasts. The illustrations that accompanied these descriptions were often partly imaginary and stylized, especially in illuminated manuscripts of the Romanesque tradition. Alexander Neckham discussed the virtues of herbs alongside the theological cause for spots on the moon and insect venoms. Studies of nature typically took the form of catalogs and encyclopedias, like that of Bartolomaeus Anglicus's *On the Properties of Things,* which became one of the earliest printed works. Bartolomaeus and others displayed great erudition in their sources and shrewd observation by adding their own opinions and commentaries to older sources. They covered herring fisheries, agriculture, mining techniques, falconry, and such like, and gave the first accounts of exotic animals, plants, and medicines brought back from early voyages of exploration. A form of emblematic natural history emerged, based on a complex system of associations and similitudes, mostly astrological and moral, that was also learned and eclectic, full of compilations from earlier texts and oral knowledge.

Highly naturalistic representations of plants and animals were displayed throughout Europe in church decorations and illuminated manuscripts. Manuscript illuminators learned three-dimensional realism from the artists of Italy and Flanders. Both the naturalistic and Romanesque traditions continued without a break into the early printed herbais. The level of popular knowledge of natural history in the medieval and Renaissance periods can be inferred from these artifacts.

After 1650, naturalists abandoned emblematic meanings in order to focus more obviously on description and anatomical investigation. They studied and collected natural objects both for themselves and as part of a broader interest in curiosities. Books such as Robert Plot's *Natural History of Oxfordshire* (1677) discussed all sorts of local features, including country houses of the region. Books based on particular geographical regions became an established genre associated particularly with the recreations of gentlefolk, the "virtuosi" or gentleman-scholars of the period. Collecting rarities, performing experiments, and traveling and discussing their finds in clubs and societies were accepted activities in European aristocratic culture. In describing curiosities, scholars consciously adopt-

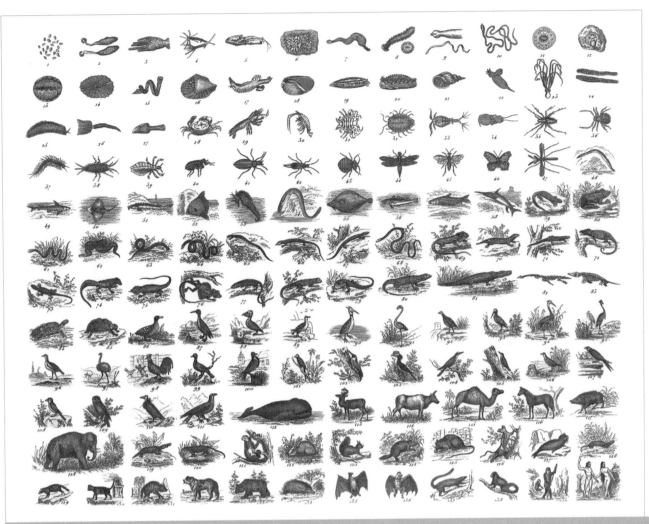

A late rendition of the animal world according to the French zoologist and paleontologist Georges Cuvier (1769–1832). The taxonomy runs from a cellular organism to man. From Johann Georg Heck, *Bild-Atlas* (1860).

ed a new style of descriptive language based on observation. Frequently, they reported measurements.

During the late seventeenth and eighteenth centuries, observations of the weather formed an important part of local natural history. Weather-books and garden calendars, in which the owner recorded the weather regularly, were introduced, emerging from the long-standing tradition of almanacs. Small museums and displays, often including antiquities, multiplied, and private menageries became popular among the wealthy. The older universities established physic gardens in which the whole of God's creation might be collected together and museums or cabinets in which curiosities from around the world could be shown.

Beginning in 1620, the Society of Apothecaries, one of the old-established livery companies of London, organized herborizing expeditions; similar expeditions followed in Edinburgh from 1670. These activities were seminal in establishing the field tradition that characterized European natural history thereafter. Since many enthusiasts for natural history were also physicians, collections often ranged widely over the disciplines, and frequently became the subject of inquiry or experiment. Putting together a "natural history of mankind" was a favorite endeavor that variously included reports of new races of humanity in exotic lands, folklore or other accounts of human societies, interesting artifacts, musings on the geographical distribution of mankind, and comparative anatomy. Natural history came to mean an account of nature based on information acquired

by observation and inquiry (including textual and verbal inquiry)—a point of view generally endorsed by forward-looking physicians. Doctors figured prominently among the early Fellows of the Royal Society, and medical societies and colleges formed some of the finest natural history collections still extant. Other enthusiasts typically formed a small club or local society to facilitate expeditions and the exchange of specimens and information. Generally these groups embraced a wide range of subject matter, and were among the first nonprofessional associations in many provincial towns in Europe. They played a major part in developing the strongly localized basis of British natural history.

During the eighteenth century, the subject's diffuse qualities gave natural history a low position in the hierarchy of the sciences. Countless descriptive papers appeared in the *Philosophical Transactions* of the Royal Society, devoid of the analytical spirit typifying French or Italian scholarly endeavor. The intellectual futility of these articles was lampooned by Jonathan Swift in *Gulliver's Travels,* and Jean Le Rond d'Alembert deprecated mere description in his preliminary discourse to the *Encylopédie* (1751).

Outside the learned world, natural history was understood to relate mostly to animals, plants, meteorology, and geology. Collecting objects and making observations became the central defining feature, encouraged by the growth of convivial clubs and outings. Techniques for recording data and collecting specimens consolidated. Naming and arranging specimens preoccupied many, both inside and outside museums. Books and catalogs were produced, and specimens sold or exchanged in a rapidly developing market economy.

In Britain, Gilbert White, the chronicler of the *Natural History of Selborne* (1789), became the exemplar of these localized pursuits. An Anglican clergyman, White regarded natural history as an appropriate way to appreciate the wonder and perfect design of God's creation. The Abbé Pluche in France wrote in much the same manner on the *Spectacle of Nature, wherein the wonderful works of Providence in the animal, vegetable and mineral creation are laid open* (1754). Natural history became closely associated with the natural theological tradition. Not all exponents made obeisance to religion, however. Thomas Pennant barely referred to the Creator in his *British Zoology* (1766), noted for its naturalistic illustrations and keen observation of bird behavior and habitat.

Fashionable interest during the eighteenth century perceived natural history as suitable for cultivation by women and gentlefolk, both literally in the development of lavish gardens and landscapes, greenhouses, menageries, and the breeding of rare livestock, and more passively in providing a responsive market for fine illustrated books, elementary teaching manuals, artworks, and newly fashionable decorated wallpapers and fabrics. Few other sciences have been taken up by consumers in such an obvious manner.

To be sure, Carl Linnaeus's simplification of classification and nomenclature enabled people who worked with animals and plants to codify their observations. Travelers and collectors could quickly assign unidentified plant specimens into a class or family. Linnaeus trained and sent plant collectors all over the increasingly accessible globe—Japan, South Africa, the Carolinas, Asia, central Spain, and so on. These men, whom he called "apostles," and others using his system, sent numerous collections back to Europe throughout the eighteenth century; Linnaeus consciously served as the hub of a botanical exploring network fanning out from his base at the medical school of Uppsala University. His classification scheme also helped botanical knowledge to move out of the restricted domain of universities, museums, and physic gardens into a broader constituency. Many eighteenth-century figures, including gentlefolk, women, and working men, are all known to have first encountered botany through popularizations of Linnaeus's system. His "sexual system" provided the basis for much cultural satire and parody, ranging from sexual innuendo about plants acting as humans to a scurrilous anti-Catholic classification of monks.

A growing interest in landscape gardening and the cult of the picturesque also stimulated interest in natural history. Plants and animals played a significant role in the life of the landed elite, who often possessed illustrated books and synopses of classification schemes in their libraries. The landed gentry patronized specimen collectors and landscape gardeners. Hothouses and stove-plants became an increasing possibility for the wealthy.

Natural history's greatest impact, however, came through geographical expeditions. These introduced a large number of new species to the West, initiating a rage for choice specimens and providing the foundations of national herbaria and museum collections. Many of these exotics came from government voyages of exploration to the Pacific, Australia, the Cape (of Good Hope), and the Americas. Living exotics could be seen at Kew Gardens (royal property until 1841), Chatsworth, or Syon Park near Chiswick, and the great European gardens such as the Jardin des Plantes in Paris. Enterprising private societies such as the Royal Horticultural Society (founded in 1804) and the Société d'acclimatisation in Paris sponsored collecting trips abroad and ran public gardens and competitions for their members. Animals were displayed in private and commercial menageries as well as in museums. The arrival of living examples of Nubian giraffes in Paris or London for these collections aroused national interest.

European prosperity overseas increasingly depended on the development of the plantation system in which staple crops such as tea or sugar-cane were relocated for colonial purposes. Local observers—frequently European expatriates—helped collectors back home. Naval officers, commercial entrepreneurs, and overseas residents gradually opened up the knowledge base of many different regions. In Britain, the East India Company took the lead in establishing botanical gardens in Saharanpore and Calcutta, and Kew Gardens, under Sir Joseph Banks, became a hub of proto-imperial science. The rich collections in Paris and the Netherlands were already the envy of Europe.

During the eighteenth and nineteenth centuries, natural history underwent a profound intellectual transformation. Interest in producing classification schemes was edged out, though never entirely replaced, by investigations into the inward functions of organisms and the history of living beings over time. Natural history itself slowly separated into subdisciplines such as paleontology, each with their own methods, agendas, and subject-matter. When the Museum d'Histoire Naturelle was reformed in post-Revolutionary France, the academic work undertaken within its domain was especially significant. Georges Cuvier explored the fossil world, and restructured classification schemes on the basis of four irreducible "types." His analysis of the elephant genus codified the concept of extinction.

Throughout Europe and America, a Christianized version of Cuvier's explanation of earth history became generally accepted. This invoked a series of creations of living communities of animals and plants periodically subject to catastrophic extinctions. Each successive creation advanced in character beyond its predecessor. The modern epoch, which included mankind, dated only from the Biblical flood, which coincided with the watery, icy period that naturalists recognized in the geologically recent past. This cold period divided the ancient history of the earth and the reign of mankind—and, if necessary, more or less matched the Biblical story. Cuvier's work was extensively popularized and had an impact on general natural history as well as in elite academic fields. The transformist schemes of his contemporary, Jean Baptiste de Lamarck, were less acceptable to the elite, but quickly spread in radically politicized form among progressive medical men in Europe.

Nineteenth-century natural history for the most part served Christianity. The geographical expansion of Europe's political and trading dominions, and the rapid economic development of North America, included a generalized Christianizing and educative mission in which natural history was frequently a significant element. Colonialists thought it important that natural history specimens, once collected overseas, be brought back to developed nations where they would be identified, itemized, and displayed as physical tokens of Western knowledge and, in many cases, colonial possession. In this fashion, butterflies from Surinam (say) served as effective devices to display scientific imperialism. Once named, said the British entomologist William Kirby, a thing becomes a possession. An extensive network of naval officers, surgeons, travelers, and local residents, distributed over the globe, contributed to a supply system—a flow of information mostly from the peripheries to the centers of knowledge in Europe's and America's capital cities. This flow of information to an administrative center, and the human networks on which it depended, mimicked the bureaucracies and administrative structures springing up in colonial countries.

Nineteenth-century natural history, like astronomy, lent itself to an imperialist structure. To a large degree, Charles Darwin's work was built on just such a structure. He considered himself a naturalist of the widest possible remit, interesting himself in turn in geology, plant life, animal breeding, coral reefs, insects, barnacles, and earthworms, and generally wrote in the pastoral mode created by Gilbert White. His work was nevertheless distinguished from the milieu in which he felt most relaxed by the strongly reductionist laws that he proposed to account for species change in nature. Since his day, natural historians have often justified their work and taken comfort from the fact that Darwin was at heart a naturalist and observer like themselves.

After reaching a peak in the middle years of the nineteenth century, the social and intellectual status of natural history underwent a relative decline with the rise of laboratory biology. During the same period, the popularization of science developed as a large-scale enterprise, disseminating scientific information of all kinds to the public at large. Natural history remained a favorite topic of books and magazines, lectures, exhibitions, and museums. This commercial success distinguished it from most of the other sciences. Lively, picturesque descriptions became the accepted norm, often featuring accounts of animal behavior.

Women formed an important category of authors, readers, and gardeners. They wrote books, attended public lectures, and encouraged the discipline in a domestic setting. An exceptionally accessible subject at a time when science was become increasingly abstract and mathematical, natural history seemed to belong to everybody. Anyone could advance it by observing or collecting. Amateur naturalists and volunteers in the field collaborated with newly professional university experts, although relationships could be tense. An indication of the growing distance between professionals and amateurs is the development of ecology. It did not emerge from field observations or inherit the characteristics of nineteenth-century natural history, even though one of its founders, Charles Elton, wrote that ecology was in essence "scientific natural history." In fact, it emerged in opposition to the natural history tradition in a movement in which professionals rejected the natural historical as amateurish and disorganized, not subject to rigorous controls or experiment.

This aura of accessibility continued to be the defining feature of natural history through the twentieth century, aided immeasurably by the development of cinema, photography, and television. Environmentalism and "green" policies have furthered the public appeal of the subject.

JANET BROWNE

NAZI SCIENCE refers in a general sense to all science, its practitioners, and its policy during the Third Reich (1933–1945), and more specifically only to those sciences directly tainted ideologically in content or in application by National Socialist policy. To the occupying powers, all scientists who remained in the Third Reich were "Nazi scientists" for purposes of denazification. For decades after World War II, the historical examination of science under National Socialism was taboo. Since the publication in 1977 of Alan Beyerchen's groundbreaking study of Nazi physics, the extent of Nazi influence has been revealed and the difference between "science in the Third Reich" and "Nazi science" has diminished. Under Hitler, nearly all areas of science, technology, and medicine, and indeed of scholarship in general, were influenced by the Nazi regime in content, practice, policy, or administration. Historians have tried to understand how and why sciences not obviously relevant to National Socialism still became more or less Nazified in content or approach. Nazi science is thus one of the most important historical examples of the relationship between science and ideology.

The most obvious of the Nazi sciences was Aryan science. The purging of Jews from state positions under the Nuremberg Laws of 1933, and the accompanying elimination of "Jewish theories," such as relativity, from textbooks, led attempts to create ethnically pure varieties of science that embodied National Socialist values. Aryan science included the application of rationality and efficiency to pressing state problems, especially the "Jewish Question" and the infamous Final Solution. It also became manifest in fields as diverse as physics, chemistry, mathematics, and psychology. Once politically objectionable individuals had left Germany, the state or party orchestrated the decline of Aryanized disciplinary science—except for certain forms of the biomedi-

The He-178, the first jet plane, designed by Heinkel in the late 1930s, made its first major flight on August 27, 1939. Its competitor, Messerschmidt's Me-262, was the first mass-produced jet fighter.

cal, engineering, and social sciences useful in attaining Nazi social and political objectives.

Although Nazi racial policy had links both to Social Darwinism in Imperial Germany (1871–1914) and the racial hygiene and eugenics movements in the Weimar Republic (1919–1932), the execution and administration of those policies were distinctive and tragic occupations of the Third Reich. Already, Weimar Germany used euthanasia in mental institutions and co-opted biology instruction, even at introductory levels, to teach racial purity, civic-mindedness, health, and hygiene. Although some biologists remained unaffected by the Third Reich, biology and the biomedical sciences were mobilized in war-related projects in research institutes or concentration camps on twins, eye color, air pressure, and reproduction. Genocide could only be accomplished with the chemical weapons created during World War I and further developed and deployed in medical settings outside the military in the 1920s. Part of Nazi racial policy involved the resettlement of Germans in eastern Europe. Area studies and spatial planning policy, using a multi-disciplinary approach based on geography, provided the practical details needed to implement the plan. This *Ostforschung,* or research on the east, presumed that the Polish, Jewish, Russian, and Ukrainian populations of eastern Europe would be expelled or murdered. The loss of the war thwarted the project to resettle the east, but the principles of urban and spatial planning developed for it remained useful. Elements of it figured in the reconstruction of West Germany, especially in handling the influx of German citizens forced to leave the eastern sections of the former Reich.

In defiance of the Versailles treaty, the Nazi regime supported military science and technology beginning with the introduction of armaments research in engineering courses at the technical universities in the early 1930s. In 1936–1937, the Reich openly supported military weapons projects; its devastating loss in the *Blitzkrieg* (lightning war) of 1941–1942 intensified its weapons research. In principle, Hitler himself had to approve all major military research and development projects, but bureaucratic conflicts led to inconsistent oversight of even the most strategic of them, including aeronautics, the uranium bomb, and rocketry.

Aeronautical research, based at Ludwig Prandtl's Göttingen institute, effectively circumvented the restrictions of the Versailles treaty, but was stymied occasionally by covert acts of resistance. Nevertheless, aeronautics became not only a Nazi strength, but later a West German one as well.

The uranium project under Werner Heisenberg, one of the most enigmatic projects of the Third Reich, failed to build a bomb; Heisenberg nonetheless went on to become the most important public spokesman for science in democratic West Germany and a major figure in promoting West German nuclear power plants. The guided missile and rocketry project under Wernher von Braun was the most outstanding technological success of the Third Reich. Under the Army's administration at first, the rocketry project expanded when the Air Force took over in 1935, and then again at Peenemünde and eventually in an abandoned mine in the Harz Mountains near Nordhausen, where concentration camp prisoners from Buchenwald supplied the labor for the protection of the vengeance weapon, the V-2, which Hitler believed would win the war. Both the Americans and the Soviets captured nearly all of Hitler's rocket scientists. During the Cold War, the Germanies had hardly any space program, while the superpowers explored space and esca-

lated international tensions with the help of former leaders of Nazi missile projects.

That the Third Reich was not more successful in science and technology has to do in large part with the fractious nature of its internal politics. A state that appeared to be run rationally was weakened by competition among power groups that precluded success in major projects. Where broad definitions and goals guided policy and administration—in matters concerning military technologies, race, gender, *Lebensraum* (living space) in *Mitteleuropa,* and *Gleichschaltung* (social coordination, or alignment with the regime)—science and technology were for the most part effectively co-opted. The most successful of the Nazi policies in science, racial cleansing and genocide, were also the most tragic. The alliance of science, technology, and medicine with the National Socialist technocracy led to a reorganization of scientific administration that survived the Reich and helped to create the big science methods of management found in both Germanies after 1945. These administrative strengths contributed significantly to the rebuilding of the scientific community after 1945, and eventually enabled both Germanies to compete scientifically with the superpowers during the Cold War. In both its short-term and long-term successes, however, Nazi science cannot evade moral judgement.

KATHRYN OLESKO

NEWTONIANISM. Isaac Newton joined terrestrial and celestial mechanics together in 1687 with the publication of his *Philosophiae naturalis principia mathematica,* transforming the two kinds of physics into a single system oriented around the inverse-square law of gravitational attraction. Twenty years after this feat of mathematical synthesis, Newton contributed to framing experimental physics in his *Opticks; or, A Treatise of the Reflections, Refractions, Inflections and Colours of Light,* first published in 1704 and going through four editions by 1730. The *Opticks* laid out an experimentally derived geometry of light-rays, including the use of prisms to analyze white light into the colors of the spectrum and then resynthesize them into white light. The *Opticks* also included a final section of "queries" containing all the unfinished business of Newton's career. By means of this laundry list, Newton set the agenda for his eighteenth-century followers. Most importantly, he proposed that weightless ethers were the medium and material cause of forces and phenomena including light, heat, electricity, magnetism, gravitational attraction, and animal sensation.

Over the past three centuries, "Newtonianism" has meant several things. On the model of the *Principia,* it has meant a mathematical, synthetic approach to physics, and more specifically, the confirmation and promulgation of inverse-square laws of force. Important examples are John Mitchell's demonstration of an inverse-square law for magnetic force (1750) and Charles Augustin Coulomb's announcement of an inverse-square law governing electrical attraction and repulsion (1785–1789). Eighteenth- and nineteenth-century Newtonians also developed the field of astronomy by testing Newton's law of gravitational attraction against new observations and resolving apparent conflicts. Alexis-Claude Clairaut's explanation of the motion of the lunar apogee (1749) and his accurate prediction of the return of Halley's comet in 1759 confirmed and vindicated Newtonian astronomy. These efforts gave rise to an increasingly complex picture of the mutual gravitational influences of celestial bodies. The culmination of eighteenth- and early nineteenth-century Newtonian astronomy was Pierre-Simon Laplace's *Traité de mécanique céleste* (1798–1827), in which Laplace used Newton's law of gravitation to develop a complete theory of the solar system, taking into account complexities such as the perturbations in the orbits of the planets and the satellites caused by their mutual attraction.

On the model of the *Opticks*, meanwhile, Newtonianism has meant an inductive, experimental approach to physics. Users of this meaning of the word cite Newton's promise, in the preface to the *Principia*, to "feign no hypotheses." An example of a Newtonian in this sense is Benjamin Franklin, who presented his electrical science as one founded in experimental tinkering rather than theory. His followers and historians have likened him, on that basis, to the Newton of the *Opticks*, the empirical essayer and querist. The empiricist meaning of Newtonianism has also referred, more specifically, to the use of analysis and synthesis experiments, for which Newton's investigations of white light served as the paradigm. The leading eighteenth-century example of experimental Newtonianism in this sense is Antoine-Laurent Lavoisier's analysis of water into hydrogen and oxygen and his resynthesis of these elements into water (1785).

The *Opticks* gave rise, finally, to a third meaning of Newtonianism, to describe the eighteenth-and nineteenth-century research program of so-called imponderable fluids that grew from Newton's hypothesis regarding force-bearing ethers. The hypothesis that an imponderable fluid medium carried each force informed theories of electricity, magnetism, heat, and light well into the nineteenth century. An eighteenth-century example of a fluid theory was Franklin's account of electricity, according to which a weightless electrical fluid, whose particles were mutually repulsive, permeated common matter, balancing the mutual attraction of its particles. Electrical effects accordingly resulted from the depletion (negative charge) or overabundance (positive charge) of the electrical fluid in a body. Another important eighteenth-century example was Joseph Black's understanding of heat. Black noticed that it took a great deal of heat simply to melt ice, without changing its temperature. He gave the name "latent heat" to the thermal fluid that seemed to disappear during phase changes, and he distinguished the quantity of this fluid in a heated object from its density, defining temperature as density of heat. An object's temperature depended, Black reasoned, upon its substance's capacity to contain the thermal fluid. These early notions of negative and positive electricity, of latent heat and of heat capacities, or specific heats, were thus informed by the Newtonian paradigm of imponderable fluids.

In addition to the work set forth in the *Principia* and the *Opticks*, another factor was crucial in shaping the meaning of Newtonianism, particularly during the eighteenth century: the contrast—partly genuine, but also overdrawn by Newton and his followers—between Newton's approach to physics and that of the French mathematician and natural philosopher René Descartes, to whose example Newton owed the beginnings of many of his ideas. Descartes notoriously allowed his rationalism and his commitment to rigorously mechanical explanations of natural phenomena to get the better of his physics. Based upon the principle that there could be no intelligible difference between matter and space, and on the conviction that physical events must have mechanical causes in the form of pushes between bits of matter, Descartes derived a picture of the universe as a great plenum in which all things were constrained to move in vortices. Newton's followers called Cartesian physics dogmatic, misguided, and arrogant in its claims to completeness. They pointed to Newton's abstention, in the *Principia*, from assigning a mechanical cause for gravitational attraction as the epitome of empiricist open-mindedness and humility. In celebration of what they took to be his epistemological modesty, Newtonians often referred to Newton's remark that he was merely collecting pretty pebbles beside the ocean of truth.

Leaving a gap at the heart of his system of mechanical causation, Newton allowed his disciples to fill in the metaphys-

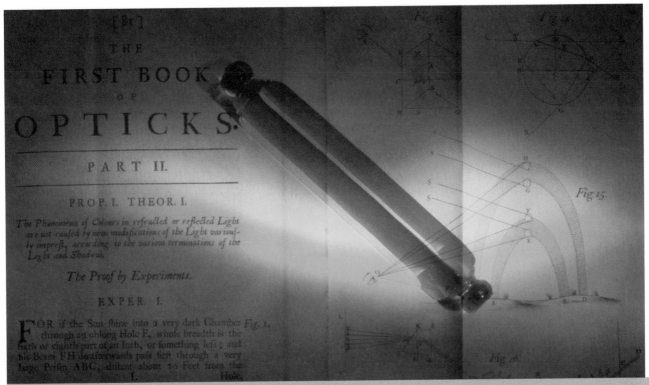

Photograph illustrating Isaac Newton's (1642–1727) ideas on the origin of the spectrum published in *Opticks* of 1704

ics of their choosing. He himself wrote, in the queries to the *Opticks,* that natural phenomena arose not from mechanical causes, but from the will of a divine intelligence. This appeal to a final cause lying beyond the efficient ones pleased Enlightenment eulogists of Newton's mechanical system, who showed a remarkable tendency to cite its breaches. An example is David Hume's satisfaction that although Newton "seemed to draw off the veil from some of the mysteries of nature," he also demonstrated "the imperfections of the 'mechanical philosophy," restoring Nature's secrets "to that obscurity in which they ever did and ever will remain" (*The History of England* [1754–1762]). Voltaire, in his *Lettres philosophiques* (1734), popularized for a French audience the contrast between Newton's heroic acceptance, and Descartes's dogmatic refusal, of obscurity.

We now have four meanings of Newtonianism: a mathematical, synthetic approach to natural philosophy (particularly one founded in inverse-square laws of force); an inductive, experimental approach to natural philosophy (particularly one founded in analysis and synthesis experiments); the attribution of forces to weightless, force-bearing ethers or "imponderable fluids"; and the appeal to final causes, manifestations of the will of a divine intelligence, as the ultimate cause of natural phenomena, in contrast with Descartes's and his followers' strict adherence, in their natural philosophy, to mechanical causes.

The promulgation of Newtonianism coincided with an increasing interest in natural knowledge among the literate public. Some of the first people to teach courses of experimental physics were Newton's propagandists: Francis Hauksbee and John Theophilus Desaguliers, demonstrators at the Royal Society of London, and Willem Jacob 'sGravesande, professor of mathematics at the University of Leiden, who was inspired by a meeting with Newton during a visit

Alfred Nobel (1833–1896), Swedish chemist, engineer, and philanthropist

to London. These lecturers professed to translate Newton's physics from the language of mathematics into the language of experience, using demonstration experiments to make complicated ideas accessible to polite audiences. Popular written expositions of Newton's physics, including Desaguliers's and 'sGravesande's published lectures, emerged during the first third of the eighteenth century. Turning Newton's natural philosophy into a source of philosophical amusement, lecturers and authors established in the minds of their public a particular model of natural knowledge: quantitative and synthetic but also rigorously experimental; materialist and mechanist but also resting upon an underlying assumption that the ultimate causes in nature were final rather than efficient, reasons rather than mechanisms. The same model of knowledge took root in universities, academies, and technical and professional schools during the eighteenth century, beginning with the Royal Society, Cambridge University, and the University of Leiden, and spreading after about 1730 to France, Italy, Russia, and Sweden, where it mixed with continental traditions informed by the work of Descartes, Gottfried Leibniz, and others. Not only mathematicians and philosophers but doctors and engineers studied and taught Newtonian curricula by the end of the eighteenth century. Thus Newtonianism, with its several meanings, permeated the emerging professional and popular cultures of the Enlightenment.

JESSICA RISKIN

NOBEL PRIZE. By his will of 1895, Alfred Nobel, inventor of dynamite and smokeless powder, left his estate to a nonexistent corporation, soon established as the Nobel Foundation. He directed that the net income from his endowment be given in equal shares for discoveries or inventions in physics, chemistry, and physiology/medicine made during the previous year that had contributed most to the welfare of mankind; and also for literature of an idealist tendency and for contributions to world peace. The prize in economics in the name of Alfred Nobel was established by the Bank of Sweden in 1968. The Royal Swedish Academy of Sciences awards the prizes in physics, chemistry, and economics, and the Karolinska Institute the prize in physiology/medicine.

The requirement that the prizes be given for current work was not observed in the first awards, made in 1901, and rarely thereafter. Since prizes can be given for old work newly recognized as significant for recent innovations, the lag can be considerable, almost fifty years in the case of one of the physics laureates of 2000. Early winners, like Wilhelm Conrad Röntgen for X rays (physics, 1901), Guglielmo Marconi and Ferdinand Braun for wireless telegraphy (physics, 1909), Adolf von Baeyer for contributions to chemical industry (chemistry, 1905), Emil von Behring for serum therapy (physiology/medicine, 1901), Ronald Ross for the etiology of malaria (physiology/medicine, 1902), and many more in physiology/medicine, were the sorts of awardees Nobel had in mind. But the requirement of applicability dissolved along with that of currency. Many of the science prizes, particularly in physics, have gone to academics for discoveries whose applications, if any, were not foreseen at the time of the award.

The distribution of awards has often been scrutinized for signs of bias and indications of national rankings. Some have noticed biases toward Germany, experimental discoveries, and exact measurement in the prizes given during the first two or three decades. But the leading theorists usually were honored if they lived long enough and the early favoritism of

N

Germans, owing to the closeness of the German and Swedish scientific communities, did not undermine confidence in the merit of the decisions. Since World War II, Americans have dominated the science prizes. The first crop of winners, in 1901, were two Germans and a Dutchman working in Germany. The prizes of 1926 (to proceed in 25-year intervals) went to two Germans, an Austrian working in Germany, a Frenchman, a Swede, and a Dane. This increase in awardees does not indicate the arrival of team research but the operation of a rule that played an important part in Nobel politics: a prize committee can hold over a prize for a year, after which it must either be awarded or pocketed by the academy for the research of those who failed to find a winner. The accounting of 1926 includes two prizes postponed in 1925.

Twenty-five years later we reach a new world. The science prizes of 1951 went to two Americans, a South African working in the United States, an Englishman, and an Irishman. (The quantity of winners reflected not belated prizes but small-team collaboration in accelerator physics.) In 1976, Americans made a clean sweep, five of them sharing the three prizes available.

Of greater interest to many winners than the competition among nations is the monetary value of their awards. Although it has varied, it has ended the century as it began, at about six times a top professorial salary. One of Nobel's purposes in making the prizes so valuable was to draw attention to the importance of science and technology. The size of the prize, inflated by the participation of the Swedish royal family in the gala award ceremony and dinner, helped make its message. Science needs no such advertisement today. Nobel had in mind the lone investigator, such as himself, working out ideas that strike only the prepared mind of an individual genius. By insisting that no more than three people can share one science prize, the Nobel Foundation has institutionalized its founder's romantic notion of scientific creativity. In our age of team research, when experiments can involve hundreds of people, Nobel's notion of a single informing creative impulse no longer catches the circumstances of science.

In this predicament, the Nobel Foundation might become more companionable, and permit the award of science prizes to groups as it does the peace prize. Failing that, it might consider enlarging the scope of science to include its history. Most historians still work alone.

J. L. HEILBRON

NOBLE GASES. The least reactive of the chemical elements proved the most fruitful guide to their interrelations. Some twenty-five years after Dmitrii Mendeleev first worked out his periodic table, Lord Rayleigh (John William Strutt), formerly James Clerk Maxwell's successor as Cavendish professor of physics at Cambridge, discovered that the nitrogen he drew from the air had a specific weight greater than that of the nitrogen derived from mineral sources. He asked publicly for ways to resolve the discrepancy and then hit on the solution himself. He read a paper, then a century old, in which Henry Cavendish mentioned an unoxydizable residue of gas he obtained after sparking atmospheric nitrogen with oxygen.

While Rayleigh tried to collect enough of this residue to weigh it, William Ramsay, a leading British chemist alerted to the problem by Rayleigh's request, isolated the residue by more effective chemical means. It weighed enough to account for the discrepancy of one part in two hundred that

A display of neon lights enhanced by mirrors

had started Rayleigh's quest. By 1895, they could announce the discovery of a constituent of the atmosphere they named "argon" (from the Greek for "lazy") because it declined chemical intercourse. Ramsay then looked for other trace gases by examining air and argon liquefied by then-new cryogenic techniques. Neon ("novel"), krypton ("hidden"), and xenon ("strange") quickly put in an appearance in the spectroscope and then the balance. So did helium, already named and known as the suppositious source of certain otherwise unattributable lines in the solar spectrum.

The sluggishness and aloofness of the noble gases put them in a class apart. Astonishingly, Mendeleev's chart could accommodate the five newcomers, confirming its importance and renewing its mystery. The only pinch came with argon, whose atomic weight placed it after potassium, but whose nobility placed it before. It took almost twenty years and the invention of the concept of isotope to resolve this problem of precedence. In 1919, Francis Aston at the Cavendish made the first crisp separation of isotopes using neon gas in a mass spectroscope he had invented. Meanwhile the reversal at argon-potassium (and at cobalt-nickel and iodine-tellurium) helped to alert chemists and physicists that something other than atomic weight regulated the properties of the elements.

The discovery of the noble gases was almost a prerequisite to unraveling the complexities of radioactivity. Ernest Rutherford and Frederick Soddy identified the "emanation" from thorium as a new and flighty member of the noble family, now called radon; the occurrence of a decaying nonreactive gas in their experiments provided the clue for working out their theory of the transmutation of atoms. Radium also gives off a radioactive emanation and the two similar (indeed chemically identical) noble gases offered an early example of isotopy. However, the lightest of the noble gases proved the weightiest. Helium is often found with uranium and other active ores. With the spectroscopist Thomas

N

The explosion at the Trinity test of the first plutonium bomb, performed at Alamogordo, New Mexico, on July 16, 1945.

Royds and an apparatus made by the virtuoso glass blower Otto Baumbach, Rutherford demonstrated in 1908 that the alpha particles emitted from radioactive substances turned into helium atoms when they lost their electric charge. In 1910–1911 he showed that alpha particles acted as point charges when fired at metal atoms, and devised the nuclear model of the atom to explain the results of the scattering and to deduce that helium atoms have exactly two electrons. The replacement of atomic weight by atomic number (the

Nuclear physicist Igor Vasilivich Kurchatov (1903–1960), leader of the Soviet atomic bomb project

charge on the nucleus) as the ordering principle of the periodic table followed. Rayleigh, Ramsay, Aston, and Rutherford all received Noble Prizes in large measure owing to their work on noble gases.

J. L. HEILBRON

NUCLEAR BOMB. After the discovery of radioactivity and the relativistic equivalence of matter and energy, scientists realized that vast amounts of energy must be stored within the atom. Most insisted, however, that the enormous potential of atomic energy for industry and also for war could never be exploited in practice. More power would have to be fed into an atomic device than could be extracted; the threat of atomic weapons was consigned to science fiction. Increasing knowledge of the atomic nucleus did not affect this assumption. Once James Chadwick in 1932 had demonstrated the existence of neutrons, Leo Szilard inferred that a nucleus would not repel a neutron as it would a positive particle and might release more neutrons than it captured, leading to a chain reaction. But he was unable to pursue his ideas further.

Meanwhile astrophysicists suggested as early as the 1920s that the energy of stars came from the fusion of hydrogen atoms to form helium. Hans Albrecht Bethe and George Gamow worked out a convincing mechanism for the process in agreement with observation in 1937–1938. Their theory was of purely cosmological interest, since nobody imagined that humans could attain the temperatures required to set the process off. But then came the surprise discovery of fission at the end of 1938 by Otto Hahn and Fritz Strassmann, as interpreted by Lise Meitner and Otto Robert Frisch. Within a month it was widely understood that nuclear fission could release energy far in excess of any chemical combustion or explosion. To achieve the necessary chain reaction required obtaining a critical mass of potentially fissile material (that is, a large enough sample that the neutrons can participate in the chain before being lost to the environment).

Szilard persuaded Albert Einstein to inform President Franklin Delano Roosevelt about the possibility of a nuclear bomb. Roosevelt set up a scientific committee under the National Bureau of Standards to look into it. Meanwhile, atomic scientists were investigating the question in Germany, France, and Britain. Niels Bohr and John Wheeler had in 1939 proposed a mechanism for fission from which it followed that uranium 235 (U-235), although only about 0.7 percent of natural uranium, would be more suitable than the common isotope U-238. In March 1940 Frisch, now in England, and another refugee, Rudolf Peierls, completed their memorandum, "On the Properties of a Radioactive Super-Bomb," which showed that the critical mass required for fission on a large scale was much less than had been presumed. The British government set up the MAUD committee to investigate; they reported in the summer of 1941 that a bomb would be feasible. They also suggested methods to enrich the proportion of U-235 in uranium. In Germany Werner Heisenberg, as head of the Kaiser-Wilhelm Institut für Physik, set out the main tasks of a nuclear energy program. For about a year German research stayed ahead of the British, who at first thought to develop their own nuclear weapon but soon felt obliged to accept the absorption of their program into America's.

Anglo-American research disclosed that the newly discovered plutonium (created by bombarding U-238 with neutrons) would probably also be fissile. The American government, through the National Defense Research Council, began to pump money into the nuclear program even before

N

Pearl Harbor. In December 1941, what was to become the Manhattan Project began to take shape. In almost exactly a year Enrico Fermi and his team at Chicago achieved an atomic pile capable of a controlled chain reaction. Their accomplishment indicated that a plutonium bomb might be no more difficult to make than a uranium bomb. Huge factories in remote parts of the United States mushroomed into life—Oak Ridge in the Tennessee Valley (for separation of U-235) and Hanford in Washington state (for production of plutonium).

A third major laboratory, established at Los Alamos, New Mexico, under J. Robert Oppenheimer, assembled many outstanding nuclear scientists, including Bohr, Bethe, and Edward Teller, to design the bombs. They decided that uranium could be detonated by firing (with ordinary explosives) two subcritical masses together, but the plutonium would fizzle if made critical so slowly. Instead, a subcritical mass of plutonium would be made critical by suddenly increasing its density via an imploding charge outside it. War ended in Europe, and the failure of the German program was known, before the test in June 1945 of the plutonium bomb. The uranium bomb fell (without prior test) on Hiroshima and a plutonium bomb on Nagasaki in August. The shock of the invincible weapon forced the military leaders of Japan to capitulate.

The United States resumed testing in summer 1946. The Soviets, who had known about the Manhattan Project, resumed their own project, spurred on after August 1945 by fears that the Americans would use atom bombs to impose their supremacy over all. Helped by espionage (just how much is still debated), the Soviet Union exploded its own bomb in 1949. Shocked by this unwelcome surprise and revelations of past spying, the American government now pressed on to develop a thermonuclear device, the so-called H-bomb (for hydrogen bomb). Some scientists involved in the Manhattan Project, Teller for example, had even then wished to work on such a weapon, nicknamed the "super," since the fission bomb would create the temperatures and pressures to make fusion feasible. Both the United States and the Soviet Union developed hydrogen bombs and tested them in the early 1950s. Meanwhile the British, feeling they had been shut out of a program to which their scientists had originally contributed much, decided in 1947 to make their own nuclear armory. They have been followed by a number of other states.

ALEX KELLER

NUCLEAR MAGNETIC RESONANCE. The technique of nuclear magnetic resonance (NMR) emerged as a consequence of quantum mechanics. The orbital motions of electrons give atoms a magnetic dipole moment, which according to quantum theory can take only particular orientations in a magnetic field. One method to explore the effect involved sending a beam of atoms or molecules from a gas through a magnetic field and measuring the deflection. The so-called molecular-beam method could also measure the magnetic moment of an atomic nucleus, which resulted from quantum-mechanical spin. In 1937, I. I. Rabi, an expert in molecular beams, proposed applying an alternating magnetic field, oscillating at radio frequency, on top of the static magnetic field. The particles in the beam would suddenly switch orientation for particular frequencies of the alternating field, and the frequency depended on the magnetic moment—in particular, when the frequency of precession of the spin axis matched, or resonated with, the frequency of the applied

magnetic field. Rabi and his group at Columbia University used the magnetic resonance technique to produce surprising results for the magnetic moment of the proton and the quadrupole moment of the deuteron by 1939.

World War II interrupted research on magnetic resonance, but also fostered the development of new radio frequency electronics that would aid future research. At the end of the war physicists resumed work with resonance. One direction led to atomic clocks, which inverted the approach and used the minute difference between quantum-mechanical energy levels as the basis for a constant frequency. Another direction looked from the gases studied in the 1930s to solid matter. In 1946, a group under Felix Bloch at Stanford University and another under Edward Purcell at Harvard succeeded in detecting nuclear magnetic resonance in condensed matter. Bloch and Purcell shared the Nobel Prize in physics for 1952 for the work; Rabi had won in 1944 for the molecular-beam resonance technique.

Subsequent research brought NMR from the nuclear physics lab into diverse fields of science. In the early 1950s, Bloch's group found that the chemical environment of the nucleus—the close presence of nuclei of other chemical elements or molecules—affected the resonance frequency, as did couplings between the spins of nearby nuclei. The so-called chemical shift and spin-spin coupling suggested a powerful tool for chemistry. Organic chemists began using resonance signatures to tease out variations in molecular structure, and increasing use of NMR in the 1950s helped transform organic chemistry from painstaking test-tube analysis of chemical reactions to a quick mechanical process

N

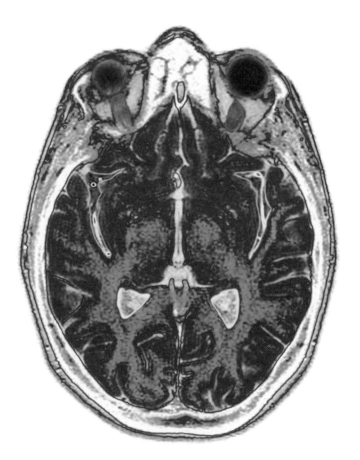

Cross-sectional magnetic resonance image of the human head

of structure elucidation. Solid-state physicists similarly took up NMR to reveal the internal structure of their samples.

The provision of standardized NMR devices spurred the spread of the technique to other fields. Varian Associates, a firm formed in 1948 near Stanford, led the market. Varian's founders had long experience with microwave electronics and close associations with Stanford physicists and engineers. These ties extended to Bloch's group, and when Bloch and Stanford lagged in pursuing a patent on NMR the company convinced Bloch to file a patent and assign it the license. Varian would also hire several students of Bloch. Varian quickly capitalized when the chemical uses of the machine became apparent; it introduced the first commercial NMR spectrometer in 1952 for $26,000 and improved models in subsequent years. The role of Varian in NMR development demonstrates the indistinct boundary between industrial and academic research, and between basic and applied science.

Yet another use for NMR, perhaps the most widely known, appeared in medicine. In 1972, the chemist Paul Lauterbur proposed to use magnetic field gradients to distinguish NMR signatures from different portions of an object. The resulting scan could identify biochemical properties across a tissue sample, such as water content, blood flow, and cancerous growths. Groups in Aberdeen, Scotland, and Nottingham, England, soon scaled up NMR scanners for human use and commercial firms brought them to the medical marketplace. In the 1980s, the technique acquired its current name of magnetic resonance imaging, or MRI, which skirted public fear of things nuclear.

PETER J. WESTWICK

NUCLEAR PHYSICS AND NUCLEAR CHEMISTRY.

Research into the atomic nucleus derived from the study of radioactivity, which flourished starting around 1900 as a program in both chemistry and physics; chemists sorted out the different radioactive elements and their decay products, and physicists elucidated the nature of the emitted rays. The physicist Ernest Rutherford, who would later deride most science outside physics as stamp-collecting, won a Nobel Prize in chemistry for his radioactivity research, but his work divided the physical from the chemical in the study of radioactivity. He posited the existence of the atomic nucleus in 1911. The subsequent atomic model of Niels Bohr, which combined Rutherford's nuclear atom with the emergent quantum theory, would establish the nucleus as the seat of radioactivity and encourage physicists to speculate about its contents. In 1919, Rutherford achieved the artificial disintegration of the nucleus by bombarding nitrogen atoms with alpha particles from radioactive substances. Hydrogen nuclei (protons) were knocked out of the nucleus by the impact of the alphas.

Most nuclear models through the 1920s built nuclei out of protons and electrons, since their opposite electric charges would prevent electrical repulsion; also, the apparent expulsion of electrons from the nucleus in beta decay argued for their inclusion. Application of the new quantum mechanics to the nucleus later in the decade, especially by George Gamow, provided a model of a liquid drop held together by surface tension, which nuclear particles could escape through quantum tunneling. But the presence of both protons and electrons defied attempts at detailed descriptions, and the nucleus seemed to reveal deficiencies in quantum mechanics. Bohr believed, characteristically, that the problem required bold steps and suggested that conservation of energy and momentum failed at the nuclear level. Wolfgang

Pauli instead proposed a new nuclear particle, later dubbed the neutrino, to save the energy balance in beta decay.

Another new particle solved the problem and reconciled nuclear models with quantum theory. In 1920, Rutherford suggested that protons and electrons could combine to form a neutral particle, a "neutron," which might reside in the nucleus. The hypothetical neutron attracted little attention, but James Chadwick, a protégé of Rutherford's at the Cavendish Laboratory in Cambridge, looked for it through the 1920s. In 1932, Chadwick found it in radiation, studied by Frederic Joliot and Irène Joliot-Curie, emitted by beryllium when it was exposed to alpha rays. Physicists soon accepted the neutron as a single elementary particle, and new models of the nucleus, notably one proposed by Werner Heisenberg, gradually accommodated the neutron alongside protons and removed electrons from nuclei. The neutrino and neutron, along with the positron (detected, like the neutrino, in 1932), were followed in the 1930s by other new particles, such as the cosmic-ray mesons. The floodgates opened to the proliferation of so-called elementary particles that emerged from the heads and machines of physicists in ensuing decades.

The neutron provided a useful projectile with which to probe the nucleus, since its neutral charge experienced no electrical repulsion. Physicists at the time were developing devices to accelerate charged particles to energies high enough to penetrate the electrical barrier of the nucleus. In another corner of the Cavendish, John D. Cockroft and Ernest T. S. Walton had built a high-voltage apparatus, which they used in 1932 to fire a proton into a lithium nucleus and disintegrate it into two alpha particles. Simultaneously, Ernest Lawrence in Berkeley was developing a circular particle accelerator as an easier route to high energies. Then in 1934, Joliot and Joliot-Curie bombarded aluminum with alpha particles from a polonium source and found that they created an isotope of phosphorous, which decayed radioactively. The process provided a way to produce radioactive isotopes in the lab. A group under Enrico Fermi in Rome quickly extended the results in a systematic bombardment of elements with neutrons; when they got up to uranium, their results suggested that neutron capture produced new transuranic elements.

The artificial production of radioisotopes, whether using rays from natural radioactivity or accelerated particles, required chemistry to disentangle the decay processes and identify short-lived parent species and their daughter isotopes by comparison to elements with similar chemical behavior. Nuclear research labs of the 1930s restored the sort of collaboration between physicists and chemists that had marked radioactivity research thirty years earlier. Lawrence, who recruited a group of chemists to his cyclotron program, noted the indistinct boundary between the existing disciplines and wondered whether to call the field nuclear physics or nuclear chemistry. An international community emerged among the major centers in nuclear science: the Cavendish under Rutherford; Lawrence's group in Berkeley; Joliot and Joliot-Curie in Paris; Fermi's group in Rome; Bohr's institute in Copenhagen; a group under Igor Vasilyevich Kurchatov in Leningrad; and the Riken laboratory in Tokyo under Yoshio Nishina.

A momentous collaboration formed in Otto Hahn's chemistry institute in Berlin, where the physicist Lise Meitner worked with chemists Hahn and Fritz Strassmann. The Berlin group began studying the decay modes of the postulated transuranics produced by neutron bombardment of uranium; after several years of analysis, Hahn and Strassmann convinced themselves that the suppositious transuranics behaved chemically like elements much further down the periodic table. The chemical evidence implied that uranium could split into two lighter elements in a nuclear version of cell fission, but the conclusion challenged the results of Fermi's group and seemed to contradict the nuclear theory developed by physicists. As chemists, Hahn and Strassman hesitated to take such a bold step. They appealed to the physicist Meitner, in exile from the Nazis, who with her nephew and fellow physicist Otto Robert Frisch showed how to reconcile fission with nuclear physics.

Physicists and chemists alike recognized the importance of nuclear fission after its announcement in January 1939, and both disciplines would play central roles in the military and industrial application of nuclear energy in World War II and afterwards. The discovery required the sort of interdisciplinary collaboration possible in Hahn's institute, which helps explain why physicists alone failed to notice the effect earlier. Fission exemplifies the interplay of chemistry and physics within a common field of nuclear science; Rutherford's early Nobel Prize symbolized the difficulties Nobel committees experienced in distinguishing physics from chemistry in the nuclear science of the 1930s.

The contributions of nuclear scientists to the war ensured public prestige and government funding for their postwar programs, which attracted new practitioners and allowed the construction of more and larger particle accelerators. The devices encouraged the separation of a new field of high-energy physics from nuclear physics, but also supported thriving research. Nuclear physicists recognized the existence of several different mesons and incorporated the various types into the theory of nuclear forces. Based on evidence of the stability of certain isotopes, Maria Goeppert Mayer postulated an alternative nuclear structure based on shells of nucleons instead of the liquid drop; theorists later reconciled the competing models in a rotational scheme combining single-particle states with surface oscillations. Nuclear chemists, especially a group under Glenn Seaborg, meanwhile were using cyclotrons, nuclear reactors, and even nuclear bombs to produce new transuranic elements up to and beyond element 100 in the period table. Both nuclear physics and nuclear chemistry earned state support by continuing as prime contributors to the military and industrial development of nuclear energy in the cold war.

PETER J. WESTWICK

NUCLEAR POWER. The dream of obtaining cheap and useful power from the atomic nucleus originated with the discovery in 1896 that energy emanated from radioactive atoms. By the beginning of the 1920s, Einstein's theory of the equivalence of mass and energy and Ernest Rutherford's experiments in nuclear disintegration together indicated that energy is contained in every atomic mass. Popularizers of the day declared that the energy in just one glass of water could power a giant ship across the Atlantic. But leading physicists at the time agreed with Rutherford in dismissing the prospect of nuclear power as "moonshine." However, nuclear power suddenly became a realistic possibility when Otto Hahn and his collaborators in Berlin in 1938 discovered that uranium is capable of fission upon bombardment with neutrons. Physicists soon learned that in the process of fission, a large quantity of energy is released along with more neutrons, possibly enough to make a chain reaction. While an uncontrolled chain reaction would make a nuclear explosion,

Ernest Ruterford (1871–1937), inventor of the nuclear model of the atom

a controlled one in a nuclear reactor would provide a source of energy that could be transformed into electrical power.

In Chicago at the end of 1942, as part of the Manhattan Project to build the atomic bomb, a team led by Enrico Fermi achieved a controlled chain reaction with an experimental nuclear reactor. The project soon established a reactor research station near Chicago at the site of what would become the Argonne National Laboratory. In 1946, the United States Congress established the Atomic Energy Commission (AEC), a civilian agency with sole control of all nuclear research. At Argonne, which in 1948 became the AEC's center for the development of reactors to produce electrical power, investigators pursued the main elements of reactor design: types of fissionable core, moderators to slow and absorb neutrons, and coolants.

In the late 1940s, as the Cold War set in, the AEC concentrated on nuclear weapons and gave nuclear power a relatively small budget. Admiral Hyman Rickover grew impatient. Rickover, a career navy officer and visionary engineer, was bent on developing nuclear-powered ships. Obtaining authority in 1947 to build a reactor for the navy, he persuaded Congress in 1949 to commit the AEC to the project. At Rickover's urging, the agency contracted with the Westinghouse corporation for a reactor suitable to power a submarine. A prototype version achieved full-power operation in 1953, and the next year a modified version of the reactor was successfully installed in the submarine *Nautilus*.

In 1954, the Republican Congress revised the Atomic Energy Act to permit private ownership of nuclear reactors and the leasing of nuclear materials to industry. The chairman of the AEC told the public that nuclear power would bring "energy too cheap to meter." Both the AEC and partisans of atomic energy in the Congress also spoke of an "atomic power race" with the Russians to bring nuclear power to the Third World. Under AEC sponsorship, Westinghouse constructed a scaled-up version of the *Nautilus* reactor for electrical power generation at Shippingport,

Pennsylvania. It went on line in 1957, generating 60 megawatts of power. That year, making conditions for private nuclear power more favorable, Congress limited industry's liability for nuclear accidents and provided hazard insurance at public expense.

More than a dozen nuclear power plants were operating in the United States by 1967. By 1975, in the wake of the Arab oil embargo and the resulting energy shortage, about 225 plants were on order, under construction, or in operation. And by the late 1970s, nuclear power plants generated 13 percent of the nation's electricity. Nuclear power was also under rapid development in France and Japan. Neither had adequate resources of coal or natural gas to fuel its power needs, and the oil embargo prompted both to intensify their commitment to reactor generation of electricity.

Meanwhile, in the United States, environmentalists had been taking aim at the rapidly developing nuclear power industry and its patron, the AEC. Critics raised questions about the disposal of the burgeoning radioactive wastes; about the safety of reactors themselves, particularly the emergency core-cooling systems designed to prevent overheating and meltdown; and about the effect of the heated water that reactors disgorged into rivers, lakes, and streams on aquatic life. In 1970, as the result of a suit brought by environmental groups, the AEC was compelled to take into account all potential environmental hazards in the licensing of nuclear plants. To many observers, the AEC seemed to have a conflict of interest because it was responsible for both the promotion and the regulation of nuclear power. In 1973, Congress broke up the AEC, awarding the agency's promotional and R&D functions to the newly created Energy Research and Development Administration (which in 1977 became the Department of Energy) and its regulatory functions to the new Nuclear Regulatory Commission.

The American nuclear power industry received a severe blow in March 1979 when operator errors at the nuclear power plant at Three Mile Island near Harrisburg, Pennsylvania, caused a failure in the cooling system, a partial meltdown of the nuclear fuel, and the expulsion of some 800,000 gallons of radioactive steam into the air above the surrounding Susquehanna Valley. Utilities canceled orders for more than thirty nuclear plants and no new orders were placed during the rest of the century. The accident at Chernobyl in 1986 further turned the public in the United States against nuclear power, and stimulated anxious questioning in Europe.

Since the 1950s, several nations have attempted to harness thermonuclear fusion for power generation. Since fusion burns hydrogen, which is abundant, fusion reactors would in principle be cheap to sustain and relatively environmentally clean. However, no nation has come close to making practical fusion reactors. Research focuses on magnetic confinement of fusion fuel, using, for example "Tokomaks," (an acronym from the Russian words for "toroidal magnetic chamber," the standard vessel used to contain the superheated hydrogen fuel) and inertial confinement fusion, which uses a fusion-fuel-containing pellet irradiated by X rays produced by high-energy lasers to symmetrically implode the pellet. Large laser facilities have been built to study ICF and the world's largest laser system, the stadium-sized 192-beam National Ignition Facility, is under construction in the United States. In the absence of a viable fusion reactor, nuclear power remains indispensable in the industrial economies of France and Japan, for example, where in the mid-1990s it provided 75 percent and 27 percent of their electricity, respectively. In recent years, the specter of global warming has revived interest in nuclear power in the West because nuclear plants do not produce greenhouse gases.

DANIEL J. KEVLES

Night view of the nuclear power plant on Three Mile Island near Harrisburg, Pennsylvania. The evaporation of water from the cooling towers kept the reactors at a safe temperature—except on March 28, 1979.

OBSERVATORY. Celestial phenomena have long been observed from buildings or sites specially equipped for the purpose. Notable examples before the early modern period include that at Hamadan (1024), established to remedy tables of planetary positions; at Maragha (1259) in northwest Persia, set up by Genghis Khan's nephew Hulagu, a devotee of astrology, and equipped with renowned astronomers from China to Spain; and at Samarkand (c. 1420), built by Ulugh Beg, grandson of Tamerlane and also a skilled mathematician and astronomer. The main instrument at Samarkand, the largest sextant ever made, consisted of two hinged rods whose free ends roamed over a circular arc 40 meters in radius. Using it, Samarkand's astronomers drew up a catalog of 1,018 stellar positions, the greatest achievement of fifteenth-century observational astronomy. Observatories were yet to be harmonized and integrated into Islamic culture, however. The Istanbul observatory, built in 1577, the year of a famous comet, did not long survive its completion. The faithful suspected that its attempt to pry into the secrets of nature had brought on misfortunes including plague, defeats of Turkish armies, and deaths of important individuals.

The comet of 1577 and an earlier supernova in 1572 undercut Aristotelian astronomical theory in Europe and encouraged the Danish nobleman Tycho Brahe to build an observatory surpassing everything before it. The Danish king, Frederick, offered him the island of Hven. There Tycho built Uraniborg, his manor and observatory, with large instruments for observing stellar and planetary positions, a paper mill and a printing press, and other necessities for self-sufficiency. Its great mural quadrant was a brass quarter-circle arc 2 meters in radius mounted to a wall oriented precisely north-south. Governmental largesse, equivalent to a great many millions in today's dollars, flowed to Tycho during King Frederick's reign and the regency of his son Christian, but shortly after Christian's coronation in 1596 it ceased.

The seventeenth and eighteenth centuries saw the rise of nation-states in Europe and growing sea trade, increasing navigational demands for accurate astronomical data. Charles II of England issued a royal warrant in 1675 appointing John Flamsteed "astronomical observator" at a salary of £100 per year to rectify "the tables of the motions of the heavens, and the places of the fixed stars, so as to find out the so much-desired longitude of places for the perfecting the art of navigation." A second warrant established a small observatory in the royal park at Greenwich. There was no provision for instruments, some of which Flamsteed paid for himself, and which his widow removed from Greenwich.

The Paris Observatory, begun in 1667, though more generously funded by the state, combined the pomp of the French court with poor design. Observing through windows rather than a rotating dome limited observations. The Cassini family ruled the observatory for four generations, until driven out during the French Revolution.

The observatory at St. Petersburg also functioned more for show than science until replaced in 1839 by the Pulkovo Observatory south of the city. Equipped with fine instruments, the new astronomical capital of the world figured as an object of high utility and importance to the scientific honor of Russia. The United States Naval Observatory, devoted, like Pulkovo, to positional astronomy, was completed in 1844, though surreptitiously in the face of congressional disapproval.

President John Quincy Adams in his message to Congress of 1825 had lamented that Europe had 130 "light-houses of the skies" and America none. Soon the United States had observatories too, mostly in colleges. Harvard lured William Cranch Bond away from his private observatory to work for no salary and supply his own instruments. They pointed out windows until interest in the great comet of 1843 led to a public subscription to construct and endow the Harvard College Observatory. The municipal Cincinnati Observatory also was funded by public subscription in 1843. Cincinnati purchased an 11.25-inch refractor from the German firm Merz and Mahler, makers of the Pulkovo 15-inch refractor, then the largest and best telescope in the world. Cincinnati's astronomer spent most of his time displaying the heavens to subscribers. Harvard, too, ordered a telescope from Merz and Mahler, and received a twin to the Pulkovo 15-inch. Trying too hard to justify its purchase, Bond mistakenly reported that he had resolved stars in the Orion nebula.

College and government observatories with precision instruments focused their efforts on positional astronomy. Individuals in small, private observatories were freer to explore new fields. The industrial revolution and British technology facilitated the construction of large metal reflecting telescopes from the 1780s to the 1860s, but steerable mountings and shelter from inclement weather, both important elements of working observatories, lagged in development, leaving the telescopes largely unusable. Application of the new technologies of photography and spectroscopy to astronomy also occurred first in private observatories. In 1854 William Huggins disposed of his silk and linen business and moved to Tulse Hill, a suburb of London, where he set up his own telescopes. By the 1870s, he was identifying elements in the spectra of stars and nebulae and detecting the motion of stars from shifts in their spectral lines.

Huggins's telescopes limited his investigations to bright, relatively near objects. Meanwhile in the United States, men wealthier than the former draper endowed the observatories with more expensive instruments: the Lick Observatory of the University of California with a 36-inch refractor (1887) and the Yerkes Observatory of the University of Chicago with a 40-inch (1897). The Lick, the first of the mountain observatories, demonstrated the value of good astronomical seeing at high altitude.

Growing interest in astrophysics and in distant stars and nebulae encouraged the development of new observatories

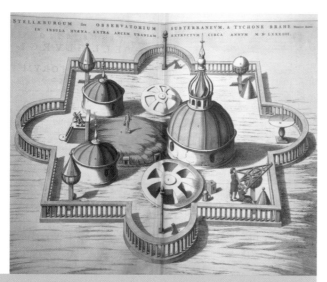

A portion of the observatory built by Tycho Brahe (1546–1601) on the island of Hven in the Danish Sound. From Willem Blaeu, *Atlas* (1665).

with large steerable reflecting telescopes suitable for photography and auxiliary instruments for the analysis of starlight. In 1902, Andrew Carnegie, rich from innovations in the American steel industry, created the Carnegie Institution of Washington to encourage investigation, research, and discovery. George Ellery Hale left the Yerkes Observatory to build, with Carnegie money, the Mount Wilson Observatory on a mountain above Los Angeles. A 60-inch photographic reflecting telescope, completed in 1908, and a 100-inch, completed in 1918, were the largest telescopes in the world and they revolutionized astronomical knowledge. Lights from the expanding city affected astronomical seeing, however, and after World War II an even larger telescope was constructed at Mount Palomar, northeast of San Diego.

The Mount Wilson observatory's relationship with physicists at the nearby California Institute of Technology was also crucial to its dominance of the study of astrophysics during the twentieth century. Many observatory staff at the beginning of the century had acute vision but little scientific education; soon a Ph.D. degree and considerable theoretical understanding were necessary for admittance.

Supposedly only men could withstand the rigors of observing all night in an unheated telescope dome, but the presence of women in observatories kept pace with their progress in university science programs. Women were first employed in an observatory in 1886, at Harvard, for lower wages than men would have received, not to observe but to examine photographs of stellar spectra and catalog the spectral lines.

World War II marked a turning point in the relationship between science and the state. The development of radar, ballistic missiles, and the atomic bomb relied on and demonstrated the power of state-sponsored and directed research and development. Observatories were a major beneficiary of increased government patronage.

Research on radar during World War II had led to the University of Manchester's Jodrell Bank Research Station and its large steerable radio telescope. Government assistance proved insufficient, however, until the observatory was rescued from financial disaster by its ability to track *Sputnik* in 1958. In 1962, British astronomers discovered a radio source that Australian astronomers identified with a faint star; but

the honor of measuring the highest redshift observed up to that time and establishing the first known quasar went to the United States, which had the only optical telescope powerful enough to study the object's spectrum. Commonwealth pride was assuaged by the creation of the Anglo-Australian Observatory in New South Wales in 1974.

The Soviet Union's *Sputnik* challenged American aerospace supremacy. The United States responded with a new institution, the National Aeronautics and Space Administration (NASA). Among its accomplishments are automated mini-observatories launched into space, topped off by the two-billion-dollar Hubble Space Telescope. This instrument, operated by the Space Telescope Science Institute, is managed by a university consortium under contract to NASA. Observatory personnel and much of the auxiliary instrumentation are earthbound. In general, NASA adjudicates questions of scientific priority and supplies the money for space observatories; industry helps build them; and universities or consortiums of universities design and operate them, and analyze the resulting observations.

The Kitt Peak National Observatory on a mountain near Tucson supports the largest collection of big telescopes in the northern hemisphere. Seventeen universities have come together in the Association of Universities for Research in Astronomy (AURA) to manage the observatory. After *Sputnik*, the National Science Foundation supplied many millions of dollars for construction of AURA facilities.

Observatories moved from cities to mountain-tops and then into space. They have also moved south, to observe the sky not visible from the Northern Hemisphere. The British Board of Longitude established the Royal Observatory at the Cape of Good Hope in 1820; the Harvard College Observatory had a southern station in Peru at the end of the nineteenth century; and Mount Wilson established a southern station in Las Campanas, Chile, in 1976. Its dark-sky site is better for extragalactic studies than Mount Wilson, which diminished its activity in the 1980s to free up funds for Las Campanas. Chile also boasts AURA's Cerro Tololo Inter-American Observatory and the European Southern Observatory. Astronomers from any institution may apply for observing time, and automation increasingly allows astronomers to control the telescopes from anywhere in the world.

It remains to be seen whether generous governmental patronage for observatories will long outlive the Cold War. Already, though, immense, technologically complex, and expensive observatories on Earth and in space memorialize our civilization as pyramids do ancient Egypt and Mexico, cathedrals the Middle Ages in Europe, and Stonehenge ancient Britain.

NORRISS S. HETHERINGTON

OCEANOGRAPHIC INSTITUTIONS. Most modern oceanographic institutions date from the second half of the twentieth century. During this period, oceanography came from the periphery of earth science to a more central position. Sea-floor studies played a crucial role in establishing current thinking about the dynamics of continents and oceans. Physical oceanographers improved knowledge of the mechanisms governing ocean circulation and the relationship between ocean and atmosphere, with important consequences for understanding climate change. From the 1980s onwards, they joined marine biologists, geologists, and chemists in the study of recently discovered hydrothermal vents and their unique faunas. These developments reflected

Amateur-astronomer night at Kitt Peak National Observatory in Arizona.
The segment of sky visible through the dome contans part of the constellation of Sagittarius.

scientific interests and oceanography's military and other applications in modern industrial society, and took place when funding for large-scale scientific projects became increasingly available. The funding made possible not only new ships and opportunities to explore the oceans on a scale not known before but also a corresponding increase in the number and scale of institutions carrying on marine research.

The first marine laboratories date from the second half of the nineteenth century. By then most nations had organizations such as the United States Coast Survey or the Meteorological Office in Britain, which functioned in the widest sense as oceanographic institutions, and also natural history museums and large aquaria. Zoologists who came to the seaside to be near fresh specimens developed the first dedicated institutions from ad hoc arrangements. A growing awareness of what could be learned about the origins, development, and physiology of living organisms from marine life powered their enthusiasm.

The first permanent institution in Europe was a laboratory dedicated to the study of marine zoology and physiology established by J. J. Coste at Concarneau, France, in 1859. A biological station at Arcachon, maintained by a local scientific society, followed in 1863. By the 1890s, marine stations could be found on the coastlines of Europe from the Black Sea to the Scandinavian Arctic. Of these early foundations the most influential was the Stazione Zoologica established at Naples by the German zoologist Anton Dohrn in 1872. Subsidized by the German government but also supporting itself by renting tables to other scientists and institutions and through the sale of specimens, the Stazione Zoologica

The Woods Hole Oceanographic Institution operates the US Navy's Deep Submergence Vehicle *Alvin* to explore hydrothermal vents.

provided (and provides) scientists of all nationalities with year-round access to research facilities where studies of the anatomy, physiology and development of marine organisms led to important advances in the life sciences.

These institutions varied considerably in their origins, modus operandi, and objectives. Félix-Joseph de Lacaze-Duthiers's stations at Roscoff and Banyuls-sur-Mer were linked to his department at the Sorbonne and welcomed visiting workers on the Naples model. Most laboratories opened only seasonally and a few, such as the station founded by the Zoological Society of the Netherlands in 1876 in its early days, occupied prefabricated buildings that could be moved from one location to another. Many of these European institutions received at least part of their funding from the state, some governments (notably the British) being stingier than others. In the United Kingdom, the Marine Biological Association established the Plymouth Laboratory in 1885. Other early British laboratories were connected with university departments (e.g., Gatty/St. Andrews and Port Erin/Liverpool), local societies, and fishery committees. Until well after 1900, British government funding for marine research was largely restricted to fisheries programs and provided at best an insecure lifeline to the independent laboratories.

Meanwhile, in the United States, marine biological laboratories were set up at Woods Hole, at Cold Spring Harbor, and elsewhere. The laboratory at Woods Hole, through its predecessors, the Penikese Laboratory established by Louis Agassiz in 1873 and the Annisquam Sea-side Laboratory of 1880, had its roots in teacher training but would later become a leading center for biological research. On the West coast, the principal centers were linked to universities—the Hopkins Marine Station of Stanford University at Pacific Grove, founded in 1892, the Scripps Institution for Biological Research (University of California), and the University of Washington's Oceanographic Laboratories.

In 1871, the U.S. Commission for Fisheries under Spencer Fullerton Baird selected Woods Hole for biological investigations and built the fisheries laboratory there a few years later. Concern over fisheries drove much organized marine research in the late nineteenth century. Norway channeled its marine research effort into specialist fisheries institutions. Scandinavian scientists soon perceived the need for more broadly based and coordinated studies of fisheries and related problems. Their initiative led to the establishment of the International Council for the Exploration of the Sea in 1900. The ICES inspired the creation of national laboratories and a short-lived (1902–1908) Central Laboratory in Christiania (Oslo) that paid special attention to the development of apparatus.

Until 1900, people considered the study of the oceans a shipboard activity. As the collections gathered in expeditions multiplied, however, land facilities for their study were required. The voyage of HMS *Challenger* (1872–1876) resulted in the creation of the Challenger Office in Edinburgh. It shut down after the completion of its report in 1895. Sir John Murray continued its work independently at the Villa Medusa until his death in 1914 but in 1884 he had established a laboratory that he hoped would be more permanent, the Scottish Marine Station for Scientific Research near Granton—the world's first truly oceanographic institution. In spite of Murray's efforts to conform to the prevailing utilitarian ethos by linking the station to long-running research by the Scottish Meteorological Society on the effects of weather on fisheries, the government refused to support it. The Marine Biological Station at Millport, established by the West of Scotland Marine Biological Association in 1897, regarded itself as Murray's successor and its work on productivity in the 1920s and 1930s followed his interdisciplinary vision.

The first permanent oceanographic institutions date from the turn of the twentieth century. The geographer Ferdinand von Richthofen established the Institut für Meereskunde in Berlin in 1900 to cover all aspects of oceanography. It sponsored the influential *Meteor* expedition in the 1920s, which resulted in the first detailed survey of the deep Atlantic circulation. After World War II the Berlin institute's work was transferred to a like-named, preexisting institution attached to the University of Kiel. Kiel was already distinguished in ocean research through the work of Otto Krümmel, whose *Handbuch der Ozeanographie* served as a standard text, and of Victor Hensen and other members of the Kiel school of plankton studies.

One of the foremost leaders of ocean research of the early twentieth century was Prince Albert I of Monaco, an enthusiast for science, education, and international cooperation. His wealth enabled him to mount numerous scientific voyages in Atlantic, Mediterranean, and Arctic waters from the 1880s till 1914. He set up his twin foundations, the Institut Océanographique in Paris and the Musée Océanographique at Monaco, both still in existence, to house his collections and promote the science of the sea through research and teaching.

After World War II, Admiralty pressure led to the establishment of a (British) National Institute of Oceanography (1949), now incorporated in the large-scale Southampton Oceanography Centre, established in 1995.

In the United States, concern about the state of marine science prompted several initiatives in the interwar period. In 1923, William E. Ritter secured the appointment of Thomas Wayland Vaughan as his successor as director of the renamed Scripps Institution of Oceanography (SIO) of the University of California. However, only after the appointment of the Norwegian physicist Harald Ulrik Sverdrup as Vaughan's successor in 1936 did work expand offshore into the Pacific Ocean. The outbreak of war postponed major development until the 1950s. Since that time SIO has been the premier U.S. West-coast oceanographic institution. On the eastern seaboard, this position is held by the Woods Hole Oceanographic Institution, founded in 1930 when a committee of the National Academy of Sciences enlisted the support of the Rockefeller Foundation for physical oceanography. A key role has also been played by the Lamont-Doherty Geological Observatory of Columbia University, founded by Maurice Ewing in 1948 as a center for seafloor studies.

The diversification of ocean science during recent decades, ranging from the deep-sea research to increasingly comprehensive observations of the oceans from space, has brought many sorts of institutions, including commercial enterprises, into oceanographic work. National and international academic cooperation now maximizes efficiency in what is still an expensive and challenging field of scientific investigation. However, large institutions continue to play an important role as centers of excellence, both in generating and supporting new research projects.

MARGARET B. DEACON

OCEANOGRAPHY, as a distinct scientific discipline, and "oceanography," as the standard term for the study of all of the marine sciences, both date from the late nineteenth century, when the first major expeditions were undertaken specifically to explore the physics, chemistry, biology, and geology of the world's oceans. But the prehistory of oceanography begins centuries earlier. Natural philosophers had given attention separately to most of the branches that now constitute oceanography—Aristotle's investigations of

The zoological laboratory on board the British research ship *Challenger* in 1874

Computer graphic indicating the changes in magnetism in sea floor volcanic rocks as Earth's magnetic field changes over time. The red strip represents the mid-Atlantic ridge (rocks 0-0.2 million years old), the purple strips the continental margins (rocks up to 200 million years old).

marine invertebrates; Robert Boyle's analysis of the temperature, salinity, and movement of sea-water; and Isaac Newton's explanation of the forces that cause the tides being among the most famous.

The first text devoted exclusively to marine science was the *Histoire physique de la mer* (1725) of Count Luigi Ferdinando Marsigli, a military man and founder of the Istituto di Bologna. From studies of the Gulf of Lyons, Marsigli assembled information about water temperature, salinity, specific gravity, tides, waves, currents, depth contours, and marine plants and animals. The diligence required in these efforts convinced Marsigli of the limitations of individual research in marine science; larger scale results required teams of investigators and government support—the hallmarks of oceanography since the nineteenth century.

The second half of the eighteenth century witnessed an acceleration of marine research. Enthusiasm for, and advances in, chemistry underpinned the chemical analysis of sea water by leading chemists, including Antoine-Laurent Lavoisier and Torbern Bergman. Salinity was also studied during voyages of exploration, such as the Danish expedition to Arabia Felix, and, especially, James Cook's expeditions in the Pacific. Meanwhile, ocean currents and circulation patterns engaged the curiosity not just of sailors but of scientists such as Benjamin Franklin, chronicler of the Gulf Stream, and Benjamin Thompson, Count Rumford, whose heat experiments led him to attribute ocean circulation to differences in water density, a theory finally accepted after a long delay.

Studies of currents and tides intensified in the early nineteenth century, exemplified by British naval surveyor James Rennell's *An Investigation of the Currents of the Atlantic Ocean* (1832). Also in the 1830s, John Lubbock and William Whewell, Lubbock's mentor at Trinity College, Cambridge, reduced tidal phenomena to mathematical analysis. And the British Admiralty helped to install tidal gauges around the southern coast of England. The limitations of the data for establishing general tidal patterns, and for drawing what Whewell dubbed "cotidal lines," led him to develop an international scheme for the collection of information about tides. The nascent British Association for the Advancement of Science soon took over the program. At the U.S. Naval Observatory, Matthew Fontaine Maury assembled data on winds, currents, and other oceanographic phenomena from ships' captains, and published the results in

his textbook, *The Physical Geography of the Sea and Its Meteorology* (8 editions, 1855–1861).

The British Association also played a key role in marine biological enterprises during the middle decades of the nineteenth century. The chief investigator was Edward Forbes, a marine naturalist and paleontologist for the Geological Survey, and a native of the Isle of Man. Excursions of small boats to ascertain the depth and distribution of bottom-dwelling species led to summer-long cruises in British waters, continued aboard Admiralty ships in the late 1860s by naturalists Charles Wyville Thomson and William B. Carpenter. The success of these efforts, and the increasing curiosity about life and conditions in the deep oceans, gave rise to the most ambitious oceanographic endeavor of the era, the expedition of HMS *Challenger* (1872–1876). Wyville Thomson headed a team of five scientists and an artist during this three-and-a-half-year circumnavigation of the globe. They oversaw dredging and trawling at more than 360 stations. International authorities in the various subspecialties analyzed the data and the specimens collected. The resulting *Challenger Reports* (1885–1895), published in fifty volumes, remain the founding benchmark of oceanographic science.

Although the supremacy of its navy allowed England to take a leading role initially, other nations used the precedent to launch important oceanographic enterprises during the late nineteenth and early twentieth centuries. Germany focused initially on the North Sea, but its S. S. *Gazelle* also operated in the Atlantic at the same time as the *Challenger,* and its S. S. *National* (1889) carried out a global Plankton Expedition. Alexander Agassiz headed American cruises in the Atlantic aboard the *Blake,* and in the Pacific aboard the *Albatross.* France, Denmark, Italy, and Russia had also launched projects by the turn of the twentieth century. This period saw the creation of the first marine biological laboratories, the prototype being the Stazione Zoologica created at Naples in 1873 by Anton Dohrn.

The two world wars provided an unprecedented stimulus to physical oceanography at the expense of marine biology. The deployment of submarines and their detection by sonar brought new urgency to studies of bathymetry and the relation of temperature, salinity, and bottom sediments to acoustic transmission. And an intimate knowledge of waves, currents, and surf conditions would become crucial later on to the success of amphibious landings. By World War II, a productive, if sometimes stormy, collaboration had emerged between civilian oceanographers and naval officers. In the United States, the principal centers of this collaboration were the Woods Hole Oceanographic Institution in Massachusetts, headed by Columbus O'Donnell Iselin, and the Scripps Oceanographic Institution in California, under the direction of Harald U. Sverdrup. In the midst of the war, Sverdrup, with co-authors Martin W. Johnson and Richard H. Fleming, published the first modern textbook of oceanography, *The Oceans: Their Physics, Chemistry, and General Biology* (1942).

After 1945, the Cold War relentlessly drove the growth of oceanography. As early as 1950, the U.S. Navy defined Soviet submarines patterned after advanced German designs seized at the war's end as the greatest maritime threat to the security of the United States. Understanding the ocean environment became critical to antisubmarine warfare. The Office of Naval Research and the Bureau of Ships quickly and regularly made resources available to address the threat, funding work by hundreds of scientists and institutions around the country. The results quickly outstripped administrative efforts to bring disciplinary coherence and recognition to oceanography, slowing the creation of degree programs and formal technical education at major universities. However, this massive investment made at a dizzying pace resulted in amazingly comprehensive ocean surveys, the understanding and exploitation of the deep sound channel, fundamental advances in sonar, the very rapid development of ocean acoustics as a field of study, the creation of the Navy's ocean surveillance system (SOSUS), the quieting of nuclear and conventional submarines, and the possibility of submerged missile launching. In addition, these circumstances effectively launched the careers of Roger Revelle, Walter Munk, J. Lamar Worzel, Dale Leipper, Waldo Lyon, Henry Stommel, Alan Robinson, and many others. The new sophistication of oceanography made it possible for American nuclear attack submarines to detect and shadow their Soviet missile-carrying counterparts. The deep ocean quickly became the front line in the Cold War.

The Russians followed suit, responding to American determination for the same reasons. While definitely competitive in terms of theoretical understanding and scientific capability, the material resources of the former Soviet Union did not permit it to keep pace. However, its scientists made very significant contributions to understanding anti-submarine acoustics, the study of the Arctic region, ocean surveying, and the construction of advanced oceanographic vessels.

Twentieth-century oceanography achieved a new, mathematically rigorous understanding of the coupling of atmospheric and oceanic phenomena, and of the climatic implications of oceanographic events such as El Niño. But after World War II, the discipline turned increasingly toward questions of marine geology and geophysics. The leading catalyst here was the continental-drift hypothesis proposed by Alfred Wegener in his book *The Origin of Continents and Oceans* (1915, first English translation 1924). Rejecting notions of continental stability and isostasy, Wegener proposed that the present configuration of the continents, and other phenomena from stratigraphy, paleontology, and biogeography, could be accounted for by assuming the gradual movement of the continents horizontally over the face of the globe. The theory gained few adherents until the 1960s, by which time new lines of evidence helped bring about the plate-tectonics revolution. Evidence came from studies of paleomagnetism and polar wandering carried out by P. M. S. Blackett, S. Keith Runcorn, and their colleagues in Britain; heat flow from mid-ocean ridges by British geophysicist Edward Bullard; seismological activity along mid-ocean ridges by Americans Maurice Ewing and Bruce Heezen; and gravity anomalies, pioneered by the Dutch geophysicist Felix Andries Vening-Meinesz and the American Harry H. Hess. In 1960, Hess proposed the hypothesis, subsequently known as sea-floor spreading, that would explain all of these phenomena. In the mid-1960s, the British geophysicists Frederick Vine and Drummond Matthews confirmed the hypothesis by analyzing patterns of magnetic anomalies around mid-ocean ridges, and the *Glomar Challenger* drilled directly into the Mid-Atlantic Ridge. J. Tuzo Wilson's 1965 concept that the earth's surface consists of several rigid but mobile plates put the finishing touch on the plate tectonics revolution.

OPERATIONS RESEARCH. One of the progenitors of Operations Research (OR), the physicist P. M. S. Blackett, defined it as "social science done in collaboration with and on behalf of executives," but this was both too modest and too limited a definition. Originally forged as a species of interdisciplinary scientific research in the fires of World War II, OR proved to be a major innovation in the management of science and in the application of natural-science models to social phenomena during the postwar period.

Autonomous microrover Genghis from MIT's Artificial Intelligence Laboratory. The overall length of this apparent monster is one foot.

OR began as an Anglo-American response to the vast expansion of the funding and organization of science by the military from 1940 onward. Mixed disciplinary units dominated by physicists rationalized the deployment of novel weapons systems such as radar and mechanized air warfare, and parlayed their scientific expertise into advice for developing a new science of war. OR arose in an Anglo-American context of science organization; the German war effort produced no equivalent, perhaps because German scientists were already well integrated into state bureaucracies. The forerunner of OR, "operational analysis," came into existence in Britain with the Tizard Committee on air defense in 1935; by 1942, several OR groups had become established in military structures in the United States. What in Britain had been a method to optimize the sinking of submarines by altering the color of the attacking airplane, the depth of the torpedo, the angle of attack, and other variables grew in America to encompass the modeling of the targeting of ICBMs as a two-player game with various technological options solved with a Monte Carlo simulation.

Having spread throughout the military in the immediate postwar period, OR subsequently entered business schools as part of the toolkit of academic training for corporate middle management. In 1952, the Operations Research Society of America was formed, providing the professional identity for a haphazard collection of trained natural scientists and mathematicians. Although OR maintained its connections to physics and other natural sciences, recruitment in the second half of the century tended to come increasingly from its own professional base. Thus it became possible to regard OR in the late twentieth century as a social science with an unusually specialized clientele.

OR cannot be reduced to a few discrete doctrines, since its methods tended to diverge between the British and American professions after World War II. Whereas British OR generally maintained its original character as a hands-on project of pragmatic modeling based on thermodynamic metaphors and statistical expertise, American OR, inspired by the contributions of John von Neumann in the areas of game theory and computers, grew into a mathematically abstract and theoretical discipline including "systems analysis" and "decision theory" at the RAND Corporation and Bell Laboratories. Some of the most illustrious scientists of the postwar period spent portions of their careers as operations researchers, including P. M. S. Blackett, J. D. Bernal, Conrad Waddington, Philip Morse, George Gamow, William Shockley, John Bardeen, Kenneth Arrow, and Ivan Getting.

The standard curriculum for an operations researcher toward the end of the twentieth century included linear programming, network models, game theory, inventory models, queuing theory, information theory, econometrics, and simulation techniques. OR progressively became allied with "behavioral science," artificial intelligence, cognitive psychology, organization theory, and neoclassical economics. It became the exemplar of the "cyborg sciences" primarily because of its heavy reliance on the computer as a source of legitimation and metaphoric inspiration, as well as its penchant for blurring the conceptual boundaries between men and machines.

Although OR and systems analysis have succeeded as intrinsically interdisciplinary professions, their practitioners experience recurrent bouts of self-doubt about the true or fundamental core competencies of the profession. Initially, the operations researcher regarded himself as a technocratic consultant who reconciled planning with market alloca-

tion or military command hierarchy. As planning ambitions receded, the role of the mathematical consultant moved to the fore. Hence, OR has never achieved an altogether stable academic identity, tending to become lodged in schools of management or public policy, but sometimes in departments of mathematics, natural science, or engineering. OR has been predominantly client-driven rather than content-based throughout its half-century of existence; nonetheless, it has played an indispensable role in forging a rapprochement between academic science and the state.

PHILIP MIROWSKI

OPTICS AND VISION. During the early seventeenth century, Johannes Kepler, echoing the earlier views of Leonardo da Vinci, likened the eye to a camera obscura, a black box containing a pinhole opening through which an image of external objects is projected on the back wall. Kepler worried that the analogy implied that the eye must invert the images it observes, but his work on light, optics, and the camera obscura forced him to accept the inference. He concluded that light forms images on the back wall of the eye, now called the retina, and not on the crystalline humor, now called the lens, as most scholars of the period thought.

Kepler argued that light as a passive entity followed the laws of geometry. His *Astronomiae pars optica* (1604) and *Dioptrice* (1611) dealt with the refraction of light, whose "law"—a relation between the angle of incidence i and the angle of refraction r—was given in 1621 by Willebrord Snel, professor of mathematics at the University of Leyden, who busied himself with astronomical and triangulation studies. Snel did not print his result; René Descartes, who may have seen it in manuscript, published it in 1637 as $\sin r = (\sin i)/n$, where n, the index of refraction, is a constant. Christiaan Huygens elaborated upon the law of refraction in his *Traité de la lumière* of 1690 by assuming that light was undulatory, rather than corpuscular, in nature. Like Kepler, Huygens believed that refraction arises because light moves more slowly in a denser than in a rarer medium.

Descartes had accounted for vision by analogy. According to him, the colors we perceive, like the impulses transmitted by a blind man's stick, result from pressure. He took color to be a secondary quality, not a property of external objects but the mind's interpretation of the pressure registered on the optic nerve. Nicolas Malebranche deepened Descartes's theory of vision in his *De la recherche de la verité* (1688). Sight cannot ascertain the truth of things in themselves; its purpose is to facilitate our navigation through the world. Further to the impugning of vision, George Berkeley (*Essay towards a New Theory of Vision*, 1709) undermined the idea that the concepts the mind creates by working on sense impressions reliably indicate the nature of things.

Isaac Newton's grand discovery, that sunlight is made up of rays of different refrangibilities, transformed the study of light and vision. Newton showed in 1672 and at length in his *Opticks* of 1704 that sunlight passed through a glass prism yielded a spectrum of rays of different colors refracted at characteristic angles; that the rays of a given color all had the same refrangibility (and so could not be further divided by a prism); and that the differently colored rays, if reunited by a second prism, again produced white light (the so-called *experimentum crucis*). Newton supposed that the different rays were made up of particles; but to explain why some rays striking glass are refracted and others reflected, as well as to model interference phenomena like the colors of the plates and "Newton's rings," he also supposed that the particles interacted with a pervasive subtle matter or ether. The emission and motion of the particles set the ether in vibration, and the particles penetrated or rebounded from a surface in accordance with the phase or "fit" of vibration of the ether there.

The different refrangibilities of rays of different colors make single lenses cast colored images. Newton thought, mistakenly, that this evil could not be cured, and he turned his attention to the construction of reflecting telescopes. In the 1750s, the instrument-maker John Dollond proved Newton wrong by manufacturing achromatic doublets made of crown and flint glass, which compensated one another's dispersion. Drawing upon Dollond's idea of an achromatic doublet, Joseph Fraunhofer, a Bavarian skilled artisan and optician working in the secularized Benedictine monastery of Benediktbeuern, improved upon a complex glass-stirring technique first developed by Pierre Louis Guinand, a Swiss bell pourer. With this method, Fraunhofer was able to manufacture flint glass of unprecedented homogeneity in the 1810s and 1820s. In addition to this crucial technological development, Fraunhofer reckoned that he could use the dark lines of the solar spectrum (later called the Fraunhofer lines), which his superior glass prisms produced, to demarcate precise portions of the spectrum. By altering the ingredients of his glass samples, he adjusted the refractive and dispersive properties in order to produce a second lens that would correct for the chromatic aberration produced by the first. After Fraunhofer's death in 1826, the British firm Chance Brothers of Birmingham and the French company Feil of Paris usurped the world's optical glass market from Bavaria. But during the 1880s, the physicist Ernst Abbe and chemist and glassmaker Otto Friedrich Schott manufactured apochromatic lenses for the Carl Zeiss Company in Jena, Germany, which would monopolize optical glass and equipment production until World War II.

During the eighteenth century, prominent natural philosophers like Leonhard Euler and Benjamin Franklin challenged Newton's particulate model of light, but their opposition, based on qualitative considerations such as the improbable loss of matter from the sun that the model implied, did not make an effective alternative. The corpuscular theory reached its pinnacle after 1800 in the school of Pierre-Simon de Laplace, which developed a quantitative theory of optical phenomena based on distance forces between light particles and the particles of ponderable matter. They managed to incorporate the polarization of light, which Huygens had known in the case of birefringent crystals and Étienne Louis Malus had discovered in 1810 in light reflected from glass, into their scheme by supposing that light particles had different properties on different "sides."

The remarkable success and high patronage of the corpuscular theory did not preserve it from an attack launched around 1800 by the English physician Thomas Young, who drew upon an analogy between sound, which was understood to be a wave motion in air, and light. Young perceived a further, and more useful, analogy between diffraction patterns and the interference of water waves. In 1807, he presented the persuasive demonstration (now famous as the Young double-slit experiment) in which light from a common source passes through two parallel narrow slits in an opaque screen. The superposition of the two transmitted beams on a surface beyond and parallel to the screen produces dark and light stripes rather than clear images of the slits.

Young's initiative was continued by a better mathematician than he, Augustin Fresnel, whose memoirs, composed between 1815 and 1827, challenged his compatriots who championed the corpuscular theory. One of Fresnel's techniques was to treat each point of the wave front as a source of secondary waves, a technique introduced by Huygens. By adding the contributions of those secondary waves in accordance with Young's principle of interference, Fresnel could determine the intensity of light in a diffraction pattern. The Laplacian Simeon-Denis Poisson deduced from Fresnel's

David Brewster (1781–1868), Scottish physicist, whose work included classification of the optical properties of crystals and minerals, the invention of the kaleidoscope, and the discovery of Brewster's law governing the polarization of light by reflection

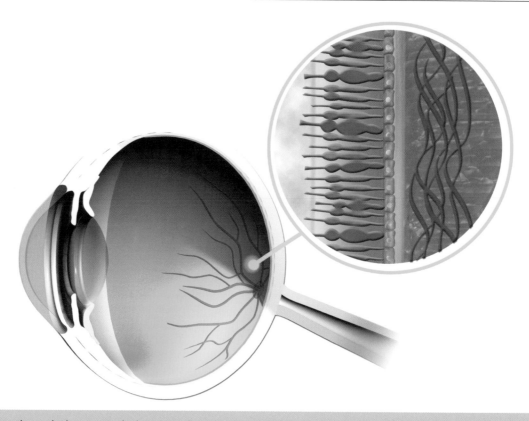

Light enters the eye through the cornea (colored grey), passes the lens (brown and pink) partly covered by the iris (blue), and lands on the retina (orange). There light receptors (red and brown) transform the stimulus into impulses fed by the optic nerve (grey) to the brain.

equations the paradoxical result that a bright spot should appear at the center of the geometrical shadow of a disk illuminated by a beam of light. The experiment decided in favor of Fresnel.

Around 1862, James Clerk Maxwell calculated that the speed of propagation of an electromagnetic field is approximately that of the speed of light. He concluded that light must consist of transverse waves of the same medium, which, according to the ideas of Michael Faraday, gives rise to electric and magnetic phenomena. British physicists attempted to ascertain the physical properties of this ubiquitous and omnicompetent ether. To incorporate polarization into the theory, both Young and Fresnel independently suggested that the vibrations constituting light are perpendicular to the direction of travel, not, as in the model proposed by Huygens and, originally, Young, in the direction of travel, as is the case of sound in air. With this addition, the wave theory bettered the corpuscular theory at its strongest point. All efforts to find a mechanical model for the ether failed, and the assumption that one might exist came into increasing conflict with electromagnetic theory. The nature of light and the fate of its medium were resolved—for the twentieth century at least—by the theory of relativity and quantum physics.

Young contributed to the study of vision as well as the theory of light by criticizing the custom of separating consideration of the physical and mental states involved in the perception of color. He argued that the eye, being far less complex than the mind, simplifies the information provided by a particular scene and channels it to the brain, which in turn paints the scene. He demonstrated that the most sensitive points of the retina, which are connected directly to the brain, can detect only the three primary colors—blue, red, and yellow. The optic nerve is composed of filaments, portions of which correspond to a pri-

mary color. The brain mixes the sensations to create all the possible colors. Young's theory was ignored until Maxwell and Hermann von Helmholtz elaborated upon his work in the mid-nineteenth century. Individuals suffering from color blindness (a disorder first recognized during Young's lifetime) have an abnormally low number of retinal cones, which detect color.

With the help of the opthalmoscope he invented in 1851, Helmholtz demonstrated that the optic nerve itself is insensitive to light. Sensory nerves apparently merely transmitted stimuli between the end organs and the sensorium. Between 1852 and 1855, Helmholtz studied color mixing and vision. He based his further work on Young's theory of three distinct modes of sensation of the retina, which he had previously rejected. He adopted the interpretation in Maxwell's paper, "Experiments on Colour, as Perceived by the Eye" (1855), which stated as Young's theory the proposition that, although monochromatic light stimulates all three modes of sensation, only one or two color responses will prevail in the resulting mixed color. This reading made one of the foundations for Helmholtz's *Handbuch der Physiologischen Optik* of 1860. In this classic work, Helmholtz developed Young's notion of three distinct sets of nerve fibers, although he observed that three distinct and independent processes might take place in each retinal fiber.

Binocular vision presented another set of physical-psychological problems. Charles Wheatstone's stereoscope, invented in 1838, played a critical role in the debate over how perception transforms two flat, monocular fields into a single, binocular field illustrating objects in relief. One group, led by David Brewster, argued for a theory of projection according to which the mind imagines lines starting at two stimulated points on the retinas and projecting outward to their point of intersection at the observed object. Another theory, proffered by the German physiologist Johannes Peter Müller, argued that retinas possess pairs of corresponding or identical points, each pair providing only one point in the unified field of vision. Wheatstone's stereoscope seemed to disprove Müller's views.

Physiologist Ewald Hering challenged Helmholtz's work on vision, declaring that four primary colors—red, blue, green, and yellow—formed the psychological basis for all color sensation. Hues arrange themselves in opposing pairs: red/green and blue/yellow. Helmholtz characterized the controversy as a clash between opposing epistemologies, nativism (Hering's position) and empiricism (his own view). At a deeper level, Hering opposed reckoning the processes of perception in analogy to functions of the human mind. He viewed vision as immediate impressions on the eyes and so rejected theories of projection in favor of a theory of identity similar to Müller's. Against Wheatstone and Brewster, Hering demanded that corresponding pairs of retinal points determine visual directions and depth perception. Helmholtz argued that the processes governing our spatial perception are psychological in nature and thus conditioned by learning and experience.

The controversy lasted well into the 1920s. Modern research affirms both the Young-Helmholtz three-color theory and Hering's four-color theory. The two theories complement one another. While the trichromatic approach explains how the eye detects and perceives color, Hering's explains how color information is encoded and sent to the brain via the nerve pathways. Research during the 1960s and 1970s confirmed that the eye contains three types of color sensors, the photoreceptors, composed of red, green, and blue cones, so-called because of their absorption of light at those wavelengths.

MYLES JACKSON

OZONE HOLE, a colloquial term for the dramatic seasonal thinning of middle atmospheric ozone (O_3, an allotrope of oxygen) over Antarctica. The controversy over the causes of this phenomenon is a defining episode in the history and politics of anthropogenic global climate change.

In the mid-1920s, the English meteorologist Gordon Dobson made observations of atmospheric ozone employing a global network of spectrophotometers of his own design. The total amount of atmospheric ozone is today expressed in Dobson Units, where 1 DU equals 0.01 mm. If all the ozone in the atmosphere were compressed into a single layer, that layer would be about 300 DU (3 mm) thick.

Between 1929 and 1931, the British geophysicist Sydney Chapman hypothesized that ozone arises by the action of ultraviolet light on molecular oxygen (O_2) in what is sometimes called the Chapman layer at about 45 km, a figure now lowered to a variable altitude between 15 and 30 km. Chapman's ideas about atmospheric ozone dominated the scene until 1964.

By 1970, it was clear that the chemistry of stratospheric ozone involved hydrogen, nitrogen (predicted by the Dutch meteorologist Paul Crutzen), and chlorine. In 1974, the Mexican chemist Mario Molina and the American chemist Sherwood Rowland argued that CFCs (chlorofluorocarbons), inert chemicals widely used for sixty years as aerosol propellants and refrigerants, were finding their way into the stratosphere, where they dissociated under intense ultraviolet radiation and produced chlorine species that combined with photolytically dissociated oxygen, thus preventing the formation of ozone; they predicted a long-term decline in the earth's protective ozone shield. It also appeared that aircraft and spacecraft exhausts (the SST and the Space Shuttle) would therefore also deplete atmospheric ozone.

Although these discoveries led to some regulatory efforts in the 1970s to reduce CFCs, especially in the form of aerosol propellants, economic and political interests, as well as legitimate scientific disagreement about the causes of ozone depletion, stymied attempts to control ozone-depleting chemicals. Debate intensified when the British Antarctic Survey reported in 1984 that Antarctic ozone levels had plummeted by a third since 1977 (to less than 200 DU). Americans initially doubted these results, since the TOMS (Total Ozone Mapping Spectrometer) on the *Nimbus-7* satellite had not detected sharply lower levels of ozone. Later analysis of the satellite's programming showed that it had been ordered to disregard such low values as outside the "reasonable range," though they had been regularly observed since 1978.

Regulatory efforts to cut CFCs and other depleting chemicals resumed in the 1980s, including the signing of the Montreal Protocol (1987). Nonetheless, the Antarctic ozone hole has continued to grow. In 1998, it covered 27 million km^2, and in 1999, total atmospheric ozone in October fell below 88 DU. The magnitudes of these changes were not predicted in 1985 by any model of stratospheric composition, even looking fifty and a hundred years ahead. Susan Solomon, the scientist who in 1987 proposed that the ozone hole was a direct consequence of the activation of anthropogenic chlorine on stratospheric ice clouds (later experimentally confirmed many times over), has said that the period of our complacency concerning this ozone hole, and our doubts as to its cause, are over.

MOTT T. GREENE

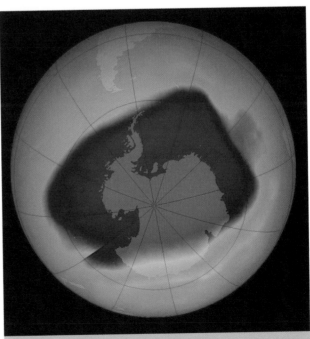

Colored satellite image of low-atmosphere ozone levels over Antarctica on September 25, 2006. The lowest level is indicated by purple, the highest by yellow; the hole pictured covers 29.5 million square kilometers, a record.

PALEONTOLOGY. Paleontology, the study of the remains of living beings and their traces in the rocks, emerged as a distinct area of investigation in the late eighteenth and early nineteenth centuries. By then, most mineralogists and naturalists concurred that fossils were the remains of living beings. The German naturalist Johann Friedrich Blumenbach went further, and argued that in the past many animals and plants had become extinct while new and different ones had been created in their place. Two of his followers, Ernst von Schlotheim and Georges Cuvier, realized this meant that extinct species and genera could be used to identify and correlate stratified rocks. In an important study of the geology of the region around Paris published in 1812, Cuvier, used fossil quadrupeds for the purpose. Schlotheim embarked on the massive task of classifying the less glamorous but much more widely distributed invertebrate fossils, as a preliminary to using them in stratigraphy. Not long after, in 1816, the English surveyor William Smith published his *Strata Identified by Organized Fossils*. By the 1830s, British geologists, ignoring the Continental tradition, claimed that Smith should be credited with the discovery that fossils could be used to identify strata.

Whatever the merits of this dispute, geologists agreed that fossils offered the best way to determine when a stratum was formed and to correlate strata over large distances. They busied themselves collecting, identifying, cataloguing, and producing monographs on the fossils most useful in stratigraphy. Overwhelmingly these were marine invertebrate fossils, usually shells of one kind or another, but also corals, trilobites, ammonites, belemnites, and so on. Geologists also studied fossil plants, especially abundant in the economically important coal-bearing formations. With the possible exception of fishes, vertebrate fossils were too rarely preserved to be of use.

In the 1870s, paleontology matured as a scientific discipline with its own specialist journals, meetings, and societies. Although university departments employed paleontologists, the new specialty derived the bulk of its institutional support by being an ancillary to stratigraphy, which was of great economic importance first in the mining industry and later in the petroleum industry as well. Jobs were offered in national geological surveys and later in laboratories run by oil companies. Because of the small diameters of the rock cores brought up in drilling for oil, paleontologists turned in earnest to the study of fossils visible only under the microscope, such as ostracods, foraminifera, and pollen grains. In 1917, the American Association of Petroleum Geologists was formed. By the end of the century, it would be the largest geological society in the world.

For stratigraphic and economic purposes, questions about the meaning of fossils—how life had been created and evolved, how dinosaurs had lived, how man had evolved—were irrelevant. Chemists, biologists, enthusiastic amateurs, and anthropologists were as likely to pursue these questions as paleontologists. Most important debates within professional paleontology dealt with matters that bore directly on stratigraphy. Was a single fossil species or genera adequate to identify a formation, or did the paleontologist have to take whole assemblages of fossils into account? Did whole fossil faunas and floras change abruptly and simultaneously, as Cuvier claimed? Or did they change slowly and gradually, as Charles Lyell contested? Were fossils reliable as indicators of the relative age of rocks? From the early nineteenth century on, geologists had recognized that different extinct species, just like different living species, lived in different environments. If so, was it possible that fossils varied with the environment in which they had been deposited, and not with time? By the late nineteenth century, geologists used the concept of facies to describe these environments, and began to factor environmental factors into their stratigraphic investigations.

In two areas, paleontologists concerned themselves with issues outside stratigraphy. One was paleo-ecology. In the late nineteenth century, German and Russian scientists

GROUP OF NEW RED SANDSTONE FOSSILS.

Restored figure of Labyrinthodon, with marks of footprints.

Stellispongia Variabilis.

Triassic Limpet. *(Lottia lineata.)*

Encrinites Moniliformis.

Ceratites Nodosus.

Star-fish.

Myophoria Lineata.

GROUP OF LIASSIC FOSSILS.

Tetragonolepis (restored form).

Gryphæa Arcuata.

Ammonites Bisulcatus.

Pecten Lugdunensis.

Spirifer Walcoti.

Belemnites.

Cidaris Coronata.

Plesiosaurus Dolichodeirus.

Historical artwork of various invertebrate and vertebrate fossils, taken from *The Circle of the Sciences*, published in 1862–7

			K = 39	Rb = 85	Cs = 133	—	—
			Ca = 40	Sr = 87	Ba = 137	—	—
			—	?Yt = 88?	?Di = 138?	Er = 178?	—
			Ti = 48?	Zr = 90	Ce = 140?	?La = 180?	Tb = 231
			V = 51	Nb = 94	—	Ta = 182	—
			Cr = 52	Mo = 96	—	W = 184	U = 240
			Mn = 55	—	—	—	—
			Fe = 56	Ru = 104	—	Os = 195?	—
			Co = 59	Rh = 104	—	Ir = 197	—
			Ni = 59	Pd = 106	—	Pt = 198?	—
Typische Elemente							
H = 1	Li = 7	Na = 23	Cu = 63	Ag = 108	—	Au = 199?	—
	Be = 9,4	Mg = 24	Zn = 65	Cd = 112	—	Hg = 200	—
	B = 11	Al = 27,3	—	In = 113	—	Tl = 204	—
	C = 12	Si = 28	—	Sn = 118	—	Pb = 207	—
	N = 14	P = 31	As = 75	Sb = 122	—	Bi = 208	—
	O = 16	S = 32	Se = 78	Te = 125?	—	—	—
	F = 19	Cl = 35,5	Br = 80	J = 127	—	—	—

The periodic table of the elements in the form first given it by Dmitri Ivanovich Mendeleyev (1834–1907) in 1869

began using fossils to reconstruct past climates, past environments, and past shorelines. They studied the environments of living marine invertebrates, for example, to shed light on the environment in which trilobites might have lived. They used the distribution of fossil coral reefs to infer what earlier climates were like.

The other area was the Cambrian boundary, below which paleontologists had failed to find any traces of life. Above it, fossils appeared abruptly as rather specialized invertebrate animals. In the mid-twentieth century, paleontologists detected microscopic unicellular animals and sedimentary structures built up of colonies of algae and bacteria (called stromatolites). The reason for the puzzlingly abrupt change, they concluded, was that until the beginning of the Cambrian, almost all life on earth consisted of simple unicellular bacteria, algae, and protozoans.

Following World War II, as funding within universities and new and powerful instruments became more readily available, paleontologists began asking a wider range of questions. Paleoecologists used the ratios of stable isotopes of oxygen in fossils to trace temperature fluctuations in past oceans. Other paleontologists used the trace amounts of nucleic compounds preserved in fossils to shed light on evolutionary affinities and relationships. More traditional paleontology used the scanning electron microscope to subdivide strata from the Mesozoic to the present in quite remarkable detail.

RACHEL LAUDAN

PERIODIC TABLE. Chemists of the early nineteenth century had to rely on indirect methods, analogies, and simplifying assumptions to determine the relative atomic weights of elements, and thus did not reach a consensus on them. Gradually, however, methods improved, and at the international Karlsruhe Congress of 1860 Stanislao Cannizzaro advocated what is, in essence, the system still in use today.

Even before agreement on a single set of atomic weights, several theorists noticed that chemical and physical properties reappeared in a regular, periodic fashion in the various elements. Among these predecessors of the periodic law were Johann Wolfgang Döbereiner, John Newlands, William Odling, and Jean-Baptiste-André Dumas. Many others proposed partial periodic classifications of the elements.

Dmitrii Mendeleev reaped the success of these endeavors. (The German chemist Lothar Meyer pursued a closely parallel path independently, and published his similar contribution shortly after Mendeleev's.) Mendeleev arranged the elements horizontally according to increasing atomic weight, and started a new row below the first whenever similar properties in the elements reappeared. The resulting semirectangular table of atomic weights showed many intriguing regularities. The horizontal rows ("periods" or "series") and the vertical columns ("groups" or "families") revealed a "periodic law." For example, Mendeleev's arrangement placed the alkali metals (sodium, potassium, and the then recently discovered rubidium and cesium) in a single vertical group with a marked family resemblance. The set of next-heavier elements to each of these alkali metals formed a second family group, the alkaline earth metals (magnesium, calcium, strontium, and barium).

This example understates the magnitude of the problems Mendeleev faced, for the elements simply failed to order themselves neatly. (Sometimes the greatest genius requires *ignoring* a certain number of anomalies, while discerning the larger pattern hidden within the data.) Lithium, for instance, fell into the alkali metal group by weight order, but it seemed to have more family resemblance to magnesium than to sodium, the element directly below it in the table. By the same token, beryllium seemed to resemble aluminum more than its putative family member below, magnesium. In certain other cases two adjacent elements seemed to come in a different order by weight from that dictated by the family groupings. For the first anomaly, Mendeleev provided an extenuating rationale; for the second, he did not hesitate to violate the weight order and reverse the two elements in the chart, hence preserving the periodicity of properties.

Despite the problems, Mendeleev had sufficient confidence in the periodic system he published in 1869 to hazard predic-

P

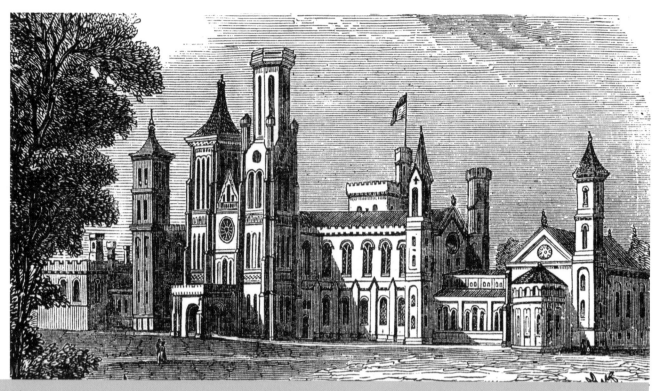

The Smithsonian Institution in Washington, D.C., in the 19th century

tions based on it. Leaving vacant places in his chart in certain critical instances, he predicted the properties of undiscovered elements. For example, he left a space between calcium and titanium, and two between zinc and arsenic. Here Mendeleev used a strategy that converted yet another anomaly—holes in his periodic table—into potentially powerful evidence for the validity of his discovery. But of course there he risked the danger that his system would fail the test of prediction.

The first of Mendeleev's predicted new elements, discovered by Paul Lecoq de Boisbaudran in 1875, was named "gallium" in honor of France. Gallium's atomic weight of about 70 came close to Mendeleev's prediction of 68, its density of 5.9 grams per cubic centimeter virtually coincided with the prediction, its valence and oxide pattern were as expected, and a long list of observed chemical properties also matched what Mendeleev had forecast. Four years later scandium filled another space, and in another seven years, germanium. Three times Mendeleev had triumphed, not only with the fact of the discoveries, but with the details of physical and especially chemical properties as well.

These confirmed predictions caught the attention of the scientific world. For the first few years after Mendeleev announced his periodic system, it received almost no notice in journals and textbooks, and much less agreement as to its utility. After the discovery of gallium, however, textbook accounts of the periodic law began to appear, and in the 1880s discussions of periodicity of the elements became a common, though not invariable, feature of chemistry textbooks.

Further developments provided both challenges to, and support for, Mendeleev's system. Chemists and then physicists confirmed the weight inversions that Mendeleev had insisted upon to preserve periodicity. A dozen or more chemically similar "rare earth elements" discovered in the last quarter of the nineteenth century presented a more worrisome problem in that they did not fit into any periodic system. Eventually chemists grouped them together in an aperiodic category as "lanthanides." In the 1890s, Wil-

liam Ramsay and Lord Rayleigh discovered the inert gases argon, helium, neon, krypton, and xenon. They fit perfectly by weight before the alkalis, and soon after the turn of the century chemists decided to create an extra group for them at one end or the other of the periodic chart.

The development of atomic physics in the early twentieth century provided an independent method for assigning positions for elements in the periodic table: the measurement of their "atomic numbers." At the same time the study of radioactivity revealed a number of apparently elementary bodies that did not fit into the table; the solution was to enlarge the concept of element. A group analogous to the lanthanides, the actinides, has been added to accommodate transuranic elements.

A. J. ROCKE

PHILANTHROPY. Rooted in the moral imperative of disinterested aid of others, philanthropy has been associated with the support of worthy causes at least since the rise of market capitalism. In the modern era, philanthropy increasingly has been directed at institutions and individuals for the increase of knowledge, distinguishing it in some degree from charity (amelioration of human misery) and patronage (support of talented individuals or groups). Substantial philanthropic support has long been a distinctive feature of modern Western science.

Many examples from the history of early modern science illustrate the point. A Medici prince supported the Accademia del Cimento in Florence (1657–1667); seventeenth-century predecessors of the Académie Royale des Sciences in France depended on patrons; and King Frederick II of Denmark financed Tycho Brahe's installation at Uraniborg. In the eighteenth century, Joseph Priestley had support from the Earl of Shelburne, Jean André Deluc from the queen of England, and many small continental academies from local magnates.

The growing institutionalization of science in the early nineteenth century is reflected in the philanthropy of Benjamin Thompson, Count Rumford, who created a research prize, helped found the Royal Institution of Great Britain, and left an endowment for a scientific chair at Harvard University. The philanthropic creation of prizes and premiums established a valuable, if post facto, source of financing. Privately endowed university chairs in the sciences helped to give science a permanent role in higher education.

Perhaps the most dramatic instance of philanthropy in science in the nineteenth century was the Englishman James Smithson's bequest of 1826 to found in the city of Washington an institution devoted to the increase and diffusion of knowledge. Finally organized in 1846, the Smithsonian Institution quickly though briefly became the most significant center of scientific research and publication in the United States. American financiers and industrialists soon began to endow chairs and to create science schools (at Harvard and Yale, for example) and entire universities (Chicago, Clark, Johns Hopkins, Stanford). James Lick, a California entrepreneur, greatly enlarged the scale of philanthropy for science by donating $700,000 to build the world's largest telescope, the 36-inch Lick refractor, which began operation in 1888.

The cumulative effect of small donations could also be substantial. Ormsby Mitchell raised funds for a telescope and observatory in Cincinnati in 1842–1843 by asking local residents for money. A public subscription to publish Louis Agassiz's natural history researches in 1855 was the first nationwide appeal in support of science in the United States; Agassiz personally raised half a million dollars from many sources for his museum at Harvard in the 1850s and 1860s. In 1885, the Pasteur Institute in Paris was founded on broad support from French citizens. Still, in most cases substantial wealth provided the infrastructure for science: Boston's monied class built Harvard's first scientific building, Boylston Hall (1858), and the executor of the Hull fortune funded the biological laboratory at the University of Chicago (1897).

Buildings, university chairs, and astronomical instruments were traditional expressions of philanthropy usually intended to memorialize the donors. Identifying worthy research and researchers required more of the giver as science developed theories and vocabularies beyond the understanding of most educated persons. To pursue leading-edge science demanded tapping various sources for support; Albert A. Michelson and Edward Morley received a grant from the National Academy of Sciences's Bache Fund for their light-wave studies in the 1880s, but their equipment came from local manufacturers who provided it free or below cost. Some philanthropists understood the need: in the 1890s Catherine Wolfe Bruce gave a cumulative $175,000 to researchers around the country to purchase astronomical research instruments, and the Naples Zoological Station in Italy received funds from Alexander H. Davis, a New York businessman, particularly to provide facilities for American researchers.

Although the organized philanthropy of large foundations became the dominant means of nongovernment support of science early in the twentieth century, private philanthropy remained important. In the United States, the Cold Spring Harbor Laboratory was established in 1923 on the basis of private gifts, as was the Institute for Advanced Study (founded 1930), a haven for exiled European scientists. In Europe the Kaiser-Wilhelm-Gesellschaft was created in 1911 with the support of many German bankers and industrialists; the Weizmann Institute of Science in Israel began with gifts that created the Sieff Research Institute in

1934; the Huancayo Laboratory of the Institute of Andean Biology in Peru was built with private funds in 1940; industrialist J. R. D. Tata endowed the Tata Institute of Fundamental Research at Mumbai in India in 1945. Typically, personal philanthropy created new scientific institutions or supported existing institutions, rather than the scientists themselves, and was increasingly shaped by both organized solicitation and tax laws.

The largest private benefactions set up medical foundations, for example, the Wellcome Trust (1936) and the Howard Hughes Medical Institute (1953). Other philanthropy focused on agricultural development, disease, environmental issues, or population control, often directing their programs toward the developing world. As the twenty-first century dawned, Johns Hopkins University received a gift of one hundred million dollars for research on malaria, a scourge of tropical Africa and south Asia.

Philanthropy on a scale that can influence science has derived largely from wealth accumulated in market-capitalist environments. While it has accounted for only a small proportion of science funding and has been limited in the developing world and virtually absent from nations with socialist systems, philanthropy has dramatically affected the conduct of science in many fields and institutions.

DARWIN H. STAPLETON

PHOTOGRAPHY. The technical history of photography comprises three parallel developments: camera negatives, monochrome positive prints, and recording color. The practice of photography was empirically led throughout its first hundred years, frequently outstripping the ability of contemporary science to explain the various phenomena.

Since the late Renaissance, it had been known that sunlight darkens salts of silver. In 1725, Johann Heinrich Schulze used sunlit stencils to cast images on suspensions of silver salts. Carl Scheele showed in 1777 that the violet rays of the prismatic spectrum were most effective in decomposing silver chloride, the dark product being finely divided silver. During the 1790s, Thomas Wedgwood sun-printed "profiles" of objects onto paper and leather moistened with silver nitrate, but could not prevent their obliteration by daylight. Images in the *camera obscura* were too faint to make any impression, but Wedgwood successfully obtained "copies" of specimens projected by the solar microscope.

The earliest extant camera photograph was not produced in silver, but by *heliography,* a copying process invented by Joseph Nicéphore Niépce in the 1820s. The process places a thin coating of bitumen on a pewter plate, selectively hardens it by sunlight, then dissolves it by oil of lavender to bring out the image. In 1827, Niépce captured the first photograph—now in the Gernsheim Collection of the University of Texas—by a heliographic camera exposure estimated to have taken several days. Heliography was better suited to providing etching-resists for photomechanical printing plates. Attention returned to silver; in 1837, Louis Jacques Mandé Daguerre discovered, fortuitously, that mercury vapor could develop camera images on iodized surfaces of silver-plated copper, the chemical prerequisite, iodine, having been discovered by Bernard Courtois in 1811. The *daguerreotype* process, first publicized in 1839, enjoyed widespread commercial success until photography on paper and glass replaced it in the mid-1850s.

Meanwhile, William Henry Fox Talbot had independently devised *photogenic drawing paper* by 1835. He had noted that the light-sensitivity of silver chloride, precipi-

P

A Talbotype photography taken in 1845 shows the printing establishment set up by William Henry Fox Talbot (1800–1877) in Reading, England.

tated within the paper's fibers, diminished with excess salt, and had thereby discovered the first method for fixing silver images. Talbot's earliest camera negative (1835) is in the National Museum of Photography, Film and Television in Bradford, England. On hearing in 1839 of Talbot's innovation, Sir John Herschel, who originated the terms "photography," "the negative," and "the positive," demonstrated that unchanged silver chloride in a photograph dissolved in a solution of hyposulfite of soda (sodium thiosulfate). Herschel's "hypo-fixing" superseded Talbot's salt-fixing, and remains in use today. In 1839, Talbot also noted the greater sensitivity of silver bromide—now the chief constituent of all modern photographic materials—made possible by Antoine Jerome Balard's isolation of bromine in 1826.

In 1840, Talbot made his third, crucial discovery: that an invisibly weak dormant picture in silver iodide could be brought out by gallic acid, effectively increasing the speed of his camera photography a hundredfold—from hours to minutes. He named this process *calotype,* and patented it in 1841. Although science could not account for these phenomena of latency and development, Talbot had set photography on the path of continuous refinement for the next 150 years. A quest was mounted for shorter camera exposures and higher resolution. The opacity and texture of paper were avoided by suspending the silver halide in organic binders, making "emulsions" (an inaccurate term, but universally employed): hens' egg-white (Claude Félix Abel Niépce de Saint-Victor, 1847), collodion (Frederick Scott Archer, 1851), and finally gelatin (Richard Leach Maddox, 1871). Emulsions were coated on transparent supports ranging from glass plates (Niépce de Saint-Victor, 1847) and waxed paper (Gustave Le Gray, 1851) to the flexible, but dangerously flammable early plastic, celluloid (cellulose nitrate), which permitted the design of roll-film cameras, introduced by George Eastman in 1888. Modern safety films employ polymer bases of cellulose triacetate (1923) or polyethyl-

ene terephthalate (1955). Parallel improvements were made in the optical design of camera lenses, notably achromats (Charles and Vincent Chevalier, 1828), large aperture lenses (Josef Petzval, 1841), rapid rectilinear lenses (J. H. Dallmeyer and H. A. Steinheil, 1866), and Zeiss anastigmats (Paul Rudolph and Ernst Abbe, 1890).

Pure silver halides respond only to blue light and the ultraviolet, whose discovery by Johann Wilhelm Ritter in 1801 represents the first contribution of photography to science. To render tonally balanced negatives, emulsions must react to the entire visible spectrum. Sensitizing with dyes, introduced in 1873 by Hermann Wilhelm Vogel, extended the response to green (orthochromatic plates, 1884), and then red wavelengths (panchromatic plates, 1904), reaching the near-infrared by the 1930s. Sensitometry, the photometric study of emulsion response, was originated by Ferdinand Hurter and Vero Charles Driffield in 1890, accompanied by extensive chemical exploration for better developers, such as hydroquinone (William de Wiveleslie Abney, 1880).

The emulsion binder in universal use by 1900, animal gelatin, displayed great variability in speed. In 1926, Samuel Edward Sheppard detected the cause: traces of sulfur-containing substances, arising from the animals' diet, could sensitize silver halides. Modern emulsion technology now uses pure gelatin, with controlled addition of sulfur and gold compounds as sensitizers. Understanding the latent image became possible with the foundation of solid-state physics and chemistry during the 1920s, especially Yakov Ilyich Frenkel's theory of ionic conductivity and A. H. Wilson's electronic band theory. In 1938, Sir Nevill Francis Mott and R. W. Gurney put forward a mechanism for the formation of the latent image that has found wide acceptance. Because of the granular structure of the developed image, photographic speed is linked inversely to resolution. This tradeoff was improved in the 1980s by controlled growth of silver halide crystals with a tabular habit, increasing their surface-to-volume ratio. The speed of modern negative emulsions is approaching the theoretical limit.

As Talbot realized in 1835, printing positives is an essential procedure to rectify the reversed tonality and handedness of camera negatives. Talbot's photogenic drawing paper served at first, but papers coated with albumen emulsion (Louis Désiré Blanquart-Evrard, 1850) displaced Talbot's *salted paper prints*. Silver images suffer from sulfiding, causing them to fade, but gold-toning (1855) mitigated the deterioration, and *albumen prints* remained the chief photographic medium until 1895.

Since speed is not paramount for printing positives, substances less sensitive to light than silver salts were employed in the quest for image permanence. Following the discovery of dichromates (Louis Nicolas Vauquelin, 1798), their light-sensitivity on paper (Mungo Ponton, 1838) led to light-hardening of dichromated gelatin (Talbot, *photoglyphic engraving*, 1852). The addition of artists' pigments to the gelatin matrix, as inert image substances, permitted the development of the *carbon process* (Alphonse Louis Poitevin, 1855; Adolphe Fargier, 1861; Sir Joseph Wilson Swan, 1864).

In 1842, Sir John Herschel discovered that iron (III) citrate was light-sensitive and could yield images in gold, silver, mercury, or Prussian blue—the *cyanotype* or blueprint, the first reprographic process. William Willis patented the analogous platinum process in 1873, and by 1900 his company's *platinotype* paper dominated the market. But demand for platinum as a catalyst in the growing chemical industry brought steep price rises; moreover, the introduction of roll-film cameras, whose small formats required enlargement onto the much faster silver-gelatin development papers, made platinotype commercially unviable by the 1930s. It remains today, together with carbon printing, a minority fine-art practice, yielding images of archival permanence. For the remainder of the twentieth century, silver-gelatin enlarging papers became the commercial norm.

Photography in natural colors was first achieved by James Clerk Maxwell (1831–1879) in 1861, using optical filters to separate three primary colors and to synthesize them additively. Ducos du Hauron published details of a three-color subtractive process, *heliochrome,* in 1869. Gabriel Lippmann, who received the only Nobel Prize (physics, 1908) awarded for photographic innovation, devised a unique interference system for recording color photographs in 1891. More successful commercially was the additive *autochrome* process of the brothers Auguste and Louis Lumière (1907), which used a mixture of starch grains dyed with three primary colors to filter the light falling on a panchromatic emulsion. Color photography progressed with research in synthetic organic chemistry of dyestuffs, notably at the Eastman Kodak Company, which produced Kodachrome in 1935: a triple-layered silver emulsion, sandwiched with subtractive primary dyes.

The scientific value of photography for faithful analogue recording is self-evident; further, by disclosing information imperceptible to the eye, photography permitted new discoveries. Early examples include the "chronophotographic" studies of animal and human locomotion (Eadweard Muybridge and Etienne-Jules Marey, 1870s); recording of shock waves (Ernst Mach, 1884); high-speed photography by stroboscopic flash (Harold Eugene Edgerton, 1932); and time-lapse photography (John Ott, 1940s).

The ability of photography to accumulate a weak optical signal over time makes its enhanced recording sensitivity particularly valuable to astronomy and optical spectroscopy.

By photographically recording galactic spectra, Edwin Powell Hubble (1889–1953) discovered in 1929 the "red shift," which implied that the universe was expanding. The response of photographic emulsions to X rays has found applications since 1895 in medicine and forensic science. The X-ray diffraction patterns for elucidating crystal structure, and electron diffraction patterns from gaseous molecules, were first recorded photographically. Antoine Henri Becquerel owed his discovery of radioactivity in 1896 to the sensitivity of emulsions to charged particles; the ensuing technique of *autoradiography* finds application in biological studies and metallographic analysis. Emulsions can register the trajectories of cosmic rays, and particle physics employs photography to record events in its cloud and bubble chambers.

With the advance of modern electronics, photoelectric devices are replacing silver-gelatin emulsions. Digitally-processed electronic imaging has reduced the role of photography in science and the lens-based media. Yet the photograph will endure in the art and archives of humanity.

MIKE WARE

PHOTOSYNTHESIS, the metabolic reactions that provide plants with a source of food, is usually referred to as fixing energy (light) from the sun in the form of carbohydrates. The term dates from 1893, when the major steps in the process were identified. Before then, by analogy with animals, most philosophers regarded plants as breathing organisms deriving their nutrients from water and the air alone. During the seventeenth and eighteenth centuries plant physiology became a branch of pneumatics. Stephen Hales, who first recorded the exchange of gases, believed that plants "perspired" during the day and "imbibed" at night. These ideas encouraged the suggestion that plants transformed stale air into fresh or sweet air and led Georg Ernst Stahl and then Joseph Priestley and others to identify the gases involved. Priestley provided evidence that green plants produced dephlogisticated air, the air that Antoine-Laurent Lavoisier redefined as oxygen (1777). Jan Ingen-Housz saw this process as a necessary counterpart to the respiration of animals. Air spoiled by the breathing of animals served as a kind of food for plants, and plants in turn supplied animals with purified air. These reciprocal actions constituted a cycle, demonstrating the economy of nature.

Biochemist Melvin Calvin (1911–1997) received the Nobel Prize in Chemistry in 1961 for identifying the path of carbon during photosynthesis.

Ingen-Housz regarded the cycle, which he described accurately, as convincing evidence of the handiwork of the creator. From 1772, Lavoisier developed the theory that combustion arose from or in the fixation or combination of oxygen in the air with any burning substance. Light and heat appeared as a result. Lavoisier later proposed that the oxidation of the carbon in food produced fixed air (carbon dioxide). The presumed goodness and efficiency of cyclical exchanges of gases, which appealed to religious sentiment as well as to reason, provided a strong basis for future research. In essence, the eighteenth century had demonstrated that plants remove carbon from atmospheric carbon dioxide and release oxygen back into the atmosphere.

With the shift in interest toward cellular activities in the nineteenth century, research began to center on the mechanisms by which plants captured carbon from the air, although only toward the second half of the century was the extent to which plants synthesize the greater part of their substance fully appreciated. Investigators soon recognized the role of light and the significance of the green pigment (chlorophyll). Julius von Sachs established the sites for absorption of gases in leaves and the biochemical pathways leading to the formation of starch and other substances. He demonstrated that the starch usually present in green cells came from the carbon dioxide absorbed and decided that starch was the primary substance produced by photosynthesis. Following up Sachs's theory, researchers discovered that starch makes up only a by-product of the assimilation process.

Subsequent investigation showed that carbon dioxide must combine with chlorophyll before chemical reduction takes place in a number of steps involving oxygen, water, and light. In 1919, Otto Warburg began work to determine the minimum number of photons required to yield a molecule of oxygen. He found it to be close to four. His initiative opened a period of research into the details of primary light conversion

using Chlorella, a unicellular green algae, as the experimental organism of choice. The prevailing view that a plant's output of oxygen derived from carbon dioxide was challenged in the 1930s by Rene Wurmser, and then by Cornelius Bernardus van Niel, at Stanford, who claimed that it must come from water. In 1937, Robin Hill in Cambridge confirmed the water origin and pointed to chloroplasts as the active sites. During the 1940s Melvin Calvin and his group at Berkeley worked out dark reaction sequences thanks in part to the availability of radioactive Carbon 14 and improvements in chromatography. Calvin received the Nobel Prize in chemistry in 1961 for unraveling the path of carbon in photosynthesis. Another member of Calvin's group, Daniel Arnon, established definitively that isolated chloroplasts could perform all the responses associated with photosynthesis.

In photosynthesis, it is now understood that water acts both as a hydrogen donor and a source of released oxygen. Only part of the process depends on illumination. An important development was the recognition that plants do not create the energy stored in their sugars, but merely fix energy radiated by the sun. Andreas Franz Wilhelm Schimper's discovery that starch stores energy allowed scientists of the early twentieth century to discuss the circulation of energy through the natural world in biochemical terms, as the synthesis and subsequent breakdown of carbohydrates and other vegetable products. From the 1960s, understanding of photochemical action has been enriched by the determination of the detailed molecular processes involved.

JANET BROWNE

PHRENOLOGY AND PHYSIOGNOMY are two methods of studying cranial anatomy as indicative of intelligence, personality, and temperament. Phrenology arose at the end of the eighteenth century, when physiognomy was in decline. Franz Joseph Gall, founder of phrenology, might have been influenced by the physiognomical tradition, but his methodology was based primarily on his own research.

Physiognomy was endorsed by the *Physiognomica,* which circulated in ancient and medieval times under the authorship (now doubted) of Aristotle. Galen connected Aristotelian physiognomy with the humoral theory of health and illness. Prominent Medieval authors developed the subject, which, however, had played out by the eighteenth century. The term "physiognomy" was in use as late as 1834 but began to be supplanted by "phrenology" in 1819.

Gall received his M.D. in Vienna in 1785 and developed a lucrative medical practice. By 1791, he had published his ideas on brain functions, which he concluded were highly localized. Personality traits and abilities supposedly depended on the size of different parts of the brain. He initiated studies on the correlation between structures and functions. However, his evidence was anecdotal, and controversy over his claims drove him to seek evidence in dissections and demonstrations. In 1800, he attracted a disciple, Johann Christoph Spurzheim, who assisted in anatomical researches until they parted company in 1813. During their collaboration they published the first two volumes of Gall's *Anatomie et physiologies du systéme nerveux* (5 vols., 1810–1819). These elaborate studies were intended to illustrate rather than test Gall's system, but they did not convince academic and medical authorities in Paris any more than his earlier research and teachings had persuaded the Viennese. A controversy arose over the grounds for this rejection. Did it have to do with substance or divisions of science? Before Gall began his teachings, brain functions

Phrenology divides the skull into areas associated with various aspects of personality and evaluates the character of an individual by the bumps and hollows.

had been explained mainly within philosophy rather than physiology.

Spurzheim traveled to London and in 1815 published *The Physiognomical System of Drs. Gall and Spurzheim*. Gall identified twenty-seven faculties of the mind, and Spurzheim thirty-five. Spurzheim won converts in both London and Edinburgh (where he lectured in 1816), but like Gall failed to win over scientific or medical authorities. Spurzheim died during a successful lecture tour in America in 1832. Gall had died in Paris in 1828.

Although Gall and Spurzheim eventually disagreed over details of investigation and interpretation, in general phrenologists used as a reference an anatomical chart of the brain with faculties of the mind labeled on its anatomical parts. The investigator needed to determine the relative size of the different faculties on his subject's brain as visible from the skull. If the subject cooperated, the investigator made careful measurements with calipers and then noted that a given faculty was "very small," "moderate," "full," or "very large." If a subject was uncooperative, an experienced phrenologist could still make a visual analysis reasonably accurately. An expert could do the same with a good portrait or bust.

Spurzheim's most important converts were George Combe, a successful lawyer in Edinburgh, and his younger brother Andrew, the most illustrious British physician to defend phrenology. They organized the Edinburgh Phrenological Society (1820) and founded *The Phrenological Journal* (1823). In 1819, George Combe published his own *Essays on Phrenology*, which he steadily revised and enlarged and eventually retitled as *A System of Phrenology* (5th ed., 1843). He outdid Spurzheim by raising the faculties of the mind to forty-five. Andrew Combe advanced phrenology in a popular textbook, *Principles of Physiology Applied to the Preservation of Health* (1834), which had fifteen editions before his death in 1847. Combe also wrote a best-seller, *The Constitution of Man* (1828).

George Combe acquired a disciple, Hewett Cottrell Watson, an Englishman who went to Edinburgh in 1828 to study medicine and phrenology, which was not taught at Edinburgh University or its medical school. Watson did well in his courses but quit medical school a semester before earning a degree, having decided that he would never practice medicine. Combe respected Watson's abilities, and Watson began publishing in *The Phrenological Journal* in 1829. After leaving Edinburgh, Watson ceased writing scientific articles on phrenology, but remained a staunch advocate. In 1836 he published *Statistics of Phrenology*, which was not a statistical analysis of phrenological data, but an account of progress made in advancing phrenology. In 1837, he became editor of *The Phrenological Journal*, hoping to raise its scientific standards. He wrote lofty editorials, but his criticism and ridicule of articles submitted only aroused the anger of authors, and in November 1839 he resigned. Watson abandoned phrenology and criticized it in correspondence with Combe until Combe died in 1858. The last serious attempt to defend phrenology was W. Mathieu Williams's *A Vindication of Phrenology* (1894).

FRANK N. EGERTON

PHYSICAL CHEMISTRY. The recognition of physical chemistry as a subfield within the broader field of chemistry is usually associated with the founding in 1887 of the journal *Zeitschrift für physikalische Chemie* by Svante Arrhenius in Stockholm, Wilhelm Ostwald in Leipzig, and Jacobus Henricus van't Hoff in Amsterdam. In his account of the history

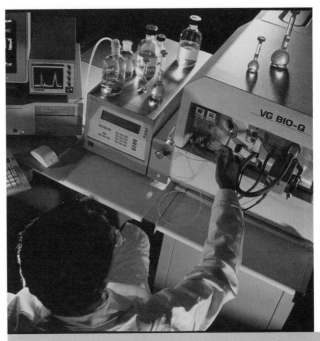

A scientist injects a sample into a Mass Spectrometer, an instrument used for protein analysis, which is used to identify chemical compounds by exploiting the behavior of their molecular ions in magnetic and electric fields.

of the discipline, Ostwald rooted its foundations in electrochemistry. Somewhat differently, Walther Nernst, in a speech at his newly built physical chemistry institute in Göttingen in 1896, described van't Hoff's work on dissociation in solutions as the path that reunited the sciences of chemistry and physics in a return to Antoine-Laurent Lavoisier's late eighteenth-century vision of a unified science.

The phrase "physical chemistry" was much in use before the 1880s, for example, by Robert Bunsen, Hans Heinrich Landolt, and Heinrich Rose, and in the title of the *Annalen der Physik und der Physikalischem Chemie* (1819–1823), which became Johann Poggendorff's *Annalen der Physik und Chemie* in 1824. Hermann Kopp received the first independently named university chair in "physical chemistry" at Heidelberg in 1863. Ost-wald's predecessor Gustav Heinrich Wiedemann set up the first German instructional laboratory for physical chemistry at Leipzig in 1871.

Increased governmental concern in the 1860s to promote scientific and technological progress made expanding resources for scientific education available first in Germany and then elsewhere in Europe and in the United States. Physical chemistry became a supplement to the curriculum in organic, agricultural, and medical chemistry that had been the heart of chemical education in universities since the 1830s.

The areas of study that defined physical chemistry at the end of the nineteenth century were thermodynamics, electrochemistry, colloid and surface chemistry, and chemical spectroscopy. They were enriched during the early decades of the twentieth century by chemical kinetics, electron and quantum chemistry, X-ray crystallography, and new kinds of spectroscopy.

In the 1850s and 1860s, Marcellin Berthelot in Paris and Julius Thomsen in Copenhagen developed theories of chemical affinity based on the assumption that the chemical force (affinity) that holds the parts of a molecule together is directly proportional to the heat evolved during its formation. By the mid-1880s, Pierre Duhem had rejected the Berthelot-Thomsen thermochemical approach. Duhem and others adopted the thermodynamical theories of Rudolf Clausius (1854, 1865), J. Willard Gibbs (1875–1877), and Hermann von Helmholtz (1882) for chemical purposes.

By the late 1880s, a stable chemical system could be defined mathematically as a state of equilibrium in which the entropy (S) of the system had reached a maximum value and the internal energy (U) a minimum. Entropy measures energy unavailable for work and "free energy" (F) the energy potentially available for work, given values for the mechanical equivalent of heat (J) and temperature (T). Thus, $F = U - JTS$; and chemical affinity is identified with free energy or with work, not with heat.

These results, based on precise experimental work, were mathematical and abstract in character. "Energeticists" like Ostwald and Duhem, who opposed the use of visualizable models in science, lauded this new physical chemistry, but mechanists like Ludwig Boltzmann in Austria and Marcel Louis Brillouin and Jean Baptiste Perrin in France preferred descriptions linked to particles in motion and the kinetic theory of gases.

Drawing on the work of Helmholtz and others, van't Hoff demonstrated in his *Etudes de dynamique chimique* (1884) that the work of chemical affinity could be calculated from vapor pressures, osmotic pressure, or electrical work in a reversible galvanic cell. His starting point in reaction velocities made a contribution to chemical kinetics. The everyday use of thermodynamics in chemical work was greatly simplified by Gilbert N. Lewis and Merle Randall's *Thermodynamics and the Free Energy of Chemical Substances* (1924), which embraced Gibbs's expression for free energy at constant pressure rather than Helmholtz's and van't Hoff's expression for constant volume.

Arrhenius took up van't Hoff's application of the ideal gas law to osmotic pressure and dilute solutions in his doctoral dissertation on electrolytic dissociation (1887). Arrhenius made the surprising argument that at infinite dilution, molecules of electrolytes break up into charged ions even in the absence of electrical current. Arrhenius's notion of independent ions built on Helmholtz's suggestion of 1881 that ions produced in electrolysis carry discrete "atoms of electricity" that might be units of chemical affinity attached to elementary substances. The physicalist electrolytic chemistry of Arrhenius, van't Hoff, and Ostwald became known as "Ionist" chemistry.

Nernst served briefly as Ostwald's assistant in Leipzig. Nernst's practical interest in electrical lamps led to his work of the dissociation of gases at high temperatures in addition to his studies of solutions, solids, and surface chemistry. Irving Langmuir, who took his doctoral degree at Göttingen with Nernst and spent most of his career at the General Electric Company's research laboratory in Schenectady, New York, investigated a similar range of subjects, which preoccupied physical chemists in the early twentieth century.

In late 1905, Nernst stated a third law of thermodynamics, which provided the means for calculating values of specific heat and for predicting the likelihood of chemical reactions from recognition that the values of entropy and specific heats approach zero at very low temperatures. Albert Einstein's quantum theory of solids, published in 1907, provided theoretical foundations for Nernst's prediction. The utility of the third law persuaded many physical chemists of the usefulness of the statistical mechanics of Gibbs and Boltzmann, as well as of the quantum theory, in chemical studies.

Optical methods have been consistently fruitful in physical chemistry. Polarimetry resulted from the discovery of Jean-Baptiste Biot and François Arago in 1840 that a monochromatic beam of plane-polarized light is twisted or rotated by solutions of sugar, camphor, or tartaric acid. The new method of study led to the recognition of asymmetries in molecular structure.

Spectroscopy in the chemical context developed from methods used by Robert Bunsen and Gustav Kirchhoff to identify chemical substances by the colors they emit in flames. In 1860, Bunsen and Kirchhoff announced the discovery of cesium, identified by its blue spectral lines; rubidinium followed in 1861, identified by its dark red lines.

In the late nineteenth century, several scientists, including George Johnstone Stoney, Arthur Schuster, and Johann Jakob Balmer, sought quantitative relations among the frequencies of the spectral lines emitted by an element. The first important success, Balmer's formula of 1885, gave the wavelengths of four lines in the visible spectrum of hydrogen in terms of integral whole numbers and a constant. In 1890, Johannes Robert Rydberg revised the Balmer formula by introducing the concept of wave number (reciprocal of the wavelength) in an equation with a constant (Rydberg constant) common to all series and elements.

Max Planck's early quantum theory resulted in a new understanding of the meaning of spectra. Heinrich Kayser incorporated Planck's radiation formula into the second volume of his *Handbook of Spectroscopy* in 1902. Niels Bjerrum interpreted spectra in terms of quantum theory in 1911, and Niels Bohr combined spectroscopic data with the quantum hypothesis in his revolutionary paper of 1913 on the hydrogen atom's electron energy.

Gerhard Herzberg's *Atomic Spectra and Atomic Structure* (1936) became one of the fundamental reference books for chemical applications of spectroscopy. By the 1950s, laser spectroscopy, nuclear magnetic spectroscopy, and other new techniques came to supplement visible, infrared, and Raman spectroscopy, the latter a technique discovered by C. V. Raman and K. S. Krishnan in 1928 for studying molecular structure based on the scattering of a beam of monochromatic light.

Mass spectroscopy, developed by Francis Aston and other physicists beginning in the 1920s, enabled chemists to sort out isotopic and molecular weights. The various spectroscopies not only identified elements and compounds, but also indicated submolecular structures, steric alignments, and bond angles.

By the 1920s, X-ray diffraction was employed to study the organization of atoms and submolecular units within molecules. Supplemented by electron diffraction after 1930, it helped to map the structure of metallic alloys, textile fibers, rubber, and large biologically significant molecules like proteins, nucleic acids, and vitamins. These methods had enormous industrial and commercial application as well as importance in fundamental research.

Paul A. M. Dirac, Max Born, and other physicists liked to say that quantum mechanics reduced chemistry to physics. Most chemists disagree. Physicists and chemists equally contributed to the development of quantum chemistry. Among the physicists, Walter Heitler, Fritz London, Friedrich Hund, and John Slater made notable contributions. But not until 1931, when Slater and Linus Pauling developed methods to explain directed chemical valence, did a truly chemical quantum mechanics exist. Their atomic orbital method was largely supplanted in chemical practice after the

1950s by the molecular orbital method developed simultaneously through the work of Hund, Erich Hückel, and, notably, Robert Mulliken.

Chemical kinetics, like quantum chemistry, became an increasingly sophisticated mathematical subject after World War I. Interest in chemical kinetics revived in the 1920s over the question whether activation energy for monomolecular reactions came from radiation or molecular collisions. Farrington Daniels, Hugh S. Taylor, and Cyril Hinshelwood developed evidence and theories for the collision hypothesis in the late 1920s, which replaced the radiation theory defended by Jean Perrin and others at the beginning of the decade. In the 1930s, Michael Polányi and Henry Eyring formulated a generalized transition-state theory for elementary chemical processes.

In the study of chemical kinetics in the late twentieth century, physical chemists employed not only the bulk experiments traditional to their field, but also molecular beams in which lasers excite reactant molecules into desired vibrational and rotational states and chemists identify the states of the products by their fluorescence. Dudley Herschbach and Yuan Tseh Lee pioneered this work.

In the development of physical chemistry, both physicists and chemists played important roles, with their work identified as chemical physics, theoretical chemistry, or theoretical physics as well as physical chemistry. The foundation in 1933 of the *Journal of Chemical Physics* marked a breakthrough in the United States for the application of sophisticated mathematical theories, including quantum mechanics, in chemistry. The journal's first volume included papers from Eyring, Herzberg, Mulliken, Pauling, Slater, and Taylor. What has most distinguished late twentieth-century physical chemistry from its late eighteenth-century counterparts have been innovations in instrumental practice and sophistication in mathematical theory.

Mary Jo Nye

PHYSICS. The development of physics provides a particularly strong example of the evolution of natural knowledge into modern physical science. Its traditional meaning of systematized, bookish knowledge about the entire physical world persisted until the eighteenth century; as late as 1798 the Académie Royale des Sciences of Paris could announce, as the subject of a prize competition in physics, "the nature, form, and uses of the liver in the various classes of animals." To be sure, the assumptions behind the question differed in an essential respect from the implications that would have been drawn a century or so earlier, when "physiologia" was often used as a substitute for "physica." This essential difference was the expectation that competitors would base their answers on experiments, at least some of which they would perform themselves.

Around 1800, "physics" in its old, inclusive sense, modified to imply experiment and some measure of research, lost out to a new division of science bearing the same name. This decisive historical fact is often veiled by the use of "physics" to refer to natural knowledge through the ages. The new physics of 1800 restricted itself to the inorganic world and, within it, to subjects open to investigation by such instruments as the air pump, electrical machine, balance, thermometer, and calorimeter. In place of the organic world, physics took on subjects previously the property of mathematics, especially mechanics and optics, and strove to quantify the fields that had distinguished physics during the eighteenth century: electricity, magnetism, heat, and pneumatics, which had gar-

nered attention as particularly suitable for catchy demonstration experiments to large and varied audiences.

The leaders in this reformulation are often grouped together as the school of Pierre-Simon de Laplace. They applied the mathematical approach developed for the theory of gravity to imponderable fluids supposed responsible for the phenomena of heat, light, electricity, magnetism, fire, and flame. The scheme of imponderables was unified by this common approach; but each fluid functioned independently and irreducibly in its theory. Neither the fluids nor the forces they were supposed to carry linked to one another in any fundamental or ontological sense. Rather, the Laplacian school and its fellow travelers deployed the fluids and forces in an instrumentalist way. It thus promoted the dismemberment of science and the dropping of scruples against instrumentalist mathematical descriptions.

The physics of 1800 differed in scope from later physics by including meteorology and parts of subjects shared with chemistry, like atomism, pneumatics, and thermodynamics. It fell far short of twentieth-century physics in eschewing models of the microworld apart from very general assumptions about the molecular constitution of bodies. A major exception to this generalization was the attachment of atomic weights to chemical atoms. The French-dominated physics of 1800 also differed from physics in 1900 or even in 1850 by having a vigorous opponent, Naturphilosophie, which depreciated mathematics and dismemberment and tried to reintegrate physics on general philosophical principles.

The basis of integration proved to be mechanics, which the Naturphilosophen disliked for its mathematics, strict-

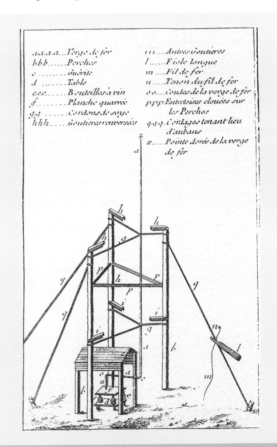

The set-up used by François Dalibard in 1752 to test Benjamin Franklin's conjecture that lightning is an electrical phenomenon. From B. Franklin, *Expériences et observations sur l'électricté*, tr. F. Dalibard (1756), and G. Dary, *A travers l'électricité* (1900).

239

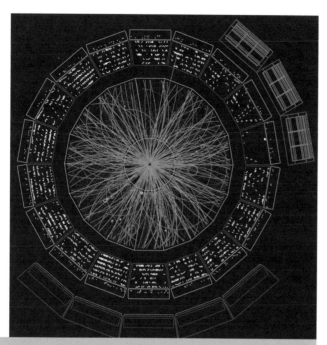

Simulated computer display of a particle collision in the large hadron collider at CERN (the European particle physics laboratory) near Geneva, Switzerland

other goings-on in the ether; in short, they could behave in many ways like chemical atoms. Thus arose the grand and remote program of complete mechanical reduction, which few physicists, perhaps, expected to see realized.

The possibility of concocting this program arose from the very substantial progress that mechanics itself had made during the middle third of the eighteenth century. The powerful mathematical theories of the behavior of fluids and solids then developed stood ready for exploitation by theorists of the ether. Also the more general formulations of mechanical principles were extended still further and adapted to electromagnetism and the kinetic theory of heat. The apparent success of the generalized mechanics in describing the phenomena of electromagnetism, light, and heat confirmed the possibility of mechanical reduction without the necessity of exhibiting an explicit model or picture. That was comforting. Of course, the scheme could be turned around and electromagnetism taken as primary. Many distinguished physicists around 1900 played with the idea of electrodynamic reduction.

The extraordinary progress of classical physics was supported by new institutional arrangements that made research as well as teaching the business of professors. The physics research of the eighteenth century, insofar as it existed at all, was primarily an easy-going affair associated with academies. Toward the end of the ancien régime and, increasingly after 1830, individual university professors were conceded the right, and then given the duty, to undertake research, usually at their own expense, as part of their jobs. Their institutions provided space, a collection of teaching apparatus, and perhaps a mechanic to keep it in order. Beginning around 1870, with the foundations of the Cavendish Laboratory in Cambridge and the Physics Institute of the University of Berlin, the idea that a professor's university should furnish him with the instruments he needed and a place to work with collaborators and advanced students steadily gained ground. (Here physics followed chemistry, whose first important university facilities for teaching and research go back to the 1830s.) The instruments employed in the institutes at first were largely home made. By the end of the century, however, most of the important equipment—electrical parts, air (or vacuum) pumps, refrigerators, batteries—came from commercial suppliers.

The recognition of the need for institutionally supported research both to advance science and to train students owed much to the demands and opportunities of the new electrotechnology and the perceived need to give doctors, engineers, and science teachers a grounding in physics. By 1900, every major university and higher school in Europe and the United States had a physics institute. By far the largest output of papers on physics came from academics. Most of them worked in Britain, France, Germany, or the United States, which then were investing the same proportion of their gross domestic product (GDP), and enlisting the same proportion of their populations, in the physics enterprise. An example of their investment, and an indication of the widening of occupational opportunities beyond the universities, was the establishment of national (or, in the case of France, international) bureaus of standards.

This enterprise reached a climax in the symbolic year 1900, when the world's physicists gathered in Paris for their first and last general conclave. They then awakened, as one participant said, to the news that the keystone of their grand synthesis might have been found. This was the electron, which, it appeared, might be the unique building block of

ness, and sobriety. This integration, which characterizes the so-called classical physics of the later nineteenth century, began around 1800 with the renewal of a quantitative wave theory of light. By 1840, most physicists (to use a word then just invented) associated light with the vibrations of a world-filling ether conceived as a medium obeying the laws of mechanics. That substituted a mechanical system for the imponderable fluid of light. As this conception crystallized, the fluid of heat vaporized; by 1860, the mechanical theory of heat and the kinetic theory of gases had replaced the old imponderable caloric. This process brought two fundamentally new concepts and techniques into physics: statistics, in the form of probability calculations about the herd behavior of molecules, and irreversibility, in the form of the thermodynamic quantity entropy.

That left the electrical and magnetic fluids, four in all, a positive, a negative, an austral, and a boreal. The discoveries of connections between electricity and magnetism beginning in 1820 led to the representation of magnetism as electricity in motion, a development completed by the demonstration of their identity in the theory of relativity. Thus, by 1860, the main imponderables of 1800 had either vanished altogether (caloric and the magnetic fluids), metamorphosed into a mechanical system (light), or remained with enhanced properties (electrical fluids). A further diminution occurred with the unexpected discovery that electromagnetism could be represented as a disturbance in the same ether whose vibrations made up light, or, stated phenomenologically, that light and other radiations were manifestations of electromagnetism, a representation confirmed by the production of radio waves in 1887.

Since the ether had been understood as a mechanical medium, physicists, particularly those trained at the University of Cambridge, tried to model electromagnetic phenomena in mechanical terms. It remained only to bring matter into the system. A way opened with the discovery that whirlpools or vortex rings in a fluid with the sorts of properties usually ascribed to the ether would last forever. These rings could link and separate in accordance with

both matter and electricity, the clue to chemical binding, the explanation of the ion, and the root of X rays and radioactivity. These considerations inspired the design of several model atoms based on electromagnetic theory. None worked well beyond the limited range of the phenomena for which it was devised, for example, magneto-optic effects and the scattering of rays from radioactive substances. Until around 1910, all these models lacked a principal ingredient that would make the theory of atomic structure into the leading sector of physics in the 1920s. The necessary ingredient was the quantum, introduced into the theory of black-body radiation in 1900. Its fundamental importance for physics had only just been recognized when the world's physicists flung themselves into world war.

The performance of physicists during World War I demonstrated their indispensability to modern society. New forms of government, foundation, and philanthropic support became available for scholarships, fellowships, and research. The worldwide activities of the Rockefeller Foundation were especially fruitful, since it favored the transfer of quantum physics from Europe to the United States and of American instrumentation, particularly cyclotrons, abroad. Basic physics, having finished provisionally with radiation and atoms, delved into the nucleus; here the United States, with sizable disposable income despite the depression, led the way into big science. American physics strengthened further as a result of the emigration of European refugees driven from their positions by fascist regimes. Nazi science policy stultified fundamental physics, in which Jews had been disproportionately prominent, in Germany and its occupied territories. As Germany declined, Japan and the Soviet Union developed their own capacities for training advanced students and set up research institutes often with liberal funding from military or industrial sources. The Soviet capacity centered on the institutes of the Akademiia nauk (Soviet Academy of Sciences) and laboratories supported by the Commissariat for Heavy Industry; the Japanese, on the imperial research institute RIKAN.

As physics spread geographically it also spread intellectually to territory newly conquered by the quantum. The study of cosmic rays, the behavior of bodies at low temperatures, the solid state, and the nucleus advanced prodigiously during the 1930s. The ascendancy of the electron was challenged or shared by the deuteron, meson, neutrino, neutron, positron, and proton. Molecular physics began to yield to new methods of calculation. Machines and ideas spun off into neighboring and even distant sciences, for example, astronomy (e.g., stellar energy) and biology (e.g., radioactive tracers). The principles of complementarity and uncertainty, invented to domesticate a mismatch between ordinary intuitions and the formalism of quantum mechanics, found applications to vitalism, psychology, philosophy, and theology.

Despite cries for a moratorium on research and movements for social responsibility among scientists, which gained some strength during the depths of the depression, the public applauded the science-based luxuries it soon found to be necessities: commercial radio, the all-electric kitchen, the long-distance telephone, air mail, air travel, and, above all, the automobile. As this easily extendable list suggests, the public did not (and does not) distinguish between science and technology. The confusion was compounded by the multiplication of industrial research laboratories, some of which, especially in the United States, permitted their technical staffs considerable leeway in choice and conduct of research. These laboratories helped to keep up demand for

physicists so that, except for the loss of a year or two's crop of new graduates, the depression had no effect on recruitment, at least in the United States.

The demand became so great during World War II that physics students who had not completed their degrees were employed on advanced research projects. Once again physicists proved their value: operations research, radar, the proximity fuse, cryptography, and the atomic bomb. The great winner in the conflict, the United States, rewarded its physicists after the war by supporting them in the manner to which they had become accustomed. The infusion of public dollars, intended to keep scientists well disposed toward government, as well as to encourage work related to weaponry, exaggerated a style already characteristic of American science: pragmatic, instrumentalist, democratic, and gigantic. The combination proved potent; countries that wanted to compete had no option but to submit to Americanization, especially in the world's most prestigious science, high-energy physics.

The United States assisted participation and competition by helping in the recovery of science in Germany (after picking some plums in Operation Paperclip, in Japan (after throwing its cyclotrons into the sea), and in Europe (by validating CERN, the Centre Européen pour la Recherche Nucléaire, which brought together nations no longer able to compete alone). The recovery called into existence new mechanisms of national support and international collaboration. As a result, Europe and Japan caught up with, and even outpaced, the United States, which, by canceling the Superconducting Super Collider in the 1990s, showed that it no longer had the will, if it had the means, to dominate the world in high-energy physics.

While the particle physicists enjoyed their limelight, their colleagues working on a smaller scale discovered or invented things of greater importance to the public than strangeness, parity nonconservation, the Eight-Fold Way, or the unification of the fundamental forces except for gravity. Radar technologies helped academic laboratories to produce the laser and airports to handle jet-setters. Research into the solid state returned with silicon chips, the computer, and high-temperature superconducting magnets. Color television, direct-dial international telephony, satellite communications, modern banking, the credit card, and so on, demonstrate that physics warmed by cold war can do wonders.

The wonders have included nuclear power and therewith the pollution that arises from the spent fuel and radioactive parts of reactors, which began to spread worldwide in the late 1950s under the American program, Atoms for Peace. The pollution, as well as the involvement of physicists and other scientists in advanced weapons projects, fuelled an antinuclear movement and wider attacks on science. The end of the cold war redirected some of this sentiment against the diffusion of high-tech industry to developing countries. Nonetheless, the spread of Western science, which began before World War I in the colonies of the European powers and produced important indigenous physics communities in the Soviet Union and Japan before World War II, continued into Latin America, the Near East, and continental Asia after 1945. An example of this diffusion of postwar physics, American style, is the synchrotron completed in Brazil in 1996.

The spread of physics to new cultures had a parallel within the old physics-producing countries in the increasing inclusion of groups whose participation had previously been marginal or restricted. Anti-Semitism lost its force in most of the world. Women gained easier access to training

P

and employment. Opportunities were extended to minority groups. Acquaintance with physical principles or gadgetry diffused widely in the general culture along with the computer, high-tech weapons, and space exploration.

On the intellectual and rhetorical side, physicists provided many good accounts of their progress toward a Theory of Everything.

The possibility of an encompassing and final theory arose at the intersection of cosmology and particle physics. Theories of the largest and smallest structures in the universe combined to make a Big Bang. Crucial evidence favoring the doctrine came from the characteristic postwar specialty, radioastronomy. The doctrine of the Big Bang and the expectation by some theoretical physicists that a complete and unified theory of the physical world might be achieved during their lifetimes provoked the interest of diverse theologians and the Vatican. In a limited region of vast extent, therefore, physics has returned to the sort of questions with which its predecessor, natural knowledge, had been engaged.

J. L. HEILBRON

PHYSIOLOGY. Originally synonymous with natural philosophy, physics, or the study of all natural bodies, the word "physiology" began to restrict its scope to the structure and composition of the human body during the sixteenth century. The French physician Jean François Fernel then defined physiology as one of the five parts of medicine—the one that "explains the nature of the healthy man, all of his faculties and functions." Fernel contrasted physiology particularly with "pathology," summarized as "the study of the illnesses and affections that can happen to man."

As the study of the structure and functions of the human body, physiology is one of the oldest fields of natural inquiry and links with fewer breaks than almost any other modern science with its roots in classical Antiquity. From Aristotle to Galen, the ancient tradition thoroughly mapped out the internal anatomy of animals closely related to humans and established the principle that the form of the parts must be related to their function. That principle has framed and guided physiological investigation ever since.

Physicians and natural philosophers of the sixteenth and early seventeenth centuries inherited an account of the functional organization of the human body based mainly on Galen. Filtered through twelve centuries and multiple layers of commentary and condensation, the complex, evolving, sometimes contradictory views of the voluminous Galenic corpus have been reduced to an easily remembered system. Despite subtle errors owing to Galen's projection of the anatomy of the apes he had dissected onto the human body he was not permitted to cut, the functional arrangements of the skeleto-muscular system had been thoroughly worked out with only secondary changes into early modern times. The system divided the body into three regions. In the uppermost of these, the head, resided the brain, the "domicile of the human spirit, the seat of thought and reason, and the source and origin of all movement and sensation." Galen had worked out the gross anatomy of the brain, the cranial nerves emanating directly from it, the spinal cord, and the peripheral nerves in considerable and mostly accurate detail, and established regions innervated by various nerves through vivisection experiments not surpassed until the nineteenth century. The heart and lungs dominated the central region, or thorax. The heart was connected with two sets of vessels: on the right side to the veins, through which nourishment, transformed to blood in several stages, most notably in the liver, flowed to all parts of the body; and on the left side to the thick-walled arteries, which also distributed blood, but of a brighter, more spirituous nature, imbued in the left ventricle with vital spirit. The lower region, or venter, was filled by the organs of digestion, through which food passed from the mouth, converted gradually, by a process known as coction, into

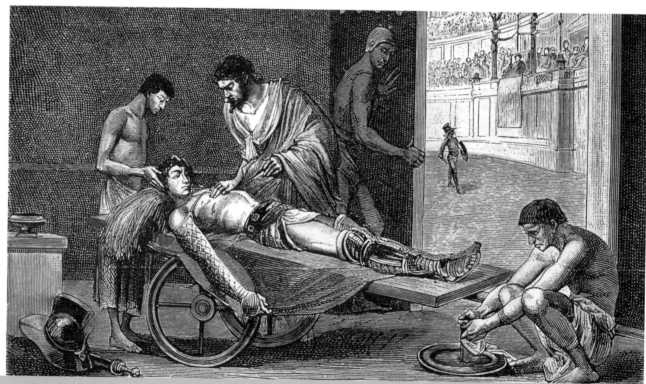

Artist's conception of the Greek physician Galen (2nd century A.D.) ministering to gladiators wounded in the arena at Pergamum.

the uniform milky chyle absorbed through the portal veins into the liver. These arrangements provided a well-integrated, comprehensible account of the relation between the observed internal structure of the human body and the primary functions essential to life, and adapted well to explanations of the humoral imbalances associated with disease.

An engineer, however, would have found some difficulties in this account. The Galenic system sometimes required fluids or pneuma to flow both ways in the same vessels, and even to pass the wrong way through valves in the heart generally understood to permit them only to move in the contrary direction. The Italian anatomist Realdo Colombo contended in 1559 that the heart did not attract blood into its ventricles in its expansion, as Galen had said, but pressed it outward in contraction, so that the arteries dilated when the heart constricted; and that the blood did not pass from right to left ventricle through pores in the septum between them, as Galen had said, but by a less direct route through the lungs. More than half a century later the questions Colombo had raised about the motions of the heart and its relation to the motions of the arteries remained controversial.

Through exquisite observations on different classes of animals, especially on the hearts of cold-blooded and dying ones, William Harvey settled to his satisfaction that Colombo's interpretation of the motions of the heart was correct: that through its active contractions it moved blood from the veins into the right ventricle, from there through the lungs to the left ventricle, and then into the arteries, which it filled, "as my breath in a glove." As soon as Harvey asked himself the further question, how much blood does the heart move in this way, he entered a pathway "so new and unheard of" that he feared "every man almost will become my enemy." No matter what quantity of blood he assumed to be driven out of the heart at each beat, the amount that passed through in an hour or a day was so abundant that it could neither be consumed in nutrition nor replenished from the food. The heart must, therefore, produce a "perpetual circular motion of the blood."

Although he did encounter some fierce resistance, Harvey prevailed over his opponents so quickly that within his own lifetime he was heralded as the founder of a new era in medicine. The discovery of the circulation not only ended centuries of domination by ancient systems of thought, but stimulated observations and experiments that brought further novelties, such as the discovery of the lacteal vessels by Jean Pecquet and a sustained collaborative effort by followers of Harvey informally associated at Oxford to understand the relation between the circulation of the blood and the process of respiration.

Harvey himself had examined physiological questions within an Aristotelian philosophical framework, which his successors soon abandoned for the newly dominant mechanical philosophy. That transition wrought a fundamental change in the relation between the living and the nonliving worlds. Where Aristotle had extended to all of nature the purposefulness evident in vital processes and activities, the new mechanical world eschewed teleology. Henceforth those who attempted to understand the underlying physical phenomena taking place in humans or other living things had the choice among explaining them in terms of the shapes and motions of the ultimate particles of matter (later also of the forces exerted between them), invoking recently discovered chemical properties (such as acidity and alkalinity), and referring vital phenomena to principles unlike those of the physical world.

The chemical and physical tools available in the seventeenth and eighteenth centuries had little capacity to explain physiological phenomena. Explanations of the formation of secretions in the salivary glands, the pancreas, or the kidney tubules remained at the level of crude images of particles of the blood that fit into holes in sieves passing through them into the secretory ducts. The new physical concepts did, however, offer more effective means to investigate the circulation, the one system in the body that seemed clearly accessible to mechanical analysis. The influential "iatromechanist" Giovanni Alfonso Borelli was the first person to attempt to determine the force exerted by the heart. The fantastically large number at which he arrived in 1678 stimulated others, such as Newton's follower James Keill, to seek more direct means to measure the force. The lack of agreement among the measurers prompted the famous measurements of the pressure in the arteries and veins that the Reverend Stephen Hales carried out early in the eighteenth century by inserting long vertical tubes into the opened blood vessels of horses and other large animals. When the medically trained mathematician Daniel Bernoulli produced a landmark treatise in 1738 that defined a new field of hydrodynamics, he quickly applied the theoretical principles and methods of calculation that he had introduced there to the study of the heart and movements of the blood.

In 1747, the Swiss professor of anatomy, surgery, and medicine at the University of Göttingen, Albrecht von Haller, published a textbook titled *First Lines of Physiology,* followed between 1759 and 1776 by an eight-volume *Foundations of the Physiology of the Human Body* that summarized and organized all previous work on its structure and functions. These massive works, which Haller intended both to teach medical students the fundamentals of the subject and to open the way to further discoveries, made physiology visible for the first time as a coherent discipline. Also a prolific experimentalist, Haller used the microscope effectively to study the circulation of the blood in the smaller arterioles and veins, and established through numerous experiments a distinction between the sensible parts (nerves) and the irritable parts (muscles) of the body. He met challenges by multiplying his own experiments and by gathering a group of followers who extended the scope of his generalization. He and his followers created an investigative field and raised the standards both for performing and reporting physiological experiments.

By the beginning of the nineteenth century, the physical sciences were supplying new, powerful methods for the investigation of physiological problems. The effects of the advances in chemistry can most easily be seen in the study of digestion. The eighteenth-century investigators René-Antoine de Réaumur and Lazzarro Spallanzani had demonstrated through experiments on various animals that foods are softened into a uniform semifluid mass during digestion, and managed to duplicate the process outside the body with gastric juice withdrawn from the stomach. Chemically, however, they could only say that the process resembled the action of an acid on a metal. During the 1820s, Friedrich Tiedemann and Leopold Gmelin used a repertoire of reagents and extraction procedures to identify the changes that foodstuffs undergo in their passage through the stomach, intestines, and lacteal vessels. Although the only definite chemical transformation they could identify was the conversion of starch to sugar, their investigation opened a continuous tradition that lasted into the twentieth century.

Between 1800 and 1810, a group of physiologists in Paris began to apply the surgical skills acquired during their

P

Hermann Von Helmholtz (1821–1894) German physicist, anatomist, and physiologist

ter such chairs spread rapidly through the major German universities.

Brücke and two other students of Müller, Emil du Bois-Reymond and Hermann von Helmholtz, committed themselves about this time, together with Carl Ludwig, to the goal of reducing physiology to physics and chemistry. This they were never able to do, but they did introduce a style of physiological experimentation based on precise instrumentation, accurate measurement, and rigorous analysis. They sought to examine the magnitude of any observed effect as an unknown function of all the conditions that influenced it and to vary one factor at a time while holding other conditions constant. "The dependence of the effect on each condition," du Bois-Reymond wrote, "can now be shown in a curve, whose exact law, to be sure, remains unknown, but whose course can, in general be outlined." In 1847, Ludwig devised a recording instrument in which the changing magnitudes of a physiological quantity such as the pressure of the blood or the length of a muscle were traced on the smoked surface of a revolving drum, soon known as the kymograph. It quickly became the operational symbol of this mode of functional analysis and a standard fixture in the physiological laboratory of the late nineteenth and early twentieth centuries. The traces recorded by kymographs filled the pages of the journals of physiology.

Meanwhile the advent of the voltaic battery, galvanic currents, and then electromagnetic phenomena had supplied other new tools for physiological experiments. Using a very sensitive galvanometer of his own design, du Bois-Reymond was able to detect, during the 1840s, delicate changes in electric potential accompanying the transmission of nerve impulses in frogs. In 1850, Helmholtz used a ballistic galvanometer to measure the velocity of the nerve impulse itself, a feat once believed to be all but impossible.

By the last third of the nineteenth century, physiologists in Germany possessed large, well-equipped laboratories in which they could not only perform complicated experiments, but train a steadily increasing number of German and foreign students. It was the golden age of physiology. No sooner, however, did physiology attain its autonomy from anatomy than it began itself to undergo a slow process of subdivision. The very tools of the physical sciences that had given it such power early in the nineteenth century now served as foundations for more specialized investigations of the phenomena of life. The first to devolve was physiological chemistry, which attained only two independent chairs in Germany in the nineteenth century, but gave rise in the early twentieth century to the dominant field of biochemistry. The study of the effects of drugs on physiological processes, initiated by physiologists, became by the late nineteenth century the domain of the emerging discipline of pharmacology. What Claude Bernard and others defined in the nineteenth century as "general physiology," or the study of the phenomena of life common to all organisms, became in the twentieth century cell biology. In this steadily expanding array of new biological disciplines, physiology functioned as a mature, or even old-fashioned, science by the middle of the twentieth century. Nevertheless, it has retained domains of its own, such as the regulation of heat, respiration, and other functions, and continues to be an active field of inquiry.

FREDERIC LAWRENCE HOLMES

medical training to make vivisection central to an emerging field in which experimentation was to be not an occasional, but the central activity in the formation of an independent scientific discipline. François Magendie became the most emphatic and persistent advocate for this viewpoint. His own discovery in 1821 of the sensory and motor roots of the spinal nerves became the starting point for mapping the sensory and motor functions of the entire nervous system. His student Claude Bernard, following his lead and succeeding to his chair at the Collège de France in 1855, made between 1848 and 1857 a series of brilliant discoveries, including the action of pancreatic juice on fats, the glycogenic function of the liver, the vasomotor nerves, and the modes of action of carbon monoxide and curare, which made him the most eminent figure of the generation in which physiology became established, both intellectually and institutionally, as the first thoroughly experimental life science.

In Germany, physiology was in the early nineteenth century combined with anatomy in the same university chair. At the Anatomical Museum of the University of Berlin, Johannes Peter Müller represented and actively pursued research in both physiology and comparative anatomy. His *Handbook of Human Physiology,* first published in 1833 and in successive editions until 1844, mastered the field more fully than any physiology text since Haller's. Müller trained students who followed him into each of the fields in which he worked, but none who could command, as he had, their whole range. By the 1840s, advances in both physiology and comparative anatomy made it imperative to separate them, and in 1847 Müller's student Ernest von Brücke accepted, at the Medical Faculty of the University of Königsberg, one of the first independent chairs of physiology. Thereaf-

PLANETARIUM denotes instruments demonstrating positions and movements of the sun, earth, moon, planets, or stars. Its earliest usage referred to Giovanni de' Dondi's clock and its astronomical dials (around 1360). It later comprised various devices: globe, armillary, equatorium, orrery, grand orrery, compound orrery, tellurian, lunarium, cometarium, jovilabe, Copernican sphere, sphère mouvante, and others. These tools have enabled scholars to pursue research and assisted lay audiences to learn basic astronomy. Since 1923, "planetarium" has connoted an optical projector, its architectural facility, and the facility's institution.

Historical planetaria fall into two categories: illustrations of the celestial sphere and associated daily motions, and representations of longer-term motions and principles pertaining to the classical planets. Instruments of the first category, including celestial and terrestrial globes and many armillaries, served as popular instruments for initial astronomical instruction long after the acceptance of Copernicanism, demonstrating earth-based observations in terms of the celestial sphere, its fixed stars, and imaginary geometrical lines. Important globes include the Atlante Farnese, and models by Ptolemy, Islamic and Chinese scholars, Gemma Frisius, Gerhard Mercator, Tycho Brahe, Jodocus Hondius, Willem Blaeu, Joseph Moxon, Vincenzo Coronelli, and the Cary family. Room-sized hollow spheres by Adam Olearius (Gottorp), Erhard Weigel (Jena), Roger Long (Cambridge), and Wallace Atwood (Chicago) provided experiences of the rotating heavens.

Instruments of the second category featured geared dials, rings, or spheres representing the seven classical planets and, later, the earth and planetary satellites in illustration of Copernican astronomy. Descendants of geared astrolabes and astronomical clocks, significant examples of these instruments include the first known tellurian, by Blaeu, and models by Ole Rømer, Christiaan Huygens, George Graham, James Ferguson, Benjamin Martin, David Rittenhouse, George Adams Sr. and Jr., and William and Samuel Jones, as well as Eise Eisenga's room-sized planetarium. Graham's proto-orrery prompted production of elaborate grand orreries for wealthy patrons and numerous inexpensive models for the adult science education market in Hanoverian England.

Instruments addressing both concepts include astronomical clocks with globes and numerous armillaries enveloping planetary models. Twentieth-century Zeiss optical projection systems synthesize the two categories somewhat, but recent computer-based technology offers more fully integrated illustrations of naked-eye observations and astrophysical principles.

Chicago, New York, Los Angeles, London, Stockholm, Calcutta, and other cities around the world feature public planetaria. School programs account for most visits, particularly in Japan, where Goto and Minolta systems are popular, and in the United States, where many Spitz models were built in response to the *Sputnik* crisis.

At times symbols of city, court, wealth, or learning, planetaria originally conveyed creation's divine order and purpose, providentially extended to human affairs. Enlightenment-era lectures and wealthier homes featured orreries illustrating the solar system's mathematical regularity, whereas early Zeiss shows competed with moving pictures for audiences seeking novel theatrical experiences. Contemporary planetaria proclaim the universe's evolutionary history alongside ever-popular presentations detailing the Star of Bethlehem's astronomy. Controversies over rival goals—education or entertainment—have accompanied planetaria for centuries, a natural consequence of their bridging

astronomy and popular culture. The mechanisms of the instruments, the techniques, skills, gender, backgrounds, and communication goals of their artisans and operators, and the desires of their audiences have reflected their cultural contexts throughout the history of planetaria, microcosms of their social and scientific macrocosms.

MARVIN BOLT

PLANETARY SCIENCE. The term "planetary science" dates from the 1950s. It applies physics, astronomy, chemistry, geology, biology, atmospheric sciences, and oceanography to discrete bodies in the solar system. Previously the study of the planets had been known as "solar system astronomy" or "solar system science." That might have been a better name, because the field takes the whole solar system, including comets, meteorites, asteroids, and planetary satellites as its object of study.

Like the parallel discipline earth science, planetary science emerged in tandem with the new technologies whose development had been spurred by World War II, rocketry and computers in particular. In 1958, the International Geophysical Year began, in large measure to take advantage of these technologies. In the same year the Soviet Union launched *Sputnik* and the space race began. In October 1958, the United States established the National Aeronautics and Space Administration (NASA), to carry on and extend the work formerly done by the National Advisory Committee for Aeronautics (NACA) and other government bodies.

The term "planetary science" first appeared in the journal *Science* in 1959 in a job advertisement put out by the Goddard Space Center. In the same year, the first specialist journal, *Planetary and Space Science,* began publication. In 1962, the American Geophysical Union set up a section

The French armillary sphere of the 18th century, can be placed in the plane of the meridian by using the compass in its base.

on planetary sciences. The journal *Earth and Planetary Science Letters* appeared in 1966. Existing institutions like the Houston Lunar Science Institute, university departments, and the journal *Meteoritics* all added "and Planetary Science" to their names.

Copernicus, Galileo, Christiaan Huygens, Gian Domenico Cassini, and William Herschel had asked questions about the configuration of the solar system (cosmology), its mechanics, and its origin (cosmogony), and little by little discovered smaller and more distant bodies in the solar system. Galileo, William Gilbert, and Thomas Harriot mapped the Moon in the seventeenth century. Michael Florent van Langren published the first large full-Moon map in 1645, though his projected series of maps showing the Moon in its different phases never appeared in print. The first full-Mars map was published in 1840. The advent of large telescopes and photography vastly improved maps of the Moon and Mars in the remaining years of the century.

Meanwhile physicists, geophysicists, and geologists as well as astronomers pursued many aspects of what would now be planetary science. They asked how the Earth differed from neighboring planets and why. In 1801, the Italian astronomer Giuseppe Piazzi detected the first asteroid. By the end of the century, Maximilian Wolf at the University of Heidelberg had invented a technique for discovering new asteroids by the streaks they left on photographic plates. Astronomers thus discovered the asteroid belt. They also discussed the origin of craters on the Moon and other planetary bodies. In 1803, Jean-Baptiste Biot confirmed that certain stones in Normandy really had fallen from the sky, thus establishing the extraterrestrial origin of meteorites.

After a period in which interest in the solar system waned, two American astronomers, Gerard Peter Kuiper and Harold C. Urey, renewed interest in the subject in the 1940s. Kuiper discovered the carbon dioxide atmosphere on Mars and a disk-shaped region of minor planets (now called the Kuiper belt) outside Neptune's orbit, which he proposed as the source of certain types of comets. He pioneered the development of infrared astronomy, helped identify landing sites for the first manned landing on the moon, and edited two influential works, *The Solar System* (1953–1958) and *Stars and Stellar Systems* (1960–1968). Urey synthesized his investigations of the distribution of elements in the solar system in his *The Planets, Their Origin and Development* (1952).

Since 1960, planetary science has developed rapidly with the help of new optical and radio telescopes. In 1990, the Hubble Space Telescope reached a position high above the distorting effects of the Earth's atmosphere. Project Apollo, which culminated in 1969 with the first human moon landing, the *Pioneer* and *Voyager* spacecraft that explored the Moon and other parts of the solar system, and the *Viking* and *Mars Pathfinder* spacecraft that investigated Mars enabled new kinds of data collection, whether by humans on the moon, by robots on the moon, or by photography and sampling of these and more distant planets. Planetary mapping, aided by radar techniques, proceeded apace. Mercury and Venus, whose surfaces had been difficult to study, Mercury because of its small size and proximity to the Sun, and Venus because of its dense atmosphere, have now been mapped.

New specialties have emerged, such as astrogeology, astrobiology, planetary atmospheres, planetary tectonics, and planetary physics. Topics of active investigation include planetary origins, the structure and composition of plan-

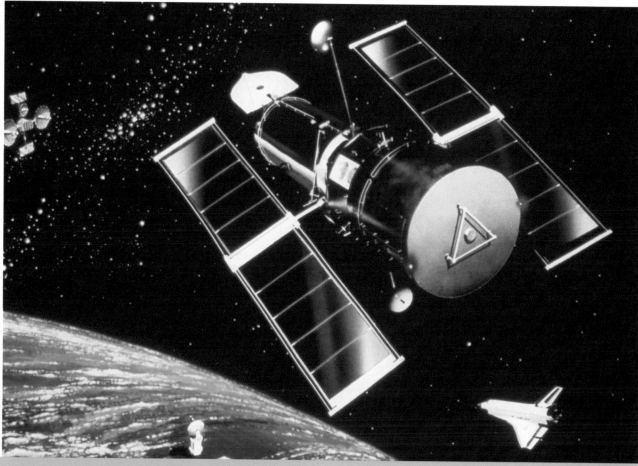

Artist's depiction of the Hubble Space telescope in orbit

ets, vulcanism and tectonic activity, the atmospheres and magnetic fields of planets, and the planets of Jupiter. Public interest in planetary science, though not as high as in the 1960s, is still fueled by dramatic photographs, press coverage, and fascination with perennial puzzles like the canals of Mars and the possibility of life elsewhere in the universe. New discoveries and up-to-date information are posted on the NASA site on the World Wide Web. Planetary scientists, who until the end of the second millennium had been concerned almost exclusively with objects within our own solar system, are beginning to pursue the increasing evidence of planets in other parts of the universe.

JOANNE BOURGEOIS

PLASMA PHYSICS AND FUSION. A plasma in physics refers to an ionized gas. Scientists first recognized the importance of plasmas in studies of the propagation of radio waves for the nascent radio industry of the early twentieth century. In seeking ways to send radio signals over long distances they realized that waves seemed to bounce off a conducting layer in the earth's atmosphere, allowing signals to travel far beyond the horizon. One of these researchers, Irving Langmuir of the United States, in the 1920s designated the atmospheric matter "plasma" and investigated its properties in gas discharges in the laboratory.

In the late 1920s, physicists began to apply new theories of atomic structure and quantum mechanics to the energy source of stars. In 1929, Robert Atkinson and Fritz Houtermans predicted that the nuclei of light atoms such as hydrogen, the primary constituent of the sun, could fuse through quantum tunneling, and that the resultant atoms would weigh less than the original constituents. Albert Einstein's mass-energy relation suggested that fusion would release vast amounts of energy, enough to power the stars. Hans Bethe and others developed the theory of stellar fusion in the 1930s, elucidating the chains of nuclear reactions by which fusion built up heavier chemical elements and calculating the reaction rates and energy release. Astrophysicists were then incorporating plasmas into theories of stellar structure and thus merged the study of plasma with fusion.

Physicists at the time recognized the potential of fusion for a new energy source, but the high temperatures required to produce it seemed out of the reach of available technology. Although World War II and the coincident discovery of nuclear fission diverted attention from fusion, they would eventually provide the motivation and means to attain it. Nuclear fission and the subsequent development of nuclear bombs brought stellar conditions down to earth and offered a way to ignite fusion. During the war scientists working on the atomic bomb project in the United States discussed thermonuclear weapons, or the hydrogen bomb (named after its fuel), with explosive force orders of magnitude beyond fission bombs. Both the United States and the Soviet Union would pursue the hydrogen bomb in the Cold War; in the meantime, work on fission bombs advanced knowledge about plasma behavior, and the complicated hydrodynamic calculations for bomb physics spurred the development of electronic computers, which would then aid the development of fusion weapons.

Research into controlled fusion revived in 1951 with the help of Juan Perón, the dictator of Argentina. A few years earlier Perón had set up a laboratory for Ronald Richter, an expatriate German with a scheme for controlled fusion power. In 1951, Perón announced Richter's successful pro-

duction of power from a fusion reactor. The news made headlines in major newspapers, and though American and European scientists quickly discounted Richter's results, they did start thinking more seriously about the problem of fusion reactions.

One physicist so inspired was Lyman Spitzer, Jr., who was familiar with plasmas from his background in astrophysics and who had just joined a group at Princeton University working on the crash program to build the hydrogen bomb in the United States. Spitzer quickly devised a device to contain a plasma at high temperatures and obtained the support of the Atomic Energy Commission for the work. Commission laboratories at Los Alamos, New Mexico; Livermore, California; and Oak Ridge, Tennessee, soon followed suit. Controlled fusion seemed to offer unlimited power from an abundant fuel without the lingering radioactivity of nuclear fission reactors, and also provided a peaceful application of nuclear research to balance the fearful implications of nuclear weapons. It hence did not lack for support; by the late 1950s the United States was spending tens of millions of dollars a year on fusion research.

Other countries joined what became an international race for controlled fusion. British scientists led by George P. Thomson began investigating fusion soon after the war, and the British government sponsored a major fusion effort at its nuclear research laboratory at Harwell. In the Soviet Union, Igor Kurchatov, Igor Tamm, Andrei Sakharov, and other scientists in the nuclear weapons project took up fusion research in the early 1950s. The connection to nuclear weapons kept work in each country secret until Kurchatov revealed the Soviet program on a visit to Harwell in 1956; an international conference on atomic energy in Geneva in 1958 opened up the field for good. Japan, France, Italy, and other nations also entered the race, but the high cost of fusion experiments spurred efforts at international collaboration.

Most fusion reactors used various configurations of magnetic fields to bottle up the charged particles of the plasma, which at the high temperatures involved proved difficult to control. Fusion research engaged scientists from diverse fields: astrophysics, cosmic ray physics, accelerator engineering, gas discharges, and weapons physics. But no unified framework emerged from this eclectic background, and the initial optimism of the early 1950s soon gave way to realization of the technical difficulty of the endeavor—skeptics compared it to trying to push all the water to one side of your bathtub with your hands—and lack of knowledge about the basic behavior of plasmas. In the late 1950s, fusion researchers instead turned to the underlying theory of magnetohydrodynamics, although work on fusion reactors continued under more empirical techniques.

In the mid-1960s, Soviet scientists provided a new impetus with their development of the tokamak, which combined linear and toroidal configurations of previous devices in a single toroidal device. In 1968, a Soviet team under Lev Artsimovich revealed the attainment of temperatures of around ten million degrees and confinement times of about a millisecond in a tokamak. The tokamak thereafter became the preferred device for fusion, but the conditions it produced remained far below those required for fusion. Only after decades of technical refinements did a tokamak at Princeton University provide the first definitive success in late 1993 and 1994, when it confined a plasma of hydrogen isotopes at 300 million degrees Celsius for about a second to produce 10 million watts of power. The Princeton toka-

P

Princeton University's Tokamak Fusion Test reactor, a large device designed to retain a plasma at temperatures high enough to fuse helium nuclei

mak, however, still consumed more power in heating and confining the plasma than it produced.

The development of lasers in the 1960s suggested another route to fusion. Focusing high-energy lasers on a stationary solid pellet of hydrogen isotopes could compress and heat the pellet enough for fusion. Laser fusion—a form of inertial confinement—offered a way around the difficult problems posed by confining hot moving plasma with magnetic fields, and several nations started laser fusion programs. But laser fusion also presented daunting technical problems, especially the manufacture of laser optics capable of the high energies necessary. Connections with nuclear weapons persisted in laser fusion, since it also offered a way to model miniature nuclear explosions, and secrecy began to return to fusion research. In the 1990s, the United States began building the billion-dollar National Ignition Facility at Livermore to substitute laser fusion for full-scale nuclear tests.

Still another route to fusion energy was announced in Utah in March 1989 by B. Stanley Pons and Martin Fleischmann, who claimed to have obtained fusion at room temperature in a cheap and simple electrochemical experiment. The announcement set off a frenzy of popular discussion of limitless energy, but attempts to replicate the experiment and to adjust theory to accommodate the results failed. In addition, the disciplinary background of Pons and Fleischmann in chemistry did not inspire confidence in the physicists who dominated the fusion community, nor did their mode of announcement, in a press conference instead of through peer-reviewed publication. Cold fusion quickly joined N rays, polywater, and other famous nondiscoveries in the history of science.

PETER J. WESTWICK

PLATE TECTONICS. The theory of plate tectonics, proposed in the 1960s, asserts that the creation, motion, and destruc-

tion of a small number of rigid plates, thin in relation to the earth's diameter, shape the earth's surface. Quickly termed a revolution, the switch to plate tectonics was one of the most exciting scientific developments of the mid-twentieth century.

The discoveries that stimulated scientists to propose plate tectonics came from paleomagnetism and oceanography. At the end of the 1950s, a small but influential group of physicists based at the universities of London and Newcastle and at the Australian National University were studying paleomagnetism. They became convinced that to explain the apparent global wandering of the magnetic pole over geological time, they had to assume that the continents had moved relative to one another. They saw this as new evidence for the theory of continental drift, still widely discussed in Britain and Australia because it had been advocated in 1945 in the *Principles of Physical Geology* by the distinguished geologist Arthur Holmes.

Meanwhile, oceanographers had been surveying the ocean floor and measuring heat flow and gravitational and magnetic anomalies. They discovered a global system of mid-ocean ridges. These enormous mountain chains had some peculiar physical characteristics, such as patterns of magnetic anomalies and a median rift valley with high heat flow. In the early 1960s, Harry Hess of Princeton University suggested that these were tensional cracks through which lava welled up, created new sea floor, and spread. His conjecture of sea floor spreading was quickly corroborated by two confirmed predictions. In 1963, Fred Vine and Drummond Matthews of Cambridge University predicted that magnetic anomalies observed on either side of the mid-ocean ridges recorded global magnetic reversals preserved in the solidified lava. Physicists had dated global magnetic reversals on the continents using radioactivity and so had a magnetic time scale. It was only necessary to find parallel zebra stripes

P

of anomalies on either side of the ocean ridges. In 1965, J. Tuzo Wilson predicted that if sea floor spreading occurred, scientists should be able to detect seismically a new kind of fault that he named "transform." In 1966, scientists at the Lamont Doherty Geological Observatory found evidence supporting both predictions.

If the sea floor was spreading, where was the new material being accommodated? Could it be that the earth was expanding? Scientists gave this possibility serious consideration. It was quickly displaced, however, by the theory of plate tectonics independently conceived by Jason Morgan at Princeton and Dan McKenzie at Cambridge in 1967 and 1968, respectively. They proposed that rigid plates, each perhaps a hundred km thick, covered the earth's surface. They, and not continents and oceans, were the important structural surface features. Created at the mid-ocean ridges, they moved apart until they sank into and were consumed in "subduction zones" signaled by intense earthquake activity and negative gravity anomalies. Abstract mathematical models of plate movements agreed well with field observations. By the early 1970s, almost all earth scientists, except in Russia, had accepted plate tectonics.

Such a rapid shift to an account of the earth so radically different from previous orthodoxy stimulated popular interest. Earth scientists published in the popular scientific press, appeared on television programs, and revised school textbooks. Once their immediate euphoria waned, many earth scientists suffered a crisis of confidence. Were they wrong to have resisted the theory of continental drift for half a century? And if science proceeded by the patient accumulation of facts, as most of them believed, was it scientific to switch in just a few years from believing that the continents stayed in place to believing that they moved?

Many earth scientists, particularly younger ones, wondered how their predecessors could have rejected continental drift and derided it as pseudoscientific when it had been supported by some evidence from similarities of paleontology and lithology on the two sides of the Atlantic and from the fit of the continents. Their reaction misread history. Continental drift, like other theories put forward when the geological synthesis proposed by Eduard Suess in *Face of the Earth* (1883–1904) collapsed in the early years of the twentieth century, had been given a serious hearing. It was widely accepted in South Africa and viewed with an open mind by geologists in the British Isles and Australia. In the 1950s, some American geologists mocked it in their undergraduate classes largely because they believed its proponents lacked evidence. Plate tectonics, with its confirmed predictions, had much stronger evidential support; moreover, it was a different theory. The introduction of plates made continental movement an incidental theoretical consequence and not the key theoretical claim.

Earth scientists still had to face the fact that the speed with which they accepted plate tectonics did not sit well with their image of science as the gradual accumulation of facts. Casting around for an alternative picture of science, they came across Thomas Kuhn's *Structure of Scientific Revolutions* (1962). By the late 1960s, J. Tuzo Wilson and Allen Cox were describing plate tectonics as a Kuhnian revolution—an attribution still debated by historians and philosophers of science.

RACHEL LAUDAN

PNEUMATICS. The discovery of the different gas types during the third quarter of the eighteenth century caused

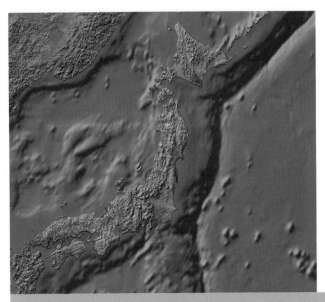

True-color satellite image of the islands of Japan. The Japan Trench (the dark line running from top right, forms part of the boundary of the Pacific and Eurasian tectonic plates. Plate movement and other tectonic features account for Japan's frequent earthquakes.

a revolution in physical science. The new field of pneumatics made large demands on experimental technique and apparatus, and required unusual accuracy in calculating the weights of small quantities of matter. It played an important part in quantifying physical science and in forging fruitful connections among the branches of natural knowledge from anatomy (as in the work of Luigi Galvani) to chemistry (Joseph Priestley and Antoine-Laurent Lavoisier), meteorology (Jean André Deluc and John Dalton), and physics (Alessandro Volta).

The English clergyman Stephen Hales, who had learned Newtonian experimentation at Cambridge around 1700, pointed the way to pneumatics in his *Vegetable Staticks* of 1727. Hales described many ways of fixing "air" in, and liberating it from, vegetable and other matter. He collected liberated air over water in a "pneumatic trough" of his invention, measured its quantity, and studied its quality; but, although he handled several chemically distinct gases,

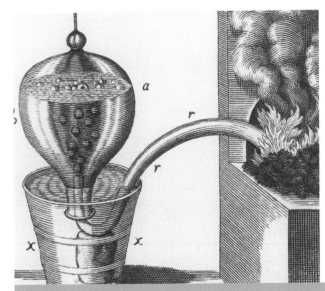

A pneumatic trough invented in the 18th century for the collection of various gas types

he regarded them all as the same basic substance. The variety and quantity of substances from which he drew his "air," however, supported his conclusion, which he expressed in the Newtonian style as a query: "may we not with good reason adopt this now fixt, now volatile *Proteus* among the Chymical principles ... notwithstanding it has hitherto been overlooked and rejected by Chymists, as no way entitled to the Denomination?"

Hales studied fixed air while following up his interest in the mechanics (physiology) of plants; Joseph Black came to the problem as a medical student concerned with kidney stones. For his doctoral thesis of 1754, he examined the air (carbon dioxide) released from magnesium alba (magnesium carbonate) when heated or treated with acid. He determined that it differed from common air in its inability to support combustion and respiration, and occurred fixed in the limestone implicated in urinary calculi. Novel airs then began to rise promiscuously. In 1766, Henry Cavendish identified a special "inflammable air" (hydrogen) as a product of metals dissolved in acids. In 1772, Priestley, teacher, divine, and experimental philosopher, inspired by reading Hales, announced the new species "nitrous air" (NO) and hydrochloric acid gas; and in 1774–1775 he introduced "eminently respirable air" (oxygen), the peculiar portion of ordinary air that maintains life. In 1776, his correspondent Volta discovered a second inflammable air (methane) while gas hunting in a swamp.

In the early 1780s, Cavendish, Lavoisier, and the inventor James Watt discovered that inflammable and eminently respirable air made water when sparked together. The rationale for the spark originated in Priestley's test for the respirability of gases: mix nitrous air with a sample under test and determine the contraction of the volume; the greater the diminution, the better the sample. (For oxygen the maximum contraction would be a third: $2NO + O_2 = 2NO_2$.) Volta had substituted inflammable gas for nitrous air and added the spark to speed up the process. He and other devotees of the new pneumatics devised "eudiometers" to test air by sparking. Thus they set up for themselves one of the grandest of all discoveries in physical science, the counterintuitive realization that gases that support combustion or burn freely combine to make the enemy of fire, water, and deprive it of its ancient right to be considered an element.

The discovery of the gas types led to a sweeping reformation of chemistry. It impelled natural philosophers to study the effects of heat on gases, which strengthened the caloric theory and supported measurements later important in thermodynamics. It had practical consequences before the end of the eighteenth century in the application of eudiometry to ventilation, in the craze of ballooning initiated by the Montgolfier brothers, and in the use of laughing gas (nitrous oxide) as an anesthetic.

J. L. Heilbron

POLITICAL ECONOMY OF SCIENCE. During the past four centuries, the political economy of science—the nature and sources of its funding and the pertinent institutional arrangements—has changed primarily, though not exclusively, according to the political regime under which science has been pursued. In medieval Europe, the Church had created what Jacques Barzun once called the "House of Intellect"—those interested in scholarly subjects, including the phenomena of nature, pursued their interests in the universities of the time, usually as ordained clergy or as candidates for ordination. There were few divisions between the academic specialties that would later constitute "natural science." The sixteenth century, however, began to see major changes in the political economy of science, setting in motion complex adjustments between science and its environment that continue to the present.

Galileo's era marks the beginning of modern science not only because of the intellectual and technological advances of his time, but also because of an important shift in science's economic and institutional foundations. As a professor of mathematics at the University of Padua, Galileo belonged to the least admired stratum of academic life, and he multiplied the fault by deriving inspiration from the activities of artisans. When he left Padua in 1611 to join the Medici court in Florence, however, he insisted on the title of Philosopher and Mathematician, a coupling of the more prestigious contemplative work with the slighted practical pursuit. This combination of philosophy (physics) and mathematics became the high road of the Scientific Revolution. That Galileo felt he had to leave the university for a court to take his first steps on this road indicate the importance of private patronage in the political and intellectual economy of early modern science.

Galileo also enjoyed membership in another extra-university institutional form of first importance in the cultivation of natural knowledge from the mid-seventeenth to the mid-eighteenth centuries. This was the Academy dei Lincei, an academy without walls, a group of correspondents promoted and supported by a prince (Frederico Lesi) to pursue natural knowledge. Lesi's academy did not survive him. Nor did the more substantial group, the Academy del Cimento (1657–1667), composed of Galileo's disciples, outlast the interest of its patrons, the Medicis. But by the 1660s, the institution of the Academy, which brought people together to investigate nature and serve their patrons, had become the most important sites for natural science. The Royal Society of London and the Paris Académie Royale des Sciences date from that decade.

The Royal Society provided its own financing via dues and subscriptions and a large membership made up primarily of gentleman drones. The Paris Academy consisted of a small number of salaried experts who advised the state on technical matters and devoted most of their effort to astronomy, geology, cartography, and other mathematical sciences. The English model was imitated in Sweden, Holland, and the French provinces, the Parisian model in Berlin and St. Petersburg. The academic movement, which reached its height toward the end of the eighteenth century, provided institutional inspiration—though seldom the laboratory space—for the advancement rather than (as was the assignment of the universities) the spread of science.

The French Revolution inaugurated a new epoch in the political economy of science. The revolutionary government suppressed both the Académie and the universities in 1793. The Académie was to some degree reborn in 1795, as the First Class of the Institut de France, but for almost a decade, scientific and technical training took place exclusively in professional schools that survived the Revolution or in the newly founded grandes école. These institutions—especially the École Polytechnique and the École Normale Supérieur in Paris—had extraordinarily good faculties and adequate facilities. Their graduates enabled France to dominate European science. However, the new regime did not succeed in replacing the old universities and Jesuit colleges with suitable higher schools, especially in the provinces. The

University of Paris had "facultés" elsewhere, but these were generally poor, small, and ineffectual.

Many analysts considered the weakness of French higher education (apart from the grandes écoles) to be an important factor in the French defeat in the Franco-Prussian War (1870–1871). A number of initiatives—including financial contributions by local magnates and industrialists—sought to transcend these restraints. In 1896, after years of study, the national government reinstated the universities as comprehensive institutions and built important new science facilities at the Sorbonne. But the patterns of centralized administrative control, concentration of resources at the center, and the resulting flow of talent to Paris still hampered development.

Napoleon's invasions of Germany had aroused powerful nationalistic reactions that prompted sweeping reforms in German-speaking territories. Illustrated by the founding of the University of Berlin in 1810, these reforms, taken together laid the basis for the shift of the leadership of science to Germany. Paradoxically because of its long history of political disunity, Germany—newly united in 1871 after three wars with neighbors—had an important institutional advantage that helped it gain ascendancy in science. Each of its constituent states—Prussia, Bavaria, Saxony, and others—had its own universities; the newly unified Reich possessed twenty-two in all, and shortly after 1900, Frankfurt and Hamburg created their own municipal universities.

These schools, together with German-speaking universities elsewhere in Europe and the better Technische Hochshule, created a cooperative-competitive system that drove its faculties toward increasingly higher performance. Professors also moved between institutions based on their accomplishments, primarily publications and to some extent reputation, and they usually made a condition of their transfer (or of their staying put) the improvement of the facilities, an increase in their research provision, or the acquisition of more technical assistance. This internal elite migration spread innovation and expertise and enlarged the disciplines. A stream of important discoveries, inventions, and publications poured out of the German universities; an impressive number of students from European and other nations flowed into them.

German-speaking higher education retained the old tradition of representing whole fields of knowledge by a single full professor who supervised the work of subordinate junior faculty or graduate students in the same specialty. Under the system, new professorships could only be created at any given university by dividing an established discipline into smaller parts. Expansion could also occur by founding an entirely new university from the ground up. A strong and innovative professor could mobilize and concentrate resources; an indifferent and negligent one could ruin his discipline in his university for decades. And in any case, the low limit on the number of professors the system could absorb eventually sapped the morale of younger scientists. The problem was addressed—though never adequately solved—by various partnerships between government and private donors. In 1887, a large donation from Werner von Siemens had facilitated the creation of the state-run Physikalische-Technische Reichsanstalt.

The Humboldt University of Berlin, the first modern German research university, was built in 1810, in emulation and defiance of French scientific institutions.

The years before World War I witnessed the founding of the Kaiser Wilhelm Society, which developed a wide network of specialized laboratories. Instigated by the chemist Emil Fischer, the humanist Adolf von Harnack, and several others, the Society attracted substantial private contributions from bankers, industrialists, and a few landed aristocrats. Their donations, together with funds allocated from the Prussian treasury, made possible the creation of an institution with historical importance for the political economy of science. But it too operated on the Führer-Prinzip: distinguished professors became institute directors with full authority—if they cared to exercise it—over their research staffs.

Invariably citing German developments in the political economy of science, the United States and Britain began to expand their educational and research facilities in the 1870s. Private capital in Sweden supported the creation of the Stockholm Högskola in 1878; dedicated almost exclusively to the natural sciences in its early years, the Högskola in 1960 became the state-run Stockholm University with a broader array of academic programs. Japan as a reformist state in the same period found both German and French models instructive. German precedents shaped the design of the so-called chair system in which a senior professor managed the budget together with the pedagogical and research activities of a subordinate younger staff. French examples influenced the national organization and important details of the internal structure. Following the Napoleonic model, Japan divided itself into regions, each of which was to have its own so-called imperial university. Each institution would have several chairs per discipline, dependent on enrollment and perceived academic needs. The one-chair rule, though widely debated, was explicitly rejected in Japan. A national system of elite universities, more equal to one another than the parent French institutions, gave rise to a competitive system favorable as such to the needs of modern science. The United States operated similarly, with multiple professorships, competitive appointments, and a unique use of government (state) and private monies. The Great War of 1914–1918 transformed the political economy of science. Geopolitical rivalries among several nations in the years leading up to the war had already stimulated greater political and financial support for science, and from a broader and more diverse stratum of society. Germany's rapidly paced industrialization between 1870 and 1914 had given it imposing strength in the realm of applied science—as in the large chemical companies and their corporate laboratories—to complement and support the strengths of science based in universities. The United States, and to some extent Britain and France, had also developed strength in company-based science; and although the German industrial research laboratories may have been more numerous and more generously funded, American corporations such as Westinghouse, AT&T, and DuPont were beginning to invest in long-term research. Germany's strength in applied chemistry enabled it to hold out against the Allied Powers until the spring of 1918. All of the leading military powers, including Japan, which entered the war on the Allied side, tried with mixed success to achieve equality with Germany in science, including its military applications.

Cut off by British blockade from its usual sources of raw materials, Germany soon ran short of strategic materials, notably nitrates for fertilizers and explosives. Fritz Haber, later director of the Kaiser Wilhelm Society's Institute for Physical Chemistry, had developed a means of producing ammonia synthetically in 1908. This achievement, when scaled up industrially, made Germany independent of imported nitrates. Haber also developed and oversaw the deployment of poison gas. The Allied nations faced the problem of finding substitutes for strategic materials previously obtained from Germany—optical glass, laboratory glassware, dyes, fine chemicals, and magnets. By the war's end, France, Britain, and the United States could make what they needed. Scientists on both sides helped to improve weapons, airplanes, radios, medical treatments, and so on. Agencies set up to mobilize scientific manpower and to provide it with resources—the Department of Scientific and Industrial Research in Britain, the National Research Council in the United States, and equivalents in the other belligerent countries—continued in many cases into the peace.

Imperial Russia was the first casualty of the war, not only because of inadequate military equipment, leadership, and training, but also because of its general backwardness in science. Following its defeat by Britain and France in the Crimean War (1854–1856), Russia had made efforts to catch its European rivals, founding several new universities, freeing the serfs, encouraging foreign investment, and promoting railway construction and industrialization. Significant weaknesses persisted, however. The underdeveloped state of Russian capitalism meant that private philanthropic support of science—increasingly important in Europe, the United States, and even Japan—had scarcely begun in Russia. With the Bolshevik Revolution in 1917, many Russians and their former allies believed that even the gains made in Czarist Russia would be lost. Nonetheless, the new regime preserved nineteenth-century advances and used them as a partial basis for subsequent development.

Several factors contributed to a smoother initial transition from one system of political economy in science to another than many observers expected. The new leadership dominated by V. I. Lenin, however autocratic by basic instinct, was flexible at first. Vigorous attempts by radical Bolsheviks to abolish the Academy of Sciences were defeated, with Lenin's concurrence. The regime desperately needed the services of the well-trained scientists and technical experts in rebuilding the country. Many professors, including leading figures like Ivan Pavlov, cooperated with the government. Moreover, the more prominent Bolshevik revolutionaries shared the Enlightenment vision of science. For them, science was not only the preeminent but also the only valid form of knowledge and the only reliable template for the reconstruction and maintenance of society.

Bolshevik radicals viewed the relatively tolerant policies of the 1920s as expedient at best, a betrayal of revolutionary egalitarianism at worst, and they were determined to dismantle the Academy of Sciences as a bastion of elitist reaction inherited from a discredited regime. Others charged the Academy with being obsessed with pure science, and insisted that all state agencies based on expert knowledge should have a strongly applied orientation. Many also favored a decentralization of research activities as a means of bringing technical knowledge closer to the clienteles that needed it. Stalin's consolidation of power created a favorable climate in which radicals might realize their vision of "science." They were only partly successful. Members of the Academy admitted a few party activists with minimally appropriate credentials, and opened its doors to engineers for the first time. Equally important in the Academy's survival was Stalin's own preference for centrally controlled institutions, even if they harbored individuals unsympathetic to his goals. The Academy of Sciences not only survived but became the institutional centerpiece and dominant agency in a new, highly centralized political economy of science. With minimal changes, this structure persisted almost to the end of the twentieth century.

Though the most extreme effects of the political economy of science were manifested in Russia, World War I had a large impact on the political economy of science in many countries. Scientists and their work in defeated Germany and Austria suffered intense privation in the first three years after the war, giving the hundreds of Japanese scientists who had earlier studied there the opportunity to repay their academic benefactors with gifts of cash, research equipment, and laboratory animals. Scientific establishments in the United States, Canada, and Britain acquired material resources on an unprecedented scale. Japanese scientists—accustomed to working under conditions of chronic privation—viewed the war as a "blessing from heaven." One consequence of the new largesse available to scientists in Japan was the founding of the Research Institute for Physics and Chemistry (1917–1922). A committee of three scientists proposed an Institute organized precisely in the manner of the Kaiser Wilhelm Society. With the active involvement of the wartime prime minister, Count Shigenobu Okuma, a finance committee raised large private gifts from the country's wealthiest citizens, the nobility, and the Imperial Family. Parliament matched these contributions, as in Germany, helping to create a more robust political economy of science than had existed in Japan previously.

Yet another result of wartime experience had broad implications for science's political economy in many—probably most—of the nations active in research. This was the establishment of formalized systems by which investigators could submit research plans to review committees of peers and request a budget for particular projects. In many countries (Germany being an exception), pre-war university budgets had made no specific provision for research activity, even though research was becoming an essential part of the academic role. Scientists who worked in specialized laboratories—the Pasteur Institute in Paris, any of the Kaiser Wilhelm Institutes, the Carnegie Institute of Washington, the Solvay Institute (Belgium), and others—naturally had budgets dedicated to research. And in many countries, scientists could and did submit ad hoc requests to governments, private foundations, and other potential benefactors. In the wake of the war, governments began to create state agencies established specifically for the purpose of funding research without respect to the particular institutional affiliations of applicants. In some cases—Britain, the United States, and Japan among them—a newly created National Research Council performed this function; Japan created a special program for grant applications by scientists through its Ministry of Education. The Conseil National pour la Récherche Scientifique (CNRS) and Consiglio Nazionale delle Ricerche (CNR) had their beginnings in the interwar period. Germany created a number of special, self-help government and private agencies during the Weimar Republic.

By the 1930s, most features of the political economy of science that would appear in the twentieth century had cropped up in one country or another. Except in the Soviet Union, academies of science had come to function—when they existed at all—mostly as institutions for honoring scientific achievement after the fact, rather than supporting it materially in advance. The fundamental reason for the decline of the academies of Western Europe from the leadership of science in the eighteenth century to purveyors of honors in the twentieth was the professionalization of science in the nineteenth century and the establishment in most countries of the modern research university.

The Japan Society for the Promotion of Science (JSPS), founded in 1932, had as its primary purpose the allocation of financial support, after reviewing proposals, to large research projects considered important to national objectives but too costly for single universities to support. Itself a product of the surging militarism that followed Japan's seizure of Manchuria in 1931, the JSPS symbolized the trend toward ever-greater state influence in, and control over, science characteristic of the dictatorial states of the twentieth century. The trend began with World War I and continued with the Stalinist program in the Soviet Union and the Nazi regime in Germany. But apart from certain police interventions, the Nazis used ideological rather than institutional tools to achieve their purpose. The pre-Nazi political economy of science in a formalist sense remained intact even as Jewish academics were ejected or imprisoned. Partly because of the Soviet Union's seemingly rapid development in the 1930s, and partly also owing to their fears of Nazism and Fascism, some scientists—especially in Britain, France, and the United States—began to promote Soviet notions of the political economy of science, or at least to debate the relative merits of democratic and socialistic support systems. Much of what transpired during World War II with respect to the political economy of science repeated the experience of the Great War on an even larger scale. The United States as well as Germany, Japan, and the Soviet Union sought to capitalize on the late 1930s discovery of fission by developing an atomic bomb for wartime use. But these projects are only the best-known examples of institutional changes in science's political economy. The earlier development of the cyclotron by E. O. Lawrence after 1929 set in motion a process of institutional growth in high-energy physics that continued almost to the present. A similar trend later appeared in other research specialties, and continues to the present, where it most recently has arrived in the biological sciences. The early decades of the Cold War saw a continuation of wartime patterns. Rivalry in almost every sphere of human activity led the United States and the Soviet Union to inexorably greater expenditures on science and technology, exemplified by the *Sputnik* program of artificial satel-

lite development and the successive *Apollo* missions of lunar exploration. The Soviet satellites followed the Soviet lead as best they could. Western Europe did the same with the United States as its model, and after Americanizing, have caught up in some respects. The innovative, cooperative research enterprise of CERN, for example, brought western Europe to parity with the United States in accelerator and particle physics, and it will soon be ahead.

Partly because of Soviet wartime successes and the evident promise of rapid economic and technological development, many developing nations after World War II tried to copy the Soviet model of the political economy of science. Building on a small-scale model developed in the 1930s before the Japanese invasion of 1937, the People's Republic of China under Mao Zedong imported hundreds of Soviet technicians and science advisers. With their help, China in the 1950s created a near-perfect replica of the Stalinist system, based on the central role of the Chinese Academy of Sciences. Attracting émigré scientists from the United States and elsewhere, the PRC managed to develop its own atomic bomb in 1964 and even more advanced weapons in later years. While the Chinese initiatives may seem extreme, the general model of state-led development in science they embodied was more broadly characteristic of the period as a whole.

It appears that the state-led pattern of growth in the political economy of science is sharply decelerating. Countries that once had no private universities, such as Australia and Britain, now have one or more; in others, such as the United States, the ranking private universities are better funded than ever, while the leading public institutions sometimes have to struggle to stay even. Japan, long a bastion of French-style étatism in higher education, has announced a plan to privatize virtually all so-called national and other public universities over the next decade or so. Russia, in the aftermath of the Soviet Union's dissolution, has begun to restore a role for the private sector in science that had disappeared in the Revolution. The government of the United States, at the insistence of Congress, in 1993 terminated the costly Super-Conducting Super Collider in Texas. And in a public-private competition between researchers investigating the human

Ernest Orlando Lawrence (1901–1958), inventor of the cyclotron and impresario of Big Science

genome, a private firm won a tentative victory over a government-funded team. How far these trends will proceed or when they might reverse cannot be anticipated. The future of the political economy of science is as difficult to predict as the future of nation-states themselves. But the two have developed in tandem, and each is a work in progress.

JAMES BARTHOLOMEW

POPULATION GENETICS is the science concerned with the inheritance and distribution of gene frequencies in a given population. Evolutionary population genetics, from which this branch of study arose, deals with changes in these distribution and inheritance patterns over time. The roots of the discipline originated in the period following the publication of Charles Darwin's *On the Origin of Species* in 1859, when a debate raged within biology about the kind of traits upon which natural selection works. Were they small physical changes in an organism, as Darwin, August Weismann, and Alfred Russel Wallace thought, eliciting a slow, gradual evolution? Or did nature proceed by jumps, fashioning new species in rapid discontinuous leaps, as Thomas Henry Huxley and Francis Gallon believed? Galton, Darwin's first cousin, argued that selection of continuous traits would be rendered ineffective by the law of regression—a mathematical formulation of the tendency of offspring characters to regress to the mean of the population. The further down an ancestral path from a new trait, such as a bent nose, the likelier it became that the nose would straighten out. If so, natural selection acting on small, continuous changes could not be responsible for evolution. Galton concluded that only by acting upon discontinuous novelties, such as a completely new nose form, could selection bring about evolution.

With the rediscovery of Gregor Mendel's laws in 1900, the old debate quickly found new proponents. The experiments of Hugo de Vries on the evening primrose in his Amsterdam garden gave rise in 1903 to the theory that spontaneous, internal, and discontinuous mutations in the hereditary substance were genetic mechanisms capable of explaining evolution. Mendelians, led in England by William Bateson, came to believe that Darwin, who thought of natural selection as a creative force, had it wrong on both counts: Evolution was neither gradual, nor brought about by selection. It was disruptive, motored by discontinuous, internal changes to the hereditary material unaffected by the environment. The most nature could do was to eliminate those deleterious varieties presented before her and propagate the rest.

A Biometric School, led by Karl Pearson and Walter Frank Raphael Weldon in England, rejected the Mendelian recourse to a heredity based on unseen, theoretical, genetic "factors." They defined inheritance instead in terms of Galton's law of regression, based on the wide range of measurable, perceivable, and continuous physical variations. Pearson argued that Galton had misinterpreted his own law: if the relation between traits of offspring to the mean of their parents, rather than that of the population, were considered, swamping (the gradual erasure of a new trait) would disappear, and Darwin's picture of gradual, continuous evolution by natural selection would be upheld. Fierce debates raged between the biometricians and the Mendelians in England. Mendelian particulate heredity and Darwinian gradual evolution by natural selection appeared to be diametrically opposed.

Darwin's proposed mechanism of natural selection was by now coming under severe attack. In 1902, the Swedish biologist Wilhelm Johannsen had shown that natural selection acting on continuous variation could not overcome Galton's law of regression: it failed to induce evolution within pure lines. Experimental Mendelians took this as strong evidence against Darwinian gradualism. They refused to admit a role for adaptation and selection in the control of those novel variations produced by mutation in their laboratories. At the opposite extreme, field naturalists, who saw variation manifested abundantly, rejected mutationism and endorsed the principle of gradualism, but advocated Lamarckian mechanisms of heredity to buttress, or replace, what they took to be inadequate selection. Embryologists and paleontologists added to the chorus of discontent with natural selection, advocating Lamarckism and other forms of orthogenetic, or directed inheritance, to explain the adaptations they recognized. The divided biological landscape made imperative the need to establish both the kind of variations upon which selection worked, and the extent to which such a force could be shown to be responsible for evolution.

The first problem was gradually settled in the first two decades of the twentieth century through the work of W. E. Castle, Edward Murray East, H. Nilsson-Ehle, and the so-called Fly Room group of Thomas Hunt Morgan. Their experimental results showed how continuous hereditary variation could be explained by discontinuous variation produced by small genetic mutations. The Biometric-Mendelian debate had been settled, but entrenched conceptions proved hard to dispel. In 1908, an English mathematician, G. H. Hardy, and a German physician, Wilhelm Weinberg, independently derived a simple yet crucial quantitative rule, expressing the idea that gene frequencies, or proportions, would remain constant unless acted upon by external forces. The Hardy-Weinberg equilibrium, $P^2 + 2PQ + Q^2 = 1$, where P is the frequency of a dominant allele A, and Q the frequency of a recessive allele a, had some very useful properties. (Alleles are alternative genes at the same locus.) In a population with a gene locus with a dominant allele A and a recessive allele a, only two phenotypes are visible: homozygous recessives aa, and a class exhibiting the dominant trait comprising a mix of AA and Aa individuals. The Hardy-Weinberg rule allowed calculation of the proportion of heterozygotes, or carriers, of recessive alleles for human genetic disease in the population, and thus a better understanding of the propagation of disease. Notwithstanding the importance of this basic and useful rule, it remained to be shown whether selection, acting on discontinuous genes and in conjunction with other variables, would explain evolution. R. A. Fisher and J. B. S. Haldane in England, and Sewall Wright in the United States, tackled this problem and founded theoretical population genetics.

Adopting a biometric, mathematical population approach, the three men defined evolution as the differential inheritance and propagation of gene frequencies over time. By assigning adaptive values with respect to fitness to different gene alleles, it became possible to calculate how selection could fashion their respective frequencies in the population. Fisher worked primarily on models with low selection pressures on individual genes in large populations; Haldane on high selection pressures on individual genes in large populations; and Wright on intermediate selection pressures on interactive gene systems in small, partially isolated, interbreeding populations. Although their models emphasized different aspects of evolution and led to disagreements, they all used the gene, not the individual organism, as the functional unit of selection. Together with the quantifiable factors of mutation and migration rate, effective population size, and mating behavior, selection was shown to suffice as a mechanism for evolution. The force it exercised was powerful enough to render Lamarckian and other forms of directed change superfluous. Haldane, for example, estimated the mutation rate of a deleterious gene in a human population, that for hemophilia, and suggested that differential susceptibility to disease might have driven much of human evolution.

Theoretical population genetics, developed in the 1920s and generally adopted after 1932, dispelled the legacy of anti-Darwinian feeling by synthesizing genetic gradualism with Darwin's theory of natural selection. But while providing a correct picture of genetic change in a given local population, what has been called the "bean-bag" genetics of these pioneers failed to explain adequately the interaction between genes and gene systems, macro-evolutionary changes such as adaptation, the origin of higher taxa and novel evolutionary forms, and the multiplication of species. In order to satisfy the organismic phenomena studied by ecologists, systematists, paleontologists, and students of behavior, and to complete what became known as the Evolutionary Synthesis, a further step of translation and modification of the mathematical models to the more complex realities of natural populations was necessary. The work of the Russian school of experimental population genetics led by Sergei Chetverikov, the interpretation of Fisher's work by the ecologist E. B. Ford and of Wright's work by the geneticist Theodosius Dobzhansky, the labors of the systematist Ernst Mayr, and the popularizations of Huxley's grandson Julian all figured significantly in this endeavor. The synthesis was generally achieved by mid-century.

Population genetics has had important implications for a range of fields from eugenics to breeding, ecology, and demography. With the development of techniques in molecular genetics, human population genetics has been employed in studies traditionally dominated by anthropology, archaeology, and linguistics to help researchers understand the history of global and local migration patterns, language evolution, and cultural and technological diffusion. Medical research has increasingly employed methods from population genetics in the study of disease.

OREN SOLOMON HARMAN

PRIMATOLOGY. Europeans who penetrated the jungles of Asia and Africa during the eighteenth century brought back tales of half-human monsters. Skeptics demanded proof, and the obliging adventurers returned to the jungles to kidnap infant chimpanzees, gorillas, and orangutans. These small animals arrived in Europe orphans—their mothers had been killed to capture them—and sick from weeks at sea and a poor diet. They seldom survived more than a year, leaving their skulls and skins for examination.

Carl Linnaeus used these relics to classify the primates, today divided into four lineages: apes, Old World monkeys, New World monkeys, and prosimians. Linnaeus lumped the tailless great apes with humans in the family *Hominoidea*. Primatology has focused on *Hominoidea*, where Linnaeus's taxonomy, though fine-tuned during the last two centuries, has persisted with surprisingly few major changes. Today some taxonomers add a fourth species to his three great apes—chimpanzees (*Pan troglodytes*), gorillas (*Gorilla gorilla*), and orangutans (*Pongo pygmaeus*); the fourth candidate, bonobo, is sometimes classified as *Pan paniscus*, a distinct species of chimpanzee, or as *Bonobo paniscus,* a separate genus. Linnaeus's arrangement of the hominids has also expanded to include the discoveries of hominid fossils, which have added extinct species to both ape and human family trees. Radiocarbon dating has shown that our ancestors diverged from the ape ancestors around thirty million years ago. DNA studies have shown the apes to be more closely related to humans than to any other primates. The chimpanzee stands genetically closest of all to *Homo sapiens.*

Charles Darwin would not have been surprised. In *The Origin of Species* (1859) he suggested that human beings share a common ancestor with other primates. Later, in *The Descent of Man* (1871), he characterized the haunting familiarity between humans and apes as a family resemblance. We

P

Jane Goodall (b. 1934), British conservationist and zoologist

share, he demonstrated, emotions and expressions as well as a similar skull and skeleton.

At the end of the nineteenth century students of the new science of psychology began exploring the abilities of the great apes in comparison to each other and to human beings. With the exception of Richard L. Garner, an American zoologist who went to West Africa in the 1890s where he sat in a cage while observing wild chimpanzees, the early primatologists studied only captive apes. In 1927, the German psychologist Wolfgang Köhler described his colony of chimpanzees on the island of Tenerife, near Spain, who stacked boxes to retrieve bananas. At about the same time in the United States, Robert Mearns Yerkes studied a pair of chimpanzees at his summer home in New Hampshire and traveled to meet and test gorillas and orangutans wherever he could find them. Eventually he established breeding colonies of apes in Orange Park, Florida. He compared the three great apes anatomically, physiologically, and behaviorally and published his results in 1929 in a massive volume, *The Great Apes: A Study of Anthropoid Life,* coauthored with his wife, Ada. Yerkes was remarkably prescient about ape intelligence and, contrary to the habits of his colleagues, he gave his experimental animals names, rather than numbers, because he found that their personalities were so distinctive as to make numbers inappropriate. Yerkes acquired his first chimp in 1923 and named him Bill, after William Jennings Bryan, the prosecutor in the Scopes Trial.

As much as he enjoyed keeping them in his laboratory, Yerkes realized the importance of observing apes in their natural habitats and found enough money in the depths of the depression in 1930 to send his student Henry Nissen to West Africa for four months. But the continued economic woes of the 1930s, followed by World War II and revolutions and civil wars in Africa and Asia, prevented the development of field studies until the 1960s. Then, at almost the same time, Dutch, Japanese, British, and American primatologists went individually and in groups to observe wild apes in Africa, Sumatra, and Borneo.

These observers habituated the wild animals to their presence and established field stations to plot the behavior of individual animals as well as groups. With support from the National Geographic Society Jane Goodall, Dian Fossey, and Birute Galdikas set up projects in Tanzania, Rwanda, and Borneo. At the same time, Junichero Itani and his Japanese colleagues began studies of chimpanzees and bonobo in central Africa. Most of these projects continued for several decades. They revealed that each ape had an individual personality that determined the nature of each family group, and that each group of apes had a separate culture. Some used tools; some hunted for meat. The primatologists who conducted these studies in the early years of the women's movement consisted of women and men in equal number. Whether gender bias had skewed earlier research is hard to assess, but research in the last decades of the twentieth century showed the powerful role of females in ape societies.

Meanwhile increasing evidence of the genetic nature of apes made them the ideal stand-in for humans in studies ranging from the evolution of the brain to medical models for HIV-AIDS. NASA's confidence in chimp intelligence led to chimpanzee "pilots" in spacecraft of the early 1960s. At the same time psychologists and linguists in the United States began experiments to test whether apes could communicate with American Sign Language and with symbols. Though their degree of grammatical mastery of language is

controversial, some chimpanzees have passed on the skills they learned to two generations of offspring.

The species most similar in behavior to humans is the bonobo, who live in a single area in the Congo. They enjoy a very complicated social life that includes frequent sexual activity, homosexual as well as heterosexual. These exchanges apparently serve as displacement behavior to avert aggression within the group.

Great apes behave differently in the wild and in captivity. Chimpanzees use tools in the wild. Gorillas do not, but in captivity perform very well on tests demanding small muscle coordination. Orangutans occasionally use tools in the wild and are especially clever at escaping from zoo confinement. All reveal a sense of humor in the way they play tricks on each other and on their human guardians.

The population of wild apes dwindled drastically in the last decade of the twentieth century as their habitats became the sites of human wars and ecological exploitation. Wild apes probably will not survive for long without dramatic policy changes. Apes in zoos and wild animal parks may live a life similar to one in the wild. Others may continue to suffer as medical models for human disease.

Philosophers and lawyers now dispute the nature of ape awareness and self-consciousness, and their entitlement to greater protection. Activists, led by Jane Goodall, are trying to have laws interpreted so as to give apes legal protection against experimentation and exploitation. Without increased protection, our fellow *Hominoidea* will soon be extinct, and their branch of primatology will become a historic science like paleontology.

BETTYANN HOLTZMANN KEVLES

PROBABILITY AND CHANCE. Civilization has always known games of chance. Throughout history, societies have guessed their future by reading entrails, tea leaves, or the accidental arrangement of other objects, and have made crucial legal decisions by lot. Christians deemed gambling a vice, but new games of chance entered Europe from the Arab world during the Crusades. In the mid-thirteenth century, about the time clocks were introduced into the town square, a poem called "De vetula" conceived of dice throwing in terms of frequencies. Cards appeared in the fourteenth century, complicating games of chance. Girolamo Cardano's *De ludo aleae* (1663) defined chance events in terms of their frequency of occurrence. During the Scientific Revolution, when the nature of evidence and causes was debated, Blaise Pascal and Pierre de Fermat corresponded about chance, Christiaan Huygens wrote a book on it, and Jakob Bernoulli I, in his *Ars conjectandi* (1713), presented the binomial distribution and considered how random events might create a regularity with more than a grain of truth.

Classical probability can be regarded as both empirical (chance as the frequency of events) and epistemic (probability as the mental state of doubt related to degrees of belief, a notion that goes back to medieval times). Probability was thus a state of opinion, perhaps related to authority and testimony, but not as demonstratively true knowledge. The empirical and the epistemic issues in probability shaped discussions on the nature and acceptability of evidence, proof, belief, and truth in early modern Europe. But the subjective and objective sides of probability could not be so cleanly separated in practice. When David Hume showed in 1737 how probability could be used to validate inductive evidence, opinion and knowledge became only differences of degree, not kind. The age of classical probability, which lasted until the mid-nineteenth century, had opened.

The shift to a mathematical theory of probability started with Pierre-Simon de Laplace's *Analytical Theory of Probabilities* (1812). Chance had begun to look lawful in the eighteenth-century analysis of errors, but now with Laplace's definition of the probability of an event as the ratio of the number of favorable cases to all possible cases, probability theory could be applied to a wide variety of events in the social and physical worlds. Yet probability continued also to refer to incomplete knowledge about matters both esoteric and everyday, about matters that possessed only partial or moral certainty, not absolute certainty. The objective and subjective sides of probability thus collapsed on one another during its classical phase; objective frequencies of events were also subjective degrees of belief. Probability had to do with uncovering the lawful in randomness, and with degrees of ignorance and doubt.

Around the mid-nineteenth century, consideration of large-scale regularities—gambling problems, actuarial computations, demographic patterns, errors as treated in the method of least squares, and the like—shifted the emphasis in probability theory more toward the frequency or ratio of events in the world and less toward assessments of epistemic certainty. Especially in what was then known as "social physics," probability appeared to be more about objectivity than subjectivity. Lambert-Adolphe-Jacques Quetelet, the founder of modern statistical methods, announced in 1844 that the error law used in astronomy could be applied to the distribution of human features, such as height: human variation thus could be understood in the same terms as errors of observation. Quetelet used the bell curve of error analysis to propose the "average man," a new object of investigation that occupied the same position on the error curve as the most probable measurement. The most likely value with the smallest error was an experimental ideal; the average man, a moral one. Mass phenomena or repeatable events became the focus of Wilhelm Lexis's sociology in his *Theory of Mass Phenomena in Human Society* (1877), and the foundation of Richard von Mises's probability calculus in 1919.

In no field was the shift to an objective probability more apparent than physics. The deterministic ideal of classical physics allowed only for an epistemic interpretation of probability (which had been the interpretation of Jakob Bernoulli and Laplace), as was the custom in error theory. Moreover, objects of investigation in physics seemed so well defined that recourse to a composite construction, analogous to Quetelet's average man, was unnecessary. But then the British physicist James Clerk Maxwell announced in 1860 that the velocities of gas molecules had a bell curve distribution, like errors. Classical physics, which was deterministic and postulated continuous (if not reversible) behavior, appeared unable to describe the intimate behavior of a system of gas molecules. Ludwig Boltzmann found that in order to understand the second law of thermodynamics—announced by Rudolf Clausius in 1850 as the irreversible increase in entropy over time—he had to use probability theory applied to molecular behavior. In Boltzmann's interpretation, entropy became a macroscopic measure of the probability of finding a system in a particular state, the most probable state being one of maximum entropy. Finally, discontinuities in matter and energy could only be understood in statistical terms. Using probability theory, Albert Einstein confirmed the existence of discrete atoms in his study of Brownian motion (1905). Discontinuous energy processes—black body radiation,

Werner Heisenberg (1901–1976), who introduced the principle of uncertainty into quantum physics, lecturing in 1936

radioactive decay, the photoelectric effect, and atomic and molecular spectra—could also only be understood through probability theory. In his study of black body radiation, Max Planck introduced what became known as energy quanta via a statistical theory of heat (1900). In quantum mechanics, in both Werner Heisenberg's matrix mechanics and Erwin Schrödinger's wave mechanics, the likelihood of measuring a system in a given state became a probability of how likely the state was to occur. Heisenberg's famous uncertainty principle incorporates the notion that at the subatomic level properties could not be measured precisely, but only given a probability distribution. Despite his reliance on the word "uncertainty," Heisenberg did not refer to degree of belief, but to the irreducibly statistical character of subatomic reality.

KATHRYN OLESKO

PROFESSIONAL SOCIETY. Societies designed to affirm and serve the professional interests of members of disciplines or other scientific groupings came into existence in the late nineteenth century. The fields that first provided professional scientific employment on a large scale were those like chemistry that found a significant role not only in the burgeoning educational system but also in industrial, commercial, and state organizations in the major economies of the world. The sharing and advancement of scientific knowledge had been the chief rationale of academies and learned societies since the seventeenth century, but professional societies had a wider occupational relationship to scientific knowledge, its possessors, and its diffusion.

Early professional societies, such as the Institute of Chemistry in the United Kingdom (founded in 1877), were designed primarily as qualifying associations. The Institute membership initially overlapped considerably with the dis-

Elizabeth Brown (1830–1899), self-taught English solar astronomer, was instrumental in setting up the British Astronomical Association, which, unlike the Royal Astronomical Society, accepted women as members.

can Institute of Chemistry (1923), the American Institute of Physics (1931), and the American Institute of Biological Societies (1947). The membership of the American Physical Society (1899) had been ambivalent about representing the employment and other interests of physicists. Most members gladly ceded this role to the American Institute of Physics (AIP). Apart from catering to the occupational and professional interests of their members, the institutes also sought to secure a sense of common identity among scientists from ever more specialized fields. The AIP consisted of the Physical Society, Optical Society, Acoustical Society, the Society of Rheology, and the American Association of Physics Teachers. More societies joined after the mid-1960s. By the 1990s, the AIP, with a staff of 500, represented over 100,000 physicists. The striving for a common identity among the biological disciplines in the United States resulted first in the American Society of Naturalists and then the American Society of Zoologists. World War II brought home the need for an integrated society in the biological sciences to make the government and the public aware of the coherent body of manpower it represented.

In Continental Europe, patterns of development differed. The Deutsche Physikalische Gesellschaft (DPG) traces its origins to the Physikalische Gesellschaft of Berlin formed in 1845. The DPG, with its range of national and professional functions, did not emerge from these local beginnings until 1899. After World War II, the DPG reformed without the Eastern bloc members and began publication of a general news magazine, *Physikalische Blätter*. By contrast, the Société Française de Physique, formed in 1873, was nationally recognized by decree in 1881 and then grew to coordinate an elaborate structure of local sections, specialist divisions, and publications, including the *Journal de Physique* and *Annales de Physique*.

Professional societies typically have several levels of membership: student (or associate), full, and fellow. Honorary fellows, presidents, and patrons selected from the disciplinary elite symbolized the bridge between the professional institutes and the more traditional learned societies. Sometimes, new institutes stimulated older societies to take on new roles. The American Institute of Chemistry was founded in part because of dissatisfaction with the professional consciousness of the American Chemical Society, which greatly expanded its role in professional affairs beginning in the 1930s. As a result, the society remained the dominant institution for rank-and-file chemists. The American Psychological Association (APA) began as a disciplinary society, saw the foundation of more professionally oriented bodies (notably the American Association for Applied Psychology, founded in 1937), and re-formed after World War II along the institute model.

Publication of research journals, abstracts, and periodicals concerned with the educational, applied, and popular aspects of their field has been a major concern of professional societies. The AIP was formed in part to publish the journals of its member societies in uniform format through a common editorial office. It subsequently acquired or established other journals, including *Physics Today*, like *Physikalische Blätter* a vehicle of news and articles of general interest to physicists. The APA bought up several psychology journals. However, its stable of journals, even as it expanded, represented a decreasing relative proportion of the psychology journals published. Compared with the United States, European and other professional societies have been less

ciplinary Chemical Society of London, but had different objectives: to promote the thorough study of chemistry and related sciences in their application to the arts, manufacture, agriculture, and public health (and thereby promote professional standards); to ensure the competence via certified training of consulting or analytical chemists; and to maintain the profession on a satisfactory basis. Acquiring a Royal Charter in 1885, the Institute gained the right to grant certificates of competence. However, the strong academic membership and the practical and ideological difficulties of representing the membership in salary questions limited its role. The Institute strenuously avoided any suggestion of trade unionism. The British Institute of Physics was established in 1921, when the expansion and diversification of physicists' employment had generated enough concern for coherent representation and promotion of their collective fortunes. The Institute of Biology (1950) met the felt need to give an authoritative voice to British biology as a whole.

The United States followed the same sequence of foundations, though telescoped in time because of the later maturity, but greater volume and more rapid growth, of scientific employment there. Thus the establishment of the Ameri-

active in publication and more reliant on private-sector science publishers.

British and American institutional models have been widely adopted elsewhere in the English-speaking world. Examples include the Royal Australian Chemical Institute, the New Zealand Institute of Physics, and the Canadian Association of Physicists. Cognate institutions exist in most developed societies. More recent foundations for physicists include Nippon Butsuri Gakkai (1946), the Israel Physical Society (1954), the South African Institute of Physics (1955), and the Dansk Fysisk Selskab (1972). The international European Physical Society (founded in 1968) represents over 80,000 physicists through 36 national member societies, for whom it acts as a federation and presents a European perspective in international forums.

The effort continues to coordinate, integrate, and effectively represent to the wider world the knowledge production and professional interests of scientific researchers and workers in the face of ever more specialization and occupational diversity.

DAVID PHILIP MILLER

PULSARS AND QUASARS. Exotic astronomical objects were first detected in the 1960s by their radio emissions, though most quasars (quasi-stellar radio sources) are radio quiet. Pulsars are pulsating radio sources.

In 1960, astronomers identified the radio source 3C48 (number 48 in the Third Cambridge Catalogue) with a star-like object. Three years later, they did the same for 3C273, which had emission lines at unusual wavelengths. Maarten Schmidt at the Mount Palomar Observatory in Southern California recognized the mysterious spectral lines as lines from common elements shifted far toward the red. One mystery solved led to another. Assuming the red shifts arose from the expansion of the universe, astronomers had to endow quasars with tremendous speeds and distances. To be visible at vast distances, a quasar would have to be enormously bright, a thousand times brighter than all the stars in our galaxy. But a quasar's rapid variation in time would require that its energy be produced in a small volume. No known nuclear process can yield the observed energy output from a small volume.

The need for new physical explanations for new astronomical phenomena expanded further. In 1967, Anthony Hewish and Jocelyn Bell at Cambridge University, looking for rapid variations in the radio brightness of quasars, discovered a rapidly pulsating radio source. The radiation had to be from a source not larger than a planet if the signal could spread so quickly across the object to trigger bursts of radiation. Hewish won a Nobel Prize for the discovery, though his student Bell made the actual observation.

The period of this pulsar, 1.3 seconds, was so regular that Hewish and Bell briefly thought it might be an interstellar beacon or radio lighthouse built by an alien civilization. Hence the name they gave the source LGM 1—LGM for Little Green Men.

A few months before the discovery, Francis Pacini published a theoretical paper showing that a rapidly rotating neutron star with a strong magnetic field could act as an electric generator and emit radio waves. (Once thermonuclear sources of energy are exhausted, stars of less than 1.4 solar mass shrink until they become white dwarfs; more massive stars continue contracting into even more dense stars composed of neutrons.) Most millisecond pulsars, pulsating many times per second, have white dwarf companions, and their amplified spins may be somehow attributable to the accretion of mass from the companion star.

The cosmological hypothesis for quasars—that their red shifts are associated with the expansion of the universe, and they are at great distances from the earth—is generally accepted. Observations by Halton Arp at Palomar, however, suggested possible physical connections between a few quasars and nearby galaxies. A committee at Palomar judged Arp's controversial research to be without value, and terminated his observing time in 1983. Quasars probably are powered by the energy released when matter falls into a gigantic rotating black hole. Why so many quasars have red shifts around 2 remains to be explained.

NORRISS S. HETHERINGTON

Computer illustration of a pulsar (a rapidly rotating neutron star) showing its emission process. Energy beams are colored blue and the magnetic fields that contain them, green. If the beams fall on Earth during the pulsar's rotation, it will appear to blink like a light house.

P

Q

QUANTUM CHEMISTRY focuses on the application of wave functions to electrons in atomic or molecular orbitals. The first successful applications of wave mechanics to a molecule occurred in the late 1920s in the work of the German physicists Walter Heitler, Fritz London, and Friedrich Hund. The first successful applications to a distinctively chemical molecule with spatially directed chemical valences was the work of the Americans Linus Pauling and John Slater in 1931.

Niels Bohr had used the quantum hypothesis in 1913 to explain the stability of the electron's orbit about a positively charged nucleus. The connection that Bohr worked out in 1913 between the periodicity of electron-shell configurations in the atom and the periodicity of properties for chemical elements in the periodic table was improved in a famous paper of 1922. Bohr worked out—but did not calculate—a neat correlation of electron levels containing 2, 8, up to 18, and up to 32 electrons in the so-called K, L, M, and N shells with chemical periodic groups containing 2, 8, 8, 18, 18, and 32 elements. By this time Bohr and others were making use of Niels Bjerrum's formulation of a quantum theory for molecules (1911–1914) that quantified a classical model of a vibrating rotator.

Werner Heisenberg's formulation of resonance in wave functions (1926) suggested a breakthrough for chemists in the long-standing puzzle of how two electrical particles of like charge can unite to form a stable covalent chemical bond. In 1927, Heitler and London successfully applied Heisenberg's resonance formulation of electron wave func-

tions to the two-atom, two-electron hydrogen molecule. At the same time Hund published a different treatment generalizing the work of the Danish physicist Oyvind Burrau on the hydrogen molecule ion, which produced reliable energy values using elliptical coordinates for the electron in orbit around two protons. Hund assumed that each electron moves in a potential field that results from all the nuclei and from other electrons present in the molecule. The Heitler-London approach became known as the atomic orbital method (AO) and the Hund approach as the molecular orbital method (MO).

Independently, Slater and Pauling developed ways to explain directed chemical valence by proposing the mixing of the s (spherical) and p (elliptical) energy levels of the four valence electrons in the carbon atom. The mixing, or hybridization, creates wave functions of equal energy with electron distributions oriented toward the corners of a tetrahedron. Pauling and Slater demonstrated that deviation from a 90-degree bond angle could be taken as evidence of mixing, or hybridization, of the electron orbitals.

During 1931–1935, Robert Mulliken used Hund's approach and Douglas Rayner Hartree's group-theoretical methods to develop molecular orbital theory, as did Erich Hückel and Bernhard Eistert in Germany. While Pauling's atomic orbital method prevailed in the United States in the next decade, in England, John Edward Lennard-Jones, Hugh Christopher Longuet-Higgins, and Charles Alfred Coulson took up the molecular orbital method with its greater potential for mathematical application and development. Coulson successfully demonstrated in 1939 how electrons in benzene move over the whole molecule instead of being restricted to the region between two particular atoms. With the development of high-speed digital computers after the war, the more mathematically difficult MO method came to be preferred by most theoretical chemists despite Pauling's argument that the AO method was more natural to the chemist and its rougher approximations often did the job. Among proponents of MO theory, Coulson persuaded many chemists (although not Pauling) that MO methods complemented AO methods and offered considerably greater capability for solving chemical problems. Coulson's influential textbook *Valence* appeared in 1952.

The development of orbital symmetry rules by Robert Simpson Woodward and Roald Hoffmann in the 1960s, which allowed highly specific predictions of stereochemical details and reaction outcomes, assisted the switch to the MO method. Building on the work of Coulson and Longuet-Higgins, the Kyoto chemist Ken'ichi Fukui developed the frontier orbital theory of reactions (1950) that showed how the progress of reactions depends upon the geometry and relative energies of the highest recipient molecular orbital of one reactant and the lowest molecular orbital of the other.

MARY JO NYE

The 5fxyz electron orbital of the 5f shell, which is partially filled out by the actinides. The orbitals are regions where electrons are most likely to appear: blue signifies a positive, yellow a negative wave function.

QUANTUM ELECTRODYNAMICS (QED) is the quantum field theory describing the interaction of charged particles with photons. It represents positive and negative electrons by a quantized field satisfying the Dirac equation in the presence of an electromagnetic (e.m.) field; charged spin 0 particles, such as pi mesons, by quantized field operators satisfying the Klein-Gordon equation; and the electromagnetic field by quantized field operators satisfying Maxwell's equations. The source terms in these Maxwell equations are the charge-currents arising from the matter field in the presence of the quantized e.m. field. The small dimension-less constant $\alpha = 2\pi e^2/hc = 1/137$, where e is the electronic charge, h Planck's constant, and c the velocity of light, measures the coupling between the charged matter field and the electromagnetic field. Since α is so small, the coupled equations are usually solved "peturbatively," that is, as a power series expansion in α. This perturbative approach has had amazing success in calculating extremely fine details in atomic spectra, accounting for the electromagnetic properties of electrons and muons, and predicting with precision the outcome of collisions between high-energy positive and negative electrons. As Toichiro Kinoshita and Donald Yennie, two theorists who have carried out some of the most extensive and difficult calculations testing the limits of QED, wrote in 1990, "it is inconceivable that any theory which is conceptually less sophisticated could produce the same results."

Richard Feynman's great contribution to QED was a technique by which perturbations could be visualized and calculated by straightforward diagrams. The diagrams indicate both why and how certain processes take place in particular systems. In Feynman's approach, as generalized by Freeman Dyson, each quantized field (and associated particle) is characterized by a "propagator" represented in a Feynman diagram by a line, which if internal connects to two vertices, and if external, that is, if corresponding to an incoming or outgoing particle, connects to a single vertex. Each interaction is represented by a vertex characterized by a coupling constant and a factor describing the interaction between the fields. For a given process, relatively simple expressions occur in the lowest order of perturbation theory. The diagrams that correspond to higher order contributions contain closed loops and entail integrations over the momenta of the propagators involved in the loops. In almost all cases these integrals diverge because of contributions from large momenta.

The anomalous magnetic moment of a (quasi-free) electron means the deviation from the value predicted by the Dirac equation. According to Dirac's theory, the electron has an intrinsic magnetic moment accompanying its spin, the value of which when expressed in the form $g_e = eh/4\pi mc$ is given by $g_e = 2$. The electron's anomalous magnetic moment is defined as $a_e = (g_e - 2)/2$.

Julian Schwinger's computation of a_e in 1947 constituted a landmark in the postwar developments of QED. It confirmed the experimental value that had been obtained by Isador Isaac Rabi and his associates and also the ideas of mass and charge renormalization in the low orders of QED. Since that time, both the experiments and the theory have been improved by several orders of magnitude and have provided the most precise and rigorous tests for the validity of QED. To date, the best theoretical and experimental values of the anomalous magnetic moment of the electron agree to ten significant figures—(in units of $eh/4\pi mc$) 1.001 159 652 17 (theoretical) against 1.001 159 652 19 (measured).

SILVAN S. SCHWEBER

QUANTUM FIELD THEORY. When initially formulated, quantum mechanics described non-relativistic systems with a finite number of degrees of freedom. The extension of the formalism to include the interaction of charged particles with the electromagnetic field-treated quantum mechanically brought out the difficulties connected with the quantization of systems with an infinite number of degrees of freedom. The effort to make the quantum theory conform with special relativity disclosed further difficulties. To address both sets of problems, Ernst Pascual Jordan, Oskar Klein, Eugene Wigner, Werner Heisenberg, Wolfgang Pauli, Enrico Fermi, and others developed quantum field theory (QFT) during the late 1920s. P. A. M. Dirac had taken the initial step in 1927 with a quantum mechanical description of the interaction of charged particles with the electromagnetic field, which he described as an (infinite) assembly of photons, that is, of massless spin 1 particles. Dirac considered "particles" (whether they had a rest mass or, like photons, had none) to be the "fundamental" substance. In contrast, Jordan insisted that fields constituted the "fundamental" substance.

The history of theoretical elementary particle physics until the mid-1970s can be narrated in terms of oscillations between the particle and field viewpoints epitomized by Dirac and by Jordan. QFT proved richer in potentialities and possibilities than the quantized-particle approach. By the mid-1930s, the imposition of special relativity on QFT had produced genuinely novel features: the possibility of particle creation and annihilation, as first encountered in the quantum mechanical description of the emission and absorption of photons by charged

Richard Feynman (1918–1988), on the right, and Paul Dirac (1902–1984), perhaps discussing quantum field theory

Italian-born American physicist Enrico Fermi (1901–1954)

Fermi took Pauli's hypothesis seriously when he heard about it for the first time at the Solvay Congress of 1933. Fermi soon formulated a theory of β-decay that marked a change in the concept of "elementary" processes. Fermi supposed that electrons do not exist in nuclei before their emission, but that (to quote his version of 1934) "they, so to say, acquire their existence at the very moment when they are emitted; in the same manner as a quantum of light, emitted by an atom in a quantum jump, can in no way be considered as pre-existing in the atom prior to the emission process. In this theory, then, the total number of the electrons and of the neutrinos (like the total number of light quanta in the theory of radiation) will not necessarily be constant, since there might be processes of creation or destruction of these light particles."

Both Fermi's theory of β-decay and quantum electrodynamics (QED) made clear the power of a quantum field theoretical description. In particular, they indicated that the electromagnetic forces between charged particles could be understood as arising from the exchange of virtual photons between the particles—virtual particles because they do not obey the energy-momentum relation that holds for free photons. When one of the charged particle emits a (virtual) photon of momentum k, it changes its momentum by this amount. When the second charged particle absorbs this virtual photon, it changes its momentum by k. This exchange is the mechanism of the force between the interacting particles. The range of the force generated is inversely proportional to the mass of the virtual quantum exchanged. Zero-mass photons generate electromagnetic forces of infinite range. Spin-zero quanta of mass m generate forces with a range of the order h/mc. This insight led Hideki Yukawa to postulate that the short-range nuclear forces between nucleons could arise from the exchange of massive spin 0 bosons. Another important lesson learned from QED and Fermi's theory of β-decay was the protean nature of particles. When interacting with one another "particles" can metamorphose their character and number: in a collision between an electron and its anti-particle, the positron, the electron and positron can annihilate and give rise to a number of photons.

By the late 1930s, physicists understood the formalism of quantum field theory and its difficulties. All relativistic QFTs have the mathematical problem that the calculations of the interactions between particles give infinite, that is, nonsensical results. The root cause—fields definable at a point in space-time of these divergences was the assumption of locality, the assumption that the local fields—fields definable at a point in space-time point—whose quanta are the experimentally observed particles interact locally, i.e. at a point in space time.

Local interaction terms implied that in QED photons will couple with (virtual) electron-positron pairs of arbitrarily high momenta, and that electrons and positrons will couple with (virtual) photons of arbitrary high momenta, in both cases giving rise to divergences. The problem impeded progress throughout the 1930s and caused most of the workers in the field to doubt the correctness of QFT. The many proposals to overcome these divergences advanced during the 1930s all ended in failure. The pessimism of the leaders of the discipline—Bohr, Pauli, Heisenberg, Dirac, and J. Robert Oppenheimer—was partly responsible for the lack of progress. They had witnessed the overthrow of the classical concepts of space-time and had themselves rejected the classical concept of determinism in the description

particles; the existence of anti-particles; and the complexity of the "vacuum." The latter was now seen to be not a simple substance but the seat of fluctuations in the measured observables, which fluctuations are the larger the smaller the volume probed.

Fermi's theory of beta-decay (1933–1934) was the important landmark of field theoretic developments of the 1930s. It had been recognized since 1915 that the nucleus was the site of all radioactive processes, including β-radioactivity. The process of β-decay—in which a radioactive nucleus emits an electron (β-ray) and increases its electric charge from Z to Z + 1—had been studied extensively during the first decade of the century. In 1914, James Chadwick found that the energy of the emitted electrons varied continuously up to some maximum at which conservation held to the accuracy of the measurements in the experiment. By the end of the 1920s, no satisfactory explanation of the continuous β-spectrum had been found and some physicists, in particular Niels Bohr, proposed giving up energy conservation in β-decay processes. In December 1930, Pauli, in a letter addressed to the participants of a conference on radioactivity, countered with "a desperate remedy." He suggested that "there could exist in the nuclei electrically neutral particles that I wish to call neutrons [later renamed neutrinos by Fermi], which have spin 1/2 .... The continuous β-spectrum would then become understandable by the assumption that in β-decay a [neutrino] is emitted together with the electron, in such a way that the sum of the energies of the [neutrino] and electron is constant."

of atomic phenomena. They had brought about the quantum mechanical revolution. They were convinced that only further conceptual revolutions would solve the divergence problem in quantum field theory.

The way to circumvent the difficulties was indicated by Hendrik Kramers in the late 1930s, and his suggestions were implemented after World War II. These important developments stemmed from the attempt to explain quantitatively the discrepancies between the empirical data and the predictions of the relativistic Dirac equation for the level structure of the hydrogen atom and the value it ascribed to the magnetic moment of the electron. These deviations had been observed in reliable and precise molecular beam experiments carried out by Willis Eugene Lamb, Jr., and by Isidor Isaac Rabi and coworkers at Columbia, and were reported at the Shelter Island Conference in the fall of 1947. Shortly after the conference, Hans Albrecht Bethe showed that the Lamb shift (the deviation of the $2s$ and $2p$ levels of hydrogen from the values given by the Dirac equation) was of quantum electrodynamical origin, and that the effect could be computed by making use of what became known as "mass renormalization," the idea that had been put forward by Hendrik Kramers.

The parameters for the mass m_0 and for the charge e_0 that appear in the equations defining QED are not the observed charge and mass of an electron. The observed mass m enters the theory through the requirement that the energy of the physical state corresponding to an electron moving with momentum p be equal to $(p^2 + m^2)^{1/2}$. The observed charge e enters through the requirement that the force between two electrons at rest separated by a large distance r satisfy Coulomb's law e^2/r^2. Julian Schwinger and Richard Feynman showed that the divergences encountered in the low orders of perturbation theoretic calculations could be eliminated by re-expressing the parameters m_0 and e_0 in terms of the observed values m and e, a procedure that became known as mass and charge renormalization. In 1948, Freeman Dyson working at the Institute for Advanced Study in Princeton proved that these renormalizations could absorb all the divergences arising in scattering processes (the S-matrix) in QED to all orders of perturbation theory. More generally, Dyson demonstrated that only for certain kinds of quantum field theories can all the infinities be removed by a redefinition of a finite number of parameters. He called such theories renormalizable. Renormalizability thereafter became a criterion for theory selection.

The idea of mass and charge renormalization, implemented through a judicious exploitation of the symmetry properties of QED, made it possible to formulate and to give physical justifications for algorithmic rules to eliminate all the ultraviolet divergences that had plagued the theory and to secure unique finite answers. The success of renormalized QED in accounting for the Lamb shift, the anomalous magnetic moment of the electron and of the muon, the scattering of light by light, the radiative corrections to the scattering of photons by electrons, and the radiative corrections to pair production was spectacular.

Perhaps the most important theoretical accomplishment between 1947 and 1952 was providing a firm foundation for believing that local quantum field theory was the framework best suited for the unification of quantum theory and special relativity. Perspicacious theorists, like Murray Gell-Mann also noted the ease with which symmetries—both space-time and internal symmetries—could be incorporated into the framework of local quantum field theory. Gauge invariance became a central feature of the quantum field theoretical description of the electromagnetic field. Subsequently, the weak and the strong forces were similarly described in terms of gauge theories.

SILVAN S. SCHWEBER

QUANTUM PHYSICS. The proximate origin of the quantum theory was a perplexing paper published by Max Planck in 1900. In it he showed that the formula he had proposed for the empirically determined spectral density of blackbody radiation could be derived by setting the energy of the collection of charged harmonic "resonators" (which he used to represent atoms capable of emitting and absorbing electromagnetic radiation) of frequency v equal to an integral multiple of hv. Here h stood for a new physical constant necessary to fit the empirical spectrum and v for the frequency of the resonator. The derivation required recourse to Ludwig Boltzmann's probability calculation for the entropy of a gas. It appears that, in adapting it to the blackbody problem, Planck did not recognize that he had made a break with the physics he had used to describe radiation.

In any case, Planck had full confidence in the representation of the electromagnetic field given by James Clerk Maxwell and Hendrik Antoon Lorentz. The unification of light with electromagnetism, the demonstration of the "reality" of electromagnetic waves by Heinrich Hertz, and the description given by the Maxwell-Lorentz equations of a multitude of wave phenomena was for Planck, and for almost all of his contemporaries, convincing evidence of the continuous nature of radiation. Albert Einstein entertained doubts. Having scrutinized the statistical mechanical foundations upon which Planck based his derivation of his formula for the spectral density of blackbody, Einstein concluded in 1905 that a few phenomena, like the photoelectric effect, could be explained easily if "the energy of monochromatic light consists of a finite number of energy quanta of magnitude hv, localized at various points of space [that] can be produced or absorbed only as units." At about the same time, Einstein realized that Planck's radiation theory required a radical discontinuity in the energy content of the individual resonators; with his "heuristic hypothesis" concerning the photo-effect, Einstein extended the discontinuity to the free electromagnetic field and to the interaction between light and matter.

Einstein's explanation in 1907 of the observed deviation at low temperature of the specific heat of simple solids from their classical value of $3Nk$ (N = the number of molecules in a gram, k = "Boltzmann's constant," a second universal constant from the blackbody formula) corroborated the quantum hypothesis. In Einstein's model of a solid, the potential that an atom experiences near its equilibrium position is the same for all the atoms of the solid. Hence for small vibrations near their equilibrium point all the atoms oscillate with the same frequency v. Quantization implies that each oscillator can only have an energy equal to $E = nhv$, and Planck's formula gives, in the limit where hv is small in comparison with kT (T = temperature), the specific heat $3Nk$. At low enough temperatures, where the limit does not hold, characteristic deviations from the classical value occur, which Walther Nernst and others detected around 1910.

In his doctoral thesis on the electron theory of metals (1911), Niels Bohr concluded that atoms constructed according to the principles of classical physics could not represent the magnetic properties of metals. Working in Ernest

Rutherford's laboratory in Manchester just after Rutherford proposed the nuclear model of the atom, Bohr seized upon it because its radical mechanical instability made it a promising candidate for repair by a quantum hypothesis. Bohr stabilized the Rutherford atom by supposing that it could exist in various "stationary states" constrained by certain quantum rules but otherwise governed by the laws of classical mechanics. However, the laws of mechanics do not hold for the transition of the system between two stationary states during which the atom radiates a quantum of energy $h\nu$ equal to the difference in energy between the two states. On Bohr's theory, radiation is not emitted (or absorbed) in the continuous way assumed by Maxwell-Lorentz electrodynamics.

Bohr's first postulate, which limited the validity of classical mechanics in the atomic domain, restricted the angular momentum of each atomic electron to an integral multiple of $h/2\pi$. The second postulate, which denied the validity of classical electrodynamics for radiative processes in atoms and made the frequencies of atomic spectral lines different from the orbital frequencies of the electronic motions, required surrendering the classical connection between the frequency ν of the emitted radiation and the mechanical frequency of the electron in its orbit.

With the help of these quantum rules, Bohr accounted for the phenomenological regularities that had been discerned in the hydrogen spectrum, in particular, the Balmer formula for transitions to the $n = 2$ level, and also, and more dramat-

ically, for the spectrum of ionized helium (1913–14). During World War I, Arnold Sommerfeld generalized Bohr's postulates to elliptical electron orbits and then to motions in three dimensions. He recorded his success in calculating regularities in doublet and triplet spectra, in the Zeeman effect, and in x-ray spectra in a long book, *Atombau und Spektrallinien* (first edition 1919), with which all physicists interested in quantum and atomic physics during the early 1920s began their work.

In the early 1920s, Bohr gave a phenomenological explanation of the periodic table based on the occupancy by electrons of Coulomb-like orbits in multi-electron atoms. Thereafter, many theorists tried to justify Bohr's explanation, but, except for Wolfgang Pauli's formulation of the exclusion principle early in 1925, none of their efforts provided a stable foundation for the dynamics of atoms. They were seminal, however, in that they made manifest the problems a more complete quantum mechanics would have to solve.

In 1917, Einstein took what in retrospect was an important step toward this mechanics. Still flirting with the corpuscular nature of radiation, Einstein introduced the concept of the probability for the spontaneous emission of a light quantum by a "molecule" in a transition from one state to another. The concept allowed an easy derivation of Planck's blackbody formula. In 1923, Arthur Holly Compton's experiment on the scattering of X rays by electrons indicated that the shift in the wave length of the scattered

Two pioneers of quantum physics, Niels Bohr (1885–1962) and (on the right) Max Planck (1858–1947), in 1930, not lecturing on quantum physics

X ray and the recoil energy of the electron could be derived on the assumption that the X rays acted as particles with energy $h\nu$ and momentum $h\nu/c$ (c the velocity of light). The positive result of the Compton experiment led Einstein to declare that there are "two theories of light, both indispensable, and without any logical connection." The corpuscular viewpoint accounted for the optical properties of atoms, whereas macroscopic phenomena like diffraction and interference required the wave theory of light. The two theories coexisted without any resolution during the early 1920s.

Another important guide to a more powerful quantum physics was the correspondence principle Bohr refined between 1913 and 1918. It stated that the frequencies calculated by Bohr's second postulate (during "quantum jumps") in the limit where the stationary states have large quantum numbers that differ very little from one another will coincide with the frequencies calculated with the classical theory of radiation from the motion of the system in the stationary states. Bohr's assistant Hendrik Kramers cleverly applied the correspondence idea to compute the intensity and polarization of the light emitted from simple atoms. Kramers and Werner Heisenberg extended the same idea to the dispersion of light and worked out ways to translate classical quantities involving a single stationary state into quantum mechanical quantities involving two or more states. Max Born, Heisenberg's teacher at the University of Göttingen, called for a "quantum mechanics" for calculating with the quantum mechanical quantities directly. That was in 1924. In less than a year, Heisenberg provided him with one. Its guiding principles were satisfaction of Bohr's correspondence principle (in the appropriate limit the theory should yield the classical results); recognition that the troubles of the "old quantum theory" arose primarily from breakdown of the kinematics underlying classical dynamics; and restriction of the theory to relations between observable quantities.

Born, Heisenberg, and a fellow student of Heisenberg's, Pascual Jordan, soon developed the new mechanics into an elaborate mathematical formalism. They built a closed theory that displayed strikingly close analogies with classical mechanics but at the same time preserved the characteristic features of quantum phenomena. Their work laid the foundations of a consistent quantum theory but at the price of relinquishing the possibility of giving a physical, visualizable picture of the processes it could calculate. Hence the relief felt by Planck, Einstein, and Lorentz when Erwin Schrödinger, who followed a route entirely different from Heisenberg's, began to publish his wave mechanics in 1926. It seemed to avoid the unconventional features of Heisenberg's formulation and rested on more traditional foundations and easier calculations: variational principles, differential equations, and the properties of waves.

Schrödinger had followed up insights and suggestions by Louis de Broglie and Einstein. In 1923, de Broglie published an idea that was the obverse of Einstein's attribution of particle properties to wave radiation—to endow discrete matter with wave properties.

By following sometimes fanciful analogies and the principle of relativity, de Broglie associated a wave of frequency ν and wavelength λ with a particle of momentum p and energy E according to $\nu = E/h$, $1/\lambda = p/h$. He thus extended the particle-wave duality of radiation to matter. Knowing the wavelength, Schrödinger soon found an appropriate differential equation for a wave of amplitude Ψ. He interpreted the Ψ function as describing a real material wave and considered the electron not a particle but a charge distribution whose density is given by the square of the wave function. In a short paper dated June 1926, Born rejected Schrödinger's viewpoint and proposed a probabilistic interpretation for the Ψ function. He stipulated that the wave function $\Psi(x, f)$ determines the probability of finding the electron at the position x at time t. In 1927, two different sets of experimentalists—George P. Thomson (the son of Joseph John Thomson) in Britain and Clinton Davisson and Lester Germer in the United States—detected diffraction patterns from an electron beam.

Several physicists proved in 1926 that wave mechanics gave the same numerical answers as the "matrix mechanics" of Born, Heisenberg, and Jordan. Together they are known as quantum mechanics. In contrast to classical physics, which contained no scale and was assumed to apply both in the micro and macro domain, quantum mechanics asserted that the physical world presented itself hierarchically. Certain constants of nature layered the world. As P. A. M. Dirac emphasized in the first edition of his *Principles of Quantum Mechanics,* Planck's constant allows the parsing of the world into microscopic and macroscopic realms.

The conquest of the microrealm during the first years after the invention of quantum mechanics stemmed from the confluence of two factors: the apperception of an approximately stable ontology of electrons and nuclei, and the formulation of the dynamical laws governing the motion of electrons and other microscopic particles moving with velocities small compared to the velocity of light. "Approximately stable" meant that electrons and (non-radioactive) nuclei, the building blocks of atoms, molecules, simple solids, could be treated as ahistoric objects, with physical characteristics seemingly independent of their mode of production and lifetimes effectively infinite. These electrons and nuclei behaved as if they were "elementary," almost point-like objects specified only by their mass, their intrinsic spin, electric charge, and magnetic moment. In addition, the members of each species were indistinguishable: all electrons are identical, as are all protons, and all (stable) nuclei of a given charge and mass when in their ground state. Their indistinguishability implied that an assembly of them obeyed characteristic statistics depending on whether they had integral or half odd integral spin (measured in multiples of $h/2\pi$). Bosons (particles with zero or integral spins) can assemble in any number in a given quantum state. Fermions (particles with half odd integral spins) do not share a quantum state. A one-particle quantum state can be characterized either by the position and the spin state of the particle or by its momentum and its spin state. Thus no two identical Fermions can be at the same position if they have the same spin. More generally, the wave function describing a system of identical bosons remains unchanged under the interchange of any two particles, whereas that describing fermions changes sign under such a transposition.

The quantum mechanical explanation of chemical bonding resulted in a unification of physics and chemistry. In 1929, following the enormous success of nonrelativistic quantum mechanics in explaining atomic and molecular structure and interactions, Dirac, a main contributor to these developments, declared that "the general theory of quantum mechanics is now almost complete." Whatever imperfections still remained were connected with the synthesis of the theory with the special theory of relativ-

Q

Physicists at the Solvay Conference of 1927, the fifth in the series of high-level meetings begun in 1911 and sponsored by the Belgian industrialist Ernest Solvay (1838–1922). The conferences considered pressing problems in physics; that of 1927, attended by Einstein, Bohr, Pauli, Dirac, Marie Curie, and Louis de Broglie, discussed the then-new quantum mechanics.

ity. But these were of no importance in the consideration of atomic and molecular structure and ordinary chemical reactions. "The underlying physical laws necessary for the mathematical theory of a large part of physics and the whole of chemistry are thus completely known, and the difficulty is only that the exact application of these laws leads to equations much too complicated to be soluble." Dirac's assertion may still have the validity it had, but, as emphasized by Phillip Anderson, "the reductionist hypothesis does not by any means imply a 'constructionist' one: The ability to reduce everything to simple fundamental laws does not imply the ability to start from those laws and reconstruct the universe. In fact, the more the elementary particle physicists tell us about the nature of the fundamental laws, the less relevance they seem to have to the very real problems of the rest of science, much less to those of society. The constructionist hypothesis breaks down when confronted with the twin difficulties of scale and complexity." Still, physics can be regarded as more foundational (not fundamental) than chemistry because the laws of physics encompass in principle the phenomena and the laws of chemistry.

J. L. HEILBRON

QUARK. During the 1950s and 1960s, progress in classifying and understanding the phenomenology of the ever increasing number of hadrons (strongly interacting microscopic particles) came not from fundamental theory but by shunning dynamical assumptions in favor of symmetry and kinematical principles that embodied the essential features of a relativistic quantum mechanics.

In 1961, Murray Gell-Mann and Yuval Ne'eman independently proposed classifying the hadrons into families based on a symmetry later known as the "eightfold way." They realized that the mesons (hadrons with integral spins) grouped naturally into octets; the baryons (heavy hadrons with half integral spins) into octets and decuplets.

The "eightfold way" can be represented mathematically in three dimensions, a property that led Gell-Mann, and independently George Zweig, to build hadrons out of three elementary constituents. Gell-Mann called these constituents "quarks" (from a line in James Joyce's *Finnegans Wake,* "Three quarks for Muster Mark!"); Zweig called them aces. The elaboration of the quark scheme is briefly indicated here as an indication of the methods and madness of elementary particle physics.

To account for the observed spectrum of hadrons Gell-Mann and Zweig defined three "flavors" of quarks (generically indicated by q), called up (u), down (d), and strange (s), each with spin $\frac{1}{2}$ but differing in two other quantum numbers (isotopic spin and strangeness) that defined them. Ordinary matter contains only u and/or d quarks. ("Strange" hadrons would contain strange quarks.) The three quarks had two other features: a baryonic mass of $\frac{1}{3}$, and an electrical charge of $\frac{2}{3}$ (for the u) and of $-\frac{1}{3}$ (for the d and s) those of the proton. This last feature startled physicists who had no experimental evidence for any macroscopic object carrying a positive charge smaller than a proton's or a negative charge smaller than the electron's.

Since a relativistic quantum mechanical description implies that for every charged particle there exists an "antiparticle" with the opposite charge, Gell-Mann and Zweig provided for antiquarks (generically denoted by $\bar{q}$) having an electric charge and strangeness opposite to those of the corresponding quarks.

Quarks bind together into hadrons as follows. An up and an antidown quark make a positive meson; two ups (with electrical charge $\frac{4}{3}$) and a down (with electrical charge $-\frac{1}{3}$), a proton. All baryons can be made up of three quarks, all mesons of one quark and one antiquark. That, however, did not provide quite enough possibilities so quarks had to have another attribute, which, in the playful quark nomenclature, was called "color." Quark color comes in three varieties (sometimes taken to be red, yellow, and blue), each of which can be "positive" or "negative." Quarks carry positive color charges and antiquarks carry negative ones. The observed hadrons have no net color charge.

In the late 1960s, the Stanford Linear Accelerator (SLAC) could produce electrons of sufficiently high energy to probe the internal structure of protons. If the proton's charge were uniformly distributed, penetrating electrons would tend to go through it without being appreciably deflected. If, on the other hand, the charge was localized on internal constituents, then—in analogy to Ernest Rutherford's demonstration of the atomic nucleus—an electron that passed close to one of them would be strongly deflected. The SLAC experiments showed this effect, which prompted Richard Feynman to suggest that the proton contained pointlike particles with spin $\frac{1}{2}$, which he called "partons." The partons soon were assimilated to the quarks, although they (the partons/quarks) appeared to be too light and too mobile to make up protons. These difficulties were eventually resolved.

The discovery in November 1974 of the J/Ψ meson gave further support for the quark picture and reason to accept a fourth quark with a new flavor, "charm" (denoted by c), whose existence had been proposed by Sheldon Glashow and others in 1964 and, with greater insistence, in 1970. The J/Ψ (its two names resulted from its simultaneous dis-

covery by two different groups) appeared to be a bound state of c and $\bar{c}$. The discovery of November 1974 revolutionized high-energy physics by establishing the representation of hadrons as quark composites. As the number of hadrons grew, however, the scheme had to be extended by the addition of the "bottom" (or "beauty," b) quark in 1977 and the "top" (t) quark in 1994. Each successively discovered quark has a larger mass than its predecessors on a scale in which the u weighs 1, the d weighs 2, the s 36, the c 320, the b 960, and the t 34,800. They all have spin $\frac{1}{2}$; partake in the strong, electromagnetic, and weak interactions; and come in pairs: up and down (u, d), charm and strange (c, s), and top and bottom (t, b). The first member of each pair has electric charge $\frac{2}{3}$ and the second $-\frac{1}{3}$. Each flavor comes in three colors.

If hadrons are made up of fractionally charged quarks, why have fractionally charged particles not been observed? Even if a plausible mechanism could be devised for confining quarks, what reality can be attached to them as constituents of hadrons if they can never be observed empirically? Quantum chromodynamics (QCD), which emerged a decade after the introduction of quarks, explained how quarks could be so strongly bound that they could never escape, while nevertheless behaving as quasifree particles in deep inelastic scattering.

SILVAN S. SCHWEBER

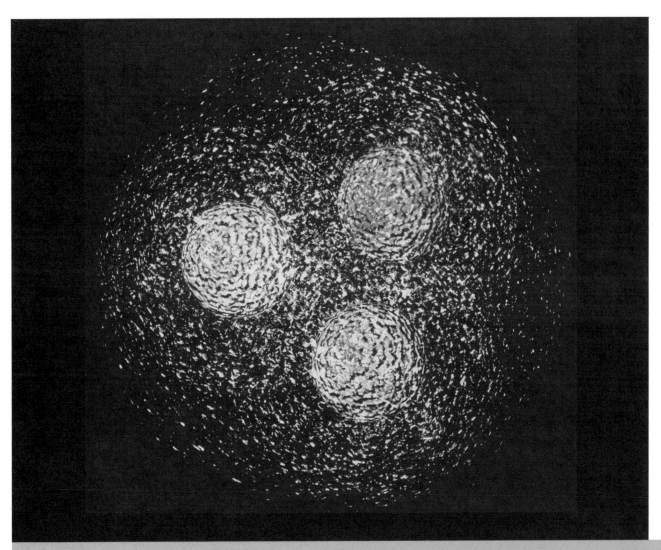

Quark structure of the proton. The quarks are the globules, green for the up quark (charge 12/3), pink for the down quark (charge -1/3), They are held together by the strong nuclear force conveyed by a cloud of virtual gluons.

RADIOACTIVITY. Studies in radioactivity produced the scientific research fields of nuclear physics, cosmic-ray physics, and high-energy physics, and also nuclear chemistry, nuclear medicine, and nuclear engineering. Beginning in 1940 with the isolation of neptunium and plutonium, the creation of short-lived transuranium elements extended the periodic table of the chemical elements into new territory.

That radioactivity has rested in the shared disciplinary terrains of physics and chemistry is indicated by the shared Nobel Prize in physics awarded to its discoverers Henri Becquerel, Marie Sklodowska Curie, and Pierre Curie, and Ernest Rutherford's receipt of the Nobel Prize in chemistry in 1908 for his (and Frederick Soddy's) elucidation of the mechanism of the radioactive disintegration of atoms.

Polish-French physicist-chemist Marie Sklodowska Curie (1867–1934) and her husband, physicist Pierre Curie (1859–1906), in their laboratory in Paris

Becquerel discovered that uranium salts emit radiation by accident while investigating whether naturally phosphorescent minerals produce the X rays discovered by Wilhelm Conrad Röntgen in late 1895. By 1897, Becquerel and others had demonstrated that uranium radiations carry electrical charge, a physical property that led Marie Curie to apply the quartz electrometer (then recently invented by her husband and his brother Jacques-Paul Curie) to a variety of minerals in search of the property that she termed "radioactivity." She identified polonium and radium as radioactive elements in 1898, and André-Louis Debierne discovered actinium in 1899. They and others found that thorium, like uranium, is radioactive.

Rutherford distinguished two kinds of radiation, which he called "alpha" (distinguished by its ready absorption) and "beta" (about one hundred times more penetrating). At the Curies' laboratory in 1900, Paul Villard discerned a gamma radiation from radioactive substances that appeared to behave exactly like X rays. By 1900, Becquerel, Rutherford, and others had established that the beta rays consist of negatively charged particles similar if not identical to electrons. In 1903, Rutherford showed that the alpha rays also carried a charge and so had to be understood as a stream of particles. By 1908, Rutherford and his colleagues had decisive evidence that the *"alpha"* radiations are helium ions. Rutherford and Soddy recognized in 1903 that thorium continuously produces a new radioactive gas (radon), and a second radioactive substance (chemically identical to radium) from which a longer line of radioactive substances descends. They settled on the hypothesis that radioactive decay is accompanied by the expulsion of an alpha or beta particle from the decaying atom and that the decay can be expressed in terms of a half life, defined as the time during which half of the mass of a radioactive element is transformed into a new substance. Rutherford's continuing study of alpha particles and their interactions with matter prompted the experiments that led to his invention in 1910–1911 of the nuclear atom.

By 1912, some thirty radioactive elements had been identified. This achievement derived from the work of Rutherford's groups in Montreal and Manchester; Marie Curie's laboratory in Paris; Otto Hahn and Lise Meitner's work in Berlin; and other investigators, including Bertram Borden Boltwood at Yale University in New Haven. They differentiated natural decay series beginning with uranium (238), actinium (227) or uranium (235), and thorium (232). In 1913 Soddy, Alexander Russell, and Kasimir Fajans independently developed a generalized radioactive displacement law. In 1911, Soddy had noted that loss of an alpha particle produced a chemical element two places to the left of the original in the periodic table. Similarly, Russell remarked that beta decays lead to the next element in the periodic table. Soddy coined the word "isotope" for radioactive elements chemically identical to another element while differing in atomic weight. Several studies confirmed in 1914 that atomic weights of lead derived from radioactive ores varied from each other and from the established value of 207.2.

Early methods for detecting radioactivity were both electrical and visual, relying initially on the electrometer and on microscopically observed scintillations of light caused as alpha particles strike zinc sulfide. Electrical methods of detection improved in 1928 when Hans Geiger and Walther Müller succeeded in making a reliable counter using the technique with which Geiger and Rutherford had counted alpha particles before the war. C. T. R. Wilson's cloud chamber, invented in principle in 1899 but not perfected until after World War I, also provided a means of "seeing" nuclear events. Using the older scintillation technique, Rutherford proposed in 1919 that collision of an alpha particle with nitrogen gas resulted in disintegration of the nitrogen atom and expulsion of a long-range hydrogen atom (proton). After automating a cloud chamber, P. M. S. Blackett in 1924 fired alpha particles into nitrogen atoms and obtained dramatic photographs, showing the path of a proton ejected from a recoiling nitrogen nucleus and the capture of the alpha particle by the nitrogen nucleus, creating an isotope of oxygen.

Francis Aston, who began his career as an assistant to Joseph John Thomson, developed a mass spectrograph that provided a photographic record of particles separated by their masses. Aston and others found evidence for isotopes not only among the radioactive and heavy elements, but also among the light elements. The concept of the isotope thus became generalized for all chemical elements.

In 1932, the same year that James Chadwick identified the neutron at the Cavendish Laboratory, John Douglas Cockroft and Ernest T. S. Walton, working with lithium, became the first scientists to split the atom by accelerating protons in a high-voltage, high-tension machine. Ernest O. Lawrence and Milton Stanley Livingston built a circular particle accelerator that provided a rival model for achieving high energies. However, alpha particles from radium provoked the first radioactivity artificially induced by humans. That was in 1934, when Frédéric Joliot and Irène Joliot-Curie produced a radioactive isotope of phosphorus from aluminum.

During the late 1920s and early 1930s, Meitner, Charles D. Ellis, and Enrico Fermi argued over the existence and interpretation of apparent anomalies in the energy in beta decay. Wolfgang Pauli proposed in 1930 that a nuclear particle with a mass similar to an electron but with no charge might be expelled with an electron in beta decay in order to conserve energy in the reaction. Fermi suggested in 1933 that Pauli's little "neutron" be renamed the "neutrino" following James Chadwick's identification of the proton-sized neutral neutron in 1932. Fermi's theory was adopted, although the neutrino eluded detection until 1956.

Rays from naturally occurring sources continued to serve nuclear physicists and chemists even in the era of the cyclotron. Fermi and his collaborators irradiated every element they could find with neutrons derived from a radon-beryllium source, discovered the efficacy of slow neutrons in inducing nuclear reactions, and, mistakenly, believed that they had made transuranic elements by shining neutrons on uranium. Meitner, Hahn, and Fritz Strassmann also used neutrons from natural sources in the experiments from which, by the end of 1938, Hahn and Strassmann obtained the results whereby Meitner (by then a refugee in Sweden)

Willard Libby (1908–1980), known for his development of radiocarbon dating, for which he received the Nobel Prize in Chemistry in 1960

and her nephew Otto Robert Frisch deduced the existence of nuclear fission.

During the course of the Manhattan Project for the development of uranium and plutonium bombs, the health hazards of radioactivity increasingly came to the fore. Radiations that had been touted since the early 1900s as a general curative and a specific agent against cancer were demonstrated to cause leukemia and other cancer-related diseases. Facial creams and mineral waters, as well as watch dials and curios containing uranium salts, disappeared from store shelves and health resorts in the 1950s as international movements against the atmospheric testing of nuclear weapons gained force from evidence of the hazards of nuclear debris or "fallout." After enthusiasm in the early 1950s for the use of nuclear energy not only as a commercial power source but also for explosives in dam-building and road-building, public suspicion of radioactivity curtailed nuclear energy projects in countries like the United States and Great Britain, although not in France or the Soviet Union.

In chemotherapy and in medical tests, radioactive isotopes continue to serve as tagging or tracer devices for studying the metabolism or pathways of iodine, barium, and other elements in the body. In his first efforts in the 1930s to get large-scale funding for his accelerator program at the University of California at Berkeley, Lawrence emphasized medical applications. Large philanthropies such as the Rockefeller Foundation increasingly turned their funding priorities to medical research in the 1930s. Lawrence and his brother John Lawrence, who served as director of the university's medical physics laboratory, argued for the medical benefits of the production of radioactive isotopes in the

R

and radiochemical techniques to unravel in detail the mechanism of photosynthesis.

Willard F. Libby attracted more public attention when he showed in 1946 that living matter contains carbon-14, produced by the collision of cosmic ray neutrons with atmospheric nitrogen, which enters the carbon dioxide and carbon monoxide metabolism. Since the quantity of carbon-14 decays after death, Libby's discovery made a brilliant new means of dating very old organic remains.

Since World War II, particle accelerators and nuclear reactors have entirely superseded natural elements as the sources of radioactive materials for laboratory experiments and medical procedures.

MARY JO NYE

RELATIVITY is a theory and program that set the frame of the physical world picture of the twentieth century. Four stages may be distinguished: the invention of the misnamed "special theory of relativity" (SRT), which covered only phenomena observed in bodies moving among themselves with constant relative velocities, in 1905; the recognition of the equivalence of a body's inertial mass (the measure of its resistance to change of velocity) and gravitational mass (the measure of the pull of gravity on it) in 1907; the removal of the restriction to constant velocities in the general theory of relativity (GRT) in 1915; and the application of GRT to cosmology especially in recent decades.

The inefficy of the term SRT involves both the "S" and the "R." It is not "special" but limited, whence the French term "restricted relativity." Again, what distinguishes SRT from classical mechanics is not "relativity"—the idea that the laws of motion look the same in all inertial frames (reference frames moving with respect to one another with constant velocity)—but rather the startling concept that all observers measure the same velocity for light in free space. This distinguishing principle is absolute, not relative. It disagrees with the principle of relativity if, as many physicists believed around 1900, radiation is reducible to mechanics. Einstein insisted on both the absolute and the relative—the constancy of the light velocity and the equivalence of inertial frames—and, in consequence, had to surrender com-

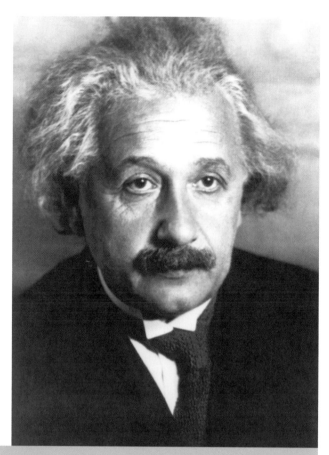

Albert Einstein (1879–1955), invented the theory of relativity at the age of 26

accelerator. One result, phosphorus-32, was used in early attempts to treat leukemia.

Radioactive isotopes had uses beyond medicine. Samuel Ruben, W. Z. Hassid, and Martin Kamen at Lawrence's radiation laboratory used carbon-11 to study the chemistry of carbon dioxide in the photosynthesis of barley and the green algae chlorella. In 1941, Ruben and Kamen identified the radioactive isotope carbon-14 produced from nitrogen in the Berkeley accelerator. Melvin Calvin followed up at Berkeley by using a combination of paper chromatography

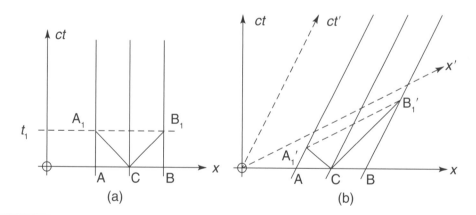

(a)   (b)

The points A and B, at rest in the system x, t, describe "world lines" parallel to the ct-(time) axis: their world position changes in time but not in space. A light signal sent from C reaches them simultaneously (at time t_1) along the "light lines" CA_1, CB_1, drawn arbitrarily at an angle of 45 degrees to the x axis. If A and B move along x at the speed v, they describe world lines inclined to x since their world positions change in both space and time. They meet the signals from C at A_1', B_1', that is, at different times measured in the x, t system. Since relativity requires the signal to be simultaneous in the system x', t' in which A and B are at rest, the x' axis must be parallel to A_1B_1; and since, in the x', t' system, A and B change their world positions only in time, the ct' axis must be parallel to AA_1' and BB_1'.

mon intuitions of space and time. One forgone concept was absolute simultaneity.

In the thought experiment Einstein often described, an observer on an embankment sees a light flash from the middle of a passing railroad carriage equipped with a mirror at either end. According to relativity, an observer seated at the center of the car would see the light returned from the mirrors simultaneously. But the observer on the embankment would see the flash from the forward mirror after that from the rear: the light has farther to go to meet and return from the forward than from the rear mirror, and the speed of light by hypothesis is the same in both directions. On a ballistic theory of light, the return flashes occur simultaneously for both parties: to the traveling observer, the light has the same speed in both directions; to the stationary one, the speed in the forward direction exceeds that in the opposite direction by twice the speed of the carriage. Further arithmetic shows that holding to the absolute and the relative simultaneously required that meter sticks and synchronized clocks moving at constant velocity with respect to a stationary observer appear to him to be shorter and tick slower than they do to an observer traveling with them.

Einstein showed that the form and magnitude of these odd effects follow from the stipulation that the coordinates of inertial systems are related by a set of equations that he called the Lorentz transformation. Hendrik Antoon Lorentz had introduced them as a mathematical artifice to make the principle of relativity apply to Maxwell's equations of the electromagnetic field. Einstein now insisted that the Lorentz transformation apply also to mechanics in place of what came to be called the "Galileo transformation" that guaranteed relativity to Newton's laws of motion. The Galilean, which transforms only space, reads, for relative motion at a constant velocity v, $x' = x - vt$, $t' = t$, where the primed letters refer to a coordinate system moving along the x axis of the unprimed system; the Lorentz transformation replaces these relations with $x' = \gamma(x - vt)$, $t' = \gamma(t - vx/c^2)$, $\gamma = (1 - v^2/c^2)^{-1/2}$. When v is negligibly small in comparison with c, the equations have the same form, but not the same meaning, as the Galilean transformation between the same variables. Since the Galilean transformation supports the Newtonian expressions for force, mass, kinetic energy, and so on, replacing it required reworking the formalism of the old mechanics. This labor, in which Max Planck and his student Max von Laue played leading parts, produced expressions differing from the Newtonian ones by factors of γ. A new form of Newton's second law emerged that satisfied the demand of relativity ("remained invariant") under the Lorentz transformation.

As an afterthought, also in 1905, Einstein argued that energy amounts to ponderable mass and vice versa. The relativistic expressions for the momentum and kinetic energy require that, for conservation of momentum to hold, the mass m of an isolated system of bodies must increase when the system's kinetic energy E decreases. The increase occurs at a rate (change of mass) = (change of energy)/c^2, $\Delta m = \Delta E/c^2$. Einstein thus united the previously distinct principles of the conservation of energy and of mass. From a practical point of view, the equivalence of mass and energy as applied to nuclear power is by far the most important consequence of relativistic mechanics.

Relativity had an enormous appeal to people like Planck, who regarded the surrender of common-sense expectations about space, time, and energy as a major step toward the complete "deanthropomorphizing of the world pic-

ture" begun by Copernicus. The mathematician Hermann Minkowski declared in a famous speech to the Society of German Scientists and Physicians in 1908 that "space by itself, and time by itself, are doomed to fade away into mere shadows, and only a kind of union of the two will preserve an independent reality." He interpreted the Lorentz transformation as a geometrical rotation in his four-dimensional space, whose points represented "world events" and whose lines represented the histories of all the particles in the universe. "The word relativity postulate ... seems to me very feeble," he said, "[to express] the postulate of the absolute world," that is, Einstein's theory as geometrized by Minkowski.

Einstein's compulsion to remove the "all too human" from physics and his desire to overcome the limitation of SRT brought him to a more profound generalization than Minkowski's. Taking the equivalence of inertial and gravitational masses as his guide, he worked out by 1911 that gravitational forces should affect electromagnetic fields (for example, by giving radiation potential energy) and deduced that the sun would bend the path of a ray of starlight that passed close to it. But the major conquest wrested from the equivalence of the masses was the elimination of gravity: all freely falling bodies in the same region experience the same acceleration because the presence of large objects distorts the space around them and the bodies have no alternative but to follow the "geodesics"—straight lines in the curved space in which they find themselves. In "flat space-time," without distorting masses, bodies move in inertial straight Euclidean lines. Falling bodies apparently coerced to rejoin the earth under a gravitational force in Euclidean space in fact move freely along geodesics in the local warp in the absolute four-dimensional space-time occasioned by the earth's presence. By 1915, Einstein had found the mathematical form (tensors) and the field equations describing the local shape of space-time that constituted the backbone of GRT and had added two more tests: an explanation of a peculiarity in the orbit of Mercury and a calculation of the effect of gravity on the color of light.

By 1910 or 1911, German theorists had accepted SRT and a few physicists elsewhere recognized its importance. Arnold Sommerfeld grafted it onto Niels Bohr's quantum theory of the atom in 1915–1916, with spectacular results (the explanation of the fine structure of helium). Physicists demobilizing from World War I interested in atomic structure or quantum physics perforce had to learn relativity and, ultimately, to find ways of employing SRT systematically in quantum mechanics. And then the positive results of the eclipse expedition organized by Arthur Eddington and other English astronomers to test Einstein's prediction of the deflection of starlight engaged the public imagination. It appeared that a lone pacifist had by pure thought bettered Newton while most of the world's scientists had devoted themselves to war. Einstein traveled, quipped, became a favorite of newspaper reporters around the world and the bête-noire of anti-Semites back home. He spent the rest of his life, in Berlin and in Princeton, trying to generalize the general by bringing electromagnetism within GRT. But neither his efforts nor those of the few other theorists who thought the game worth the candle managed to reduce electricity and magnetism to bumps in space.

Application to cosmology at first seemed more promising. A solution to the field equations by Aleksandr Friedmann in 1922 indicated the possibility of a finite expanding universe.

The concept agreed with measurements of red shifts in galaxies. The notion of the origin of the universe in a compact space, or "cosmic egg," was bruited by Georges Lemaître in 1927. The resultant Big-Bang universe, with origin in time (initially set at two billion years ago from the accepted value of the Hubble constant), gained some acceptance but little development until the 1960s. Then discoveries in astronomy (quasars, pulsars, supposititious black holes, the cosmic background radiation), laboratory demonstrations of the gravitational red shift and tests with rockets and atomic clocks, and advances in particle physics and the mathematics of gravity made GRT fashionable. Relativistic astrophysics now has the panoply of journals, textbooks, meetings, and money that mark a flourishing science. Although gravity remains outside the unified forces of the Standard Model, the pursuit of the vanishingly small and the ineffably large depend upon GRT for clues to the origin and evolution of the universe.

J. L. HEILBRON

RELIGION AND SCIENCE. Religion and science are both so important and diverse that any attempt to encapsulate their interrelations is bound to fail. Their interaction is also a topic that attracts not only scientists and theologians but also an interested and concerned public. Yet contemporary discussion of religion and science is dominated by partisan writers who promote grand but simplistic theses—some proclaim science to be in perpetual conflict with religion while others posit complete harmony. Moreover, much current discussion draws heavily on such historical episodes as the Galileo affair. The historical study of religion and science has therefore an important contemporary role since it can illuminate the complexity of religion-science interrelations, place the grand popular theses in context, and inject a dose of critical analysis.

Centrality of Religion to the Scientific Revolution

Most of the major figures associated with the rise of modern science in the sixteenth and seventeenth centuries paid close attention to the religious issues and their bearing on science. Thus Francis Bacon could both advocate the separation of science from religion and stress the religious character of science, since the study of nature displayed "the footprints of the Creator." In many cases, too, religion provided the motivation for pursuing science. Johannes Kepler felt compelled to discover the harmony, order, and (ultimately) mathematical laws governing the motions of the planets by the conviction that God had created the universe on a mathematical model. Isaac Newton, who likewise saw the physical world manifesting divine design, adopted a priestly role in determining the laws that God had imposed on matter at the creation. Of the many points of contact between his science and his religion, Newton's innovative concept of "force" possessed strong theological significance since he considered all force to be derived from God. Newton's religious writings were not confined to physicotheology; he also wrote extensively on biblical chronology and prophesy. Nor were his theological views conventional; he

Artist's depiction of Italian astronomer Galileo Galilei's (1564–1642) trial for heresy by the Roman Catholic Church

tried to conceal his Socinianism (denying the divinity of Christ) in order to avoid the charge of heresy.

The Galileo affair, culminating in his censure by the Roman Catholic church in 1633, has often been portrayed as a conflict between reactionary clerics and the harbinger of scientific progress. Yet, despite the heavy-handed action of a committee of the Holy Office that prohibited Nicholas Copernicus's book, this is an untenable interpretation since not only did many church members support Galileo, especially in the 1610s and 1620s, but he himself also remained a staunch Catholic. The affair raises many substantive issues including the meaning of certain scriptural passages that might bear on astronomy, the relation of empirical knowledge to theology, and the strength of Galileo's arguments in favor of Copernicus's theory. (He failed to prove the truth of the Copernican system.) Other factors that bear directly on this episode were Galileo's ability to create enemies and his refusal to heed Cardinal Robert Bellarmine's advice to treat the Copernican system as a mathematical hypothesis and not as physical truth. Galileo can also be seen as a pawn in the vicious political struggles between the Pope, the Dominicans, and the Jesuits. More controversially, some scholars have interpreted the 1633 trial as the final act in Galileo's long-running battle over atomism with his Aristotelian opponents, who believed it challenged the doctrine of the eucharist. From this perspective the theological acceptability of Copernican astronomy was not at issue. The jury is still out, but historians continue to discover new interpretations of the Galileo affair.

Since early modern science was a product of Christians, some have argued that Christian theology provided the necessary conditions for the rise of science. In particular, Christianity specifies a rational creator who constructed a lawlike universe; these laws can, in turn, be decoded by scientists. While this argument might bear on the rise of science, it fails to explain why modern science was delayed a millennium and a half after the rise of Christianity. Likewise, in a classic article first published in 1938, the sociologist Robert K. Merton attributed the values required for the rise of science in the seventeenth century to the "Puritan ethic"—the assurance of salvation among English Protestants, which found expression in good works, science included. Science was therefore the offspring of a religious system. While his argument applies reasonably well to Britain, it makes it difficult to understand how Catholics contributed to science. Yet many eminent seventeenth-century natural philosophers were Catholic, including Galileo, René Descartes, and Marin Mersenne. Through their schools and colleges, Jesuits were particularly active in teaching modern science. The structure of the Society of Jesus also aided the acquisition of natural knowledge since Jesuits traveled widely and transmitted astronomical data and botanical specimens through their diplomatic channels.

Many of the major intellectual controversies of the seventeenth and eighteenth centuries manifested both religious and scientific dimensions. For example, in the controversy between Gottfried Leibniz and Samuel Clarke (a follower of Newton's), in 1715–1716, Leibniz criticized not only Newton's views about space, time, matter, and force, but also his theology, which emphasized God's will. This is a classic example of a controversy in which scientific and theological issues were thoroughly intermixed. Moreover, "scientists" were not pitted against "theologians"; instead different theologies and different natural philosophies clashed. It is also typical in possessing political and personal connotations,

since both Leibniz and Newton were seeking the patronage of the newly enthroned King George I.

Many of those who challenged Newton's science drew attention not only to its scientific difficulties but also to its philosophical and theological defects. For example, Newton considered space to be empty, except for widely dispersed atoms, but his critics seized on emptiness as wasteful and incompatible with a divinely planned universe in which the principle of plenitude applies. Moreover, they objected that Newton's philosophy encouraged pantheism by attributing activity to matter and thereby failing to differentiate the creation from the creator. These critics were not antiscience *per se,* but rather adopted alternative natural philosophies, such as the "scriptural physics" of John Hutchinson, which they considered truly Christian.

Local Contexts

Owing to the diversity of religious traditions, each with its own complex history, it is difficult to draw any global generalizations about science-religion interactions. We should also recognize the existence of local scientific traditions; for example, in France responses to Newton's ideas were affected by both the dominance of Catholicism and by commitments to Cartesian natural philosophy. Much recent research on science and religion has indicated the importance of specific religious and scientific traditions within local contexts. The following examples, which are drawn from English history, illustrate typical loci of science-religion interaction but are not necessarily applicable to other locations. During the eighteenth and nineteenth centuries science proved particularly attractive to religious dissenters, such as Unitarians and Quakers, who emphasized education and promoted science in their schools. For example, the Unitarian Joseph Priestley, best known for his work on gases, was connected with Warrington Academy (county of Cheshire, England) and published a number of educational works, while the Quaker schoolmaster John Dalton began research in meteorology and subsequently developed his theory of the chemical atom. There are many reasons why dissenters were attracted to science: they were not from the land-owning establishment nor did they have access to some traditional routes for social advancement. Instead they were drawn to new and precarious ventures in science and technology—thus many dissenters became prominent in key industries, such as iron smelting and later railway construction. Since dissenters could not graduate from either Oxford or Cambridge Universities until the repeal of the Test Acts in 1871, many studied abroad or in Scotland, where scientific and medical education was of a far higher standard. Thus in many British cities dissenters promoted the provision of hospitals and dispensaries for the poor. Quakers in particular gravitated to pharmacy where their reputation for honesty and their ability at networking worked to their advantage.

The audience for science increased significantly in eighteenth- and nineteenth-century Britain, with a plethora of itinerant lecturers and publications aimed at the upper, middle, and (increasingly) working classes. Often science was presented in a theological frame, a strategy that not only helped legitimate science but also conveyed its intellectually integrity. Thus signs of design, such as the webbed feet of water birds (enabling them to walk on water) or the appropriateness of the distance of the earth from the Sun (preventing the earth from being fried or frozen), were interpreted as evidence of God's wisdom, power, and good-

R

ON

THE ORIGIN OF SPECIES

BY MEANS OF NATURAL SELECTION,

OR THE

PRESERVATION OF FAVOURED RACES IN THE STRUGGLE
FOR LIFE.

By CHARLES DARWIN, M.A.,

FELLOW OF THE ROYAL, GEOLOGICAL, LINNÆAN, ETC., SOCIETIES;
AUTHOR OF ' JOURNAL OF RESEARCHES DURING H. M. S. BEAGLE'S VOYAGE
ROUND THE WORLD.'

LONDON:
JOHN MURRAY, ALBEMARLE STREET.
1859.

Title page of Charles Darwin's *On The Origin Of Species By Means of Natural Selection*, written in 1859

ness. Despite being disparaged by David Hume, design arguments remained very popular, as can be seen from the frequent reprinting of such works as John Ray's *The Wisdom of God Manifested in the Works of Creation* (1691), William Paley's *Natural Theology* (1802), and the Bridgewater Treatises of the 1830s. Design arguments performed many functions and were capable of many different modalities. They could, for example, perform an irenic function by appealing to all denominations. By demonstrating the harmony and integrity of God's creation they also functioned as a creative aesthetic. Many people who would not otherwise have known much science studied it in popular natural theology texts.

Following the French Revolution fear of a popular uprising was fuelled by the materialism and atheism associated with such leading French scientists as Pierre-Simon de Laplace, Jean-Baptiste de Lamarck, and Georges-Louis LeClerc, Comte de Buffon. Over the next few decades the "The March of the Mind," as manifested by Mechanics' Institutes, popular science lectures, and cheap books and periodicals, added to this concern. Attitudes to science became increasingly divergent in Britain. Some saw it as a legitimate hand-maiden of religion, while others conceived it as materialistic and destructive to the old social and religious order. The success of such "alternative sciences" as phrenology (often painted as materialist) and spiritualism (antimaterialist), both of which attracted large followings, further challenged the established church. Secular theories in geology and natural history likewise questioned not only the biblical narrative but also the notion of a divinely crafted

universe. By the early nineteenth century, few writers maintained a six thousand year-old Earth, most others being prepared to accept a nonliteral interpretation of Genesis.

The Challenge of Evolution

The publication of Charles Darwin's *On the Origin of Species* in 1859 drew fire from other simmering controversies. As with the Galileo affair, responses to Darwin cannot be reduced to a simple conflict between science and religion—although this interpretation was constructed and widely publicized by some of the protagonists. Historians have uncovered diverse responses from writers holding widely different religious commitments, ranging from those who tried to keep evolution at bay to those who welcomed the new theory as advancing our understanding of how God governs the universe through laws. The short-term impact of evolution on religion is difficult to determine since the "Victorian crisis of faith" had no single cause and the decline in religious observance resulted as much, if not more, from demographic changes and from the impact of such publications as *Essays and Reviews* (1860), which questioned the basis of revealed religion.

In the long term, however, evolution has been central to discussions of science and religion. The *Origin of Species* acted as a rallying point for a number of scientists who not only questioned the truth of Christian belief but also challenged the political power vested in the established church. Thomas Henry Huxley, Joseph Dalton Hooker, John Tyndall, and others—through to Richard Dawkins and Peter Atkins in our own day—have alighted on evolution as the scientific theory with considerable antireligious potential. Following the publication of Darwin's theory it became far more difficult to articulate views of special creation and the argument from design took a severe blow. Nevertheless the polarization that has occurred around evolution is not simply a result of Darwin's theory but also demonstrates the impact of social and political factors. For example, in the southern United States, evolution encountered relatively little opposition until the 1920s when it became the focus for many local grievances and the foe of fundamentalists. The 1925 trial of John Scopes, who defied the law and taught evolution in the public schools of Tennessee, has often been used to symbolize the conflict between science and religion. Opponents of "evilution" have more recently developed "creation science" as an alternative to evolutionary science. Thus they have sought to redefine the conflict between science and religion as a disagreement between two scientific theories.

Darwin's theory also fed into a much more protracted philosophical dispute that challenged Christian ontology. For many Christians, science is suspect if it implies that all phenomena can be reduced to inert matter and a set of laws. Not only does this reductionism portray the universe as inhospitable, but it removes God from nature. Materialists also deny the need for any form of creator, instead attributing natural phenomena to the properties of matter. Huxley, who coined the word "agnostic" to describe those who refused to accept a creator-God owing to lack of evidence, was an ardent materialist. Yet the most conspicuous site of conflict was the meeting of the British Association for the Advancement of Science in 1874 when Huxley's friend John Tyndall devoted his presidential address to the topic. Tyndall traced the history of materialism from the ancients to contemporary ideas about evolution, showing that the advance of science had been achieved through our increasing understanding of matter. Although Tyndall was no naive materialist or reductionist, he was widely attacked as an atheist and for supporting a thoroughly materialistic view of science.

In contrast to Tyndall, religious writers have repeatedly challenged materialism by affirming that the physical world is dependent on God—as creator and/or conserver of the world. Thus Newton asserted that if God were not in continual interaction with the universe it would simply stop, like a clock whose mechanism has run down. More recently, and in very different theological contexts, quantum theory has proved a boon to those who wish to inject mind or spirit into the universe. Scientists of a religious disposition have often been more attracted to such fields as cosmology, astronomy, and physics—as opposed to the biological sciences—where considerable scope exists for natural theological speculation.

In the second half of the nineteenth century, the Roman Catholic church implemented a number of measures that, in the eyes of its detractors and not a few of its members, made it increasingly rigid and inhospitable to new ideas, especially developments in science. Science was made subservient to theology, while scholastic philosophy and the power of the papacy were enhanced. Among the indirect reactions to this increasing conservatism was the publication in 1874 of John William Draper's *History of the Conflict between Science and Religion,* which portrayed Catholicism as the natural enemy of science. In this classic statement of the conflict thesis, science and Catholicism are two opposing forces that have been played out in history. In response to this interpretation, many Catholic scientists, historians, and theologians have tried to rescue the church by offering less antagonistic accounts of the Galileo affair. Particularly since the Second Vatican Council positions have shifted significantly and in 1979 Pope John Paul II conceded that the church had made a mistake. In 1992, following a report by the Pontifical Commission, the church acknowledged that the Galileo affair resulted from "tragic reciprocal incomprehension."

Beyond Christianity

An interesting twist to science-religion interactions has been the development of "scientism," the view that science can be extended beyond its usual disciplinary boundaries to encompass all other areas, religion included. For example, the late nineteenth-century chemist Carl Wilhelm Wolfgang Ostwald advocated a substitute religion based on contemporary scientific ideas, especially thermodynamics. He believed that his new "religion" would fulfill the psychological functions traditionally performed by Christianity, which he utterly rejected. He envisaged a secular festival that would replace Christmas at which candles would be lit and hymns sung in praise of "energy." The example of Ostwald's new religion and the many subsequent versions of scientism raise the question whether it is a religion or an antireligion.

The literature on science and religion has been dominated by writers seeking to defend or attack Christianity. Little attention has been paid to other religious traditions, which have often experienced far less difficulty in relating to mainstream science. In Judaism, for example, there has been relatively little antagonism to science. Jewish participation in science was however often limited by the civil and educational disabilities imposed by the countries in which Jews lived. Paradoxically, in the late nineteenth and early twentieth centuries Jews tended toward science since other professions were closed to them. Thus Jews made up a significant proportion of scientists, especially in German-speaking countries. Many of them were subsequently forced to leave owing first to the economic recession during the inter-war years and later to Hitler's purges. American, British, and Russian science benefited.

China developed independent scientific traditions commensurate with the religious philosophies of Buddhism and Taoism, often emphasizing human harmony with nature rather than nature's exploitation for human ends. Since the seventeenth century, there has been considerable but selective interchange of Western science and technology for alternative medical therapies. Probably the most important contemporary encounter is between Western science and Islam. Drawing on both the Koran and its early encounters with Greek science there is a strong Islamic tradition of analyzing the physical world. Yet the contemporary encounter with Western science is also deeply marked by the various politically charged responses to Western culture and capitalism.

GEOFFREY CANTOR

SCIENCE FICTION. Given the human affinity for storytelling, the rise of modern science inevitably prompted narratives involving science. One of the first writers of science fiction was Johannes Kepler, whose posthumously published *Somnium* (1634) explained and defended the heliocentric model of the solar system by describing the astronomical observations of a man transported to the Moon by demons. Unmemorable as literature, *Somnium* indicated that scientific discussions in fictional contexts might have special virtues.

Despite sporadic attention to figures like Kepler and Jonathan Swift for his satirical *Gulliver's Travels* (1726), historians of science fiction emphasize four figures of the nineteenth and early twentieth century as central to its origins and development. They accept Mary Shelley, author of *Frankenstein* (1818), as the first science fiction writer. Jules Verne achieved popular success with adventurous novels featuring new means of transportation and journeys into exotic realms. H. G. Wells effected a brilliant synthesis of earlier writers' generic models—including Shelley's Gothic horror, Verne's travel tales, Swift's satire, and Edward Bellamy's utopia *Looking Backward* (1888)—to produce several famous novels, including *The Time Machine* (1895), *The Island of Dr. Moreau* (1896), *The Invisible Man* (1897), *The War of the Worlds* (1898), and *First Men in the Moon* (1901), which established patterns for all later science fiction writ-

ers. Hugo Gernsback named the genre "science fiction" and transformed it into a recognized category of literature by editing the first science fiction magazine, *Amazing Stories,* beginning in 1926.

Despite Gernsback's lasting influence on the American variety of science fiction, not all writers and editors shared his devotion to science, and the genre expanded and diversified in magazines of the 1930s and 1940s. Like Gernsback, editor John W. Campbell, Jr., of *Astounding Science-Fiction* favored scrupulously scientific stories, or "hard science fiction," but other magazines like *Planet Stories* emphasized the subgenre of "space opera," exciting interplanetary adventures that might display little awareness of scientific realities. Such stories were also prominent in the science fiction films and television programs of the 1950s and 1960s. Despite the genre's burgeoning presence in these and other media like comic books and (later) video games, science fiction enjoyed little success in theater and radio, with exceptions like the depictions of humanoid robots in the play *R.U.R.* (1920) by Czech writer Karel Čapek and the 1938 radio adaptation of Wells's *The War of the Worlds* (1898).

After World War II, English-language science fiction dominated the world, led by major writers like Isaac Asimov, Arthur C. Clarke, Robert A. Heinlein, and Frank Herbert, all capable of crafting both realistic accounts of near-future developments and expansive visions of humanity's distant future. Science fiction that stressed literary values more than science was produced by Ray Bradbury, Kurt Vonnegut, Jr., Philip K. Dick, Ursula K. Le Guin, J. G. Ballard, Harlan Ellison, Samuel R. Delany, and other writers who sometimes labeled their work "speculative fiction." Non-English science fiction usually dwelt more on satire than on science, though intriguing speculations about alien life and technological breakthroughs came from Russia's Boris and Arkady Strugatsky, Poland's Stanislaw Lem, and Japan's Kobo Abe.

In the 1970s and afterwards, the *Star Trek* television series and *Star Wars* films brought new popularity to space opera, in print and film. New schools of science fiction emerged, including outspoken feminists led by Joanna Russ and Pamela Sargent, and "cyberpunks" like William Gibson, Bruce Sterling, and Neal Stephenson, who were fascinated by technology and committed to literary sophistication. Other distinctive new voices like Kim Stanley Robinson and Octavia E. Butler resisted easy categorization.

While science fiction has grown more variegated to appeal to wider audiences, many still believe that science fiction should have a strong relationship with the scientific community. In his essay "Old Legends" (1995), physicist and writer Gregory Benford reports that many scientists—himself, Freeman Dyson, Stephen Hawking, Edward Teller, Steven Weinberg, and researchers of the Manhattan Project and at Livermore National Laboratory—often read and discussed science fiction stories. Carl Sagan, who later advocated scientific searches for alien life, stood under the stars

Johannes Kepler (1571–1630), the German astronomer who devised the three fundamental laws of planetary motion

as a child and longed to be transported to Mars like John Carter, hero of several novels by Edgar Rice Burroughs. Leo Szilard read Wells's *The World Set Free* (1913), which first predicted atomic bombs, during the 1930s, when he was developing the idea of a chain reaction leading to an explosion. Gerald Feinberg first envisioned faster-than-light tachyons after reading "Beep" (1954) by James Blish. And following Kepler's example, some scientists, including Fred Hoyle, Marvin Minsky, Szilard, and Sagan, have moved from reading to writing science fiction.

Gernsback had expressed hopes of institutionalizing science fiction as a stimulus to scientific advances: Writers would send stories with promising ideas to magazines, experts would review submissions to ensure their scientific plausibility, and scientists reading the stories would be inspired to build new inventions. Although Gernsback's plans (which included allowing science fiction writers to patent their ideas) have been ridiculed, the notion of mining science fiction for potentially useful concepts endured. In 2000, the European Space Agency's Innovative Technologies from Science Fiction project enlisted scholars to compile ideas from futuristic stories that might lead to new scientific initiatives. A possible illustration of the process would be the artificial hands used to manipulate radioactive material, named "waldoes" to acknowledge their first appearance in Heinlein's "Waldo" (1942). The terms "astronaut," "genetic engineering," "robotics," and "terraforming" also originated in science fiction stories.

Campbell extended Gernsback's theories to suggest that development of scientific ideas in narrative form could provide scientists and policymakers with important insights not obtainable from everyday scientific activities. Campbell's suggestion might apply to works like Heinlein's "Solution Unsatisfactory" (1940) and Lester del Rey's "Nerves" (1942), which predicted not only atomic energy but also the technical and political problems it might engender.

Along with its potential power to predict future inventions and their effects (which many would argue is illusory or unimportant), science fiction may also encourage worthwhile exercise in scientific thinking. The spectacular but scientifically plausible new worlds created by masters of science fiction like Hal Clement and Larry Niven enable thoughtful readers to critique or expand upon the scientific logic deployed. When Niven posited a huge artificial ring around a star in *Ringworld* (1970), students analyzing the concept determined that such a structure would not be mechanically stable, which prompted Niven to add "stabilizing rockets" to the construct in *Ringworld Engineers* (1979). Other provocative subjects for informed scrutiny surfaced in Hoyle's *The Black Cloud* (1957), featuring an intelligent cloud traveling through space, and Robert F. Forward's *Dragon's Egg* (1980), describing the evolution of life on the surface of a neutron star. Science fiction might also be lauded for sustaining interest in the possibility of time travel during the decades when working scientists dismissed the idea as fanciful.

In addressing the general public, science fiction has affected attitudes toward science and influenced policy decisions. Gernsback hoped science fiction would educate readers about science and encourage them to support scientific progress. At times it has done so. In the 1950s, novels like Clarke's *Prelude to Space* (1951) and films like *Destination Moon* (1950) portrayed and advocated human flight into space; in the 1970s, the American government exploited the popularity of *Star Trek* to publicize the space shuttle. The National Aeronautics and Space Administration

Arthur C. Clark (1917-2008), writer and scientific visionary, pictured at his home in Sri Lanka

(NASA) named its prototypical shuttle the Enterprise after the ship in *Star Trek* and enlisted cast members for promotional films and appearances. H. Bruce Franklin's *War Stars* (1988) suggests that an American tradition of future-war novels featuring successful superweapons may have inspired Harry S. Truman to use atomic weapons.

Science fiction works have also helped to hinder or prevent scientific developments. The nightmarish scenario of a totalitarian government's employing ubiquitous surveillance technology in George Orwell's *Nineteen Eighty-Four* (1947) sparked determined efforts to prevent that future from occurring. Likening plans for space-based antimissile devices to the death rays in the space battles of *Star Wars*, opponents derided the proposals as "Star Wars" systems. And since science fiction, particularly the celluloid variety, has perpetuated stereotypical images of "mad scientists" who thoughtlessly pursue dangerous projects leading to monsters, mutations, and mayhem, researchers seeking to bioengineer new plants and animals are obliged to proceed carefully, anticipating public fears of new "Frankenstein monsters."

GARY WESTFAHL

SEISMOLOGY, a branch of geophysics, examines the behavior and products of elastic (seismic) waves traveling within the earth. Earthquakes are the most significant generators of these waves. Other sources include volcanic eruptions, explosions (including nuclear explosions), and meteorite impacts. Trucks, trains, and thunder produce seismic "noise." The discipline of seismology covers documentation of events and effects (observations, maps, catalogs), instrumentation and analysis, theory and application. Because large earthquakes can be detected worldwide, the science is international.

Since ancient civilizations arose in earthquake-prone country, a long history of observation and speculation about

A geologist at the US Geological Survey monitors seismograph readings from a recording station in California

earthquakes exists. Aristotle proposed a classification of earthquakes while the Chinese philosopher Chang Heng is credited with designing an inertial seismoscope in A.D. 132 that could determine the source direction of an earthquake. Many early treatises attributed earthquakes to the movement of air or water vapor within the earth. The role of rock fracturing in earthquake generation was not realized until the mid-nineteenth century.

The great Lisbon earthquake and tsunami (tidal wave) of 1755 mark the beginning of the systematic study of earth-

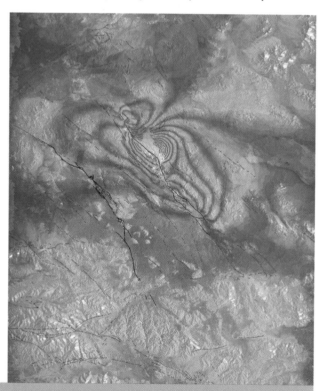

Image made from data collected by satellite radar interferometry of the earthquake at Hector Mine, California, on October 16, 1999. The colored contours indicate displacements in multiples of ten centimeters increasing toward the fault at upper center. The quake registered 7.1 on the Richter scale.

quakes in western science. For the next century or so, studies of earthquakes consisted primarily of observations of how earthquakes behaved, their geological effects, catalogs of historical events, and continued speculation about their causes. By the early eighteenth century, inertial seismoscopes in Europe included pendulums and bowls of liquid mercury. Earthquake catalogs and other regular observations of earthquakes were widely compiled. By 1840, enough information had accumulated for Karl Ernst Adolf von Hoff to produce the first global historical catalog of earthquakes.

Around 1850, seismology began to take shape as a separate field of inquiry. Robert Mallet studied the great Italian earthquake of 1857 and wrote the landmark *First Principles of Observational Seismology.* Johann J. Noggerath in 1847 first used isoseismals to map earthquake intensity, Luigi Palmieri produced an electromagnetic seismograph first used in 1856, and M. S. de Rossi and François Alphonse Forel cooperated to publish the first widely used, standardized intensity scale in 1883. By the end of the century, scientists were designing the first reliable seismographs (recording instruments). They sought ways to reduce friction between the recording needle and recording paper, to damp triggered motion in the instrument, and to eliminate local disturbance of the mechanism. In 1892, John Milne in Japan produced the first compact, simple (though still not entirely accurate) seismograph. Boris Golitsyn's galvanometric seismograph, perfected in 1911, suspended the pendulum in an electromagnetic field, but largely independently, scientists developed the basic theory of elastic wave behavior. Simeon-Denis Poisson worked out a theory for the primary and secondary (P and S) waves; George Gabriel Stokes and Lord Rayleigh made further contributions; and the effort culminated with the publication of theoretical work on surface and other seismic waves by Horace Lamb in 1906 and A. E. H. Love in 1911.

By the early twentieth century, international cooperation and the standardization of observations worldwide, including accurate timing mechanisms and travel-time tables, allowed the development of new standard scales of magnitude and detailed maps of global seismicity. Using Milne's seismograph scientists in the British empire had set up the first uniform, international network. In the 1930s, Charles Francis Richter and Beno Gutenberg developed a standard scale to measure the relative sizes of earthquake sources, commonly called the Richter scale. It is one of several magnitude scales in use today. Gutenberg and Richter also wrote textbooks that became standards in the field. Seismology figured among the founding six sections at the first meeting of the International Union of Geodesy and Geophysics (IUGG) in 1922. The International Association of Seismology and Physics of the Earth's Interior (the IASPEI), a branch of the IUGG, continues to coordinate international seismological research.

The twentieth century saw major advances in geophysics as a result of the accumulation of seismic data and analysis. In the first half of the century seismologists and geophysicists such as Gutenberg, Richter, Hugo Benioff, Inge Lehmann, Harold Jeffreys, and Francis Birch delineated the interior, layered structure of the earth. By the end of the century investigators were mapping heterogeneity in the earth's mantle and its boundaries using a method called seismic tomography. A second important spin-off followed from the more accurate location (both geographically and within the earth) of earthquake sources and the differentiation of fault motions, known as focal mechanisms. This

S

information played a major role in the development of the theory of plate tectonics. A third area of importance was the investigation of the structure of the crust itself. During World War II, Maurice Ewing and others developed the technology to make seismic investigations offshore. This allowed the mapping of layered strata beneath the sea floor. The investigation of the earth's crustal structure, at ever greater depths and resolution, has continued to the present day, particularly in the field of seismic stratigraphy.

From the 1920s on, seismology has been put to practical uses like the search for oil and gas in the subsurface by using artificial sources of elastic waves, primarily dynamite explosions. Beginning in the 1950s, seismology has been used for monitoring nuclear testing and for understanding other seismic events caused by humans such as those triggered by pumping fluids such as water or oil into or out of the ground. Volcanic seismology has improved to the point that it can help predict volcanic eruptions. While seismologists still cannot predict earthquakes with accuracy, they have done much to explore their preconditions. As human population has increased, more funding has been devoted to earthquake preparedness, including the design of structures, the education of the public, and hazard analysis. In places where the historical record of earthquakes is too short to analyze earthquake probability, workers in the field of paleoseismology use geological evidence to document prehistoric earthquakes.

Satellite and digital technology, notably the Internet, have had major effects on seismology. In 1984, a consortium of American universities founded the Incorporated Research Institutions for Seismology (IRIS) to develop, deploy, and support modern digital seismic instrumentation. By the year 2000, IRIS had more than ninety member institutions and four major programs: the Data Management System (DMS), the Global Seismographic Network (GSN), a program for the study of the continental lithosphere (PASSCAL), and an education and outreach program.

JOANNE BOURGEOIS

SEX. Societal taboos still significantly affect the dispassionate study of sex. Investigations have been discontinuous and scattered, findings contradictory, and samples small and often not directly comparable. There has been little interdisciplinary discussion.

A necessary precondition for a scientific study of sex was the perception that it had medical and social, not just individual moral, repercussions. These became more apparent as urban spaces enabled semivisible homosexual subcultures and other manifestations of "deviancy," providing many opportunities for sexual gratification away from its "legitimate" locus within marriage. By the late nineteenth century, several factors facilitated the emergence of a sexual science. These were a growing awareness of the serious consequences of venereal diseases and the role of accepted sexual mores (the "double standard") in disseminating them; anthropological reports destabilizing assumptions of one "natural" pattern of sexual behavior; increasing refusal among homosexuals to accept stigmatization, with a search for validatory models; and the influence of Darwinism and evolutionary theory in which sexual selection played the central role.

In the 1860s, Karl Heinrich Ulrichs, a German lawyer, argued from theories of embryological development that homosexuality was neither a crime nor a disease but an inborn condition whereby one individual might have characteristics of the other gender to the one externally appar-

William Howell Masters (1915–2001), American gynecologist, and his wife, psychologist Virginia E. Johnson (b. 1925), who together studied sexual activity under laboratory conditions

ent, leading to sexual desire for the same, rather than the other, sex. In the following decades, French psychologist Alfred Binet defined "fetishism," and Italian criminologist Cesare Lombroso's writings on the sexually deviant gained wide currency. The German psychiatrist Richard von Krafft-Ebing's *Psychopathia sexualis* (1886) cataloged a vast variety of deviations; recent scholarship locates him as a champion of the homosexual against the notorious Prussian Code. He listened to and learned from the numerous homosexuals of good social position who consulted him. Magnus Hirschfeld, who argued in early-twentieth-century Berlin for the rights of the "third sex," followed Krafft-Ebing's lead in an even more radical direction.

In Britain, works by self-acknowledged "inverts" such as John Addington Symonds and Edward Carpenter drew on a range of contemporary scientific discourses to reinforce their arguments that homosexuality was not a crime, a disease, a sin, or a vice but "natural" and inborn in certain individuals, even benign in its effects. Havelock Ellis, a friend and colleague of Symonds and Carpenter, gave an exhaustive review of human sexuality in his seven-volume *Studies in the Psychology of Sex* (1897–1928), displaying a grasp of several intellectual disciplines and the international literature. Other significant figures in this endeavor were the Swiss Auguste-Henri Forel and the Russian-German Iwan Bloch. Sigmund Freud took a different approach, penetrating the depths of the human psyche rather than scanning cross-cultural differences. Meanwhile biologists began to investigate the "sexual secretions" significantly later than the products of other endocrine glands. By the early 1930s, they had discovered that no male or female secretion existed; though differing in their proportions, testosterone and estrogen were found in both sexes. In the United States, a few pioneering social

Printed tables, slide rules, and scientific calculators give values for logarithms to ease multiplication and division.

scientists started to survey what people actually did. Alfred Kinsey's huge report of 1948 on the sexual life of the American male revealed the extent of the disjunction between conventional assumptions about sexual life and the doings in the bedrooms of the nation. During the following decade, William Howell Masters and Virginia E. Johnson mapped the orgasm using human subjects in the laboratory.

The advent of the AIDS-HIV epidemic directed attention to the magnitude of ignorance about human sexuality and behavioral motivation. Claims to have discovered the biological basis for sexual orientation or intellectual and behavioral differences between the sexes routinely arrive, receive widespread publicity, and soon fade. In spite of increasingly meticulous attention to the vexed questions of research methodology and problems of population sampling, surveys by social scientists on individual sexual attitudes and behavior continue to be criticized as unrepresentative, methodologically flawed, or based on deceitful responses, and therefore invalid, even though ever since Krafft-Ebing and Ellis, personal testimonies have demonstrated the mismatch between reality and conventional assumptions. As we enter the twenty-first century, sex remains an area of contested knowledge.

LESLEY A. HALL

SLIDE RULE. The slide rule served generations of scientists, engineers, and technical professionals as a quick, convenient, and portable calculating device. First devised in the seventeenth century, it achieved its widest use in the nineteenth and twentieth centuries before being rapidly eclipsed by handheld electronic calculators in the early 1970s.

The most basic of slide rules are particularly suitable for multiplication and division. With additional scales, the instrument can tackle trigonometric problems and higher-order tasks such as the extraction of roots. By modifying standard scales, formulas and constants for a myriad of special-purpose calculations can be incorporated into the design of the slide rule.

Slide rules have been made in a variety of formats, with scales arranged on straight rules, circles, cylinders, and spirals. The key ingredient common to all types is the logarithmic scale. First described by the Scottish mathematician John Napier in 1614, logarithms were quickly adopted and reformulated by his contemporaries in London. Arranged in printed tables, logarithms translated lengthy multiplications and divisions into much simpler additions and subtractions.

Edmund Gunter made the first logarithmic instrument by placing logarithmic scales on a ruler and performing calculations with the help of a pair of dividers. Introduced in 1623, the Gunter rule was soon transformed into a self-contained slide rule by the simple expedient of placing two rules side by side. Although surrounded by considerable controversy, the first to devise this arrangement was probably William Oughtred, who also invented the first slide rule in a circular format.

The slide rule stood briefly at the forefront of innovation in practical mathematics, but soon found its niche as a routine tool for particular trades and professions. Early designs for gauging, excise calculations, and carpenter's work were gradually supplemented by new applications in navigation and surveying. During the nineteenth century, the predominantly British slide rule became a genuinely international instrument. As a general-purpose calculator, its design was standardized, while the number of its specialized uses—from chemistry to monetary calculation—continuously increased.

By the middle years of the twentieth century, slide rules could be found in almost any activity requiring calculation, from engineering construction and electronics to meteorology and black-body radiation. In addition to the professional market, their use in schools created a demand for literally millions of instruments. Traditionally hand-divided on wood, slide rules appeared from the late nineteenth century in celluloid (and other plastics), bamboo, magnesium, and aluminum. New manufacturing methods such as machine dividing and printing increased the accuracy and rate of production.

While efforts were made in the late nineteenth century to produce slide rules operating to four and even five significant figures, precision remained subsidiary to ease of use, low cost, and speed. The introduction of handheld electronic calculators in the 1970s combined these benefits with high precision, and within a very few years the mass market for slide rules collapsed. Some specialist niches survive—slide rules can still be found as circular bezels on watches for aviators and divers—but most instruments are now collector's pieces.

STEPHEN JOHNSTON

SLOGANS FROM SCIENCE. "Eppure si muove" ("Still it moves"), quipped Pope John Paul II after hobbling to the podium on a new hip. He was quoting Galileo Galilei, who is said to have muttered the words after repudiating the Copernican theory under the persuasive pressure of the Inquisition. "Eppure si muove" is an example of "slogans from science," phrases born in or around science and used widely outside it.

It was a "Eureka moment" when "Newton's apple" struck young Isaac. It caused him to associate the force that drew the apple to the earth with the force that retained the moon in its orbit ("essentia non multiplicanda sine necessitate"). Two decades later, Newton had tied the universe together by gravity, without presuming to know its cause ("hypotheses non fingo"). He did know that God had to intervene now and again to keep the planets going, which God did until Pierre-Simon de Laplace showed that no intervention was necessary ("Sire, je n'ai pas besoin de cette hypothèse"). No wonder France had decided that "la République n'a pas besoin des savants."

Changing topics in a "quantum leap," we observe that although "Cogito ergo sum" may be a good test for the existence of a philosopher, it was fatal for "Buridan's ass." Nature is interested in the "survival of the fittest," not of the smartest. That makes no difference in the long run, however, since despite the vast and constant quantity of energy in the universe ("$E = mc^2$," "$E = h\nu$"), "die Entropie strebt einen Maximum zu"; not even "Maxwell's demon" can save the cosmos from "heat death." Of course, war or pollution may get us first. "Nuclear winter" would be followed by a very "silent spring," which could also be achieved by baking ("greenhouse effect") or grilling ("hole in the ozone layer") the creatures of the earth. Whether "ontogeny recapitulates phylogeny" then would not even be of academic interest. Since "ex nihilo nihil fit," there would be little comfort in knowing that "ex ovo omnia" and that life was a "double helix."

J. L. HEILBRON

SOCIAL RESPONSIBILITY IN SCIENCE requires recognition of the social, political, and cultural context and consequences of scientific activity. These consequences include potential risks to health, safety, and the environment. Social responsibility requires acknowledgement of the fact that the institutions in which scientists work also have agendas that go beyond research for the sake of research (e.g., national laboratories for defense, profit-making corporations). On the epistemological level, social responsibility involves discussion of the extent to which scientists have a privileged view of nature and ought to involve the public in decisions about the direction of research.

Between 1600 and 1750, natural philosophers and other creators or disseminators of natural knowledge did not recognize social responsibility beyond loyalty to the patrons who supported them and to devotion to the topic at hand. The patrons included wealthy individuals from the growing mercantile class like the Medicis of Florence; the state and the church seeking technical advice about draining mines and swamps, canalizing rivers, navigating oceans, mapping lands, managing forests; universities and other higher schools; and academies of science.

Between 1750 and 1920, social responsibility evolved in concert with Enlightenment thought and the expanding institutional bases of science. The Enlightenment recommended the study of nature for the advancement of human well-being. The philosophes' engine, the *Encyclopédie* of Denis Diderot and Jean d'Alembert, indicated the responsibility of savants—men of science—to rationalize arts and manufactures. On the eve of World War I, this Enlightenment tradition came together with strong scientific institutions developed in and around the universities. In public health, scientists conducted epidemiological studies, built hospitals, and planned water works and sewer systems to fight epidemics in burgeoning cities. In agriculture, they organized experimental plots and sought new hybrids, fertilizers, and methods of pest control. In the forest and along bodies of water they studied how to manage resources "scientifically" to ensure their availability for present and future generations.

After the war, scientists publicly recognized their responsibility to society. The process centralized in professional societies founded in the late nineteenth century to lobby the government to secure the privileges of recognition, licenses, and financial reward in exchange for service to the greater interests of society. Participation in the war was such a service but an equivocal one. The improvement of the means of destruction, especially chemical weapons, prompted a reevaluation of the potential human costs of research.

The economic depression of the 1930s, together with the claims of the leaders of the Soviet Union that its scientists served the interests of the masses, rather than the profit motive and the capitalist, contributed to debate about the moral and social compass of scientists. Scientists like John Desmond Bernal in his book *The Social Function of Science* (1939) asked about the impact of science on society, its role in warfare, employment, and social forecasting. The American and the British Associations for the Advancement of Science set up special sections to air these questions.

Three major arenas of scientific activity after World War II forced scientists to engage the notion of responsibility more intimately. The first concerned arms control and disarmament. In the late 1930s, physicist Leo Szilard, with the hope of slowing weapons development, urged his counterparts throughout the world not to publish nuclear research. Early in 1945 scientists in the Metallurgical Laboratory in Chicago issued the so-called Franck Report (named after the chairman of the committee that produced this memorandum, James Franck), recommending all steps possible to avoid the use of nuclear devices. In the postwar years, a large number of scientific groups condemned these new weapons as immoral. They called for a moratorium on their development, outlawing of their use, international control of materials, and sharing of knowledge. Those who spoke out against nuclear weapons included the Federation of American Scientists, the One-World-Or-None movement, and such prominent figures as Niels Bohr, Albert Einstein, and Bertrand Russell. These three and several others established the Pugwash organization, named after Pugwash, Nova Scotia, where scientists from around the world first met in 1957 to pursue verifiable arms control agreements. On behalf of Pugwash, Joseph Rotblat received the Nobel Peace Price in 1995; another arms

S

control organization, Physicians for Social Responsibility, received the Nobel Peace Prize in 1985.

The second arena raising new questions of social responsibility concerned eugenics, medicine, and other biological sciences. Eugenics, the effort to improve the hereditary quality of society, was a mainstream science. But its notorious manifestations, ranging from antimiscegenation policies and laws that barred the "unfit" from reproducing to the sterilization of tens of thousands of allegedly feeble-minded people throughout the world, and especially the horrors of National Socialist "racial hygiene," led the vast majority of scientists to decry biologically determinist arguments. The extreme determinist argument—humans are entirely the product of their genetic material, and programs to improve their circumstances are futile—reached its obscene logical endpoint in the Nazis' Final Solution and horrific experimentation on humans. Another grotesque violation of the sanctity of human life was the so-called Tuskegee experiment initiated during the 1930s. The U.S. Public Health Service observed the path of secondary and tertiary syphilis in four hundred black American males while providing no therapeutic treatment. Although a lead editorial in the *Journal of the American Medical Association* (*JAMA*) condemned the Nazi research in 1948 as totally without merit and morally bankrupt, the Tuskegee experiment continued for nearly forty years. Meanwhile the U.S. Atomic Energy Commission conducted experiments on unwitting subjects in prisons and on Army recruits. An editorial in *JAMA* in 1965 that promulgated a strict definition of informed consent forced many scientists to reconsider their obligations to society. Proper consent took precedence over data generation. This shift in values evolved into institutional commit-

ments such as research advisory committees in government, medical centers, and universities to consider potential risks before the initiation of biomedical research. By the 1990s, the Ethical, Legal and Social Implications program of the Human Genome Project incorporated the commitment to social responsibility directly in genomic research. Some scientists understood that if they did not regulate research activities from within their disciplines, public officials, responding to public concerns, might impose standards that scientists would find too restrictive.

The third major arena for issues of social responsibility concerned the research and production of new pesticides, herbicides, and fertilizers (much of which grew out of chemical weapons efforts) and the well-intended but too frequently disastrous attempts to produce new drugs and food additives, illustrated by the thalidomide birth defects of the late 1950s and early 1960s. Increasing evidence that overuse of chemicals had significant environmental and public health consequences contributed to stricter controls on the development of various chemical products and gave rise to the environmental movement in which many scientists took part.

In many countries of the postwar world, scientists' notion of their social responsibility also came to include obligations to the state in the name of the public welfare, national security, and international prestige that often superceded notions of human welfare. Many scientists have justified research as "science for its own sake," claiming that scientific activity is apolitical (even, and perhaps especially, when it is defined as patriotic). Scientists who embraced internationalist notions of human welfare frequently came under pressure to conform to national norms. In France, for example, Frédéric Joliot became the first high commissioner for atomic energy

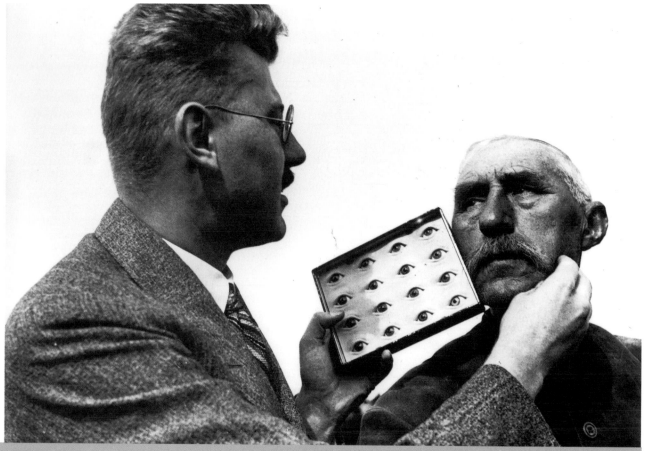

Comparison of eye shapes and colors to determine ethnic characteristics at the Institute for Anthropology of the University of Kiel, Germany

S

and directed the construction of the first French atomic pile. Yet he was relieved of his duties in 1950 because of his communist leanings. Scientists and politicians feared he might interfere with national programs to develop nuclear power.

In the Soviet Union, the notion of social responsibility was tied directly to state programs for economic growth and the production of nuclear weapons. Scientists who embraced a Western view of responsibility, such as Andrei Sakharov, and who attempted to advance the notions of academic freedom, the right of contact with foreigners, and human rights issues, usually were demoted or lost their positions. Sakharov and many others were exiled or sentenced to terms in psychiatric hospitals or labor camps.

In Germany, scientists who had been connected with the Nazi war effort—in V-2 rockets, the atomic bomb, or cruel "medical" research conducted at concentration camps—were either "denazified" or co-opted by the new governments. Denazification penalties were determined on the basis of the severity of the activities committed, the date of entry into the Nazi Party, and functions held in both state and party during the National Socialist period. In some cases, this meant prison or loss of job. But many Nazi scientists claimed they had been coerced into research and bore no responsibility for their actions. Many others were useful to German (East and West), Soviet, and American bomb and rocket programs, and willingly declared allegiance to their new states. As a result, denazification was ineffective and inconsistent, and many Nazis who were considered "rehabilitated" never addressed publicly notions of social responsibility. By the 1970s, these forces had generated significant discussion among many scientists about the need to engage society—the public, government officials, corporate leaders, university and laboratory personnel—in considering the potential risks of unregulated research and development. These scientists and engineers sought to encourage a culture in which scientists need not fear reprisals, reassignment, or dismissal for raising concerns over risky science and technology. They were involved in the creation of public interest science groups and the formation of national and international organizations to spread the cause of social responsibility. These include environmental and consumer product organizations.

PAUL R. JOSEPHSON

SOLAR PHYSICS. As with many topics in the history of astronomy, solar physics started with Isaac Newton and his *Principia mathematica* (1687). Using his new theory of gravity, the contemporary values for both the Earth-Sun and Earth-Moon distances, and the length of the year and the month, Newton calculated the Sun/Earth mass ratio. Because the Earth-Sun distance was inaccurate, Newton obtained a mass ratio that was eight times too small. By the time of the second edition of *Principia* (1715), however, a better value for the Earth-Sun distance gave the astonishing result that the Sun was about 330,000 times more massive than the earth, and 110 times larger. Doubts about why the earth should orbit the Sun and not vice versa evaporated.

Newton also concerned himself with the source of the solar energy. In his *Opticks* (1704), he often treated the "rays" of light as corpuscular. On this view, the Sun, in emitting light, lost mass. If the loss were not made good, the Sun should dwindle. For Newton, the great comet of 1680 came to the rescue. He calculated that it had passed within 250,000 km of the solar surface. Newton suggested

Image of a solar flare or prominence erupting from the chromosphere (colored orange), which lies above the sun's visible surface. The image was taken by Skylab 1.

that comets that came closer would fall into the Sun and thus provide it with new fuel and light.

Worries about the solar energy source resurfaced in the nineteenth century with the realization that the earth, and thus the Sun, had to be much older than the 6,000 years allowed by Bishop Ussher, who in the seventeenth century had calculated from Biblical chronology that creation had occurred in the last week of October 4004 B.C. Measurements by Claude-Sevais-Mathias Pouillet in 1837 of the flux of radiation passing the earth indicated that the sun had a luminosity of about 3.8×10^{26} watts. The suggestion that the sun compensated for this continuous energy loss by accreting meteorites was discarded on the realization that a mass equivalent to about 86 percent the mass of the Moon would have to hit the Sun each year, a gain that results in an unobserved annual increase in the length of the year of 1.5 seconds. In 1854, Hermann von Helmholtz suggested that the sun was contracting and thus converting potential energy into radiated energy. Even though the required rate amounted to only 91 m per year, the accumulated reduction of the Sun's diameter of 50 percent over 5 million years was regarded as untenable. The discovery of radioactivity in 1895 opened the possibility of another source of solar heating. The solution to the problem came closer with Albert Einstein's deduction of the energy equivalent of mass. The direct conversion of solar mass into energy became more plausible in the early 1920s when mass spectroscopy disclosed that four hydrogen atoms outweighed one helium atom. In the mid-1920s, spectroscopic analysis by Cecilia Payne-Gaposkin indicated that about 75 percent of the solar mass was in the form of hydrogen. Astrophysical modeling of the solar interior by Sir Arthur Eddington made the Sun gaseous throughout, and fixed the central temperature high enough, at 15 million degrees, for collisions between nuclei to lead to fusion and energy release. The physicist Hans Bethe worked out the nuclear chemical equations governing the conversion of hydrogen into helium in 1939. It became clear that the sun could produce energy at its present rate for a further 5,000 million years.

The relationship between solar astronomy and physics also appears in the problem of surface temperature. The sun's radiant power was known, but not its law of cooling.

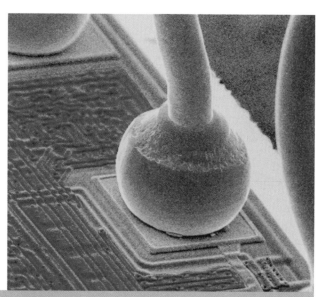

Micro-wires bonded onto a silicon chip as seen by a scanning electron microscope

Father Pietro Angeli Secchi assumed Newton's exponential formula for cooling held, and calculated in 1861 a surface temperature of 10,000,000° K. At the same time, J. M. H. E. Vicaire used the empirical power law proposed by Pierre Louis Dulong and Alexis Thérèse Petit and obtained a value of 1750° K. The introduction of Stephan's law (bodies radiate as the fourth power of their temperature) in 1879 and Wien's law in 1896 pointed to 5,770° K.

Pieter Zeeman's observation of the splitting of sunspot spectral lines enabled George Ellery Hale to measure the magnetic fields in these temporary refrigerated dark regions on the surface (1910). These fields change polarity every cycle, indicating that solar activity varied with a period of around 22 years. Harold D. Babcock and his son Horace W. Babcock used a magnetograph in the late 1940s to show how the magnetic fields of sunspots related to the general solar magnetic field. By the 1960s, the Babcocks had linked the 11-year sunspot cycle, the 22-year magnetic cycles, the magnitude of the general solar magnetic field, and the way in which the solar spin-rate varied with latitude.

Solar flares in the vicinity of bipolar spot groups lead to the ejection of clouds of plasma from the overlaying solar corona. Richard C. Carrington and Edward Sabine in the mid-nineteenth century had related the occurrences of these solar phenomena to the observations of aurorae and geomagnetic storms on Earth. It takes a day or two for the charged particles to travel between the Sun and the earth. Eugene N. Parker put forward a hydrodynamical model that explained how the continuously expanding high-temperature corona produces a solar wind that expands past the planets into interstellar space (1958).

Robert B. Leighton's high-precision Doppler spectrometry of 1960 has measured the velocity of the solar surface along the line of sight and has revealed that the whole solar surface oscillates vertically. Analysis of the modes of this oscillation allow astrophysicists to determine the conditions inside the sun.

DAVID W. HUGHES

SOLID STATE (CONDENSED MATTER) PHYSICS. The publisher's note of Galileo's last work, *Dialogues Concerning the Two New Sciences* (1638), informs the reader that the author considered "the resistance which solid bodies offer to fracture by external forces a subject of great utility, especially in the sciences and mechanical arts, and one also abounding in properties and theorems not hitherto observed." By the 1660s, Robert Hooke had discovered the proportionality of stress and strain. Notwithstanding the amazing volume of empirical data amassed by engineers and craftsmen up to the mid-seventeenth century concerning the elastic properties of materials, only in Galileo's and Hooke's work did characteristic features of what came to be known as solid state physics surface: specific assumptions to simplify calculations, which, nevertheless, express underlying physical processes and mechanisms, together with the introduction of "constants" specific to each substance.

Jakob Bernoulli initiated the mathematical study of elasticity, which his nephew Daniel Bernoulli and Leonhard Euler developed in the eighteenth century. By the middle of the nineteenth century the systematic experimental and theoretical investigations of these and other phenomena of the solid state were closely associated with engineering. Slowly the study of solids independently of the problems encountered in their practical use led to the establishment of the first laboratories devoted to work in solid state physics. The main areas of study have been elasticity, crystal structure, strength of materials, thermal and electrical conductivity in metals, thermoelectricity, optical, magnetic, and electric properties of solids, the Hall effect, low and high temperature superconductivity, incandescent lamps, semiconductors, transistors, and computer chips. The amazingly successful explanations of these phenomena rested on general theories such as electrodynamics and quantum mechanics and many new specific concepts. The development of calibration instruments, the needs for standardization, the extensive use of X-ray diffraction, and the attainment of temperatures close to absolute zero helped further to consolidate the study of solids. The discovery of the electron in 1897, the establishment of quantum theory, and, most importantly, the advent of quantum physics in 1926 provided the framework encompassing almost all of the phenomena of condensed matter physics, as solid state physics was called at the end of the twentieth century.

In 1827, Augustin-Louis Cauchy considered solids as continua and proposed a theory of elasticity involving the use of a large number of disposable parameters that could not readily be determined by experiment. The study of crystals brought about a significant change in the treatment of solids. Louis Pasteur discovered in 1848 that tartaric acid can have two distinct crystal forms, each polarizing in a different direction. He inferred that crystals acted as an aggregate of "unit cells" rather than of atoms. The shift from a strict atomic viewpoint facilitated the introduction of symmetry techniques and the understanding of a number of properties as deviations from symmetry.

In 1900, Paul Drude, using the methods of the kinetic theory of gases, showed that the quotient of thermal conductivity and electrical conductivity was proportional to the absolute temperature. This derivation of the empirical Wiedemann-Franz law rested on the assumption that the conduction electrons in a metal could be considered as a free gas. Hendrik Antoon Lorentz proceeded to refine the calculations of Drude by taking into consideration the statistical distribution of the electron velocities and their collision with what he considered to be positively charged atomic cores. His results, which differed from Drude's by a factor of 1/2, also explained other properties such as normal and anomalous dispersion of light, rotation of polarization, and the Zeeman effect.

The experimentally determined dependence of specific heats on temperature at low temperature could not be understood with the model of the free electron gas in solids. It appeared necessary either arbitrarily to reject the gas equation for free electrons or to make the number of free electrons much smaller than the number of atoms in the metals. By 1905, Walther Nernst formulated his heat theorem and surmised that as temperature goes to absolute zero, the specific heat of a body must approach a limiting value independent of the nature of the body. Experimental corroboration in 1910 of the behavior predicted by Nernst helped to consolidate Albert Einstein's treatment in 1907 of specific heats using Max Planck's radiation law.

Undoubtedly the most decisive developments concerning solid state physics resulted from the advent of quantum mechanics in 1926. The electrical conductivity of metals, paramagnetism, diamagnetism, ferromagnetism, magneto-resistance, the Hall effect, the behavior of semiconductors, and superconductivity found a satisfactory explanation within the framework of quantum mechanics. Theoretical solid state physicists faced two particularly vexing problems in their attempts to solve the wave equation in a periodic crystalline potential: the numerical solution of the Schrödinger equation for the problem and the establishment of the proper expression for the potential used in the equation, which involved approximating interelectron effects.

Long before the extensive use of digital computers, physicists developed effective numerical solutions. They handled interelectron effects by likening a solid to a periodic array of associated nuclei and their core electrons immersed in a sea of valence or conduction electrons. The treatment of conduction electrons in solids as nearly free particles occupying a series of energy bands that correspond to the electronic shells of atoms turned out to be so successful that the success itself required an explanation. Why did the electrostatic interactions among the electrons not restrict their freedom? Lev Landau showed in 1950 that a system of strongly interacting fermions (particles that, like the electron, have half-integral spin) can be regarded as a collection of "quasi-particles" resembling free fermions. This idea underlay the development of the excitation model of the solid that formally solved the puzzle of how supposedly highly correlated electrons can act as if free.

The understanding of the magnetic properties of matter remained elusive for a long time. Empirical methods and a mass of data about magnets provided sufficient information for the construction and manipulation of magnetic and magnetized materials. By 1903, Joseph John Thomson had come to consider magnetism as a property of atoms and to attribute both paramagnetism and diamagnetism to the motion of the atomic electrons under their reciprocal repulsions and the externally applied field. Pierre Curie's systematic experimental treatment of magnets and his empirical law that the magnetization of a paramagnetic body is proportional to the intensity of the magnetic field divided by the absolute temperature became the background for Paul Langevin's theory of 1905. This theory, based on ideas of Thomson and Lorentz's electrodynamics, derived para- and diamagnetism from magnetic moments arising from motion of the atomic electrons. In the late 1920s, Werner Heisenberg showed that the exchange interaction between electrons might be the key to an understanding of the success of Langevin's approach.

In 1926, Wolfgang Pauli calculated the paramagnetic susceptibility quantum mechanically on the assumption that an electron gas consists of free fermions. In contrast to the prediction of the classical treatment, Pauli found that at low temperatures the susceptibility approached a constant. Only electrons in metals within a certain small range of energy can be aligned by the magnetic field, an effect that dramatically decreases the magnetic susceptibility in metals.

The electron theory of metals was systematically developed after 1928, the year that Felix Bloch defended his doctoral dissertation under Heisenberg at the University of Leipzig. Bloch assumed that the electrons did not act on one another and that they moved freely through a lattice (the metal). A perfect lattice of identical atoms would give an infinite conductivity; electrical resistance resulted from lattice imperfections or ionic motion. Bloch also proved that if the electron Fermi distribution was in equilibrium and at rest with respect to the lattice, and if it had the same temperature as that which the lattice vibrated, then the electrons and the vibrations would be in equilibrium. In this case the motion of electrons did not have any consequences for the thermal motion in a solid. From these considerations Bloch derived a temperature dependence for electrical resistivity.

Hans Bethe's doctoral dissertation with Arnold Sommerfeld was another turning point of the electron theory of metals. He showed that electrons with negative potential energy in a metal have a larger kinetic energy inside it than outside, and concluded that the crystal shortened their wavelengths. This explained the positions of the maxima in electron-diffraction experiments, which did not agree with the predictions of the previous theory. Two additional notions associated with Bethe's close friend Rudolph Peierls—holes and band gaps—became important in understanding the conduction processes in metals. In his attempt to deal with the anomalous Hall effect, Peierls found that the Hall constant in the limit of a slightly filled energy band had the same value as that derived by the classical electron theory. In a nearly full band, it again had the value derived by the classical electron theory, but now for carriers of positive charge equal in number to the unfilled states in the band. These vacancies or holes in an otherwise full band behaved as positively charged bodies. Since, as Peierls showed, electrical conductivity vanished in the case of completely occupied bands, the holes (the negative electrons in Paul Dirac's quantum electrodynamics) became an indispensable notion for understanding the behavior of electrical insulators.

In 1934, Eugene Wigner and Frederick Seitz calculated the bands of sodium, a monovalent metal. They modeled the crystal as a network of identical cells surrounding single metallic ions and thus considered the conduction electron in each cell to be influenced only by its "own" ion's field. This calculation initiated other studies of band structures of real materials.

The nearly free electron model could not account for low temperature phenomena such as superconductivity and superfluidity or for phase transitions and critical (or collective) phenomena. Here interactions between the electrons became important. Not until after Wold War II, however, were the necessary many-body methods developed. New concepts like elementary excitations (phonons, spin waves, quasi-particles), macroscopic wave functions (long range order), order parameters and changes of symmetry in phase transitions, collective modes, low-lying excitations above the ground state, Bose-Einstein condensation, pairing, and broken symmetries played an important role in understanding these interactions. The articulation of the notion of macroscopic quantum effects, first formulated by Fritz London in 1936, brought about a deeper understanding of these phenomena.

Electronic conductivity of semiconductors and the mechanical properties of metals are controlled by minute additives of foreign atoms or by irregularities in crystalline structure. Small concentrations of defects in a largely undisturbed lattice have strong effects on macroscopic crystal phenomena such as optical properties and electrical conduction. Semiconductors (flawed crystals) became a separate class of materials and the objects of intensive research, much of it done in industrial laboratories. In one of the largest of them, Bell Laboratories in the United States, researchers invented the transistor. The contact of two crystals, one with a minute excess of electrons and the other with a predominance of holes, formed the so-called p-n junction, the basis of the transistor. The need for purer materials, the understanding of structure-dependent properties, and the introduction of specific impurities defined the possibilities of semiconductors, and led to the elucidation of their most important property, the rectifying contact that made the transistor practicable. Lasers soon followed.

Research and development in many universities and industrial research laboratories, the direct and intense interest of the military, and the profitability of the new materials and inventions based on the understanding of the many properties of the solids played a decisive role in shaping the characteristics of solid state physics. These characteristics derived from many schools of thought and experimental practices from all over the world.

Henri Poincaré (1854–1912), French mathematician and mathematical physicist, who made important contributions to the theory of relativity

The only person to have been awarded the Nobel Prize twice for the same science was John Bardeen, who shared the physics prize for his work on semiconductors and again for his work on superconductivity, in 1956 and 1972, respectively. This unique honor reflects solid state physics' idiosyncratic inheritance of diverse phenomena, intriguing problems, and miscellaneous methods.

KOSTAS GAVROGLU

SPACE AND TIME. The evolution of the modern understanding of space and time, which is closely related to the formation and development of physical sciences, can be divided into three stages dominated by Newton's absolute space and time, Minkowski's spacetime, and Einstein's spatial and temporal structures constituted by gravitational fields interacting with material bodies or other physical fields.

Absolutism

The scientific revolutionaries of the seventeenth century rejected the scholastic view of space and time as accidents of substance along with most other fundamental tenets of Aristotelianism. Against this view, which left no room for a void and assumed that time was the same everywhere at once, the revolutionaries flirted with atomism and other systems that gave space an independent existence.

Here, René Descartes took an intermediate position. Although he rejected the notion of space as an immaterial, infinite, immobile container with indistinguishable parts, he did allow it an independent, even a material, existence, by characterizing it by its extension and identifying it with matter. He thus rejected a vacuum in favor of a plenum, and deduced that motion can be transmitted only by impact, that motion of a body can be measured only relative to other bodies, and that the total motion in the universe is conserved. Conservation of motion suggested to him a principle of inertia, according to which uniform rectilinear motion is equivalent to rest, but rest requires for its definition an immobile frame of reference, which, alas, cannot be supposed within the ceaselessly moving Cartesian universe.

In forming his theory of motion, Isaac Newton recognized the importance of Descartes's principle of inertia, transformed it radically, and provided it with new conceptual foundations. By conceiving the inertia of a body not as an expression of the conservation of its motion, but as its inertness measured as its mass, Newton purchased ground for taking force, an external mover of inert matter, as a primitive entity existing independently of bodies. To give meaning to the revised notion of inertia and to make the revised law of inertia self-consistent, Newton promoted the atomists' void into a primitive entity.

If motion occurs only relatively to other bodies, immaterial and immobile space as a frame of reference is dispensable; but if absolute motion exists, then the frame of reference has to be taken as a primitive concept (absolute space). Newton adduced the motion of water in a rotating vessel as evidence of a centrifugal force generated by a rotation in absolute space. He described this space eloquently as an entity that, in its own nature, without relation to anything external, remains always similar and immovable. In the same manner, without much argument, Newton defined true time as absolute time, which, of itself and from its own nature, flows equably without relation to anything external. He understood absolute space and absolute time as attributes of God, one expressing divine omnipresence, the other divine eternity.

Newton's absolutist view of space and time came under criticism from Christiaan Huygens and Gottfried Leibniz. Huygens tried to interpret rotation as a relative motion of the parts of the rotating body, driven to different sides and in different directions, and argued that this relative motion gave the appearance of centrifugal force in Newton's bucket experiment. But this argument failed because in a rotating coordinate system, parts rest but the centrifugal force does not disappear. Leibniz employed his principles of the identity of indiscernibles and sufficient reason to dismiss Newton's absolute spatial and temporal relations and to insist, characteristically, that in Newton's homogeneous absolute space, God would have had no reason to create the world in the way he did rather than in infinitely many other ways. But since Leibniz had to accept rotation as an example of absolute motion, and offered no relational theory to accommodate it, his metaphysical arguments did not carry much force for his contemporaries.

In the two centuries after Newton, natural philosophers accepted absolute space and time as the bedrock of physical theory. The only significant challenge came from Immanuel Kant. In his influential teaching, space and time are imposed by us on the world as the ground or possibility of our intuitions of it. Kant's *a priori* view of space collapsed with the discovery of non-Euclidean geometry in the mid-nineteenth century. But his transcendental arguments about space and time as necessary prerequisites for experience was revived by Niels Bohr and many others concerned to anchor quantum physics on classical observables in space and time.

Spacetime

Newton defined absolute space in terms of the resting center of gravity of the world. However, for the validity of mechanics, any "inertial system," that is, any body moving uniformly with respect to absolute space, could serve as a reference system. The question of inertial systems in mechanics was entangled with the question of the ether, the carrier of electromagnetic waves, in the late nineteenth century. Since physicists tended to identify the ether with absolute space, they expected to be able to detect the effect of motion relative to it. The negative result of the Michelson-Morley experiment (1887) posed a puzzle, explained away by the hypothesis, suggested by George Francis FitzGerald and Hendrik Antoon Lorentz, that moving bodies, owing to their interactions with the ether, contract along their line of motion. Lorentz's explanation (1895, 1902), also proposed by Joseph Larmor in 1900, made use of a quantity they called "local time," different for different observers, which they regarded as a mathematical artifice. When local time was taken to be the real time for a moving observer, first by Henri Poincaré in 1902 and then by Albert Einstein in 1905, the absolutist notion of a single universal time collapsed, and absolute simultaneity could no longer be defined. Times and locations can be defined meaningfully only in accordance with the states of motion of inertial systems. The relation between the space and time coordinates in two inertial systems in relative motion can be obtained mathematically from the principle of relativity (physical laws take the same form in all inertial systems) and the postulate of the constancy of the speed of light, first suggested by Poincaré in 1902, without resorting to the contraction hypothesis.

In 1905, Poincaré noted that the mathematics (Lorentz transformations) that relate spatial and temporal intervals of inertial systems to another mixed spatial and temporal coordinates, but left the formula for the spacetime intervals

The Austrian physicist Ernst Mach (1838–1916) influenced the creation of the quantum theory (via Planck) and relativity (via Einstein) through his philosophy of science and ideas about space, mass, and measurement.

between events the same in all coordinate systems. Poincaré observed further that this formula behaved as if it represented a four-dimensional analogue of a line in three-dimensional space, so that the Lorentz transformations could be pictured as four-dimensional analogues of ordinary rotations. These observations suggested a complete change in the ideas of space and time to Hermann Minkowski. He conceived the relative spaces and times of inertial systems as projections of an absolute four-dimensional spacetime manifold, the true and independent stage for physical events to occur, onto the three-dimensional space of the observer. .

Absolute spacetime has richer structures than absolute space had. Most important among them is the light cone, defined at each point by the events that can be causally related to the observer and those that lie absolutely elsewhere and absolutely elsewhen. Minkowskian spacetime, together with its kinematic and causal structures, has replaced Newtonian absolute space and time and played a foundational role in all forms of relativistic dynamical theories, including quantum mechanics and quantum field theories, except for the general theory of relativity and its variations.

Dynamical Spatial and Temporal Structures

Non-Euclidean geometries make possible use of intrinsic local variations of curvature to designate positions in space without resorting to a material coordinate system and thus opened the way to a new version of absolute space. But Bernhard Riemann observed in 1854 that since the structure of physical space had to be determined by physical forces, the new notion of absolute space could not be sustained. Einstein vigorously pursued Riemann's idea in developing his general theory of relativity. Here Einstein's work shows the influence of Ernst Mach, whose program

S

of freeing science from metaphysics included ridding the world of the concept of absolute space. In 1883, he rejected Newton's crucial bucket experiment with the argument that the centrifugal forces on the water arose because of its relative motion with respect to the mass of the earth and the other celestial bodies. Mach thus replaced absolute space with the cosmic distribution of matter, which would determine the inertia of bodies and the spatial structures of local inertial systems, and thus provide dynamics with a relationist foundation.

Einstein's general relativity (1915) has a spatial structure (curvature or metric) that varies with the distribution of matter. But an interpretation of general relativity along Mach's lines ran into trouble with the discovery of the "vacuum solution" to the theory's equations, which showed that spatial structures exist in the absence of matter. Further reflection showed that any description of the properties and state of matter necessarily involves a metric as an indispensable ingredient, and thus presupposes the existence of spatial structure. Thus, although Einstein initially liked Mach's idea, which, in 1918, he raised to "Mach's Principle," he later (1953) rejected it. In his final formulation, dynamical (gravitational or metric) fields, but not masses, determined the spatiotemporal structures that grounded the dynamic behavior of everything in the world. Spacetime as a quality of the field had no independent existence.

There seems to be unanimity that spatiotemporal structures are not conventional, but specified or constituted by metric fields or their variations. Serious disagreements nevertheless persist over the ontological status of spacetime. Substantivalists ascribe spatial-temporal positions and structures directly to the individual points of a spacetime manifold, and only in a derivative sense to physical entities occupying points of the manifold; relationists claim that the spacetime characteristics of a physical entity belong to it in a primary and underived sense.

Some ardent substantivalists argue that an immovable spacetime substratum as a primitive existence has to be presumed if we wish to ground absolute motions and field theories. The relationist counters that absolute motions can be measured by deviations from geodesic motions and that chirality (right- or left-handedness), as Kant had realized, cannot be understood by reference to the points in absolute space. It is an intrinsic spacetime characteristic of physical entities and belongs to them in a primary sense.

TIAN YU CAO

SPACE SCIENCE. The term "space science" came into use in the late 1950s just after the Soviet Union launched *Sputnik I,* but it had antecedents in the 1930s, when astronomers climbed mountains to observe the heavens and meteorologists and physicists sent instruments aboard highflying balloons to study cosmic rays.

After World War II, captured German V-2 missiles and their immediate successors, like the Navy's *Viking* or the long line of Soviet missiles based upon V-2 technology, carried probes into near space to examine Earth's upper atmosphere, the nature of cosmic rays, the Sun's high-energy spectrum, and the particles and fields contained within Earth's magnetic system. After *Sputnik,* space science research relied on rockets powerful enough to send nuclear warheads ballistically to another continent or satellites into orbit. Space science identified its programs in terms of the capabilities of specific transport vehicles—balloons, aircraft, sounding rockets, satellites, and space probes.

In Britain, most of the activity in the 1950s centered on the Gassiot Committee of the Royal Society and on less formal splinter groups at major university centers. The society's members had established interests in the physics of the upper atmosphere and had followed closely the progress of the rocketry groups in the United States. Starting in 1955, they championed what became known as the *Skylark,* a sounding rocket on the scale of the American *Aerobee,* and eventually gained access to space post-Sputnik with the Ariel series of scientific satellites sent up by American vehicles. Meanwhile other British launchers were being developed—*Blue Streak* (based on preexisting military systems) and *Black Knight* (developed out of research programs)—but they did not survive as scientific launchers once Britain decided to work within an international structure.

In the United States, those who instrumented the V-2s between 1946 and 1951 came from disciplines that traditionally had not inquired into the natural phenomena they now addressed with rockets. They were practical, tool-making, problem-solving physicists and engineers experienced in building and maintaining long-range radio networks, rugged and reliable high-speed optical systems, proximity fuses for artillery shells, and radiation detectors for atomic tests. These were the skills needed to make an instrument perform delicate observations in the violently hostile realm of the rocket.

A second generation of practitioners, typically trained in the university groups that had access to rockets in the 1950s, did postdoctoral work in military laboratories. They tended to identify more with the disciplines they could address with the instruments they built than with the objects of their handiwork. Starting in the 1960s, leading academic scientists like Lyman Spitzer, Jr., at Princeton, Leo Goldberg at Harvard, John Simpson at Chicago, James van Allen at Iowa, Fred Whipple at Harvard, Charles Hard Townes at Berkeley, Joshua Lederberg at Wisconsin, William Dow at Michigan, and Joseph Kaplan at UCLA supported graduate students and assistants on contracts from NASA, the Air Force, and the Navy to develop instruments and techniques to pursue science from space.

Graduate students in astronomy were attracted to groups conducting solar physics from rockets, and became specialists in methods most suited to studying the Sun from space. Many went on to satellite-based research in the 1960s and to manned orbiting platforms in the 1980s and 1990s. As the generational cohorts established stronger and stronger interdisciplinary ties with traditional areas of research, they migrated more freely within their subject matter disciplines; generally they no longer moved from one scientific discipline to another but were attracted to problems within their discipline where they could exploit their expertise with rocket and satellite technologies.

Space science thus came to lie at the intersection of three elements: a technical capability (the use of rockets and satellites as platforms to make observations of any accessible phenomenon) with a scientific interest (framing problems that can be addressed by observations from rockets and satellites) and a military or commercial need (creating a capability to use and manage space for communication, weapon delivery systems, reconnaissance, and command and control). At the intersection, expensive, government-sponsored technologies made research in space possible.

Scientific satellite development roughly followed the growth of the launch capabilities of the vehicles. The very first American scientific satellites, those typical of the long-lived Explorer series, were single-purpose instrument

A composite image of the Chandra X-ray (blue) and Palomar infrared (red and green) observations of the supernova W49B reveals a barrel-shaped nebula consisting of bright infrared rings around intense X-radiation along the barrel's axis.

packages weighing thirty to one hundred pounds. They contained primitive telemetry systems, on-board data storage, and rudimentary temperature stabilization. By the early 1960s, spin-stabilized "observatory" class satellites (the Orbiting Solar and Geophysical Observatories) and the multifunctional but unstabilized Ariel series were flying. These satellite series coexisted throughout the 1960s and offered access to a wide range of electromagnetic phenomena from the Sun, Earth's magnetosphere, and the interplanetary medium. Dedicated sounding rockets and a few experimental high-energy satellites began to detect nonsolar X-ray sources: the first fully dedicated X-ray mapping satellite, *Uhuru*, was launched only in 1970 as the forty-second in the Explorer series.

The first of the OAO series appeared in 1968. With the OAO, in a weight class of thousands rather than hundreds of pounds, lead times crept up during the 1970s from a few to many years and began to slow the pace of training and advancement in the participating disciplines. Astronomers have called OAO-2 the first true observatory in space because the scale and resolution of its instrumentation complemented those available on the ground. It operated from December 1968 to January 1973 and could achieve a pointing accuracy as good as 1 minute of arc with a stability of some seconds of arc providing the capability to secure sustained photometric and spectroscopic data from tiny celestial sources.

In the post-Apollo era, two drivers of the American space program both propelled and severely limited the continuing development of science satellites. The primary driver was NASA's preoccupation with establishing a permanent human presence in space. As the Apollo program wound down in the wake of the successful lunar landings between 1969 and 1972, NASA decided that national goals could best be met in a reusable launch system, the Space Shuttle. Accordingly it concentrated access to space in the Shuttle bay, severely reducing or eliminating altogether suborbital and orbital programs based upon conventional launch vehicles. This had the effect of requiring even the smallest packages to be rated for human space flight, vastly increasing costs and lead times for development and testing.

At the same time, NASA's propensity for mission-based, rather than problem-based, programming drove up the scale of successive satellites. While the OAO's were flying and scientific groups tried to keep alive programs in the Explorer and smaller observatory and planetary probe classes, NASA and a vocal faction within the scientific community set their sights on a "great observatory" class of satellites, instruments that would fill the Shuttle bay and offer truly high resolution and broadband access to the faintest of celestial sources. This older class had been wildly successful beginning in the 1970s. By the end of the century, all the planets save Pluto had been visited, mapped, revisited, and, in the cases of Mars

S

and Venus, investigated by landers. In the 1980s and 1990s, however, the costs of these probes were competing directly with the great observatories like the Hubble Space Telescope, the Compton Gamma Ray Observatory, the Advanced X-Ray Astronomy Observatory (AXAF, renamed *Chandra*), and the Space Infra-Red Telescope Facility (SIRTF). Pressure mounted under competition from satellites of the European Space Agency and Japan.

For these reasons, as well as a lack of public enthusiasm for the continuation of NASA programs at the levels enjoyed in the Apollo era, American promoters of space research increasingly sought out new and more substantial modes of international cooperation at all levels, from Explorer to great observatory class. Few nations have the resources to conduct science from space. The United States from the start entertained an international program, mainly to launch instruments, and in some cases, satellites, for other countries. The Soviet Union soon followed, and all eventually recognized the need for the creation of a new international body, now the Committee on Space Research (COSPAR), that would coordinate international participation in space research. Many countries, including Great Britain, created new organizational structures to communicate with the international body. Thus, COSPAR formed and quickly assumed far broader international responsibilities.

At the same time, the United States announced that it would provide launch vehicles for COSPAR countries as its contribution to international cooperation. Initially western Europe, Great Britain, and the Commonwealth countries dominated COSPAR, with a strong representation from the United States and hardly any from the Soviet Union and Eastern Bloc. This was not satisfactory to member countries

of ICSU, and eventually the Soviet Union joined COSPAR, which thus became an important forum for international cooperation, eventually as an agency within the United Nations. Its existence, and the American offer of launch vehicles, weakened British resolve to purchase its own systems. The United States sealed the arrangement when it announced at a meeting of COSPAR in March 1959 that it would provide launch systems without charge.

The emergence of the European Space Research Organization (ESRO), and out of that the European Space Agency (ESA) in the 1960s, even with Britain's initial reluctance to join in, marked the completion of the overall structure for space science in Europe and the Americas. Led by France, ESA produced a competitive launch vehicle, *Ariane,* which prompted creation of similar-scaled vehicles in China and Japan. Thus at the beginning of the twenty-first century there exist five competing national—or, in the case of ESA, transnational—sources for placing satellites into orbit. Before the multinational armada of space probes that met Halley's Comet in the spring of 1986, the United States and Soviet Union were the only countries actively supporting interplanetary probes, landers, and orbiters. By 2000, at least four of the five major launching programs were considering new probes, orbiters, and landers.

DAVID DEVORKIN

SPECTROSCOPY is the science on the borders of chemistry and physics that studies the properties of matter by analyzing, usually prismatically, the light it emits when rendered incandescent. Spectroscopy's progress has depended on the development of the necessary equipment. It uses physical methods to study chemical phenomena. Not until a chemist and a physicist collaborated in working on spectra did spectroscopy begin to yield useful chemical knowledge.

While working to improve optical glass, Joseph von Fraunhofer found that flame spectra were characterized by discrete bright lines. He also found a number of dark lines crossing the continuous spectrum of the sun and noted that their positions did not change with intensity. These dark lines, subsequently named after him, still bear the letters he used to designate them.

While spectral lines facilitated the calibration of optical instruments, their meaning eluded satisfactory explanation for many years. The physical interpretation of the lines played a major role in the wave-particle debate over the nature of light that raged, especially in Great Britain, during the 1820s and 1830s. William Henry Fox Talbot suggested in 1826 that spectral lines might be used for chemical analysis. This idea, however, was not pursued, largely because the generally poor quality of glass prisms made it difficult to achieve replicable results, as did the impurities present in chemical substances. Attempts in the 1840s and 1850s to analyze the spectra of electric sparks also came to little, although the theory behind them favored the development of spectroscopy.

From his work on photochemistry in the 1850s, Robert Bunsen, professor of chemistry at the University of Heidelberg, became convinced that the light emitted from flames was uniquely characteristic of the chemical elements present. He pursued this idea with the school's professor of physics, Gustav Kirchhoff. Together they showed conclusively, in 1859, that a chemical element emitted a uniquely characteristic spectrum that could be used for chemical analysis.

In 1860–1861, using what was then known as spectrochemical analysis, Bunsen detected and then chemically

The spectrum of a pure element is unique to it. The spectra pictured here belong, from top to bottom, to bromine, deuterium, helium, hydrogen, krypton, mercury, neon, water vapor, and xenon.

S

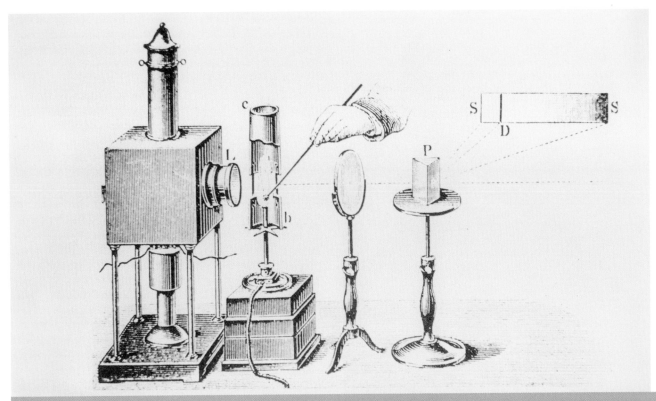

Spectroscope dating from around 1900. The illuminated specimen contains sodium, whose prominent D line is indicated in the absorption spectrum beyond the prism at P.

isolated two hitherto unknown chemical elements, cesium and rubidium, which occurred in trace quantities in mineral waters. In 1861, William Crookes in London discovered the chemical element thallium using spectrochemical methods. These discoveries placed the new method on a secure evidential basis. Furthermore, they helped popularize knowledge of the new method and to arouse widespread interest. In 1865, August Wilhelm von Hofmann demonstrated spectroscopy to Queen Victoria at Windsor. Thus publicized, the method quickly became established as an invaluable laboratory technique.

During the same period, Bunsen also collaborated with Kirchhoff to show experimentally that the bright yellow lines characteristic of sodium corresponded with Fraunhofer's dark D lines in the solar spectrum. Kirchhoff provided a thermodynamic explanation of the coincidence. This extension of chemical analysis to the sun and stars (entities that the French philosopher Auguste Comte had pointed to in 1835 as examples of things forever unknowable) led to the new science of astrophysics. In the ensuing decades, spectroscopic observations allowed astronomers to develop theories of the evolutionary sequence of stars. Measurements made in the late 1890s on the spectrum of cavity radiation prompted Max Planck's quantum theory. Somewhat later, using the measurements and analyses of the distribution of lines emitted by particular elements, physicists began to investigate the internal composition of matter, leading to Niels Bohr's theories of atomic structure. The discovery of the diffraction of X rays in 1911 led to high-frequency spectroscopy with crystals rather than glass prisms as analyzers, and to important information about the deeper reaches of atoms.

The obvious benefit of the spectroscope to a wide range of scientific and technical activities prompted its commercial manufacture by a large number of instrument makers throughout Europe. The instrument was refined and developed during the late nineteenth century by substitut-

ing diffraction gratings or hollow prisms filled with carbon bisulphide for the glass prism. Some spectroscopes had prisms so arranged that they appeared to resemble telescopes. The basic principles and uses of the spectroscope did not undergo any fundamental change until the invention of the mass spectrograph in 1919.

FRANK A. J. L. JAMES

SPONTANEOUS GENERATION. "Spontaneous" or "equivocal" generation denotes the widespread belief in the production without parents and by chance of living beings either from decomposing living matter (heterogenesis) or from nonliving matter (abiogenesis). This belief, which dates back to ancient times, has often taken the form of sophisticated doctrines related either to the generation of specific living beings like insects, infusoria, and bacteria, or to the origin of life itself.

Like the ancients, most authors of the seventeenth century believed that flies sprang from rotting meat. By experiments and microscopic observations Francesco Redi demonstrated that the maggots observed in rotting meat came from eggs laid by flies (*Esperienze intorno alla generazione degl'insetti*, 1668). Jan Swammerdam and Marcello Malpighi, who showed that plant galls also resulted from insect eggs, confirmed Redi's results.

Although the microscopist John Turberville Needham (1713–1781) explicitly rejected the doctrine of equivocal generation, his complex theory of generation by vegetation seemed to most of his contemporaries and successors to support it. He carried out observations on the animalcules arising in infusions and explained their generation as the result of the decomposition of living matter, which released "active" forces able to produce new "vegetations" (*Nouvelles observations microscopiques*, 1750). In 1765, Lazzaro Spallanzani argued against Needham's active forces, proposing instead that the animalcules were true animals

Lazzaro Spallanzani (1729–1799), Italian naturalist

generated from eggs present in the air that contaminated the infusions. By repeating Needham's experiments with sealed and heated infusions, Spallanzani showed that if boiled infusions were placed in previously heated hermetic flasks to destroy all existing eggs, no animalcules would be generated. By contrast, if air entered the flasks animalcules proliferated.

Between 1858 and 1864, a fresh controversy took place in France. Félix-Archimède Pouchet claimed that airborne contamination of infusions was unlikely because he had rarely found spores and living particles in air. Therefore only spontaneous generation could account for the microorganisms found in infusions (*Hétérogénie,* 1859). Stimulated by the debate begun by Puchet, Louis Pasteur filtered air with an instrument of his own making and concluded that air did contain microorganisms and that flasks with sterilized sugared yeast water remained sterile if not contaminated by it.

At the same time that the doctrine of spontaneous generation seemed to have been finally superseded by the postulate that life could only be transmitted by preexisting life, some evolutionists posed the question of the origin of life in general from nonliving matter. New terms were introduced to indicate the passage from ordinary to living matter: "abiogenesis" by Thomas Henry Huxley, "archeobiosis" by Henry Charlton Bastian, and "Urzeugung" (primordial generation) by many German authors. According to August Weismann, spontaneous generation was a logical necessity notwithstanding the failures to demonstrate it. In 1924, the Russian biochemist Aleksandr Oparin argued that life did not arise immediately but slowly emerged from a long-term chemical evolution. His ideas, expressed in many widely circulating books, received near-universal acceptance.

RENATO G. MAZZOLINI

STANDARD MODEL. During the 1980s, physicists who worked on elementary particles came to agree that matter consists of three pairs of leptons—very light and even weightless particles—and their antiparticles (of which electrons and their corresponding neutrinos are the exemplars) and three pairs of quarks and their antiparticles (of which protons, neutrons, and other heavy particles, or "baryons," are made). So much for the bricks. The mortar that holds the quarks together (the "strong force") comes in eight kinds of "gluons"; the cement that binds leptons to one another and to quarks (the "electroweak force") consists of the photon (the electrical part of the force) and three adhesives, W^+, W^-, and Z^0 (the weak part). The detection of the W and Z particles and the top quark in 1982–1983 completed the experimental identification of the elements of the standard model. The successes of this model gave impetus to Grand Unified Theories (GUTs), intended to unify the strong and electroweak forces, and to dreams of Theories of Everything (TOEs).

Some particle physicists, notably Steven Weinberg (who won the Nobel Prize in physics in 1979), have asserted that now that the guts of GUTs are in place, the final TOE will soon follow. A glance at earlier claimants to the status of "standard model" does not give cause for confidence in his prediction. To go back no further than 1800, the system of imponderables developed by Pierre-Simon de Laplace and his school seemed capable of describing all the phenomena then known in the same terms (though not the same language): several leptons (the weightless "fluids" of electricity, magnetism, heat, light, and so on), a baryon (the particles of "common matter"), and forces of attraction and repulsion. Many natural philosophers looked forward to a unified theory that would connect the various "fluids" (leptons), a project encouraged by the discoveries of radiant heat and electromagnetism. But with difficulties in the theory of heat and new fashions in science, the imponderable fluids evaporated. A new standard model was drawn up, based on the unification of light with electromagnetism, heat with kinetic energy, and magnetism with vortical motion, which strove to manage with one sort of material substrate, or ether, subject to the laws of mechanics. In the most austere of these GUTs, the "vortex atom," developed especially by William Thomson (Lord Kelvin), James Clerk Maxwell, and Joseph John Thomson, all physical phenomena were to be referred to motions of a single, perfect, incompressible space-filling medium.

The program of mechanical reduction, the standard model of the late nineteenth century, collapsed under experimental discoveries and difficulties in the theories of radiant heat and electrodynamics. The discovery of the electron and subsequent speculation about atomic structure suggested that matter might be built from three ingredients: in today's language, a negative lepton (electron), a positive baryon (proton), and, after the Compton effect, a neutral photon. But the study of the nucleus and cosmic rays between the world wars, and the building of ever more powerful accelerators after World War II, revealed many more "particles" than three. The gigantic instrumental and theoretical effort to classify and comprehend this cornucopia resulted in the standard model of the 1980s.

Like the decuplet of five pairs of twin brothers who ruled Atlantis, the standard model with its three pairs of leptons, eight gluons, and so on, will slip into the sea. Its place may be taken by uncountable numbers of unimaginably small, wriggling, vibrating bits, as in string theory, the latest candidate for the Theory of Everything.

J. L. HEILBRON

S

STEREOCHEMISTRY. Although the founder of the atomic theory, John Dalton, speculated about the three-dimensional arrangements of atoms within molecules, chemists customarily specified formulas without any indication of the structure of molecules, much less the arrangements of their atoms in space, until the 1850s.

Jean-Baptiste Biot noted in 1811 that quartz crystals were "optically active;" when he directed polarized light through them, the plane of polarization rotated. This asymmetrical effect on light suggested that the atoms of the crystals might be arrayed asymmetrically. Further studies revealed that certain organic materials were also optically active, even in solution. Since a dissolved substance cannot have a crystal array of any sort, the asymmetry in these instances had to inhere in each molecule.

In his first important scientific investigation (1848), Louis Pasteur studied the crystal structures of the salts of the optically active tartaric acid and of an isomeric substance, the optically inactive "racemic" acid. He discovered that a certain racemate salt consisted of intermixed crystals, all of which appeared to be identical. More careful examination, however, revealed minute differences of form, from which Pasteur could distinguish mirror-image pairs of crystals, half right-handed and half left-handed. Separating them painstakingly by hand, Pasteur showed that the two mirror-image crystals rotated polarized light in equal but opposite directions. It was then clear that the natural racemate was optically inactive only because the two kinds of crystals were normally present in equal numbers, canceling out each other's activities. The artificially separated right-handed racemate was identical in optical activity to the naturally active tartrate.

Pasteur's research gave impetus to the chemical study of the three-dimensional structure of molecules (later called "stereochemistry"), but real progress came only after the formulation of the theory of chemical structure (1858), when chemists first began to have confidence in their ability to discern molecular architecture. The chief architect, August Kekulé, regarded designing molecules in three dimensions as still too difficult, hence premature. Kekulé proposed that every carbon atom could form bonds to precisely four other atoms—that it was tetravalent. In this way carbon atoms could link up together to form chains, the backbones of organic molecules.

A Dutch student of Kekulé's, Jacobus Henricus van't Hoff, provided the first substantial development of stereochemistry in 1874. (Entirely independently, a Frenchman, Joseph Le Bel, published a substantially similar exposition just two months later. Curiously, the two men had studied together with the noted Parisian chemist Adolphe Wurtz earlier that year, but apparently owed nothing to one another.) Van't Hoff taught that the four bonds of the carbon atom should be positioned as far apart from each other as possible, or (equivalently) that they be symmetrically situated in space. Uniform distribution of four bonds coming from a central point in two dimensions would place them at right angles, but in three dimensions they would have to be arranged tetrahedrally, with angles of about 109 degrees between adjacent bonds.

Van't Hoff demonstrated the empirical power of this purely theoretical idea by referring to the numbers of isomers known for various formulas. If carbon compounds were flat, there would have to be many more isomers than chemists had found to date. If carbon bonds formed symmetrically in three dimensions, on the other hand, the predicted isomer numbers matched those known. A crucial case emerged whenever the four groups attached to a given carbon atom were all different. Van't Hoff showed that in the tetrahedral bonding situation, exactly two different

John Ellis (b. 1946), a British theoretical physicist, helped to unify string theory and the standard model, and coined the phrase, "Theory of Everything," on which he appears to be working here.

Polarized-light micrograph of crystals of tartaric acid, one of a pair of compounds that gave rise to the concept of molecular isomerism

arrangements of the four groups in the form of nonsuperimposable mirror images would be possible. One of these molecules would be right-handed, the other left-handed. An organic molecule with such asymmetry should normally exhibit optical activity.

And so it was, at least to a first approximation. The accepted formula of Pasteur's tartaric acid showed the presence of two asymmetric carbons. The two possible mirror-image formulas centered on one of these atoms suggested the existence of a right- and left-handed version of the acid. Such "optical" isomers became known as "enantiomers," and any equal mixture of two enantiomers became known in the general case as a "racemic mixture." After a decade of hesitation, most chemists accepted the van't Hoff-Le Bel theory, and began to pursue the new field of stereochemistry with enthusiasm.

The earliest supporter of van't Hoff had been the Leipzig chemist Johannes Wislicenus. In 1887, Wislicenus published a pathbreaking study of what he called "geometric" isomerism, a kind of stereoisomerism not related to optical activity. In Heidelberg, Victor Meyer (who coined the term "stereochemistry") demonstrated the chemical effect of large space-filling groups on organic molecules; he called this phenomenon "steric hindrance." In Zurich, Arthur Hantzsch and Alfred Werner investigated the stereochemistry of organic compounds containing nitrogen, and Werner later applied stereochemical precepts to the chemistry of inorganic coordination compounds. Emil Fischer in Berlin used stereochemistry to interpret his fundamental research on carbohydrates.

These examples only highlight the vigorous activity in the new field toward the end of the century. In the next generations, many new ideas and research programs appeared alongside established ones. From early important work by Adolf von Baeyer on the stereochemical analysis of cyclic organic compounds came a substantial research program on "conformational analysis." Other chemists showed that Meyer's phenomenon of steric hindrance gave rise not just to stereoisomers, but in certain circumstances to optical activity. The problems of determining not just the relative, but the absolute configurations of atoms have been solved. The stereochemistry of ever more complex natural products was slowly unraveled. Today, chemists talk about the orientation of invisibly small atoms in space as comfortably as they talk about directions on a street map.

A. J. ROCKE

STRATIGRAPHY AND GEOCHRONOLOGY. The principles of stratigraphy—the study of the earth's strata or layers of sedimentary rock—and of geochronology—the naming and describing, though not necessarily dating, of the periods of earth history—were established rapidly between 1810 and 1840. For the next century, stratigraphers filled

Looking southwest from Bright Angel Point at Grand Canyon National Park.

S

in the details of the stratigraphic column with ever-greater precision. Much of this research could be put to good use by the mining industry, and from the 1920s and 1930s by the petroleum industry.

Although stratigraphy flowered in the first half of the nineteenth century, it had its roots in the seventeenth century. The Danish Cartesian Niels Stensen (or Steno), in his *Produmus to a Dissertation on Solids Naturally Contained within Solids* (1669), considered bodies that made up the earth, particularly fossils, crystals, and strata. In any sequence of undisturbed strata, he concluded, the oldest strata would be on the bottom and the youngest on the top. This was an early version of the first of the three major principles of stratigraphy—the principle of superposition.

The second principle—that rock types or lithology usually occur in a predictable sequence—followed from the work of eighteenth-century mineralogists in the German states, Italy, France, the British Isles, and Russia. Independently of one another, they became convinced that the strata of the earth occurred in the same order everywhere. On the small scale, they knew that in an individual mining area, for example, they would find the same rocks in the same sequence in adjoining shafts. On a grander scale, they believed that around the globe, the rocks could be sorted into three main groups that appeared to represent a time sequence: the primary rocks, hard and often crystalline; the secondary rocks, softer, layered, and often fossiliferous; and the tertiary rocks, the topmost and softest rocks. Unfortunately, the principle of superposition failed when strata had been disturbed subsequent to deposition, and the principle of lithological regularity broke down when rocks of the same lithology occurred more than once in the sequence.

By the second decade of the nineteenth century, the third principle of stratigraphy—that fossils can be used to identify and correlate strata—had been established. For the next century and a half, paleontology was to be chiefly a tool for stratigraphy. Armed with these three principles, geologists between 1820 and 1840 established and named the greater part of the stratigraphic column, an accomplishment that has held up in outline to the present day. In practice, it involved one controversy after another about particular puzzles in the sequence. The British played a large part, perhaps because the strata of England are relatively straightforward.

In 1815, a mineral surveyor, William Smith, had published a map of the strata of England that although not fully correct, made a good start. Charles Lyell gave names to the epochs of the Tertiary—Pleistocene, Pliocene, Miocene, and Eocene—and distinguished them by their proportion of still extant fossils. Adam Sedgwick renamed the older part of the Secondary formations, the Paleozoic. With Roderick Murchison, he introduced the names Cambrian, Silurian, and Devonian. The Carboniferous and the renaming of the upper part of the older Secondary Mesozoic were English suggestions. The renaming gave birth to Permian (another Murchison coinage), Triassic (a German suggestion), Jurassic (largely French), and Cretaceous (Belgian). The establishment of geochronology was a magnificent achievement. Museum panoramas and book illustrations showing the development of life forms still encapsulate what the general public understands by geology.

More important within professional geology were stratigraphic maps, topographic maps colored to show the strata that outcrop at the surface of the earth. Geological mapping developed with great speed between the 1780s and the 1830s when most of the techniques employed until World War II were at hand. As cartography progressed and accurate topographic base maps that showed change of elevation by contours became more widely available, the task of making geological maps became easier. Stratigraphers used maps both as a record of their fieldwork and as a way to extract new information. Using them in conjunction with the stratigraphic column—a theoretical reconstruction of the strata arranged according to age—and the section—the vertical arrangement of strata along some line or traverse across the surface of the map—they could construct a mental picture of the three-dimensional structure of the strata and thus predict what would be found beneath any spot on the earth's surface.

Until the 1950s, most geological education gave priority to teaching students to construct and interpret maps, and professional stratigraphers were largely occupied with mapping the earth's surface. During the nineteenth century, they extended their mapping beyond northwestern Europe. They resolved problems about the Cambrian-Silurian boundary by introducing the Ordovician Period. American stratigraphers found that the Carboniferous did not work well for their territory, and replaced it with Mississippian and Pennsylvanian. The Canadians began trying to make sense of the afossiliferous pre-Cambrian rocks that made up much of their country.

Stratigraphers saw themselves as men who traveled widely, scaling mountains and descending mines, hammer, notebook, and map in hand, returning to their bases with packages of fossils and rocks to add to growing collections. Some were independently wealthy, but most found employment in universities and national geological surveys. In 1878, at the first International Geological Congress in Paris, they began the huge task of codifying stratigraphic nomenclature, a task that still continues.

Stratigraphers puzzled about how to reconcile the distinct breaks in the fossil record with the gradual changes predicted by evolutionary theory, writing at length about how elevation and erosion had destroyed part of the record. They worried that fossils might indicate changes in the environment of deposition rather than in the time of deposition. Walking through a gorge with sloping strata might be a walk through time or it might be a walk through space, from the deep ocean to a continental shelf to a brackish delta. With the growth of the petroleum industry, further subdividing the stratigraphic sequence became a necessity. New tools were developed, such as well logs and microscopical examination of microfossils, particularly foraminifera.

By World War II, the intellectual excitement in stratigraphy had evaporated. It revived after the war when stratigraphy was subsumed under the earth sciences, with their host of new concepts and sophisticated instruments.

RACHEL LAUDAN

SUPERNOVA. Supernovae have been observed on several occasions, recently and spectacularly in 1885, when Ernst Hartwig saw a new star brighten the Andromeda galaxy by 25 percent. Six months later this supernova was ten thousand times fainter.

In 1911, the American astronomer Edward Charles Pickering differentiated between low-energy novae, often seen in the Milky Way galaxy, and novae seen in distant nebulae like Andromeda. By 1919, Knut Lundmark had realized that low-energy novae occurred commonly, whereas the brighter novae, up to tens of thousands times more luminous, occurred rarely. The 1920s saw two theories of these

Image of the Crab nebula (M1), a remanent of the supernova seen on earth in 1054 A.D.
The picture comes from data collected by the Hubble Telescope.

brighter novae (named "supernovae" by Fritz Zwicky and Walter Baade in 1934), one relying on runaway instabilities in stellar interiors, the other (by Alexander William Bickerton) suggesting that collisions had occurred between stars.

Zwicky started the first supernova detection patrol in 1933; J. J. Johnson joined him in 1936. Using the new 45-cm Palomar Schmidt Telescope they found twelve new supernovae in three years based on 1625 photographs of 175 extragalactic regions. The new 1.2-m Palomar Schmidt came into use after 1958, and by 1977 the supernova tally had reached 450.

In 1981, Gustav Tammann estimated that around three supernovae occurred every century in the Milky Way galaxy. Most go undetected due to obscuring interstellar material. During the last millennium local supernovae were detected only in 1006, 1054, 1572, 1604, and 1667.

The Taurus supernova of 1054 was extensively recorded in the East, being visible in daylight and reaching -5 in the magnitude scale. (The magnitude scale is a logarithmic scale of stellar brightness in which the brightest naked eye star is of magnitude 1, the faintest of magnitude 6. Hence, a negative magnitude denotes a body that is brighter than the brightest naked-eye star.) John Bevis discovered the expanding cloud of material that resulted in 1731. In 1758, Charles Messier labeled the cloud Ml, the first entry in his catalogue of nebulae. By 1937, OH, O III, N II, and SII emission lines (spectral lines emitted by excited atoms as they decay) had been found in the cloud. Owing to the large expansion velocity produced by the stellar explosion, the emission lines were particularly broad. After 1948, astronomers found several supernova radio sources.

In 1934, two years after the discovery of the neutron, Baade and Zwicky suggested that supernovae arose when giant stars became neutron stars. Their view became generally accepted after Jocelyn Bell Burnell discovered pulsars in 1967. The Crab Nebula pulsar came to light in 1969.

Over 120 supernova remnants have been discovered in the Milky Way. One type, exemplified by Cassiopeia A and the Veil nebula in Cygnus, has a ring-like structure. Others are irregular with a central brightening, like the Crab.

In the mid-1950s, astronomers recognized two supernova varieties. Type I are binary white dwarfs. Mass accretion, pushing the star beyond the Chandrasekhar limit, triggers a wave of nuclear reactions and a flood of neutrinos, either destroying the star completely or leaving behind a neutron star. Type II results from the explosion of a young, massive giant star that has exhausted its nuclear fuel. In February 1987 a Type II supernova exploded nearby, in the Large Magellanic Cloud. The pre-nova star was a supergiant. In exploding, its brightness increased by 10^8 in a few hours. The visible energy release of 10^{44} joules was dwarfed by the 10^{46} joules of high-energy neutrinos, many of which were captured by atomic nuclei thus manufacturing elements heavier than iron. The explosion scattered these elements far and wide throughout the galaxy.

DAVID W. HUGHES

SYMPATHY AND OCCULT QUALITY. Aristotelian physics was strong on classification (four elements, four causes, types of motion, categories of being) but weak on dynamics (generation, corruption, physical interaction). Bodies acted on one another primarily through the "manifest active qualities" of the elements predominating in their constitutions: hotness, coldness, dryness, and moistness. Thus, to take a complicated example used by Aristotle, the sun melts wax and dries mud, the different consequences of the same manifest quality (hotness) depending on the elementary makeup of the recipient body. Two other widespread attributes of matter, gravity and levity, were often treated as if they were manifest qualities, since they characterized the four elements even though they could not be reduced to the tangible qualities hotness, coldness, and so forth, to which Aristotle gave priority.

The world has many physical properties less widely encountered than gravity and levity but, like them, not easily or obviously explainable in terms of the action of manifest qualities. Later Peripatetic philosophy designated these properties "occult," because, although evident in their consequences, their causes were hidden. The exemplar of an occult quality was magnetism. The ancients knew it as the ability of a peculiar rock to draw bits of iron to it—but why only iron? The answer lay, according to the natural philosophy taught when Galileo was in school, in an innate sympathy or harmony between lodestones and iron. This example indicates the level of explanation that, in the seventeenth century, made "occult" a byword for nonsense. Originally an expression that aided the classification of properties whose causes were provisionally unknown, the occult became a trash heap of innate and irreducible qualities. A purge or poison, the deadly glance of the basilisk, astrological influences, the powers of talismans, and the force by which that small pesky fish, the remora, stops big ships—all operated by occult sympathies and antipathies between agent and recipient. Molière neatly satirized the level of explanation afforded by the occult in his *Malade imaginaire* (1673), in which he praises a doctor for ascribing the soporific quality of opium to an occult "dormative virtue."

The mechanical philosophy, especially in its radical form of René Descartes's limitation of the affections of matter to extension, shape, and motion, appealed to the scientific revolutionaries of the seventeenth century because it

annihilated the complex of qualities taught by the traditional philosophy they opposed. Even manifest qualities had to go; the hot, cold, moist, and dry became secondary effects arising from the interaction of the few primary qualities of extended, moving, material bits with the human sensory apparatus. Explanations in mechanical terms, like Descartes's referral of thunder and lightning, and rains of blood, to the precipitous fall of one cloud on another, might appear no more persuasive than magnetic sympathies; nonetheless, the corpuscular philosophy, by seeking a mechanical account of properties held by its opponents to be innate and irreducible, opened the possibility of further analysis. Robert Boyle's concept of the "spring of the air," for which he offered several mechanical analogies, and Descartes's representation of magnetism by a vortex of specially shaped particles, suggest the range and limitations of seventeenth-century mechanical models.

Against the rhetorical and explanatory advantages of the corpuscular philosophy, Isaac Newton's apparent invocation of an occult sympathy—the "universal attraction" of the *Principia* (1687)—seemed retrograde to many natural philosophers enlightened by Descartes. They were both right and wrong. Newton did return to an occult quality, but in its most useful and responsible form: a widespread property of matter, exactly described, whose cause had not yet been found. Newton's famous phrase "hypotheses non fingo" ("I feign no hypotheses") meant that, as far as he was concerned, gravity would remain occult. Until we have a Theory of Everything, and perhaps even then, scientists necessarily will continue to invoke occult qualities.

J. L. HEILBRON

Bene qui latuit, bene vixit

René Descartes (1596–1650), French mathematician and philosopher, whose mechanical world picture had no place for occult qualities

TELESCOPE. Lenses for reading were available in Italy in the thirteenth century, but not until the seventeenth century did spectacle makers in the Netherlands put together a device "by means of which all things at a very great distance can be seen as if they were nearby." In 1609, Galileo Galilei heard rumors of spyglasses, made more powerful ones, and pointed them at the heavens. In 1611, Johannes Kepler explained the path of light rays through lenses and the formation of images. The improved Kepler telescope formed images in its focal plane, where they were viewed by a magnifying lens.

Anything placed in the focal plane of a telescope appears sharply alongside the celestial object, as the Englishman William Gascoigne noticed in about 1640 when a spider spun its web inside his instrument. Astronomers inserted cross hairs, facilitating precise alignment of telescopes on objects, and micrometers, to measure small angular distances and diameters. They also developed, though more slowly, stable, precise mountings and large arcs with precisely divided and marked scales against which the telescope's alignment could be noted when pointed at a celestial object. Still their instruments suffered from chromatic and spherical "aberrations"—fuzziness of the image—arising from the

The one-arm Estonian-German optical engineer Bernhard Voldemar Schmidt (1879–1935), known for the design of the Schmidt telescope, in which a glass corrector plate of complicated figure placed in front of the primary mirror creates an instrument almost free from optical aberrations. Usually used as a camera, the Schmidt telescope revolutionized optical astronomy.

fact that different wavelengths or colors of light are refracted by different amounts, and light incident on the periphery of the lens focuses closer to the lens than does light striking near the center. To reduce the aberrations, astronomers ground lenses with very long focal lengths, which led to long and unwieldy instruments. In 1757, the Englishman John Dollond perfected the achromat, a combination of glass lenses that brought rays of different colors to the same focus, enabling more precise measurements of positions of faint stars by means of shorter instruments easier to use. Inability to make large pieces of optical-quality glass, however, limited the size of refracting telescopes, in which light passes through transparent lenses.

In 1668, Isaac Newton, having decided that chromatic aberration in lenses could not be defeated, built the first successful reflecting telescope. It employed a concave mirror to collect light and form the image. William Herschel in England built telescopes with large reflecting metal mirrors in the 1780s and William Parsons in Ireland built the 6-foot "Leviathan of Parsonstown" in 1845. Giant reflectors, though producing spectacular observations, ultimately were disappointing: the mirrors flexed under their immense weights and tarnished quickly.

The second half of the nineteenth century saw advances in refracting telescopes, especially by the Boston firm of Alvan Clark and Sons. Their metal tubes were stiffer yet lighter than wooden telescopes. Larger pieces of optical glass were now available, from France and England, and five times the Clarks figured the lens for the world's largest refracting telescope, culminating in a 40-inch lens in 1897. It is yet to be surpassed in size. Larger pieces of optical glass are difficult to cast; heavier lenses flex more; and thicker lenses absorb more light.

Lenses also absorb strongly in the blue region of the spectrum, where photography is most effective. A new interest in astrophysics and distant stars required a new technology. George Willis Ritchey made the photographic reflecting telescope the basic instrument of astronomical research, constructing at the Mount Wilson Observatory a 60-inch telescope in 1908 and a 100-inch in 1918. Later the Rockefeller Foundation paid for a 200-inch reflecting telescope at nearby Mount Palomar. Corning Glass Works cast the mirror in 1934 as a thin piece of Pyrex glass with a system of ribbing in the back. Grinding the lens removed five tons of material, leaving sixteen tons of curved mirror, which received its reflective coating of aluminum in 1949.

To circumvent the problems of casting and supporting large mirrors, many small mirrors can be assembled into a close array. The Keck Telescope, erected in Hawaii in 1993, has thirty-six 1-meter mirrors mounted together on a tracking structure, and the European Southern Observatory in Chile links four 8-meter and three 1.8-meter mirrors into one very large telescope. Its huge cost is shared among nine countries.

Reflecting telescopes bring only rays from stars in the center of the viewing field to a sharp focus. Given a usable field of view of 15 seconds of arc, approximately a million photographic plates would be required to cover the entire sky. In 1930, Bernhard Schmidt, an Estonian-born optician at the Hamburg Observatory, designed a reflecting telescope with a usable field of view of 15 degrees. The Schmidt telescope has a simple spherical mirror plus a thin correction plate for spherical aberration. Palomar completed a 1.2-meter Schmidt telescope in 1948.

Non-optical telescopes can detect radio and gravitational waves unblocked by the earth's atmosphere. Other non-optical telescopes rise above the earth's atmosphere. There X rays incident on mirrors at small "grazing angles" are reflected into a detector, where their interaction with an inert gas generates countable electrons. The telescope, with several mirror surfaces nested concentrically within it, looks like a funnel. Telescopes in space also detect infrared emissions and gamma rays.

The Hubble Space Telescope enables traditional, optical astronomers to escape our atmosphere. The telescope's primary mirror is eight feet in diameter. Including recording instruments and guidance system, the telescope weighs twelve tons. It has been called the eighth wonder of the world; critics say it should be, given its cost of two billion dollars. It was as much a political and managerial achievement as a technological one; approval for it came only after a political struggle lasting from 1974 to 1977. In 1990, after overcoming a host of problems, its designers launched it into space, only to discover that an error had occurred in the shaping of the primary mirror. One newspaper reported "Pix Nixed as Hubble Sees Double." Addition of a corrective mirror solved the problem.

Over four centuries the telescope has evolved from two small glass lenses affordable and operable by an untrained individual of no great wealth into an immense political, managerial, and technological undertaking beyond the reach of all but the wealthiest countries. Our understanding of the universe has expanded apace, as ever larger, more expensive, and technologically sophisticated telescopes range over ever more of the electromagnetic spectrum to detect ever more distant objects.

NORRISS S. HETHERINGTON

TERRESTRIAL MAGNETISM. Practical needs, particularly of navigators, have inspired interest in terrestrial magnetism since at least the fifteenth century. Equally important have been conceptual puzzles about how to reconcile terrestrial magnetism with basic physical theory and with theories based on laboratory studies of magnetism. Consequently interplay between field studies and experimental studies has been a regular feature of the history of geomagnetism. So has a tension between explaining the ultimate causes of geomagnetism, usually in terms of some kind of fluid movement in the interior of the earth, and surveying the spatial and temporal variations of geomagnetic declination, dip, and intensity.

Serious work on geomagnetism began in 1600 with the publication of William Gilbert's *De magnete*. By that date, navigators knew that their needles sometimes pointed at an angle to true north (declination) and that sometimes they inclined from the horizontal (dip). Philosophers generally assumed that the earth's magnetism arose through the occult properties of the mineral magnetite or by some Neoplatonic correspondence between the polestar in the heavens and the magnetic north pole on Earth.

Making a magnet by hammering a hot iron rod aligned with the earth's magnetic field. William Gilbert, De magnete (1600), color added.

Gilbert, a member of the Royal College of Physicians in London, discussed the five motions associated with magnetism—attraction (he called it coition), orientation, declination, dip, and rotation—as a preliminary to presenting his theory of earth magnetism. Experiments with small magnetic needles on a small spherical lodestone (called a terella) showed that irregularities in the lode-stone changed the orientation of the needles. They also demonstrated that needles parallel to the surface of the sphere at the equator gradually dipped to a vertical as they moved to the position at the poles. The Earth, he concluded, was a giant lodestone with an immaterial rotating magnetic soul.

Because magnetism, including geomagnetism, seemed an exemplary occult force, mechanical philosophers had to find an alternative explanation in terms of matter in motion. In his *Principles of Philosophy* (1644), René Descartes traced the earth's magnetism to circulating streams of corkscrew-shaped particles. From this suggestion arose the tradition, predominant until the 1820s, of attributing the earth's magnetism to subtle active magnetic fluids. Edmond Halley in 1683 and again in 1692 proposed that the earth consisted of an inner sphere and outer shell. They rotated at different speeds and each had a north and south pole. The interactions between these four poles accounted for the variations in declination and dip. Between 1698 and 1700, Halley sailed the Atlantic, measured the variations in declination, and charted them on a pioneering map that appeared in different editions between 1701 and 1703.

Descartes's effluvial theory continued to be important until the early nineteenth century. The alternative, most fully articulated by Charles Augustin Coulomb and Simeon-Denis Poisson—whose theory presented to the Paris Academy in 1826 represented the culmination of the tradition—assumed distance forces resulting from fluids locked in magnetic substances. Other important figures in the debate were Gavin Knight; Leonhard Euler, who with others won the prize of 1746 offered on the subject by the Paris Académie des Sciences; Franz Aepinus; and Jean-Baptiste Biot. Many researchers attempted to deal with earth magnetism though the requisite mathematics was dauntingly complex. During the 1820s and 1830s, theories (like Poisson's) based on "austral" and "boral" fluids were losing

T

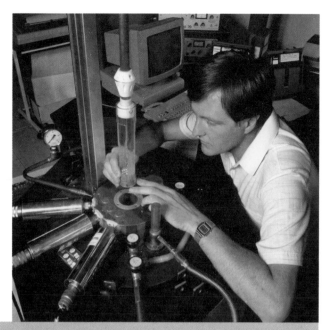

The investigator is placing a rock core sample in a cryogenic magnetometer to determine the strength and alignment of its magnetic field.

their luster. Christopher Hansteen revived Halley's two-axis-four-pole model in his *Investigations Concerning the Magnetism of the Earth* (1819). To look for poles, defined either as regions of maximum magnetic intensity or of vertical dip, Hansteen traveled to Siberia around 1830 and James Clark Ross went to Canada. Although the two-axis theory did not win acceptance, the reintroduction of poles as an object of investigation, the attempt to mathematize the theory, and the expeditions brought fresh ideas and evidence to geomagnetic studies. In the same decades, Hans Christian Ørsted's discovery in 1820 that electric currents produce magnetic effects, Thomas Seebeck's discovery of thermoelectricity in 1822, and Michael Faraday's discovery in 1831 that magnetism can produce electric currents gave rise to new questions and possibilities concerning earth magnetism. Alexander von Humboldt, who had been fascinated by the global variations of magnetism since the 1790s, speculated about the similarities between lines of equal magnetic intensity and isothermal lines and about interconnections between geological, meteorological, and magnetic phenomena. In 1805, he reported that magnetic intensity varied across the earth's surface. To plot these variations, Humboldt encouraged the establishment of a network of magnetic observatories. By 1834, the twenty-three European observatories had detected the phenomenon of magnetic storms. In the fifth volume of his *Cosmos* (1845), Humboldt summed up the state of knowledge of magnetic variation, distribution, and storms.

In the 1830s, Carl Friedrich Gauss and his younger collaborator Wilhelm Weber took over from Humboldt as leaders in geomagnetism, tackling problems from instrumentation to basic theory. Early in the decade Gauss designed the bifilar magnetometer, developed for the first time an absolute measure of magnetic intensity, and launched his own version of the Magnetische Verein (magnetic union) to establish a network of magnetic observatories worldwide. The results from these observatories came out in six volumes, *Resultate aus den Beobachtungen des magnetischen Vereins*, between 1836 and 1841. With new data about variations of magnetic intensity in hand, Gauss could publish his math-

ematical analysis of the vertical and horizontal components of earth magnetism in 1839. He analyzed the magnetic potential at any point on the earth's surface by an infinite series of spherical functions. Not dependent on a theory about the ultimate causes of geomagnetism, his method of analysis shaped theoretical work on geomagnetism for the rest of the century.

In Britain, a follower of Hansteen, Edward Sabine, fretted that Britain was letting slip the chance of contributing to the growing field of geomagnetism. In 1838, he enlisted the astronomer John Herschel to help him raise support for a British magnetic survey. The publication of James Clerk Maxwell's *Treatise on Electricity and Magnetism* in 1873 encouraged investigators to speak of the earth's magnetic field, not its magnetic forces, and gave them another set of mathematical tools.

Between 1890 and 1900, geomagnetism began to take on the trappings of a separate discipline. A new generation of mathematically trained physicists, notably Arthur Schuster, continued working on mathematical analyses of the earth's field although they did not propose new comprehensive theories. With the establishment of national surveys and observatories, the amount of data available multiplied. The beginning of submarine warfare accelerated military interest in geomagnetism. International organizations expanded; in 1896 the journal *Terrestrial Magnetism* was founded. Another period of rapid breakthroughs in geomagnetism occurred in the years following World War II. In 1947, following measurements of the magnetic fields of the sun and some stars, the English physicist Patrick Blackett suggested that magnetism (including the earth's magnetism) might be a property common to all rotating bodies. A decade earlier, Göttingen-trained physicist Walter Maurice Elsasser had published a series of papers suggesting that a self-excited magneto hydro dynamo in the earth's core created its field. For a few exciting years, scientists explored the consequences of the two theories in the hope of deciding between them. Then in 1952, after obtaining negative results from an experiment intended to detect the effects of rotation in the laboratory, Blackett himself rejected his own theory. Versions of Elsasser's theory held sway for the rest of the century.

Other major developments, interesting in their own right and for what they contributed to plate tectonics, occurred in paleomagnetism. Already in the nineteenth century, scientists had detected remanent or fossilized magnetism. They noticed that ferrous minerals in baked clays and cooled lava flows preserved the alignment of the earth's main field as it was when they had cooled. In the late 1950s, physicists in London, Newcastle, and the Australian National University who systematically surveyed remanent magnetism found that the magnetic north pole appeared to have wandered widely over the globe in the past. They proposed various hypotheses to explain this result: their instruments created the effect, the earth's field had not always been dipolar, the continents had moved relative to one another, or the earth's magnetic poles had wandered independently. By the end of the decade, a small but influential group of scientists, Keith Runcorn prominent among them, had convinced themselves that the continents had moved. This served to give the largely discredited theory of continental drift new life.

In the 1920s and 1930s, scientists had discovered another peculiarity about remanent magnetism. In some rocks the magnetism had a polarity opposite to that of the present geomagnetic field. In the 1940s, researchers in the Carnegie Institution of Washington developed a spinning magnetometer capable of detecting weak magnetic fields. From the 1950s through the 1960s, paleomagnetists at the United States Geological Survey and the Australian National University raced to reconstruct the history of these reversals, using radioactive dating to determine their sequence. By the mid-1960s, they had constructed a fairly complete scale. It proved to be a key piece of evidence for the theory of sea floor spreading.

RACHEL LAUDAN

THERMODYNAMICS AND STATISTICAL MECHANICS.

The development of the theory of heat in the first half of the nineteenth century, which eventually led to thermodynamics, was linked with the technology of steam engines. Their operation was originally analyzed in terms of the caloric theory, which represented heat as a conserved imponderable fluid. In 1824, the French military engineer Sadi Carnot employed the caloric theory in his analysis of an idealized heat-engine, which aimed at improving the efficiency of real engines. On the basis of an analogy with the production of work by the fall of water in a waterwheel, Carnot assumed that a heat-engine produced work by the "fall" of caloric from a higher to a lower temperature. The analogy suggested that the work produced was proportional to the amount of caloric and the temperature difference of the two bodies between which caloric flowed. Carnot proved that no other engine could surpass his reversible ideal engine in efficiency by showing that the existence of a more efficient engine would imply the possibility of perpetual motion. In 1834, a mining engineer, Benoit-Pierre-Émile Clapeyron, reformulated Carnot's analysis, using calculus and the indicator (pressure-volume) diagram. Carnot's theory was virtually ignored, however, until its discovery in the mid-1840s, via Clapeyron's paper, by William Thomson (Lord Kelvin), and Hermann von Helmholtz.

James Joule's experimental work of the 1840s, which indicated the interconversion of heat and work, undermined the caloric theory. His precise measurements supported the old idea that heat consists in the motion of the microscopic constituents of matter. The interconversion of heat and work, along with other developments spanning several fields (from theoretical mechanics to physiology), led to the formulation of the principle of energy conservation. In the early 1850s, all these parallel developments were seen, with the benefit of hindsight, as "simultaneous" discoveries of energy conservation, which became the first law of thermodynamics.

Joule's experiments, however, presented a problem for Carnot's analysis of a reversible heat-engine based on the assumption of conserved heat. In the early 1850s, Thomson and the German physicist Rudolf Clausius resolved the problem by introducing a second principle. Carnot's analysis could be retained, despite the rejection of the conservation of heat, because, in fact, it dealt with a quantity—the amount of heat divided by the temperature at which the heat is exchanged—that is conserved in reversible processes. During the operation of Carnot's engine, part of the heat dropped from a higher to a lower temperature and the rest became mechanical work.

In 1847, Thomson diagnosed another problem, also implicit in Carnot's analysis. Carnot had portrayed heat transfer as the cause of the production of work. In processes like conduction, however, heat flows from a warmer to a colder body without doing any work. Since the heat does not spontaneously flow from cold to hot, conduction resulted in the loss of potential for doing work. Both Joule and Thomson agreed that energy cannot perish, or, rather, that only a

divine creator could destroy or create it. Thomson resolved the difficulty in 1852 by observing that in processes like conduction, energy is not lost but "dissipated," and by raising the dissipation of energy to a law of nature. "Real"—that is, irreversible—processes continually degrade energy and, in a good long time, will cause the heat-death of the universe. The Scottish engineer William Rankine and Clausius proposed a new concept that represented the same tendency of energy toward dissipation. Initially called "thermodynamic function" (by Rankine) or "disgregation" (by Clausius), it later (in 1865) received the name "entropy" from Clausius, who grafted onto the Greek root for transformation. Every process (except ideal reversible ones) that takes place in an isolated system increases its entropy. This principle constituted the second fundamental law of thermodynamics, and its interpretation remained the subject of discussion for many years.

The dynamical conception of heat provided a link between mechanics and thermodynamics and led eventually to the introduction of statistical methods in the study of thermal phenomena. In 1857, Clausius correlated explicitly thermodynamic and mechanical concepts by identifying the quantity of heat contained in a gas with the kinetic energy (translational, rotational, and vibrational) of its molecules. He made the simplifying assumption that all the molecules of a gas had the same velocity and calculated its value, which turned out to be of the order of the speed of sound. Clausius's idealized model faced a difficulty, however, as pointed out by the Dutch meteorologist C. H. D. Buys Ballot. On the model, gases should diffuse much faster than actually observed. In 1858, in response to that difficulty, Clausius attributed the slow rate of diffusion to the molecules' collisions with each other and introduced the new concept of "mean free path," the average distance traveled by a molecule before it collides with another one.

In 1859, James Clerk Maxwell became aware of Clausius's kinetic interpretation of thermodynamics and, in the following years, developed it further by introducing probabilistic methods. In 1860, he developed a theory in which the velocities of the molecules in a gas at equilibrium distrib-

A fanciful presentation of James Prescott Joule (1818–1889) conducting his measurement of the conversion of electrical energy into hat. The measurement dates from 1840, the picture (from *Physique populaire*) from 1891.

301

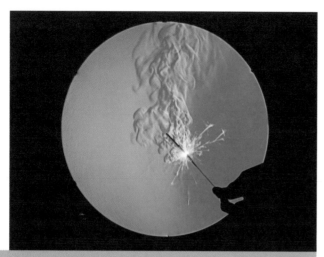

Areas of different temperature on this sparkler are brought out by a technique that makes use of the dependence of the index of refraction of liquids on temperature.

ute according to the laws of probability. He inferred from "precarious" assumptions that the distribution followed a bell-shaped curve, the so-called normal distribution, which had been familiar from the theory of errors and the social sciences. Following up these ideas, he published in 1871 an ingenious thought experiment that he had invented four years earlier to suggest that heat need not always flow from a warmer to a colder body. In that case, the second law of thermodynamics could have only a statistical validity. A microscopic agent ("Maxwell's demon," as Thomson called it), controlling a diaphragm on a wall separating a hot and a cold gas, could let through either molecules of the cold gas faster than the average speed of the molecules of the hot gas, or molecules of the hot gas slower than the average speed of the molecules of the cold gas. Heat thus would flow from the cold to the hot gas. This thought experiment indicated that the "dissipation" of energy did not lie in nature but in human inability to control microscopic processes.

Ludwig Boltzmann carried further Maxwell's statistical probing of the foundations of thermodynamics. In 1868, he rederived, in a more general way, the distribution of molecular velocities, taking into account the forces exerted between molecules as well as the influence of external forces like grav-

Glass thermometers made for the Florentine Accademia del Cimento, which operated from 1657 to 1667

ity. In 1872, he extended the second law of thermodynamics to systems not in equilibrium by showing that there exists a mathematical function, the negative counterpart of entropy, that decreases as a system approaches thermal equilibrium. This behavior was subsequently called the "*H*-theorem."

Furthermore, Boltzmann attempted to resolve a severe problem, pointed out by Thomson in 1874 and Joseph Loschmidt in 1876, which undermined the mechanical interpretation of the second law. The law defines a time asymmetry in natural processes: the passage of time results in an irreversible change, the increase of entropy. However, if the laws of mechanics govern the constituents of thermodynamic systems, their evolution should be reversible, since the laws of mechanics run with equal validity toward the past and the future. *Prima facie,* there seems to be no mechanical counterpart to the second law of thermodynamics.

Boltzmann eluded the difficulty in 1877 by construing the second law probabilistically. To each macroscopic state of a system correspond many microstates (particular distributions of energy among the constituents of the system), which Boltzmann ranked as equally probable. He defined the probability of each macroscopic state by the number of microstates corresponding to it and identified the entropy of a system with a simple logarithmic function of the probability of its macroscopic state. On that interpretation of entropy, the second law asserted that thermodynamic systems have a tendency to evolve toward more probable states. The interpretation came at the cost of demoting the law. A decrease of entropy was unlikely, but not impossible.

Maxwell's and Boltzmann's statistical approach to thermodynamics was developed further by J. Willard Gibbs, who avoided hypotheses concerning the molecular constitution of matter. He formulated statistical mechanics, which analyzed the statistical properties of an ensemble, a collection of mechanical systems. This more general treatment proved to be very useful for the investigation of systems other than those studied by the kinetic theory of gases, like electrons in metals or ions in solutions.

THEODORE ARABATZIS

THERMOMETER. The notion of a scale or degrees of heat and cold dates back at least to the second-century physician Galen, as does the idea of using a standard—such as a mixture of ice and boiling water—as a fixed point for the scale. Ancient philosophers' experiments, such as Hero of Alexandria's "fountain that drips in the sun," demonstrated the expansion of air with heat, and were known among natural philosophers of the sixteenth century. In the second decade of the seventeenth century, Galileo, Santorio Santorio, and others began to use long-necked glass flasks partially filled with air and inverted in water to measure temperature, applying them to medical and physical experiments and keeping meteorological records. The first sealed liquid-in-glass thermometers, filled with spirit of wine, were constructed for the Accademia del Cimento in Florence in 1654 by the artisan Mariani; though not calibrated from fixed points, his thermometers agreed very closely among themselves.

The succeeding century saw experimentation with thermometric liquids, among which spirit of wine was favored for its quick response and because no cold then known would freeze it. Several natural philosophers, including Robert Hooke, Christiaan Huygens, and Edme Mariotte, worked out methods for graduating their instruments from a single fixed point, typically the freezing or boiling point of water. Toward the end of the seventeenth century, Italian investigators began using two fixed points, as did the Dutch instrument maker Daniel Fahrenheit in the first few decades of the eighteenth century. Fahrenheit's excellent thermometers spread his method and his preference for mercury throughout England and the Low Countries, while the dominance of France and the fame of its Académie Royale des Sciences secured the position of academician René-Antoine Ferchault de Réaumur's thermometer on the rest of the Continent.

Réaumur and his contemporaries despaired of precision in their instruments. The inconstant composition of spirit of wine; air dissolved or trapped in the liquid, whether mercury or spirits; the lack of good glass—these and the lack of motivation to precision rendered the thermometer's readings at best qualitative indications of the temperature. After the Seven Years' War, the rational bureaucratic state and industrial manufacturers generated pressure for precise measurement for cartography and navigation, enclosures and canals, and the construction of steam engines and other machinery. In England, instrument making grew from a handicraft to an operation of industrial scale, exploiting advances in glassmaking and metallurgy and serving an international clientele. The thermometer played an auxiliary role in the precise measurements of the late Enlightenment, but from about 1760, the Genevan natural philosopher Jean-André Deluc developed methods for rigorously calibrating the instrument and for using it in exhaustive series of systematic measurements. In England, a committee of the Royal Society of London under the chairmanship of Henry Cavendish worked out methods in 1776 of setting the upper fixed point in a water bath, methods that remain in use today. Late-eighteenth-century thermometers achieved a precision of 1/10° F. The chief development of the nineteenth century was the discovery that the glass of new thermometers contracted in time so that their zero point fell; in the 1880s, glasses were developed that did not experience these effects.

THEODORE S. FELDMAN

TRANSURANIC ELEMENTS. Glenn T. Seaborg popularized the term "transuranic elements" after the declassification of information on the elements with atomic numbers greater than uranium's.

The Rutherford-Bohr model of the atom, established between 1911 and 1922, explained for the first time why the lanthanides had similar properties—namely that they possessed identical outer electronic configurations and slightly different numbers of electrons in interior subshells. Both Johannes Rydberg in 1913 and Niels Bohr in 1921 speculated that a similar group of heavier elements might exist, and Vicktor Goldschmidt proposed that they should be named the neptunium group. Following the discovery of nuclear fission in 1939, Edwin M. McMillan and Philip H. Abelson, working at the University of California at Berkeley, showed that neutron bombardment of uranium produced a synthetic radioactive element. Because of its position in the periodic table following uranium (with its association with the planet Uranus), they followed Goldschmidt in naming it neptunium. At the same time, and using the Berkeley 150-cm (60-inch) cyclotron, Seaborg and his colleagues prepared plutonium (element 94) by the beta-decay of neptunium. McMillan and Seaborg received the Nobel Prize in chemistry in 1951 for this work. During the war, Seaborg found time to pursue further examples of synthetic transuranic elements. Americium and curium were identified between 1944 and 1945, and berkelium, californium, ein-

steinium, fermium, and mendelevium by 1953. Altogether Seaborg participated in the identification of nine of the fifteen actinides (as chemists called Goldschmidt's neptunides) between 1940 and 1970.

Although the chemistry of neptunium and plutonium proved analogous to uranium's, their successors did not. This anomaly forced a reexamination of their place in the periodic table. As early as 1944, Seaborg noted that elements 95 and 96 should have properties analogous to those of the lanthanides europium and gadolinium. He therefore suggested that elements 90–92 (thorium, protactinium, and uranium) should be moved from the seventh period of the periodic table to form a second rare earth (actinide) family of elements that extended from 89 (actinium) to 102 (nobelium), and subsequently to lawrencium, made in an accelerator in Berkeley in 1961 under the leadership of Seaborg's colleague Albert Ghiorso. This amendment to the periodic table proved the key to discovering the remaining elements. The preparation and confirmation of a few fleeting atoms of synthetic transactinides beyond lawrencium saw rival groups from the Soviet Union and Germany competing with the Americans. Settling the names of these synthetic elements, rutherfordium, dubnium, seaborgium, bohrium, and meitnerium, proved controversial and protracted. In the fifty years between 1940 and 1990, seventeen new elements were added to the periodic table beyond uranium.

Seaborg also speculated that beyond transuranic elements 113 and 164 there may be islands of stability containing super-heavy elements with long radioactive half-lives that would allow detailed comparisons with natural elements in their group positions within the periodic table. Besides forming an outstanding example of twentieth-century big science, the investigation of the transuranic elements has shown the continuing value and power of Dmitrii Mendeleev's periodic table.

WILLIAM H. BROCK

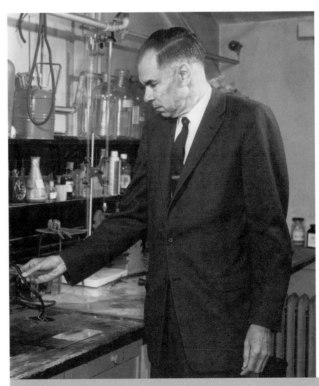

American nuclear chemist Glenn T. Seaborg (1912–1999), photographed in his laboratory at the University of California, Berkeley, in 1962

UNIVERSE, AGE AND SIZE OF THE. At the end of the seventeenth century, Isaac Newton's concept of an infinite universe created instantaneously by God rendered the question of the size of the universe moot and the question of its age a matter for historical rather than scientific determination. For more than two centuries after the publication of Newton's *Principia,* efforts to measure astronomical distances were confined to our solar system and a few nearby stars. Ever larger telescopes and the development of photography and spectroscopy greatly increased the variety and accuracy of the data available to astronomers, but at the end of the nineteenth century, the size of our own Milky Way galaxy was still unknown and, despite earlier speculations about the possibility of other systems, few, if any, astronomers believed that anything existed outside our own galaxy in the infinite void of the universe.

Between 1910 and 1930, new techniques for estimating interstellar distances finally enabled astronomers to determine the approximate size and shape of the Milky Way galaxy. During the same period, Vesto M. Slipher and Edwin Hubble measured the red shift in the spectra of a number of spiral nebula, and determined that almost all of them were moving away from the earth at high radial velocities. By 1929, Hubble had also calculated the distance to several nebula, and for the first time had provided convincing evidence that spiral nebula were clusters of stars (he did not identify them as galaxies) far beyond the borders of our own galaxy. Even more significantly, Hubble had found that the farther away the nebulae were, the greater their radial velocities away from the earth. Hubble's discoveries not only populated Newton's cosmic void with myriads of stars, they also suggested that the universe itself was expanding rather than static. The concept of an expanding universe had already been proposed theoretically by Willem de Sitter (in 1917), Alexander Freedman (1922), and Georges Lemaître (1927) as a way to resolve an anomaly in the solution to Einstein's theory of general relativity, but it was Hubble's work that caused astronomers to begin seriously to consider the idea of an expanding universe and the implication that it had a calculable age and size.

The key to calculating the age, and hence the size, of an expanding universe is the determination of the intergalactic velocity/distance ratio (which became known as the "Hubble Constant"). In the 1930s, Hubble's original value for the velocity/distance ratio produced an estimate of about 2×10^9 years for the age of the universe. This result briefly created the curious anomaly of a calculated value of the age of the universe that was smaller than radiometric measurements of the age of the earth. The work of Walter Baade in the 1940s and Allan Sandage in the 1950s resulted in substantial revisions in the accepted value of Hubble's Constant, and by the 1960s astronomers agreed that the universe was between 10 and 20×10^9 years old, with a corresponding size of the order of 10^{10} light-years. Also by the 1960s, the success of the "Big Bang" Hypothesis had provided astronomers with a causal physical model of an expanding universe with an instantaneous beginning and a finite age and size. Since the 1950s, the rapid proliferation of new techniques and technologies has enabled astronomers to probe ever closer toward the outer edge of the universe, and in the 1990s, a more precise rede-termination of the Hubble Constant was made a priority of the new Hubble Space Telescope. The results of the several independent efforts to recalculate the Hubble Constant were not consistent among themselves, however, and the late 1990s saw renewed controversy over the age and size of the universe. At the century's end, some astronomers believed that the universe's age had been determined to lie within the range of 12 to 15×10^9 years, while their more cautious colleagues remain unwilling to allow for a greater certainty than the earlier 10 to 20×10^9 years. The size of an expanding universe, of course, depends on its age, but recent cosmological theories, such as Alan Guth's inflationary model, suggest the possibility that our observable universe may be only a small part of a much larger structure.

JOE D. BURCHFIELD

Edwin Powell Hubble (1889–1953), US astronomer and cosmologist, using the 48-inch Schmidt telescope at Palomar Observatory, California

VACUUM. Nature abhors a vacuum. So said medieval natural philosophers, following Aristotle. Against the ancient atomists, who held that material atoms move in an infinite void, Aristotle presented several arguments for the impossibility of a vacuum: the lack of resistance would produce infinite velocities; the homogeneity of the void precluded natural motion, which for Aristotle relied on a distinction between up and down; and the void likewise prevented violent motion, which needed an external medium for continued propulsion. The plenum persisted into the seventeenth century, notably in the system of René Descartes, who identified matter with space. But the possibility of the void received some discussion from medieval scholastics, who wondered in particular about the space beyond the stars, where God perhaps resided.

Experimental refutation of the *horror vacui* came in the seventeenth century. Mining pumps of the time operated according to the abhorrence of the vacuum, up to a point—thirty feet, in fact, above which they could not draw water. In 1644, an Italian mathematician, Evangelista Torricelli, explained the limitation by a mechanical equivalence between the weight of atmospheric air and the weight of the column of water, and demonstrated it using a glass tube, closed at one end, inverted in a basin of mercury. The mercury rose to a height one-fourteenth that to which water attained. Torricelli's new device—what we now call a barometer—figured in a famous experiment four years later by Blaise Pascal, who initially doubted Torricelli's explanation of the barometer and thought it showed only the limits to the force of a vacuum. Pascal pursued barometric experiments with a variety of liquids and glass tubes up to 14 m (46 ft) long, for the latter relying on the state-of-the-art products of the glass factory in his hometown of Rouen. In the decisive experiment, Pascal in 1648 sent his brother-in-law up a mountain in France with a barometer; the lower level of the mercury at the peak convinced Pascal and others that the weight of the atmosphere, not the vacuum inside the barometer, was forcing up the mercury in barometers and the water in mining pumps.

Otto von Guericke soon provided an equally famous demonstration using his new air pump, a piston-driven suction pump with valves that could suck the air out of sealed chambers and thus make a vacuum. In 1657, in Magdeburg, where he was the mayor, Guericke worked his air pump on

The experiment of the Magdeburg spheres (1654), named after the hometown of the inventor of the air pump, Otto von Guericke. A pair of hollow hemispheres easily separable under ordinary conditions could not be pulled apart by teams of horses when put together, sealed hermetically, and exhausted of air.

two copper hemispheres stuck together and showed that a team of horses could not pull them apart; the force of the vacuum—or, rather, of the air on the outside of the hemispheres—held them together. Robert Boyle developed the air pump into a means of easy production of a vacuum. When Boyle placed a barometer inside a glass globe, the level of mercury descended as the pump evacuated the enclosed space until the mercury no longer stood. Boyle's account of the results, *New Experiments Physico-Mechanicall Touching the Spring of the Air* (1660), showed along the way that cats and candles could not survive in a vacuum but that electric and magnetic effects could.

The technology of the vacuum would henceforth be crucial for modern science. The fruitful program of experiment with evacuated cathode ray tubes in the nineteenth century relied on a new generation of vacuum pumps, the first major advancements over von Guericke's original design; in particular, a pump made by German instrument-maker J. H. W. Geissler using a mercury column instead of pistons, which improved residual pressures from one inch to one millimeter of mercury. Rotary pumps made by Wolfgang Gaede in Germany in the early twentieth century proved crucial for the development of vacuum tube technology in the commercial electronics industry. High-energy particle accelerators later in the century required further advances in the production of large empty spaces.

The vacuum of physicists since the early modern period has not been empty. The imponderable fluids of electricity, light, and magnetism in Laplacian physics pervaded it, as did the ether and electromagnetic fields of Maxwellian electromagnetism. Even after Albert Einstein banished the ether, his postulated equivalence of energy and mass implied that matter could still intrude in empty space, and fields, electron holes, and ghost particles continue to clog up the vacuum of modern physics.

PETER J. WESTWICK

VIROLOGY. The term "virus" in its original Latin meaning (poison, morbid principle) was used up until the beginning of the twentieth century to indicate the causative agent in the transmission of a specific disease, as in the virus of cholera or the virus of rabies. In 1892, Dmitri Ivanovsky found that the virus of tobacco mosaic disease passed through a filter believed to trap all known bacteria. This observation gave rise to the concept of "filterable viruses." Martinus Willem Beijerinck conceived of this infectious agent as a "living contagious fluid" on the basis that only true fluids were filterable. Filtration made possible a new classification of infectious agents. Soon clinicians recognized that, in addition to tobacco mosaic virus (TMV), the agents of many well-known diseases such as rabies, hog cholera, influenza, poliomyelitis, herpes simplex, and vaccinia were filterable viruses. Thomas M. Rivers's influential textbook *Filterable Viruses* (1928) was the last major work to retain the term "filterable virus"; by the mid-1930s, "virus" alone would do. From 1900 to about 1930, some authors used the term "ultravirus" to emphasize the invisibility of these filterable agents to light microscopy, but this terminology was not widely adopted.

Although Beijerinck's concept of a contagious fluid would suggest a continuous, nonparticulate nature, except for bacteriophages (bacterial viruses), there seemed to be little challenge to the belief in the particulate nature of viruses. The bacteriological paradigm of tiny organisms seemed to dominate thinking about viruses, filterable and nonfilter-

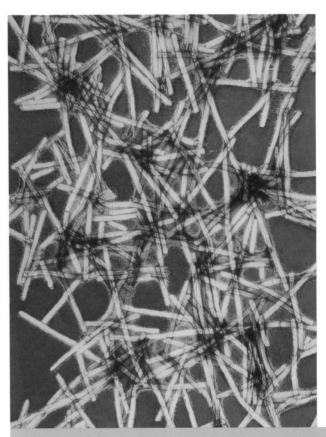

False-color transmission electron micrograph of the rod-shaped particles of tobacco mosaic virus

able. The only controversy concerned the nature of bacteriophages. Their codiscoverer Félix d'Hérelle conceived of them as filterable viruses that infect bacteria. Scientists who believed in the simplicity of bacteria as a class of organisms fundamentally distinct from complex multicellular organisms resisted this concept. They also pointed to experimental results confounded by lysogenic behavior of some phage isolates. Lysogenic bacteria harbor the genetic material of a bacterial virus in a repressed state; under certain conditions, the virus can be induced to enter its regular growth cycle, which often kills the host cell. The analogy between the process of lysogenic virus induction to the then-recently discovered autocatalytic activation of proteases was advocated from 1920 to the mid-1940s by two Nobel Prize–winners, Jules Bordet and John H. Northrop. Their authority relegated the bacterial virus model for bacteriophage to a secondary status corrected only when electron microscopy made possible visualization of phages.

The microbial conception of viruses prompted attempts to study their metabolism and their growth in pure culture. It proved impossible to grow viruses in the absence of living host cells, and viruses were reconceptualized as obligate intracellular parasites. Viruses could be obtained only from infected plants, animals, or bacteria. Embryonated chicken eggs, and later animal cells in tissue cultures, became the standard laboratory media for growing animal viruses for diagnosis and study. Bacterial cultures, both in liquid media and on solid agar plates, provided the cells for growing. In a classic study of a virus disease, Edward Jenner confirmed common folk wisdom that prior sickness with a benign disease of cows, cowpox, protected humans from subsequent susceptibility to a lethal disease, smallpox. He exploited this finding to develop the procedure of vaccination. Louis Pasteur extended this procedure to several other diseases,

V

both bacterial and viral. The use of attenuated or weakened strains of virus to induce mild or subclinical illness that confers immunity is the basis for vaccines developed against poliovirus through the work of John Franklin Enders and his colleagues Jonas Salk and Albert Sabin.

In the mid-1930s, Ernst Ruska and his colleagues turned the electron microscope they invented to the study of viruses. The higher resolution obtained with this instrument revealed the regular structures of virus particles, but also showed that viruses exist in many shapes, from simple rods such as TMV to elaborately tailed and "decorated" structures such as the T-even bacteriophages.

Chemical analysis of viruses became possible in the 1930s because of their purification by sedimentation in the ultracentrifuge. Initial analyses of some viruses such as TMV and poliovirus suggested that they were composed entirely of proteins, a finding that fit well with the notion that viruses resembled enzymes in both specificity and catalytic power. Soon, however, it was discovered that purified viruses always contained phosphate in the form of nucleic acids. The conception of viruses as simple nucleoprotein particles raised the conundrum of the living nature of such simple chemical entities. This paradox became especially acute when Wendell Stanley crystallized TMV and poliovirus in 1935, since crystallization was believed to be the ultimate criterion for chemical purity.

The chemical simplicity and rapidity of growth of viruses and the observation that they had heredity properties (such as the range of host species on which they grow) led investigators in the late 1930s to employ viruses to study the chemistry of the gene. Max Delbruck, Alfred D. Hershey, and Salvador Luria used bacteriophages as a model for gene replication and heredity transmission; their work helped to set the current directions of molecular biology. Alfred Geirer, Gerhard Schramm, and Heinz Fraenkel-Conrat used biochemical approaches to show that the genetic properties of TMV resided in the RNA component of the virus, not in the protein coat.

As more viruses were isolated from nature and studied, their diversity became apparent. One class, first represented by a virus that causes cancers in chickens (Rous sarcoma virus), was found to copy its RNA genome into DNA and integrate this DNA provirus into the host cell chromosome. This mechanism, first proposed by Howard Temin, seemed implausible because it required a reverse of the normal flow of genetic information. In 1970, both Temin and David Baltimore discovered the enzymatic mechanism for this process, demonstrating that it characterized a large class of RNA viruses, now known as retroviruses. When a mysterious immune deficiency disorder appeared in epidemiologically recognizable groups in 1982, virological studies soon identified the causative agent as a retrovirus, now called the human immunodeficiency virus (HIV).

WILLIAM C. SUMMERS

Computer artwork of T-bacteriophages (phages) attacking a bacterium, which will die after they have used its machinery to replicate themselves

V

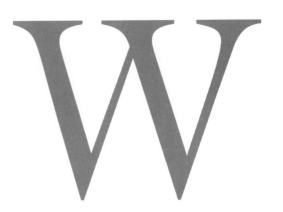

WOMEN IN SCIENCE. Women have been and remain underrepresented in science. During the Scientific Revolution of the seventeenth century aristocratic women were active as both patrons and interlocutors of natural philosophers. For example, Queen Christina of Sweden patronized many natural philosophers, astrologers, and astronomers, including René Descartes and Gian Domenico Cassini; Princess Caroline of Wales coordinated Leibniz's activities in England, especially his debate with Isaac Newton via Samuel Clarke; and Queen Charlotte Sophia of England supported Jean André Deluc.

Some women gained access to the practice of science as wives or relatives of scientists who worked at a home base, whether an observatory or a museum—Caroline Lucretia Herschel, for example, who discovered eight comets, the sister of William Herschel and the aunt of John Herschel, England's leading astronomers for half a century. A few women attained positions of scientific leadership. The marquise du Chatelet, the friend of several eighteenth-century philosophers, notably Voltaire, made the first complete translation of Newton's *Principia* into French. Laura Bassi, professor of physics at the University of Bologna, was a protégée of the city's cultural aristocracy. Most women in science, however, were relegated to the supporting cast—collecting, illustrating, or entertaining.

In the nineteenth century, the professionalization of science and its increasing location in the laboratory moved science away from its domestic base. The transition further excluded women from science, because social pressure kept them tied to the home and child rearing. Nevertheless, some women made important contributions: Mary Somerville and Jane Haldimand Marcet in England through their informal textbooks and Maria Mitchell in the United States, who detected comets and taught science to many women at Vassar College. The rise of women's colleges in the last third of the century, as well as the willingness of some universities to allow foreign women to study or even graduate created the first generation of formally educated women scientists. For example, Sonya Kovalevsky, a Russian-born mathematician, obtained a Ph.D. in Germany in 1874, became a professor at Stockholm Holgsholz, a private school, and wrote books and plays advocating women's equality through education. In the twentieth century, the shortage of technical personnel during the two world wars temporarily opened further opportunities for women in science.

Women's place in science tended to vary significantly by discipline. They encountered substantial resistance in the laboratory sciences. They were more readily accepted in observational sciences such as botany and classical astronomy, where the need for large-scale collecting and observing encouraged the persistence of an amateur subculture for both men and women. Theoretical sciences—except for mathematics, in which there was an often explicit bias against women—also presented fewer barriers since the equipment and facilities required were minimal. Both observational and theoretical pursuits seemed tolerably compatible with women's primary familial responsibilities; observation additionally belonged to a socially acceptable tradition of amateur practice.

During the twentieth century, an increasing number of women, many of them aided by enlightened male mentors, excelled in the experimental as well as in the theoretical sciences. Among them were Marie Sklodowska Curie, a codiscoverer of radioactivity and radium, who worked in state-funded laboratories in Paris and won two Nobel Prizes; her elder daughter, Irène Joliot-Curie, who shared the 1935 Nobel Prize in chemistry with her husband Frédéric Joliot for discovering artificial radioactivity; Hertha Ayrton, who worked at the interface of physics and engineering with support from the feminist Langham Place Group and from her physicist husband William Ayrton, and who became the first woman nominated for fellowship in the Royal Society of London; Lise Meitner, a protégée of Max Planck, who headed the physics division at the Kaiser Wilhelm Institute for Physical Chemistry between the wars and figured in the

German chemist Ida Tacke Noddack (1896–1978) around 1930

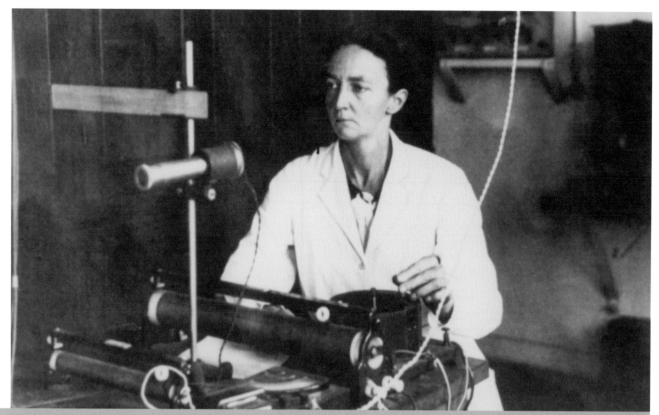

French nuclear physicist and Nobel laureate Irène Joliot-Curie (1897–1956), at work in the Radium Institute in Paris in the 1930s

discovery of nuclear fission; and Rita Levi-Montalcini, who shared a Nobel Prize for her research in neurobiology.

British culture proved relatively conducive to the enrollment of women in science, to some extent because the British Empire provided scope for imagination, independence, and travel for women of the middle upper class. The biologist Dorothy M. Wrinch, born in the British colony in Argentina, distinguished herself in mathematics at Cambridge, became the first woman to receive a doctorate in science from Oxford (1929) and a pioneer of research in protein structure and molecular biology.

In Britain during the 1930s, socialist commitments helped others flourish within scientific partnerships such as those of Dorothy and Joseph Needham, Tony and Norman Pirie, and Kathleen Yardley Lonsdale and Thomas Lonsdale. Among the accomplished women scientists from this group was Dorothy Crowfoot Hodgkin, who won a Nobel Prize in chemistry (1964) for solving the structure of key biomedical compounds, most notably penicillin and vitamin B-12. Still others made their marks by venturing into offbeat areas of their disciplines, a career path exemplified by Barbara McClintock, who in 1983 received the Nobel Prize for her discovery of genomic transposition (jumping genes).

Still women continued to face discrimination in most fields of science, and many found it difficult to reconcile the demands of research with those of home and family. Some women scientists, believing that the demands of science could not be squared with the traditional role of women, remained single. Three-quarters of women scientists who did marry collaborated with their scientist husbands. But while a scientific marriage often facilitated acceptance into a broader scientific community, it often led colleagues to assume that the work of the wife was secondary to that of the husband.

Women scientists often had difficulty isolating the role of gender discrimination in their professional lives. For example, socialist women scientists who believed in the Marxist emphasis upon class as the dominant social relation long resisted the idea of struggling against gender bias because it would detract from the presumably more basic class struggle. Many other women scientists disliked claiming attention as women, as opposed to being acknowledged as just (presumably gender-neutral) scientists.

Beginning in the 1960s, the civil rights movement and the women's movement combined to subject gender inequality in science to social, cultural, and legal scrutiny. Overt discrimination became illegal. Shortages in scientific personnel in the late 1980s led to development of a gender-responsive science policy that would enable more women to become scientists and combine their professional careers with diverse family choices. Several policy initiatives by the National Science Foundation, the National Institutes of Health, and other agencies made significant headway on the problem of recruitment. Nevertheless, gender segregation continues to plague fields such as medicine, where most women congregate in pediatrics, obstetrics, and psychiatry. New fields such as biotechnology and informatics also display a consistent pattern of gender hierarchy, inequality, and de facto segregation.

In the late twentieth century, the sociocultural expectation that women are the primary family caregivers remained a major bottleneck in reaching gender parity in science. A combination of science policy and social policy has been suggested as a plausible solution. In the twenty-first century, as innovation in reproductive biology redefines the concept of the family, and as globalization eases national and cultural constraints upon formerly dominated groups such as women, science may become a vanguard of gender equality.

PNINA G. ABIR-AM

X RAYS. When the president of the Berlin Physical Society spoke at its jubilee in 1896, he could not manage much enthusiasm about the future of its science. Later he said that, had he known about the discovery of X rays, he would instead have expressed his joy "that the second fifty years in the life of the society had begun as brilliantly as the first." His reaction was representative: from the minute Wilhelm Conrad Röntgen made known his discovery, physicists recognized it as a tonic to their senescent science. X rays challenged theory, abetted experiments, made a public sensation, and gave doctors a diagnostic tool of unprecedented power. Until the medical profession could provide itself with the necessary apparatus, people who swallowed pins or stopped buckshot appealed to physicists to locate the mischief.

X rays refused easy classification into the available categories. They did not bend in electric or magnetic fields and thus did not belong among charged particles; and since they could not be reflected or refracted, they failed the test for light. Most physicists supposed them to be a peculiar form of electromagnetic radiation. The peculiarities of X rays included behavior unbefitting a wave, however. As the English physicist William Henry Bragg stressed, an X ray could impart to an electron almost as much energy as had gone into the ray's creation. But if a wave, the ray should have spread out from its point of origin, diffusing its energy; how then could the entire original energy reassemble when a small section of the wave front encountered an electron? This difficulty appeared the stronger when in 1912 Max von Laue and his colleagues at the University of Munich, and in 1913 Bragg and his son William Lawrence Bragg, then a student at Cambridge, showed, respectively, that a crystal can both refract and reflect X rays. Röntgen's discovery thus appeared to have properties characteristic of a wave and of a particle.

At first physicists did not worry over the properties that conflicted with the wave model confirmed by the diffraction experiments. The wave model allowed investigations of crystal structure, pioneered by the Braggs. It also made possible determination of the frequencies of the characteristic X rays emitted by the elements. These rays resemble the visible line spectrum but are simpler, depending only on the atomic number, Z, and a "screening constant" σ, indicative of the place within the atom where the electron involved in the emission of a given line ends up. The study of characteristic X-ray spectra thus helped to elucidate atomic structure. In his influential theory of the constitution of atoms of 1922, Niels Bohr made systematic use of X-ray data to determine the quantum numbers of atomic electrons. The doublet structure of some X-ray lines helped Samuel Goudsmit and George Uhlenbeck to construct the concept of electron spin in 1925.

Meanwhile, the American physicist Arthur Holly Compton reopened the shelved problem of the nature of X rays by his discovery in 1922 of what was soon called the Compton effect. According to Compton, a high-frequency X ray collides with an electron as if both were billiard balls. From relativity and the quantum theory Compton assigned the X ray a frequency, v; an energy, hv; and a momentum, hv/c. By assuming that energy and momentum are conserved in the collision, he obtained a relation between Δv (the ray's loss in frequency), T (the electron's gain in momentum), and the angles between the velocities of the interacting particles.

Measurement confirmed Compton's equations and lent such support to the material conception of X rays that thereafter atomic theorists felt obliged to work both particle and wave properties into their descriptions. Louis de Broglie moderated the behavior of photons (the word Albert Einstein introduced in 1905 for hypothetical particles of high-frequency light) by coupling them to unobservable waves;

William Henry Bragg (1862–1942) and William Lawrence Bragg (1890–1971), father and son, co-inventors of the technique of X-ray interference by reflection from crystals, for which they received the Nobel Prize in Physics in 1915. This photograph dates from February 1942.

Bohr, Hendrik Kramers, and John Slater abandoned the conservation of energy in considering the relation between electron jumps and emitted light. Erwin Schrödinger followed up de Broglie's lead, and Werner Heisenberg reworked the Bohr-Kramers-Slater approach and other work of Kramers to arrive at their alternative versions of quantum physics.

The completion of the quantum theory of the electronic cloud of the atom did not end the usefulness of characteristic high-frequency radiation in studying the fundamental structure of matter. Nature produces very hard X rays in spontaneous nuclear decay. Beginning in the 1930s, physicists analyzed the energies of these "gamma rays" for data about nuclear transformations and for help in specifying nuclear energy levels. More recently, X rays from stars have given information about stellar processes.

The diagnostic uses of X rays soon gave rise to a new profession, radiology, and, when their effect on lesions and tumors was noticed, to therapeutics against skin diseases and cancers. Demand for more penetrating and more plentiful X rays prompted a rapid development of apparatus, culminating just before World War I in the high-voltage, heated-cathode Coolidge tube. The modest gains of physics from these developments rapidly multiplied after the war, in part because of wartime electrical engineering and surplus electrical equipment. Pioneers in California—at the newly established Caltech in Pasadena and at the University of California at Berkeley—pushed X-ray generators to gigantic sizes to produce radiation that could reach deep-lying tumors. Medically they achieved little, but technically they advanced substantially the art of high-power electrical engineering in the service of science. Some of the techniques and funding for these machines supported the early development of particle accelerators for nuclear physics.

The capacity of X rays to peer into previously secret places has had many applications beyond medicine. They have been used to inspect welds, test materials, fit shoes, detect dental cavities, search pyramids for mummies, etch circuits, and so on. The use of characteristic X-ray spectra to analyze the elementary makeup of even minute samples of materials became a staple in chemical assays. The optimism immediately inspired by Röntgen's discovery, and reaffirmed in the presentation to him of the first Nobel Prize in physics (1901), has been justified repeatedly in the sciences, medicine, and industry, although long exposures and inappropriate therapies have claimed martyrs among physicians and patients.

J. L. Heilbron

X

ZOOLOGY. Many early modern medical treatises entitle the section or book devoted to the remedies and drugs obtained from animals "Zoology." The word's current meaning as the general science of animals emerged later, with the splitting of the old domain of natural history into several branches during the eighteenth century. Already in the sixteenth and seventeenth centuries, however, the study of animals and subfields like ornithology and entomology were the subject of independent studies by Guillaume Rondelet, William Turner, Konrad Gesner, Pierre Belon, Ulisse Aldrovandi, Thomas Moffett, John Jonston, Thomas Willis, John Ray, and Filippo Buonanni.

In 1728, the map of knowledge provided by Ephraim Chambers's *Encyclopaedia* depicted zoology as a branch of natural history, on par with meteorology, hydrology, mineralogy, and "phytology," that is, botany. The *Encyclopédie* of Denis Diderot and Jean d'Alembert (1751) placed under "zoologie" a list of subjects ranging from anatomy and medicine to hunting and falconry. The first edition of the *Encyclopaedia Britannica* (1771) devoted the entire article "Natural history" to zoology, reserving separate articles for botany and mineralogy. Its compilers adopted for the animal kingdom the system of classification provided by Carl Linnaeus, which they presented as the best and the least understood among the many systems that had been invented to introduce some order into the diversity of animal life.

In the meantime, French naturalists like René-Antoine de Réaumur, Mathurin-Jacques Brisson, and George-Louis LeClerc, Comte de Buffon, and their collaborators had devoted studies of unprecedented thoroughness and breadth to whole or parts of the animal kingdom, inspiring frequent imitation. In the second half of the eighteenth century, a growing number of authors used "zoology" in the title of books devoted to the description of the animals living in a certain region or country. From the 1770s, these local and national zoologies became a successful genre; naturalists throughout Europe and the colonies felt pressed to contribute the zoology of a region to the growing body of knowledge about animals. Similar works later became the source for the new field of biogeography.

Recognition of the independence of the study of animals came in the later 1790s with the creation at the Musée d'Histoire Naturelle in Paris of chairs devoted to specialized areas of zoological research. Jean-Baptiste de Lamarck, Georges Cuvier, and Étienne Geoffroy Saint-Hilaire were among those appointed. While adhering to diverse, often conflicting views on broad, potentially inflammatory issues such as science and religion, science and politics, evolution, and the fundamental properties of life, these naturalists and their followers in several countries shared basic notions concerning form, function, development, and classification. They also shared basic working tools offered by the cognate fields of comparative anatomy, physiology, embryology, and paleontology. During the central decades of the nine-

teenth century these common notions and tools—together with the widely perceived significance for culture at large of the areas of disagreement within the science of animals—helped zoologists to establish a new, powerful academic field. Among the milestones in its development were the establishment in 1848 of the *Zeitschrift für Wissenschaftliche Zoologie* by Rudolf Albert von Kölliker, the creation in 1826 of the Zoological Society that ran the London Zoo (soon imitated by similar societies elsewhere), the foundation in 1859 of the Museum of Comparative Zoology at Harvard on the initiative of Louis Agassiz, and the creation of *specialized* zoological departments within the natural history museums set up in several countries during the second half of the century. Beginning around 1860, universities throughout Europe recognized zoology as a major specialty within their natural science schools; chairs devoted to zoology multiplied in the following decades.

John James Audubon (1785–1851), French-American naturalist

Between the 1870s and the 1890s, institutional development profited from the appeal of evolutionary theories. The fame of well-known supporters of evolution like Carl Gegenbaur and Ernst Haeckel, and the renown of the teaching in German universities, attracted zoology students from other European countries and North America. The establishment of the Zoological Station in Naples (1872) on the initiative of the German Anton Dohrn, supported by Charles Darwin, and of the International Commission on Zoological Nomenclature (1895) indicated the international perspective of zoologists of the period.

Mainstream late-nineteenth-century zoology centered on morphology, the determination of phylogenetic relationships among living forms. From the 1890s, however, a new generation of zoologists trained within that same tradition launched a "revolt from morphology," adopting an experimental rather than a descriptive approach. The protagonists of the new trend were the German zoologists Wilhelm Roux, Theodor Boveri, Hans Driesch, and Hans Spemann and the Americans Edmund Beecher Wilson and Thomas Hunt Morgan. With their work, substantial portions of zoological research moved from natural history into experimental biology, which had developed in the meantime, pursuing goals set by experimental physiology and embryology.

In the new context, which characterized much twentieth-century frontier biology, zoology and its specialties provided convenient frameworks for teaching and institutional organization rather than major subjects for research. Yet the fundamental contributions of zoologists to the evolutionary synthesis; the introduction of new fields of study like ethology, behavioral ecology, and mathematical biology; and the discovery in the 1990s of organisms in environmental niches formerly regarded as impossibly hostile have kept zoology a thriving branch of the life sciences.

GIULIANO PANCALDI

Z

Acknowledgments from Oxford Edition

The Editor expresses his heartfelt thanks to his associate editors and consultants, whose names appear on page 316. The contributors who have written over 20,000 words each deserve special thanks not only for their articles but also for helping to insure that the *Companion* has the character the editors desired. To create this character they assembled in New York City a lustrum ago at the invitation of Linda Halvorson Morse of Oxford University Press, who conceived the notion that the history of science might make a suitable subject for a *Companion*. That two-day meeting, in which James Miller, who helped to turn the plan into action, also participated, was the best of seminars. Even before the first article was assigned, the *Companion* had revealed to its editors many new facets of the business they had been engaged in for decades.

The major work at the Press has taken place in the Trade Reference Department headed by Nancy Toff. There Fritz McDonald and, since January 2001, Martin Coleman have been chiefly responsible for the *Companion's* fate. Martin, on whom the major burden of dealing with contributors has fallen, deserves the thanks and gratitude of everyone associated with the book for his tact, resourcefulness, and unfailing dependability.

Editors and Consultants from Oxford Edition

Editor In Chief

J. L. Heilbron, *Professor of History and The Vice Chancellor, Emeritus, University of California, Berkeley, Senior Research Fellow, Worcester College, Oxford*

Editors

James Bartholomew, *Professor of History, The Ohio State University*

Jim Bennett, *Director, Museum of the History of Science, University of Oxford*

Frederic Lawrence Holmes, *Avalon Professor of the History of Medicine, Section of the History of Medicine, Yale University*

Rachel Laudan, *Guanajuato, Mexico*

Giuliano Pancaldi, *Professor of History of Science, University of Bologna*

Consultants

Theodore S. Feldman, *Boston, Massachusetts*

Loren R. Graham, *Professor of History of Science, Massachusetts Institute of Technology/Harvard University*

Norriss S. Hetherington, *Director, Institute for the History of Astronomy, and Visiting Scholar, University of California, Berkeley*

Mary Jo Nye, *Thomas Hart and Mary Jones Horning Professor of the Humanities and Professor of History, Oregon State University*

Kathryn Olesko, *Associate Professor, Georgetown University*

Naomi Oreskes, *Associate Professor, University of California, San Diego*

Alan J. Rocke, *Henry Eldridge Bourne Professor of History, Case Western Reserve University, Cleveland, Ohio*

Directory of Contributors from Oxford Edition

Finn Aaserud, *Director, Niels Bohr Archive, Copenhagen, Denmark*

Pnina Abir-Am, *University of California, Berkeley Women in Science*

Theodore Arabatzis, *Assistant Professor of History and Philosophy of Science, University of Athens*

Hervé Arribart, *Scientific Director, Saint-Gobain Recherche*

Jon Arrizabalaga, *Department of History of Science, Institución Mila I Fontanals, Consejo Superior de Investigaciones Científicas (CSIC), Barcelona, Spain*

Lawrence Badash, *Professor of History of Science, University of California, Santa Barbara*

James Bartholomew, *Professor of History, The Ohio State University*

Jim Bennett, *Director, Museum of the History of Science, University of Oxford*

Bernadette Bensaude-Vincent, *Professor of History and Philosophy of Science, Université de Paris X*

Mario Bertolotti, *Professor of Physics, University of Rome*

Alan Beyerchen, *Professor of History, Ohio State University*

Mario Biagioli, *Professor of History of Science, Harvard University*

Marvin Bolt, *Associate Curator, History of Astronomy Department, Adler Planetarium & Astronomy Museum*

Joanne Bourgeois, *Associate Professor of Geological Sciences, University of Washington, Seattle, Washington*

Jonathan Bowen, *Professor of Computing, South Bank University, London*

Brian Bowers, *Retired Senior Curator (Electrical Engineering), Science Museum, London*

Bruce Bradley, *Librarian for History of Science, Linda Hall Library of Science, Engineering & Technology*

Robert Brain, *Associate Professor of History of Science, Harvard University*

Jeffrey C. Brautigam, *Assistant Professor of History, Hanover College, Indiana*

Paolo Brenni, *Istituto E Museo di Storia della Scienza, Florence*

William H. Brock, *Professor Emeritus of History of Science, University of Leicester*

John H. Brooke, *Andreas Idreos Professor of Science and Religion, University of Oxford*

Randall Brooks, *Curator, Physical Sciences and Space, Canada Science and Technology Museum*

Laurie M. Brown, *Professor of Physics and Astronomy, Emeritus, Northwestern University*

Janet Browne, *Reader in the History of Biology, Wellcome Trust Centre for the History of Medicine, University College, London*

Jed Buchwald, *Dreyfuss Professor of History, California Institute of Technology*

Victor P. Budura, *Vice President for Space Support, East West Enterprises, Inc., Huntsville, Alabama*

Joe D. Burchfield, *Associate Professor of History, Northern Illinois University*

Piers Bursill-Hall, *Department of Pure Mathematics and Mathematical Statistics, University of Cambridge*

Johannes Büttner, *Univ. Professor, Medizinische Hochschule Hannover*

Helen Bynum, *Honorary Research Fellow, Wellcome Trust Centre for the History of Medicine, University College, London*

William Bynum, *Professor of the History of Medicine, Wellcome Trust Centre for the History of Medicine, University College, London*

Regis Cabral, *International R&D Manager, Uminova Center, Umeå University, Umeå, Sweden*

David Cahan, *Professor of History, University of Nebraska-Lincoln*

Geoffrey Cantor, *Professor of the History of Science, University of Leeds*

Tian Yu Cao, *Associate Professor of Physics, Boston University*

Andrea Carlino, *Maître d'Enseignement et de Recherche, Institut d'Histoire de la Médecine et de la Santé, Université de Genève*

Kenneth J. Carpenter, *Professor Emeritus of Experimental Nutrition, University of California, Berkeley*

David C. Cassidy, *Professor of Natural Science, Hofstra University*

Paul Ceruzzi, *Curator, Aerospace Electronics and Computing, Smithsonian Institution*

Allan Chapman, *Member of the Faculty of Modern History, University of Oxford*

Gail Charnley, *Healthrisk Strategies, Washington, D.C.*

Guido Cimino, *Professor of History of Science and Psychology, Università di Roma*

Eugene Cittadino, *New York University*

William T. Clower, *Research Associate, Department of Neurobiology, University of Pittsburgh*

I. Bernard Cohen, *Victor S. Thomas Professor of the History of Science, Emeritus, Harvard University*

H. Floris Cohen, *Professor Emeritus of History of Science, University of Twente*

Roger Cooter, *Professor of History of Medicine, Wellcome Unit for the History of Medicine, University of East Anglia, Norwich*

Pietro Corsi, *Professor of the History of Science and Directeur d'Etudes, Université de Paris and Ecole des Hautes Etudes en Sciences Sociales*

Patrick Curry, *Associate Lecturer, Centre for the Study of Cultural Astronomy and Astrology, Bath Spa University College, London*

Olivier Darrigol, *CNRS, Paris*

Edward B. Davis, *Distinguished Professor of the History of Science, Messiah College, Granthan, Pennsylvania*

Alexis De Greiff, *Assistant Professor, Observatorio Astronómico Nacional, Universidad Nacional de Colombia at Santafé de Bogotá*

Margaret Deacon, *Southampton Oceanography Centre, University of Southampton*

Suzanne Débarbat, *Astronome Titulaire Honoraire, Observatoire de Paris*

Robert J. Deltete, *Professor of Philosophy, Seattle University*

Michael Dettelbach, *Associate Director, Corporate and Foundation Relations, Boston University*

David DeVorkin, *Curator, History of Astronomy, National Air and Space Museum, Smithsonian Institution*

Matthias Doerries, *Professor of the History of Science, Université Louis Pasteur, Strasbourg, France*

François Duchesneau, *Professor of Philosophy, University of Montreal, Canada*

Jacalyn Duffin, *Hannah Chair, History of Medicine, Queen's University, Kingston, Ontario, Canada*

William Eamon, *Professor of History, New Mexico State University*

Frank Egerton, *Professor of History, University of Wisconsin*

Ralph Eshelman, *Principal, Eshelman and Associates, Lusby, Maryland*

Henry Etzkowitz, *Director, Science Policy Institute, State University of New York at Purchase*

Isobel Falconer, *Research Associate, Open University, United Kingdom*

Bernardino Fantini, *Director, Louis-Jeantet Institute for the History of Medicine, Geneva, Switzerland*

Patricia Fara, *Fellow of Clare College, University of Cambridge*

Theodore S. Feldman, *Boston, Massachusetts*

Maurice A. Finocchiaro, *Distinguished Professor of Philosophy, University of Nevada, Las Vegas*

Paul Forman, *Curator, Modern Physics Collection, National Museum of American History, Smithsonian Institution*

Robert Fox, *Professor of the History of Science, University of Oxford*

Tore Frängsmyr, *Professor in History of Science, Uppsala University*

Alan Gabbey, *Professor of Philosophy, Barnard College, Columbia University*

Elizabeth Garber, *Associate Professor of History, State University of New York at Stony Brook*

Thomas P. Gariepy, *Professor of the History of Science, Stonehill College, Easton, Massachusetts*

Kostas Gavroglu, *Professor of History of Science, University of Athens, Greece*

Owen Gingerich, *Research Professor of Astronomy and History of Science, Harvard-Smithsonian Center for Astrophysics*

Tal Golan, *Assistant Professor of History, Ben Gurion University, Israel*

Gregory A. Good, *Associate Professor of History of Science, West Virginia University*

Michael Gordin, *Assistant Professor of History, Princeton University*

Gennady Gorelik, *Research Fellow, Center for Philosophy and History of Science, Boston University*

Penelope Gouk, *Senior Research Lecturer, Wellcome Unit for the History of Medicine, University of Manchester*

Anthony Grafton, *Henry Putnam University Professor of History, Princeton University*

Loren R. Graham, *Professor of History of Science, Massachusetts Institute of Technology/Harvard University*

Ivor Grattan-Guinness, *Professor of the History of Mathematics and Logic Emeritus, Middlesex University*

Jeremy Gray, *Senior Lecturer in Mathematics, The Open University*

John L. Greenberg, *Paris*

Mott T. Greene, *John Magee Professor of Science and Values, University of Puget Sound*

Anita Guerrini, *Associate Professor of Environmental Studies and History, University of California, Santa Barbara*

John F. Guilmartin, *Associate Professor of History, Ohio State University*

W. D. Hackmann, *Emeritus Senior Assistant Keeper, Museum of the History of Science, Oxford*

Roger Hahn, *Professor of History, University of California, Berkeley*

Lesley A. Hall, *Archivist, Honorary Lecturer in History of Medicine, London Wellcome Library, University College, London*

Karl Hall, *Assistant Professor, Central European University, Budapest*

Robert Dale Hall, *Rabat American School, Morocco*

Anne Hardy, *Reader in the History of Medicine, Wellcome Trust Centre for the History of Medicine, University College, London*

Oren Solomon Harman, *History of Science, Harvard University*

P. M. Harman, *Professor of the History of Science, Lancaster University*

Takehiko Hashimoto, *Professor of History of Science and Technology, University of Tokyo*

J. L. Heilbron, *Professor of History and the Vice Chancellor, Emeritus, University of California, Berkeley; Senior Research Fellow, Worcester College, Oxford*

Arne Hessenbruch, *Researcher in the Project on History of Recent Science and Technology on the Web, Dibner Institute, Massachusetts Institute of Technology*

Norriss S. Hetherington, *Director, Institute for the History of Astronomy, And Visiting Scholar, University of California, Berkeley*

Frederic Lawrence Holmes, *Avalon Professor of the History of Medicine, Section of the History of Medicine, Yale University*

Gerald Holton, *Mallinckrodt Professor of Physics and Professor of History of Science, Emeritus, Harvard University*

R. W. Home, *Professor of History and Philosophy of Science, University of Melbourne*

David W. Hughes, *Professor of Astronomy, University of Sheffield, Department of Physics and Astronomy*

Bruce J. Hunt, *Associate Professor of History, University of Texas*

Myles W. Jackson, *Assistant Professor of the History of Science, Willamette University*

Margaret Jacob, *Professor of History, University of California, Los Angeles*

Stephen Jacyna, *Wellcome Trust Centre for the History of Medicine, University College, London*

Frank A. J. L. James, *Reader in History of Science, The Royal Institution of Great Britain*

William T. Johnson, *Mesa, Arizona*

Jeffrey Allan Johnson, *Associate Professor of History, Villanova University*

Stephen Johnston, *Assistant Keeper, Museum of the History of Science, University of Oxford*

Paul Josephson, *Associate Professor of History, Colby College, Waterville, Maine*

Lily Kay, deceased

A. G. Keller, *Department of History, University of Leicester*

Bettyann Holtzmann Kevles, *Lecturer, Department of History, Yale University*

D. J. Kevles, *Stanley Woodward Professor of History, Yale University*

Peggy Kidwell, *Curator of Mathematics, National Museum of American History*

Rudolph Kippenhahn, *The Max Planck Institute of Astrophysics at Garching (retired)*

Sally Gregory Kohlstedt, *Program of History of Science and Technology, University of Minnesota*

Alexei Kojevnikov, *Associate Professor of History, Department of History, University of Georgia, Athens*

Helge Kragh, *Professor of History of Science and Technology, University of Aarhus, Denmark*

Jan Lacki, *Assistant Professor of History and Philosophy of Physics, University of Geneva*

Marcel C. LaFollette, *Washington, D.C.*

L. R. Lagerstrom, *Senior Lecturer, Electrical and Computer Engineering, University of California, Davis*

Rachel Laudan, *Guanajuato, Mexico*

Peretz Lavie, *André Ballard Professor of Biological Psychiatry, The Technion Sleep Laboratory, Haifa, Israel*

Susan E. Lederer, *Associate Professor, History of Medicine, Yale University*

John E. Lesch, *Professor of History, University of California, Berkeley*

Bruce V. Lewenstein, *Associate Professor of Science Communication, Cornell University*

Henry Lowood, *Curator for History of Science and Technology Collections, Stanford University Libraries*

A. J. Lustig, *Postdoctoral Fellow, Dibner Institute, Massachusetts Institute of Technology*

Marjorie C. Malley, *Cary, North Carolina*

Joan Mark, *Research Associate in the History of Anthropology, Peabody Museum of Archaeology and Ethnology, Harvard University*

Ulrich Marsch, *Max Planck Gesellschaft Munich, Germany*

Ben Marsden, *Cultural History Programme Coordinator, School of History and History of Art, University of Aberdeen*

Pauline M. H. Mazumdar, *Professor Emeritus of the History of Medicine, University of Toronto*

Renato G. Mazzolini, *Professor of History of Science, Università degli Studi di Trento, Italy*

Domenico Bertoloni Meli, *Professor of the History of Science, Indiana University*

Andrew Mendelsohn, *Governor's Lecturer in History of Science and Medicine, Imperial College, University of London*

David P. Miller, *Senior Lecturer, School of History and Philosophy of Science, University of New South Wales, Sydney*

John Mills, *Adjunct Professor of Psychology, University of Calgary, Calgary, Alberta, Canada*

Philip Mirowski, *Carl Koch Professor of Economics and the History and Philosophy of Science, University of Notre Dame*

Susan Mossman, *Curator of Materials Science, The Science Museum, London*

Shigeru Nakayama, *Professor Emeritus, Kanagawa University, Tokyo*

Meera Nanda, *West Hartford, Connecticut*

Simon Naylor, *Lecturer in Human Geography, University of Bristol*

William R. Newman, *Professor, Department of History and Philosophy of Science, Indiana University*

Thomas Nickles, *Professor and Chair, Philosophy Department, University of Nevada, Reno*

Vivian Nutton, *Professor of the History of Medicine, University College, London*

Mary Jo Nye, *Thomas Hart and Mary Jones Horning Professor of the Humanities and Professor of History, Oregon State University*

Robert C. Olby, *Research Professor, Department of the History and Philosophy of Science, University of Pittsburgh*

Kathryn Olesko, *Associate Professor, Georgetown University*

Paolo Palladino, *Senior Lecturer in History of Science, Technology, and Medicine, Lancaster University*

Frank A. Palocsay, *Emeritus Professor, Department of Chemistry, James Madison University, Harrisonburg, Virginia*

Giuliano Pancaldi, *Professor of History of Science, University of Bologna*

John Parascandola, *Public Health Service Historian, U. S. Department of Health and Human Services*

Manolis Patiniotis, *Lecturer, Department of History and Philosophy of Science, Athens University*

John Powers, *Instructor, New School University, New York*

Lewis Pyenson, *Research Professor, University of Louisiana at Lafayette*

Jessica Ratcliff, *Museum of the History of Science, University of Oxford*

Scott C. Ratzan, *Editor,* Journal of Health Communication: International Perspectives, *George Washington University School of Public Health*

Philip Rehbock, *Professor, Department of History, University of Hawaii*

Richard Rice, *Florence, Montana*

Robert J. Richards, *Professor of History and Philosophy of Science, The University of Chicago*

Robert C. Richardson, *Professor of Philosophy, University of Cincinnati*

Michael Riordan, *Adjunct Professor of Physics, University of California, Santa Cruz*

Jessica Riskin, *Assistant Professor of History, Stanford University, California*

Guenter B. Risse, *Professor, Department of Anthropology, History, and Social Medicine, University of California, San Francisco*

Alan J. Rocke, *Henry Eldridge Bourne Professor of History, Case Western Reserve University, Cleveland, Ohio*

Nicolaas A. Rupke, *Professor of the History of Science and Director of the Institute for the History of Science, Göttingen University*

Arturo Russo, *Associate Professor of History of Physics, University of Palermo*

Rose-Mary Sargent, *Professor of Philosophy, Merrimack College, North Andover, Massachusetts*

Sara Schechner, *David P. Wheatland Curator, Collection of Historical Scientific Instruments, Harvard University*

Jutta Schickore, *Research Fellow, Department of History and Philosophy of Science, University of Cambridge*

Londa Schiebinger, *Edwin E. Sparks Professor of History of Science, Pennsylvania State University*

Steven E. Schoenherr, *Professor, Department of History, University of San Diego*

Silvan S. Schweber, *Professor of Physics and Richard Koret Professor in the History of Ideas, Brandeis University, Waltham, Massachusetts*

Robert Seidel, *Professor of History of Science and Technology, University of Minnesota*

Dennis Sepper, *Professor of Philosophy, University of Dallas*

H. Otto Sibum, *Associate Professor, Research Director, Max Planck Institute for the History of Science, Berlin*

Ruth Lewin Sime, *Professor Emeritus of Chemistry, Sacramento City College*

Crosbie Smith, *Professor of History of Science, University of Kent at Canterbury*

Vassiliki B. Smocovitis, *Associate Professor of History, University of Florida*

Darwin Stapleton, *Executive Director, Rockefeller Archive Center*

F. Richard Stephenson, *Professorial Fellow in Astronomy, Department of Physics, University of Durham*

Robert K. Stewart, *Sing Tao Professor of International Journalism, Ohio University*

James Strick, *Assistant Professor, Science, Technology, and Society Program, Franklin and Marshall College, Lancaster, Pennsylvania*

W. T. Sullivan, *Professor of Astronomy, University of Washington*

William C. *Summers, Professor of Therapeutic Radiology, Molecular Biophysics and Biochemistry, and Lecturer in History, Yale University*

Abha Sur, *Lecturer, Department of Urban Studies and Planning, Massachusetts Institute of Technology*

Liba Taub, *Curator and Director, Whipple Museum of the History of Science*

Mary M. Thomas, *Department of History of Science and Technology, University of Minnesota*

Phillip Thurtle, *Assistant Professor of Anthropology and Sociology, Carleton University, Ottawa, Ontario, Canada*

Daniel P. Todes, *Associate Professor, The Johns Hopkins University*

Maria Trumpler, *Lecturer, Department of the History of Science, Harvard University*

Robert C. Ulin, *Professor of Anthropology, University of Western Michigan*

Anne van Helden, *Museum Boerhaave, Leiden, The Netherlands*

Denys Vaughan, *Research Fellow, Science Museum Library, London*

Theo Verbeek, *Professor of Early Modern Philosophy, Utrecht University*

Christiane Vilain, *Assistant Professor of Physics and Epistemology of Physics, University Denis-Diderot, Paris*

James Voelkel, *Professor, Department of the History of Science, Johns Hopkins University*

J. Samuel Walker, *Historian, Nuclear Regulatory Commission*

Alice N. Walters, *Associate Professor of History, University of Massachusetts, Lowell*

Mike Ware, *Honorary Fellow in Chemistry, University of Manchester*

Stephen J. Weininger, *Max-Planck-Institüt für Wissenschaftsgeschichte*

Kathleen Wellman, *Professor of History, Southern Methodist University*

Petra Werner, *Berlin-Brandenburgian Academy of Science*

Gary Westfahl, *Instructor, University of California, Riverside*

Peter Westwick, *Senior Research Fellow in Humanities, California Institute of Technology*

Curtis Wilson, *Tutor Emeritus, St. John's College, Annapolis, Maryland*

Eric Winsberg, *Assistant Professor, Department of Philosophy, University of South Florida*

Alison Winter, *Associate Professor of History, University of Chicago*

Roland Wittje, *Norwegian University of Science and Technology*

Richard Yeo, *Professor, History of Science, School of Humanities, Griffith University, Australia*

Further Reading

Readers who seek more information than entries in this *Companion* can provide will find a rich array of reference sources relevant to history of science. In particular, those in search of biographical information about people who are not given separate entries here will find in the *Dictionary of Scientific Biography (DSB)*, ed. Charles C. Gillispie (18 vols., including supplements and index, 1970-1990), compact accounts of life and work for figures from antiquity through the middle of the twentieth century, as well as information about major publications and archival sources. Among other specialized biographical sources are *World Who's Who in Science: A Biographical Dictionary of Notable Scientists from Antiquity to the Present*, ed. Allen G. Debus (1968); *The Biographical Dictionary of Scientists*, ed. Roy Porter and Marilyn Ogilvie (3rd ed., 2000), with "historical reviews of the sciences" as well as biographical entries; *Biographical Encyclopedia of Scientists*, ed. Richard Olson (5 vols., 1998); David Millar et al., *The Cambridge Dictionary of Scientists* (1996); and Robert M. Gascoigne, *A Historical Catalogue of Scientists and Scientific Books from the Earliest Times to the Close of the Nineteenth Century* (1984).

Many entries in *McGraw-Hill Modern Scientists and Engineers* (3 vols., 1980) are autobiographical.

Of particular relevance to historians of science is a bio-bibliographical project of broad scope and long standing: Johann Christian Poggendorff, *Biographisch-literarisches Handwörterbuch der exakten Naturwissenschaften* (1863–); vols. 1–7:1 are now available on CD-ROM, ed. Sächsische Akademie der Wissenschaften zu Leipzig (2000), facilitating searches across volumes. See http://www.poggendorff.com/.

Those who wish to pursue topics addressed in this *Companion* will also profit from a bibliography of admirable scope and complexity, the annual *Current Bibliography of the History of Science and Its Cultural Influences* (formerly *Critical Bibliography* [etc.]), which appears in the journal *Isis;* various cumulations under the title *Isis Cumulative Bibliography* cover 1913–1965 (ed. Magda Whitrow), 1966–1975, 1976–1985, and 1986–1995 (ed. John Neu). Both annual and cumulative versions cover general topics in history of science, as well as specific scientific subjects and periods. The online *History of Science, Technology, and Medicine (HSTM)* bibliographical database made available by the Research Libraries Group (http://www.rlg.org) now integrates four bibliographies: the Isis *Current Bibliography of the History of Science* (as described above), the *Current Bibliography in the History of Technology* (as published in the journal *Technology and Culture*), the *Bibliografia Italiana di Storia della Scienza* and the *Wellcome Library for the History and Understanding of Medicine*. Updated annually, the database covers 1975 to the present. History of science is an international field, as the coverage of the DSB, the *Isis Current Bibliography*, and the HSTM database make amply clear; this essay, however, emphasizes sources in English, and is, of necessity, highly selective.

Guides To Reference Sources For History of Science

The field of history of science benefits from numerous lists of specialized reference sources, among them *Reference Books for the Historian of Science: A Handlist*, ed. S. A. Jayawardene (1982), and the section on reference sources in Gordon L. Miller, *The History of Science: An Annotated Bibliography* (1992). The possibility of browsing (print) titles added annually makes Doug Stewart, *History of Science/Science Studies: Reference Sources* (http://www.wsulibs.wsu.edu/hist-of-science/) especially useful. *Starting Points in the Study of Science, Medicine and Technology* (comp. Ed Morman, 1996; rev. Christine Ruggere, 1999, http://www2.h-net.msu.edu/~smt/starting-points.html) includes chronologies, biographical sources, dictionaries and encyclopedias, periodical lists, and manuscript lists and archival guides, among other categories. The WWW *Virtual Library for the History of Science, Technology, & Medicine*, established in 1994, is now available through *echo: Exploring & Collecting History Online* (http://echo.gmu.edu/center/). See also Ronald C. Tobey, Horus *Gets In Gear. A Beginner's Guide to Research in the History of Science* (http://www.horuspublications.com/guide/tpl.html) and "History of Science" at *Teaching History's World Wide Web Links for History Teachers* (http://www.emporia.edu/socsci/journal/links.htm). Sites that are updated frequently are less likely to be compromised by broken links.

Dictionaries, Thesauri, Encyclopedias, Chronologies, Bibliographies

The tradition in reference sources represented by *A Guide to the History of Science* (1952) by George Sarton, founder of *Isis*, has continued. Research guides, dictionaries, thesauri, encyclopedias, and chronologies in English include *Companion to the History of Modern Science*, ed. R. C. Olby et al. (1990); *Dictionary of the History of Science*, ed. W. F. Bynum et al. (1981); Anton Sebastian, *A Dictionary of the History of Science* (2001); *Companion Encyclopedia of the History of Medicine*, ed. W. F. Bynum and Roy Porter (2 vols., 1993); *Encyclopaedia of the History of Science, Technology, and Medicine in Non-western Cultures*, ed. Helaine Selin (1997); *Infor-*

mation Sources in the History of Science and Medicine, ed. Pietro Corsi and Paul Weindling (1983), especially part II on reference materials and sources; *Reader's Guide to the History of Science,* ed. Arne Hessenbruch (2000); and Ellis Mount and Barbara A. List, *Milestones in Science and Technology* (2nd ed., 1994). Such works as Robert M. Gascoigne, *A Chronology of the History of Science, 1450–1900* (1987); Alexander Hellemans and Bryan Bunch, *The Timetables of Science* (1988; 1991), *The History of Science and Technology: A Narrative Chronology* (2 vols., 1988, trans. of *Scienza e tecnica,* 1975); and Claire L. Parkinson, *Breakthroughs: a Chronology of Great Achievements In Science and Mathematics, 1200–1930* (1985) aid the chronologically inclined. For others, see Stewart and Morman/Ruggiere's online guides.

Works of somewhat closer focus still contain much of general interest. Routledge, for example, has published encyclopedias for history of mathematical sciences, of medicine, of technology, and of Arabic science. The series *Garland Encyclopedias in the History of Science* includes works on science and religion, science in the United States, astronomy, and scientific instruments. William E. Burns, *The Scientific Revolution: An Encyclopedia* (2001) addresses a period of central importance; Stephen G. Brush, *The History of Modern Science: A Guide to the Second Scientific Revolution, 1800–1950* (1988) is intended for undergraduate students and those who teach them. Similar sources appear in other major languages. *The Magic Lantern: A Guide to Audiovisual Resources for Teaching the History of Science, Technology, and Medicine,* ed. Robert K. DeKosky et al. (1997), produced under the auspices of the History of Science Society, and Paul S. Cohen and Brenda H. Cohen, *America's Scientific Treasures. A Travel Companion* (1998) serve specialized purposes.

Several series of reference works afford bibliographical guidance for both primary and secondary sources. These include Berkeley Papers in History of Science, Uppsala Studies in History of Science, and Garland Bibliographies of the History of Science and Technology.

Many encyclopedias, research guides, dictionaries, and similar reference works concerning science more generally may also prove useful, especially for studies of recent science. Examples include Rudi Volti, *The Facts on File Encyclopedia of Science, Technology, and Society* (3 vols., 1999); *Science & Technology Encyclopedia* (2000); and *Academic Press Dictionary of Science and Technology,* ed. Christopher Morris (1992). The *Guide to Reference Books,* ed. Robert Balay (11th ed., 1996) lists more.

Historians of science often turn to general encyclopedias in various editions. For entries on scientific subjects, see, for example, the *Encyclopedia Britannica* (first published 1771; current ed. at http://www.eb.com/); Ephraim Chambers, *Cyclopaedia* (first published 1728); John Harris, *Lexicon Technicum* (first published 1704-1710; 1st ed. reprinted 1990, 1997); and the *Encyclopédie* of Diderot and d'Alembert (1751-1765; available online at http://www.lib.uchicago.edu/efts/ARTFL/projects/encyc/).

Other Biographical Resources

Among bibliographies of biographies with special reference to science are E. Scott Barr, *An Index to Biographical Fragments in Unspecialized Scientific Journals* (1973); *Biographical Sources in the Sciences,* comp. Janet Turner et al. (1988); Leslie Howsam, *Scientists since 1660: A Bibliography of Biographies* (1997); *Prominent Scientists: An Index to Collective Biographies,* comp. Paul Pelletier (3rd ed., 1994), supplementing Norma Olin Ireland, *Index to Scientists of the World from Ancient to Modern Times: Biographies and Portraits* (1962); Roger Smith, *Biographies of Scientists: An Annotated Bibliography* (1998). Of broader scope is K. G. Saur Publishing, World Biographical Index (1998–; online at http://www.biblio.tubs.de/acwww25u/wbi_en/wbi.html and on CD-ROM as *Internationaler biographischer Index*).

Other useful biographical dictionaries take a national tack, as in *American Men and Women of Science* (20th ed., 1998–1999, now included in *SciTech Reference Plus* on CD-ROM, 1989–).

Biographical and bio-bibliographical undertakings focused on particular fields, time periods, or both—e.g., R. V. and P. J. Wallis, Biobibliography of British Mathematics and its Applications (1986–)—note those not necessarily honored by inclusion in Poggendorff or national compilations. Stewart's online guide and *The History of Women and Science, Health, and Technology: A Bibliographic Guide to the Professions and the Disciplines,* ed. Phyllis Holman Weisbard (2nd ed., 1993), now available online through *BiblioLine* as *Women's Resources International* (1989, 1996–), are convenient sources for titles concerning women in science.

Published Scientific Works

Compilers of the Royal Society *Catalogue of Scientific Papers, 1800–1900* (19 vols. in 4 series with supplements 1867–1902, 1914–1925; continued as the *International Catalogue of Scientific Literature* covering 1901–1914 in 33 vols., 1902–1921) tried to capture a broad array of scientific literature published in periodicals, society proceedings, and so on. Stewart and Morman/Ruggiere list numerous guides to twentieth-century scientific periodicals, including those in individual fields and subspecialties. Works like Denis Grogan, *Science and Technology: An Introduction to the Literature* (3rd ed., rev. 1976); Saul Herner et al., *A Brief Guide to Sources of Scientific and Technical Information* (2nd ed., 1980); Bernard Houghton, *Scientific Periodicals: Their Historical Development, Characteristics, and Control* (1975); David M. Knight, *Natural Science Books in English, 1600–1900* (1972); H. Robert Malinowsky, *Reference Sources in Science, Engineering, Medicine, and Agriculture* (1994, especially the general descriptions in part I of scientific information practices and products); *Development of Science Publishing in Europe,* ed. A. J. Meadows (1980); Krishna Subramanyam, *Scientific and Technical Information Resources* (1981); and Richard D. Walker and C. D. Hurt, *Scientific and Technical Literature* (1990) examine scientific publishing in the print era. Recent studies such as Carol Tenopir and Donald W. King, *Towards Electronic Journals: Realities for Scientists, Librarians, and Publishers* (2000) and position papers (e.g., Jean-Claude Guédon, "In Oldenburg's Long Shadow: Librarians, Research Scientists, Publishers, and the Control of Scientific Publishing," http://www.arl.org/arl/proceedings/138/guedon.html) consider electronic possibilities. Dramatic growth and pricing policies of a few commercial science publishers have drawn particular fire: see documents concerning the case of Gordon & Breach v. American Institute of Physics and American Physical Society at www.library.yale.edu/barschall/and http://barschall.stanford.edu/. The Scholarly Publishing and Academic Resources Coalition (http://www.arl.org/sparc/) and HighWire Press (http://highwire.stanford.edu/), among others, offer alternatives.

Those in quest of specific published works have long relied on such national resources as The [U.S.] *National Union Catalog, Pre-1956 Imprints* (754 vols., 1968–1981), the *Union List of Serials in Libraries of the United States and Canada,* ed. Edna Brown Titus (3rd ed., 5 vols., 1965), and the British Library *General Catalogue of Printed Books to 1975* (360 vols., 1979–1987), with their supplements. Online library catalogs such as *WorldCat* (http://www.oclc.org/firstsearch/), the *RLG Union Catalog* (http://www.rlg.org/libres.html), and the *British Library Public Catalogue* (http://www.bl.uk/catalogues/blpc.html) enable creative bibliographic searches; the utility of such databases depends, however, on the extent to which participating libraries have converted paper catalog records to machine-readable ones. Such projects as JSTOR (http://www.jstor.org/) make long runs of periodicals, including the *Philosophical Transactions* of the Royal Society, *Proceedings* of the (U.S.) National Academy of Sciences, and *Science,* available online.

Catalogs of specific library or personal collections often provide detailed information on individual books. For history of science, examples include *The Barchas Collection at Stanford University* (1999); Louis A. Kenney, *Catalogue of the Rare Astronomical Books in the San Diego State University Library* (1988); and

Catalog of the Naval Observatory Library (6 vols., 1976). Judith Ann Overmier, *Scientific Rare Book Collections in Academic and Research Libraries in Twentieth Century America* (1985) provides an overview. Although William A. Cole, *Chemical Literature, 1700–1860* (1988) grew out of a personal collection impressive in its own right, its coverage is much broader, as the subtitle indicates: *A Bibliography with Annotations, Detailed Descriptions, Comparisons, and Locations.* Book dealer and auction catalogs, current and otherwise, are likewise useful. See such examples as Zeitlin & Ver Brugge, *The Physical World Encompassed* (1979) and *Classics of Science ... Including Many Titles from the Robert B. and Marian S. Honeyman Collection* (1981), and Christie's auction catalog for *The Haskell F. Norman Library of Science and Medicine* (3 vols., 1998). The Antiquarian Booksellers Association of America (http://search2.abaa.org/abaa/searchform.php3) permits searches across the catalogs of multiple dealers, including those with a specialty in history of science.

Collectors' guides and exhibit catalogs offer both overview and detail, sometimes ornamented by useful images. *Thornton and Tully's Scientific Books, Libraries, and Collectors: A Study of Bibliography and the Book Trade in Relation to the History of Science,* ed. Andrew Hunter (1999) is a thorough revision of John L. Thornton and R. I. J. Tully, *Scientific Books, Libraries and Collectors* (1954; 1962; 1971). Among relevant exhibit catalogs are William B. Ashworth, *Theories of the Earth 1644–1830* (Linda Hall Library, 1984) and Anthea Waleson, *Nature Disclosed: Books from the Collections of the John Crerar Library Illustrating the History of Science* (1984). Exhibit catalogs now enjoy online counterparts, often containing more illustrations than print versions permit—e.g., "Women and Nature," http://www.library.wisc.edu/Kbraries/SpecialCollections/womennature/index.html.

The number and use of image compilations continue to grow. The *Album of Science Series,* ed. I. Bernard Cohen (1978–1989) is now supplemented by specialized online image collections like the *Caltech Archives PhotoNet* (http://archives.caltech.edu//photoNet.html), *Emilio Segrè Visual Archives* at the Center for History of Physics (http://www.aip.org/history/esva/), the Edgar Fahs Smith collection at the University of Pennsylvania (http://dewey.library.upenn.edu/sceti/smith/), and online catalogs of instruments compiled at http://www.mhs.ox.ac.uk/links/.

Guides To Unpublished Sources

Historians of science rely heavily on unpublished sources, and have both benefited from and undertaken ambitious projects to collect, describe, and/or reproduce manuscripts and other unpublished resources. Cumbersome searching in multi-volume printed guides such as the *National Union Catalog of Manuscript Collections,* or NUCMC (1959/61–1992), has been eased by its availability online and by online library catalogs that contain descriptions of archival holdings. The Library of Congress provides at http://www.loc.gov/coll/nucmc/ a *Gateway to the Archival and Mixed Collections (AMC)* file in the *RLG Union Catalog.* Finding aids in paper to archival collections are sometimes published: e.g., Mary F. I. Smyth, *Catalogue of the Archives of the Royal Observatory, Edinburgh 1764–1937* (1981); and Jeannine Alton and Julia Latham-Jackson, *Report on the Papers and Correspondence of Otto Robert Frisch (1982).* Most online finding aids follow the standards of Encoded Archival Descriptions, as in the Bancroft Library Finding Aids (http://bancroft.berkeley.edu/

collections/findingaids.html), part of the Online Archive of California. Such finding aids can be "populated" by digital images of items in the collections thus described. *Archives USA: Integrated Collection and Repository Information* (http://archives.chadwyck.com/) and RLG Archives Resources (http://www.rlg.org/arr/index.html) combine collection descriptions and links to online finding aids.

National, regional, and institutional archival guides such as Peter Harper, *Guide to the Manuscript Papers of British Scientists* (1993); *Guide to the Archives of Science in Australia: Records of Individuals,* comp. and ed. Gavan McCarthy (1991); Ann Mozley Moyal, *A Guide to the Manuscript Records of Australian Science* (1966); Edwin T. Layton, *A Regional Union Catalog of Manuscripts Relating to the History of Science and Technology Located in Indiana, Michigan, and Ohio* (1971); Keith Moore, *A Guide to the Archives and Manuscripts of the Royal Society* (1995); and Grazyna Rosi'nska, *Scientific Writings and Astronomical tables in Cracow: A Census of Manuscript Sources (XIVth-XVIth Centuries)* (1984) point to research possibilities.

A subject approach with chronological boundaries characterizes such projects as *Archival Sources for the History of Biochemistry and Molecular Biology,* ed. David Bearman and John T. Edsall (1980); Bruce Bruemmer, *Resources for the History of Computing: A Guide to U.S. and Canadian Records* (1987); *Understanding Progress as Process: Documentation of the History of Post-war Science and Technology in the United States,* ed. Clark A. Elliott (1983); Thomas S. Kuhn et al., *Sources for History of Quantum Physics: An Inventory and Report* (1967); David C. Lindberg, *A Catalogue of Medieval and Renaissance Optical Manuscripts* (1975); and Bruce R. Wheaton, *Inventory of Sources for History of Twentieth Century Physics* (1992).

Guides like Roger Hahn, *The New Calendar of the Correspondence of Pierre Simon Laplace* (1994) and *The Letters of Georges Cuvier: A Summary Calendar of Manuscript and Printed Materials Preserved in Europe, the United States of America, and Australasia,* ed. Dorinda Outram (1980) and editing projects like the Einstein Papers Project (http://www.einstein.caltech.edu/) and the Darwin Correspondence Project (http://www.lib.cam.ac.uk/Departments/Darwin/) have cast their net widely. SiliconBase (http://www-sul.stanford.edu/siliconbase/) about Silicon Valley's past and present, the Ava Helen and Linus Pauling Papers (http://www.orst.edu/Dept/Special_Collections/subpages/ahp/), the Memory Bank within *echo* (see above), and the History of Recent Science & Technology project (http://hrst.mit.edu/hrs/public/SiteInfo.htm), among others, exploit new technologies to preserve and collect unpublished sources and make them available for teaching and research. The pioneering *arXiv.org E-Print Archive* (http://arXiv.org/), as conceived by Paul Ginsparg in 1991, also deserves note: in this context "e-print" denotes "self-archiving by the author."

While this essay suggests the breadth of reference sources for history of science, it does not provide a comprehensive list of general sources. It only hints at the array of specialized reference works within history of science. It also excludes regions of overlap between science and technology, medicine, and literature, and fields of philosophy and sociology of science and science studies more generally. However, the HSTM database, along with other bibliographies cited in this essay, provide valuable guidance to such collateral subjects as well.